PARAGRAPH PUBLISHING

Paragraph Publishing, Grosvenor House, 112-114 Prince of Wales Road, Norwich, Norfolk, NR10 5DJ.
Tel: 01603 633 808 Fax: 01603 632 808
Email: info@gardenersatlas.co.uk
Web site: www.gardenersatlas.co.uk

The Gardeners' Atlas

Scale 1: 175,000

First Paragraph Publishing edition: March 2001

British Library Cataloguing-in-Publication Data. A catalogue record for this book is available from the British Library.

ISBN 0-9537771-6-2

Reprographics by Anglia Colour, Norwich, Norfolk. Printed and bound by Heron Print, UK. Distributed by MDL, Houndmills, Basingstoke, Hampshire RG21 6XS.
9 8 7 6 5 4 3 2 1

EDITOR & PUBLISHER Damian Riley-Smith
DESIGN Stephen Bird
  Lorna Crosbie-Smith
PRODUCTION Brigid James
  Pippa Riley-Smith
  David Stirk
RESEARCH & SALES Joanne Morley
  Jonathan Collen
SOFTWARE Kingswood
DISTRIBUTION Littlefield Brown
FINANCE Trudi Foster

Photographs on map pages © PhotoEssentials
http://www.photoessentials.canon.com.au/
and © Corbis Corp.
http://www.corbisimages.com

With thanks to Rolf Stricker, Wimpey Knott, Beverly Cutress and Gillian Cutress.

2000-20

GARDENERS' ATLAS

FIND YOUR WAY TO BRITAIN'S

- Gardens • Nurseries
- Garden centres • Water garden specialists

THE MAPS
NUMBERS 1 TO 147

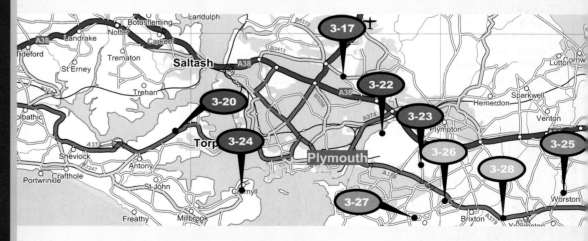

INTRODUCTION

WELCOME to the 2001 edition of the **Gardeners' Atlas**. It has been a busy year in the world of gardening, and we have been working hard to keep apace. I would like to thank the many of you who wrote, emailed and called us with ideas. As a result we have made a number of changes and improvements, namely;

- We have introduced a new category, 'garden & nursery', to reflect the fact that many gardens have nurseries and many nurseries have wonderful gardens. At the same time, producers of garden equipment have moved from the Atlas and are now to be found on our web site, **www.gardenersatlas.co.uk**

- The large number of outlets represented by B & Q, Homebase, Great Mills and Focus Do It All have been presented on *page xii* .

- We have increased the coverage on all entries, so that each one includes at least the address, county and telephone number, and extended entries now show their web, email address and up to five specialities.

- We have provided a more helpful index. Not only can you find an outlet listed by its type (nursery or garden, for example) but they are also provided in a full A-Z list. In addition, we have added a gazetteer so your **Gardeners' Atlas** can more easily double up as a road atlas.

Research from the last edition has shown us that you spend much of your time travelling the country. Often this is for reasons other than gardening, but it is clear that reaching out for the Atlas is proving invaluable in encouraging diversions from your planned route. More than 35% of you visited more than 20 gardens last year, and more than half of you visit a garden centre every week.

I hope that the **Gardeners' Atlas** makes your visits that little bit easier, and encourages yet more exploration and discovery.

Damian Riley-Smith

HOW THE GARDEN

The **Gardeners' Atlas** shows the way to thousands of places in Scotland, England and Wales that are of interest to gardeners and garden-lovers.

Our aim is that when planning visits to a part of the country you will be able to find all the locations of gardening interest through the clear and simple maps. The **Gardeners' Atlas** can also live in your car, so when you find yourself passing through any county you can quickly spot all the gardening splendours.

We have tried to include every garden centre, nursery and water garden specialist which welcomes visitors as well as all gardens open to the public for at least five months of the year.

Each is clearly identified with its own unique number shown in a coloured lozenge. This number is shown on the map, in the text and in the index. For ease of reference the numbers on the map increase as you go down the page.

We have included a different scale for parts of the country where the density of gardens and gardening retailers makes this necessary, and we hope this makes the maps even easier to use.

As in previous editions we have asked owners with enhanced entries to supply their own descriptions. We have not included our own opinions or preferences, but rather seek to provide a comprehensive range of all the relevant outlets and hope you will enjoy coming to your own views. Every entry lists the name, address and telephone number, along with which category the location falls in to. We suggest you call before driving long distances, as some gardens and nurseries have restricted opening times.

OPENING TIMES

Where provided, opening times have been supplied by the people concerned. Remember that nurseries can be flexible with their dates and hours of opening and that climate conditions can influence availability.

ENTRY COSTS

We have included entry costs where gardens have full listings. The first cost is for adults, and any concessions are listed afterwards. If in doubt please call before visiting, particularly if in a group as discounts often apply.

FACILITIES

Those entries with full listings also show all the facilities available. The facilities highlighted in yellow are available, and those in light blue were not available at the time of going to press.

The facility boxes appear in the order below:

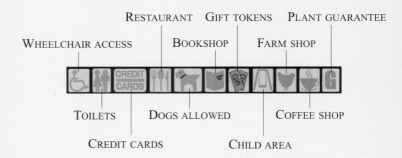

RESTAURANT   GIFT TOKENS   PLANT GUARANTEE
WHEELCHAIR ACCESS   BOOKSHOP   FARM SHOP
TOILETS   DOGS ALLOWED   COFFEE SHOP
CREDIT CARDS   CHILD AREA

ENTRY GROUPS

GARDEN

We include over 600 gardens, many of them the greatest gardens in the world. The criteria we have used for their selection is that they are open at least five months of the year, at least five days in a week and at least six hours in each day. In other words, they are generally open to the public and accessible throughout the key garden visiting months. Opening times may vary between the seasons so we suggest you telephone the garden first if you are making a special trip from afar.

RS' ATLAS WORKS

GARDEN CENTRE

We have included all garden centres, big or small, independent or part of a group. Small garden centres often carry a large range of popular plants and garden equipment. Medium-sized garden centres are able to carry a much wider range, including gifts, books, garden furniture, paving and sheds. Large garden centres are often like department stores with restaurants and a wide range of items less directly related to gardening.

GARDEN & NURSERY

Many gardens have specialist nurseries, and often a nursery will have created a garden nearby, and so we needed a separate category. Because they are tending both a garden and a nursery we do suggest you always call first to confirm opening times and seasonal variations.

NURSERY

All nurseries that welcome visitors (or that are generally open throughout the summer months) have been included. It is always safest to call before visiting to avoid disappointment. All nurseries offer expert advice and many have particular areas of speciality. If you want to find nurseries who sell particular plants, try our web site **www.gardenersatlas.co.uk** and select Nurseries and then the Speciality you are looking for.

NURSERY & GARDEN CENTRE

These are grouped together because some nurseries also operate garden centres and some garden centres have their own nurseries. Most nurseries grow their own plants from seeds and cuttings or buy stock to grow-on, whereas most garden centres buy in plants ready to sell. Many would rather be known for both areas and so when requested they have been included under this category.

WATER GARDEN SPECIALIST

These are often on the same sites as garden centres but are separate businesses. They usually sell fish, plants, ponds, liners and equipment needed by beginners and experts alike. As their specialist names suggest these are staffed by experts who are able to offer advice and who can help ensure you get the best from your water garden.

INTERNET

The **Gardeners' Atlas** is also available on the internet, at **www.gardenersatlas.co.uk**. Here you can find the outlets in the region you choose, by speciality, by location, by outlet type or by name. Maps are perfectly suited to the internet, so enjoy the 3-D effect of finding your favourite gardening outlet online.

FEEDBACK

We have done our best to ensure that all the information in the **Gardeners' Atlas** is correct, but know, reluctantly, that errors may have occurred. Please let us know if you notice any errors, or if we have left anyone out whom, in your opinion, meets our criteria. Call us on 01603 633 808, or enter the details on **www.gardenersatlas.co.uk**. We look forward to hearing from you.

CALENDAR OF GARDEN

In association with

The gardening calendar is filled for the year, and we have identified as many shows and plant fairs as possible. The location of each event can be found by looking for its map page or location number. For up-to-date information and tickets, please contact the numbers provided.

DATE	CONTACT	MAP
11 - 31 MARCH	01392 425 426	1, 2 & 3
Cornwall's Festival of Spring Gardens		
12 - 27 MARCH	01444 450 326	17-26
Rhododendron and Azalea Time		
Borde Hill Garden, Balcombe Road, Haywards Heath, W. Sussex		
12 - 18 MARCH	01732 865 224	147-16
Spring Flower Week		
Hever Castle Gardens, Edenbridge, Kent		
13 - 14 MARCH	0870 906 3721	141
RHS London Flower Show		
RHS Horticultural Halls, Greycoat Street, Vincents Square, London		
16 - 18 MARCH	0870 906 3721	141
RHS London Orchid Show		
RHS Horticultural Halls, Greycoat Street, Vincents Square, London		
17 - 18 MARCH	01539 432 252	88
Ambleside Daffodil and Spring Flower Show		
Kelsick Centre, Ambleside, Cumbria		
20 - 22 MARCH	01702 233 123	52-53
The Suffolk Spring Garden Show		
Suffolk Showground, Bucklesham Road, Ipswich, Suffolk		
23 - 27 MARCH	020 8781 9500	140-20
Florimania		
Hampton Court Palace, East Molesey, Surrey		
24 - 24 MARCH	01438 869 668	39
Great Plant Sale		
Benington Lordship, Stevenage, Hertfordshire		
28 - 29 MARCH	01733 465 000	141
RHS Flower Show		
Lawrence Hall, London		
31 - 1 APRIL	01622 765 400	29-32
Gardeners' Weekend		
Leeds Castle, Maidstone, Kent		
5 - 7 APRIL		40
Essex Garden Show		
North Weald Airfield, Merlin Way, North Weald Essex		
5 - 8 APRIL	0870 155 1996	39-42
London Garden Show		
Alexandra Palace, Wood Green, London		
6 - 8 APRIL		39-30
Spring Gardening and Country Show		
Capel Manor, Bullsmoor Lane, Enfield, Middlesex		
7 - 8 APRIL	01382 433 815	117
Dundee Spring Flower Show		
Caird Hall, City Square, Dundee, Angus		
7- 8 APRIL	0191 433 3000	102
Gateshead Spring Flower Show		
Gateshead Nurseries, Whickham Highway Gateshead, Tyne & Wear		
8 APRIL	01565 777 353	77-42
Rare and Unusual Plant Fair		
Arley Hall & Gardens, Arley, Great Budworth Northwich, Cheshire		
10 - 11 APRIL	01733 465 000	141
Daffodil Show		
Lawrence & Lindley Halls, London		
10 - 11 APRIL	0870 906 3721	141
RHS London Flower Show		
RHS Horticultural Halls, Greycoat Street, Vincents Square, London		
13 APRIL	01248 714 795	64-3
National Gardens Scheme Open Day		
Plas Newydd, Llanfairpwyll, Anglesey, Gwynedd		

DATE	CONTACT	MAP
14 APRIL	01395 273 636	3, 4 & 9
The South West Alpine Flower Show		
West Exeter Technology College, Exeter, Devon		
15 APRIL	01626 352 233	3, 4
Nursery Tour		
Burnham Nurseries, Forches Cross, Newton Abbot, Devon		
16 APRIL	01444 400 589	17-22
Daffodil Time		
High Beeches Woodland & Water Gardens, Handcross, West Sussex		
17 APRIL	01483 304 440	143-22
Getting Ready for Summer		
Loseley Park, Compton, Guildford, Surrey		
20 - 22 APRIL		52, 53
Suffolk Spring Garden Show		
Suffolk Showground, Bucklesham Road, Ipswich, Suffolk		
21 - 22 APRIL	024 7685 8300	48
Amateur Gardening Spring Show		
NAC, Nr Kenilworth, Warwickshire		
21 APRIL	01277 356 635	144
Grow: the Surrey Garden Show		
Sandown Park, Esher, Surrey		
22 APRIL	020 8366 4442	39-30
Herts and Beds NCCPG Sale		
Capel Manor, Bullsmoor Lane, Enfield, Middlesex		
26 - 29APRIL	01423 561 049	85
Harrogate Spring Flower Show		
The Great Yorkshire Showground, Harrogate, North Yorkshire		
26 - 30APRIL	01580 200 692	19-16
Tulip Festival		
Pashley Manor Gardens, Ticehurst, Wadhurst, East Sussex		
28 - 29 APRIL	0870 906 3721	141
RHS London Flower Show		
RHS Horticultural Halls, Greycoat Street, Vincents Square London		
3 - 5 MAY	01403 891 212	17-28
Bonsai Weekend		
Leonardslee Gardens, Brighton Road, Lower Beeding Horsham, West Sussex		
5 - 7 MAY	01225 482 624	23-34
Bath Annual Spring Flower Show		
Royal Victoria Park, Bath, Somerset		
5 - 7 MAY	01565 777 353	77-42
Bluebell Days		
Arley Hall & Gardens, Arley, Great Budworth Northwich, Cheshire		
5 - 7 MAY	020 8366 4442	39-30
North London Cactus and Succulents Show		
Capel Manor, Bullsmoor Lane, Enfield, Middlesex		
5 MAY	01775 724 843	60-71
Spalding Flower Parade		
Springfields Exhibition Centre, Camel Gate, Spalding, Lincolnshire		
5 - 6 MAY	01799 522 399	51-30
Spring Gardeners' Weekend		
Audley End House, Audley End, Saffron Walden, Essex		
5 - 7 MAY	01732 770 929	18, 19, 28, 147 & 142
Tonbridge Gardening Show		
Sports Ground, Tonbridge, Kent		
6 MAY	01938 554 338	55-13
Plant Hunters' Fair		
Powis Castle & Gardens, Welshpool, Powys		
7 MAY	01444 400 589	17-22
Bluebell Time		
High Beeches Woodland & Water Gardens, Handcross, West Sussex		

DATE	CONTACT	MAP
8 MAY	01248 714 795	64-3
Walk with the Gardener		
Plas Newydd, Llanfairpwyll, Anglesey, Gwynedd		
11 - 13 MAY	01626 352 233	3, 4
Chelsea Preview		
Burnham Nurseries, Forches Cross, Newton Abbot, Devon		
11 - 13 MAY		60
East of England Garden Show		
East of England Showground, Peterborough, Cambridgeshire		
11 - 13 MAY	01684 584 924	46
Malvern Spring Gardening Show		
Three Counties Showground, Malvern, Worcestershire		
12 - 13 MAY	01938 200 022	7-1
Isle of Wight Garden Show		
Osbourne House, York Avenue, East Cowes, Isle of Wight		
12 - 27 MAY	01444 450 326	17-26
Rhododendron and Azalea Time		
Borde Hill Garden, Balcombe Road, Haywards Heath, West Sussex		
12 - 18 MAY	01580 200 888	19-16
Sculpture Week		
Pashley Manor Gardens, Ticehurst, Wadhurst, East Sussex		
12 MAY	01697 724 476	95, 99 & 100
Spring Orchid Show		
Carlisle College, Victoria Place, Carlisle, Cumbria		
13 MAY	01233 861 493	20-29
Plant and Garden Fair		
The South of England Rare Breeds Centre, Ashford, Kent		
13 MAY	01423 322 583	90-15
Spring Plant Fair		
Newby Hall & Gardens, Ripon, North Yorkshire		
13 MAY	01798 344 972	15, 16, 17 & 146
Spring Plant Fair		
Petworth House & Park, Petworth, West Sussex		
13 MAY	01834 811 885	31-6
Spring Plant Fair		
Colby Woodland Garden, Amroth, Narberth, Pembrokeshire		
17 - 31 MAY	01444 450 326	17-26
Special Camellia Days		
Borde Hill Garden, Balcombe Road, Haywards Heath, West Sussex		
18 - 20 MAY	01727 850 461	38-27
Spring Garden Weekend, Royal National Rose Society		
The Gardens of the Rose, Chiswell Green, St Albans, Hertfordshire		
19 - 20 MAY	01438 812 661	39-5
Herts Garden Show		
Knebworth House, Knebworth Park, Knebworth, Hertfordshire		
20 MAY	01565 777 353	77-42
Spring Garden Day		
Arley Hall & Gardens, Arley, Great Budworth, Northwich, Cheshire		
20 MAY	01580 200 692	19-16
Spring Plant Fair		
Pashley Manor Gardens, Ticehurst, Wadhurst, East Sussex		
21 - 25 MAY	0870 906 3781	141-19
Chelsea Flower Show		
Royal Hospital, Ranelagh Gardens, Royal Hospital Road, London		
27 - 31 MAY	01305 854 892	5-2
Athelhampton Flower Festival		
Athelhampton House, Athelhampton, Dorchester, Dorset		
27 - 28 MAY	01795 474 660	28, 29
Kent Garden Show		
Kent County Showground, Maidstone, Kent		
28 MAY	01444 400 589	17-22
Azalea Time		
High Beeches Woodland & Water Gardens, Handcross, West Sussex		

SHOWS & PLANT FAIRS

DATE	CONTACT	MAP
28 MAY	01580 211 702	19-7
Spring Garden Fair and Flower Festival		
Finchcocks, Goudhurst, Kent		
29 MAY	01437 751 326	31-4
RHS Lecture at Picton Castle & Woodland Garden		
Haverfordwest, Pembrokeshire		
1 - 3 JUNE	0131 333 0964	112
Gardening Scotland		
Royal Highland Centre, Ingliston, Edinburgh, East Lothian		
1 - 3 JUNE	01539 558 328	89-17
Holker Garden Festival		
Holker Hall, Cark-in-Cartmel, Grange-over-Sands, Cumbria		
2 - 7 JUNE	01363 772 865	9
Flower Festival and Exhibition - 2001 Odyssey		
Church of the Holy Cross, Crediton, Devon		
8 - 10 JUNE	023 9241 2265	15
The Garden Show		
Stansted Park, Chichester, West Sussex		
8 - 10 JUNE	01525 290 666	50-33
Woburn Garden Show		
Woburn Abbey, Woburn, Bedfordshire		
13 - 17 JUNE		57, 58
Members: 0121 767 4505 Non-members: 0121 767 4111		
BBC Gardeners' World Live		
NEC, Bickenhill Lane, Birmingham, West Midlands		
13 - 14 JUNE	01903 882 297	15-16
Corpus Christie Carpet of Flowers and Floral Festival		
Cathedral of Our Lady and St Philip, Cathedral House,		
Parsons Hill, Arundel, West Sussex		
14 - 17 JUNE	01580 200 692	19-16
Summer Flower Festival		
Pashley Manor Gardens, Ticehurst, Wadhurst, East Sussex		
15 - 18 JUNE	01202 861 686	12-27
Flower and Garden Festival		
Stapehill Abbey Crafts & Garden, 276 Wimborne Road, West Stapehill		
Ferndown, Dorset		
16 - 30 JUNE	01444 450 326	17-26
Days of English Roses		
Borde Hill Garden, Balcombe Road, Haywards Heath, West Sussex		
20 - 24 JUNE	0906 470 1777	141 & 142
Covent Garden Flower Festival		
London		
22 - 28 JUNE	01732 865 224	147-16
Rose Week		
Hever Castle & Gardens, Edenbridge, Kent		
22 - 24 JUNE	01359 268 614	51
The East Anglian Flower and Garden Show		
Bourn Airfield, Cambridge, Cambridgeshire		
23 - 24 JUNE	01565 777 353	77-42
Arley Garden Festival		
Arley Hall & Gardens, Arley, Great Budworth, Northwich, Cheshire		
23 - 25 JUNE	01300 320 296	5,11
Flower Festival		
St Peter & Paul Church, Dorchester, Dorset		
23 - 24 JUNE	01243 818 210	15-22
Garden Festival		
West Dean Gardens, West Dean, Chichester, West Sussex		
23 - 24 JUNE	01805 624 067	8-14
Rose Festival		
Rosemoor Gardens, RHS, Great Torrington, Devon		
23 - 24 JUNE	01444 450 326	17-26
Sussex Garden Show		
Borde Hill Garden, Balcombe Road, Haywards Heath		
West Sussex		
23 - 24 JUNE	01707 262 823	39-14
The Festival of Gardening Hatfield Park		
Hatfield House, Hatfield		
Hertfordshire		

DATE	CONTACT	MAP
26 JUNE	01483 304 440	143-22
Rose Day		
Loseley Park, Compton, Guildford, Surrey		
29 JUNE - 1 JULY	023 8083 2525	13, 14
Southampton Balloon and Flower Festival		
Southampton Common, Southampton, Hampshire		
1 - 8 JULY	01624 686 801	137
Manx Heritage Flower Show		
Isle of Man		
3 - 8 JULY	01727 850 461	140-20
British Rose Festival		
Hampton Court Palace, East Molesey, Surrey		
3 - 8 JULY	0870 906 3791	140-20
Hampton Court Palace Flower Show		
Hampton Court Palace, East Molesey, Surrey		
9 - 14 JULY	01534 500 700	137
Jersey Garden Festival		
14 - 15 JULY	01903 742 021	16
Parham Garden Weekend		
Parham House & Gardens, Parham Park, Pulborough,		
West Sussex		
18 - 22 JULY	0870 906 3811	77-40
RHS Flower Show at Tatton Park		
Knutsford, Cheshire		
19 - 22 JULY	01622 765 400	29-32
Festival of Summer Floral Art		
Leeds Castle, Maidstone, Kent		
19 - 23 JULY	0870 906 3810	141, 142
RHS Flower Show		
RHS Horticultural Halls, Greycoat Street, Vincents Square		
London		
20 - 22 JULY	01483 304 440	143-22
The Great Gardening Show		
Loseley Park, Compton, Guildford, Surrey		
25 JULY	01485 540 860	61-72
Sandringham Flower Show		
Sandringham Park, King's Lynn, Norfolk		
26 - 27 JULY	01834 811 885	31-6
Pembrokeshire Flower Arrangers' Competition		
Colby Woodland Garden, Amroth, Narberth, Pembrokeshire		
28 - 29 JULY	0191 433 3000	102
Gateshead Summer Flower Show		
Gateshead Central Nurseries, Whickham Highway		
Lobley Hill, Gateshead, Tyne & Wear		
4 AUGUST	01580 880 467	19, 20 & 29
Annual Fuchsia Show		
Brede Village Hall, Brede, East Sussex		
4 AUGUST	01342 822 2372	18
Summer Flower Show		
Town Croft, Hartfield, East Sussex		
5 AUGUST	01444 450 326	17-26
Fuchsia Show		
Borde Hill Garden, Balcombe Road, Haywards Heath		
West Sussex		
10 - 11 AUGUST	01743 234 050	55
Shrewsbury Flower Show		
Quarry Park, Quarry Lodge, Shrewsbury, Shropshire		
11 - 12 AUGUST	01661 881 636	101-5
Fuchsia Show		
Belsay Hall, Belsay, Newcastle Upon Tyne, Tyne & Wear		
16 - 18 AUGUST	01704 547 147	75
Southport Flower Show		
Victoria Park, Southport, Merseyside		
19 AUGUST	01444 400 589	17-22
Gentian Time		
High Beeches Woodland & Water Gardens, Handcross, West		
Sussex		
25 - 27 AUGUST	01799 522 399	51-30
Summer Gardeners' Weekend		
Audley End House, Audley End, Saffron Walden		
Essex		

DATE	CONTACT	MAP
27 AUGUST	01288 352 114	8
Bude Horticultural Show		
Park House Centre, Bude, Cornwall		
1 - 2 SEPTEMBER	01903 742 021	16
Autumn Flowers		
Parham House & Gardens, Parham Park, Pulborough		
West Sussex		
1 SEPTEMBER	0121 303 3022	57, 58
Birmingham Gardeners' Weekend		
Kings Heath Park, Vicarage Road, Birmingham		
West Midlands		
2 SEPTEMBER	01565 777 353	77-42
Arley Plant-Hunters' Fair		
Arley Hall & Gardens, Arley, Great Budworth		
Northwich, Cheshire		
7 - 9 SEPTEMBER	01749 822 200	11
National Amateur Gardening Show		
The Royal Bath & West Showground, Shepton Mallet, Somerset		
8 - 9 SEPTEMBER	01938 200 022	7-1
Isle of Wight Garden Show		
Osbourne House, York Avenue, East Cowes		
Isle of Wight		
9 SEPTEMBER	01444 450 326	17-26
Rare Plants Fair		
Borde Hill Garden, Balcombe Road, Haywards Heath		
West Sussex		
14 - 16 SEPTEMBER	01423 561 049	85
Harrogate Great Autumn Flower Show		
The Great Yorkshire Showground, Harrogate		
North Yorkshire		
15 - 16 SEPTEMBER	01359 268 614	51
Autumn Garden and Craft Show		
Newmarket Racecourse, Newmarket, Cambridgeshire		
16 SEPTEMBER	01938 554 338	55
Autumn Plant Fair		
Powis Castle & Gardens, Welshpool, Powys		
18 - 19 SEPTEMBER	0870 906 3721	141
The Great Autumn Show		
RHS Horticultiral Halls, Greycoat Street, Vincents Square		
London		
29 - 30 SEPTEMBER	01684 584 924	46
Malvern Autumn Garden and Country Show		
Three Counties Showground, Malvern, Worcestershire		
30 SEPTEMBER	01661 881 636	101-5
Fungus Foray		
Belsay Hall, Belsay, Newcastle Upon Tyne		
Tyne & Wear		
8 - 14 OCTOBER	01732 865 224	147
Autumn Colour Week		
Hever Castle & Gardens, Edenbridge, Kent		
9 - 10 OCTOBER	0870 906 3721	141
RHS London Flower Show		
RHS Horticultural Halls, Greycoat Street, Vincents Square		
London		
10 - 14 OCTOBER	01622 765 400	29-32
Autumn Gold Flower Festival		
Leeds Castle, Maidstone, Kent		
13 - 15 OCTOBER	01580 211 702	19-7
The Finchcocks Autumn Fair		
Finchcocks, Goudhurst, Kent		
14 OCTOBER	01444 400 589	17-22
Autumn Splendour		
High Beeches Woodland & Water Gardens, Handcross, West		
Sussex		
20 - 21 NOVEMBER	0870 906 3721	141
RHS London Flower Show		
RHS Horticultural Halls, Greycoat Street, Vincents Square		
London		
11-12 DECEMBER	0870 906 3721	27
RHS Christmas Show		
Greycoat Street, Vincents Square		
London		

THE NATIONAL TRUST
GARDENS
rooted in history, growing forever

YORKSHIRE — Beningbrough Hall & Gardens 86-2

Beningbrough, York,
North Yorkshire, YO30 1DD
TEL: 01904 470 666
WEB: www.nationaltrust.org.uk
Beningbrough Hall and Gardens (pictured), one of eight inspiring flower/landscaped gardens in Yorkshire. Tel 01904 702 021 for a copy of our regional visitors' guide.
OPEN: 1 Apr–29 Oct: daily except Thu & Fri, 11–5.30.
Jul & Aug: daily except Thu, 11–5.30.
ENTRY COSTS: Adult £3.50, Children £1.70, Family £8.70.
SPECIALITIES: Bedding plants, Climbers, Garden & conservatory furniture, Roses, Shrubs, Trees, Conservatory Plants.

SOUTHERN — Nymans Garden 17-23

Handcross, Haywards Heath, W. Sussex,
RH17 6EB
TEL: 01444 400 321
WEB: www.nationaltrust.org.uk
Make time to enjoy Nymans Garden, West Sussex (seen here in summer) and other great gardens of the South, including Clandon Park, Claremont Landscape Garden, Ham House, Hatchlands Park, Hinton Ampner, Morden Hall Park, Mottisfont Abbey, Petworth Park, Polesden Lacey, Standen, Uppark and The Vyne.
OPEN: Mar–Oct 11–6 Wed–Sun; Nov–Feb 11–4 Sat & Sun.
ENTRY COSTS: Adult £6, Family £15.
SPECIALITIES: Bulbs, Rare and exotic species, Wild garden, Woodland walks.

SEVERN — Upton House 48-37

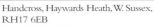

Banbury, Oxfordshire, OX15 6HT
TEL: 01295 670 266
WEB: www.nationaltrust.org.uk
The Garden is spectacular in all seasons, taking full advantage of the surprises created by the natural lie of the land, with wide lawns near the house and terraces descending to pools in the valley. The terraces are full of colourful herbaceous borders and a highly productive kitchen garden. Late colour is provided by the National Collection of Asters (Michaelmas Daisies).
OPEN: 31 Mar–31 Oct daily except Thu & Fri, 1–5.
ENTRY COSTS: Adult £5.50, Family £13.75. Garden only £2.70.
SPECIALITIES: Herbaceous plants, Roses, Trees

THAMES & CHILTERNS — Cliveden 138-3

Taplow, Buckinghamshire, SL8 0JA
TEL: 01628 605 069
WEB: www.nationaltrust.org.uk
Get inspiration from our fabulous gardens in Bedfordshire, Berkshire, Buckinghamshire, Hertfordshire, Oxfordshire and London.
OPEN: Estate & Garden: 13 Mar–31 Dec, daily 11–6 (closed at 4 from 1 Nov). Mansion: Apr–Oct, Thu & Sun: 3–6, Octagon Temple: as Mansion. Spring Cottage Garden: Jun–Oct, Thu 3–6. Woodlands car park: all year, daily, 11–6.
ENTRY COSTS: Adult £5, Children £2.50, Family £12.50, Group rate £4.50, Child £2.25. Woodlands car park £3.
Mooring Charge on Cliveden Reach £6 (24hrs), £2 (4hrs).
SPECIALITIES: Scented garden for blind, Roses, Water features, Wild flowers, Woodland plants, Water plants.

NORTH-WEST — Sizergh Castle & Garden 89-8

Sizergh, Kendal, Cumbria, LA8 8AE
TEL: 01539 560 070
WEB: www.nationaltrust.org.uk
In the Lake District, visit a range of Trust Gardens from lakeside parks to Sizergh's rock garden.
OPEN: 1 Apr–31 Oct, daily except Fri & Sat 12.30–5.30.
ENTRY COSTS: Adult £4.80, Children £2.40, Family £12. Garden only @£2.40
SPECIALITIES: Bulbs, Herbaceous plants, Rock garden, Wild flowers.

NORTHUMBERLAND — Wallington Hall 101-4

Cambo, Morpeth, Northumberland,
NE61 4AR
TEL: 01670 774 283
WEB: www.nationaltrust.org.uk
Visit Wallington's walled garden, Cragside's formal garden and the landscaped park at Gibside.
OPEN: Walled garden, daily. 1 Apr–30 Sep 10–7, Oct 10–6, Nov to Mar 10–4. Grounds, daily in daylight.
ENTRY COSTS: Adult £5.50, Family £13.75. Walled garden & grounds only £4.
SPECIALITIES: Conservatory, Herbaceous plants, Winter park & garden

Did you know?

Over 200 National Trust Gardens and landscape parks are open to the public throughout England, Wales and Northern Ireland, for everyone to enjoy. The National Trust is the world's leading conservation charity concerned for the long term future of our garden heritage.

The National Trust looks after the largest and most important collection of historic gardens and cultivated plants in the world.

For information, opening times and admission prices please call: **0870 458 4500**, *9am–530pm Mon–Fri, 9am–4pm weekends*

If you are calling from overseas, please call **+44 20 8315 1111.** Or visit our website: **www.nationaltrust.org.uk**

GARDENERS' ATLAS

MAPS

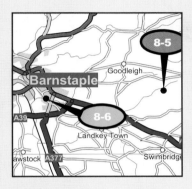

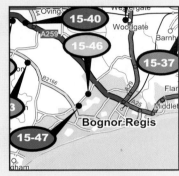

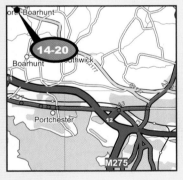

- ⬤ GARDEN
- ⬤ GARDEN CENTRE
- ⬤ GARDEN & NURSERY
- ⬤ NURSERY
- ⬤ NURSERY & GARDEN CENTRE
- ⬤ WATER GARDEN SPECIALIST

CORNWALL

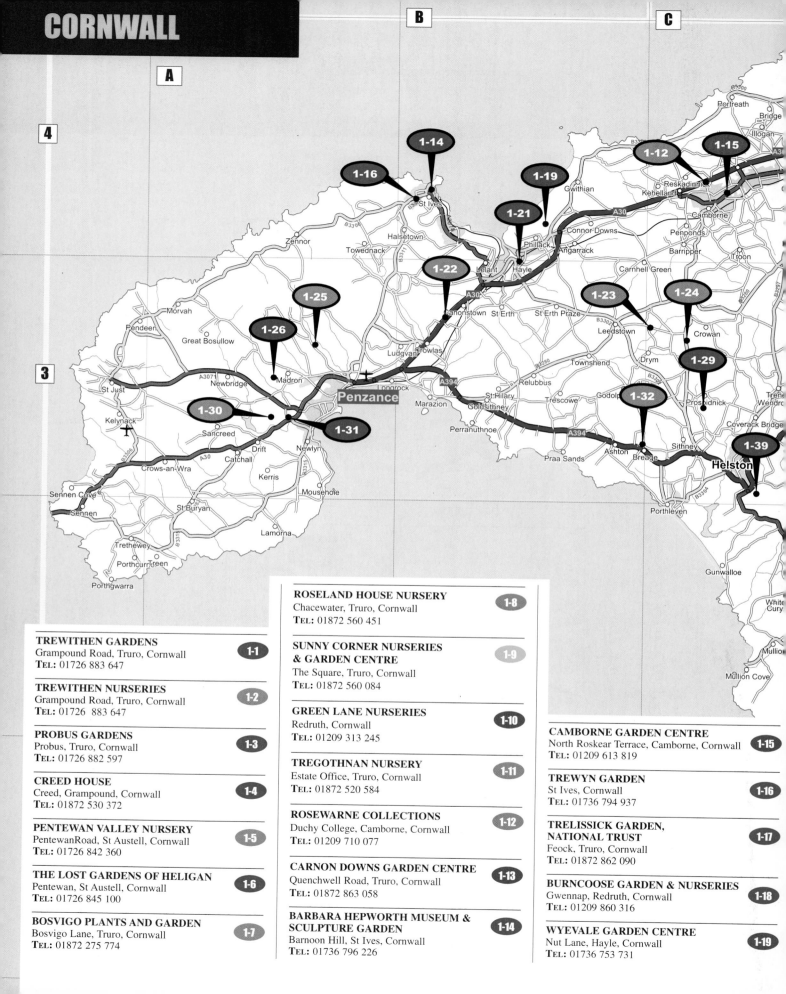

TREWITHEN GARDENS 1-1
Grampound Road, Truro, Cornwall
TEL: 01726 883 647

TREWITHEN NURSERIES 1-2
Grampound Road, Truro, Cornwall
TEL: 01726 883 647

PROBUS GARDENS 1-3
Probus, Truro, Cornwall
TEL: 01726 882 597

CREED HOUSE 1-4
Creed, Grampound, Cornwall
TEL: 01872 530 372

PENTEWAN VALLEY NURSERY 1-5
PentewanRoad, St Austell, Cornwall
TEL: 01726 842 360

THE LOST GARDENS OF HELIGAN 1-6
Pentewan, St Austell, Cornwall
TEL: 01726 845 100

BOSVIGO PLANTS AND GARDEN 1-7
Bosvigo Lane, Truro, Cornwall
TEL: 01872 275 774

ROSELAND HOUSE NURSERY 1-8
Chacewater, Truro, Cornwall
TEL: 01872 560 451

**SUNNY CORNER NURSERIES
& GARDEN CENTRE** 1-9
The Square, Truro, Cornwall
TEL: 01872 560 084

GREEN LANE NURSERIES 1-10
Redruth, Cornwall
TEL: 01209 313 245

TREGOTHNAN NURSERY 1-11
Estate Office, Truro, Cornwall
TEL: 01872 520 584

ROSEWARNE COLLECTIONS 1-12
Duchy College, Camborne, Cornwall
TEL: 01209 710 077

CARNON DOWNS GARDEN CENTRE 1-13
Quenchwell Road, Truro, Cornwall
TEL: 01872 863 058

**BARBARA HEPWORTH MUSEUM &
SCULPTURE GARDEN** 1-14
Barnoon Hill, St Ives, Cornwall
TEL: 01736 796 226

CAMBORNE GARDEN CENTRE 1-15
North Roskear Terrace, Camborne, Cornwall
TEL: 01209 613 819

TREWYN GARDEN 1-16
St Ives, Cornwall
TEL: 01736 794 937

**TRELISSICK GARDEN,
NATIONAL TRUST** 1-17
Feock, Truro, Cornwall
TEL: 01872 862 090

BURNCOOSE GARDEN & NURSERIES 1-18
Gwennap, Redruth, Cornwall
TEL: 01209 860 316

WYEVALE GARDEN CENTRE 1-19
Nut Lane, Hayle, Cornwall
TEL: 01736 753 731

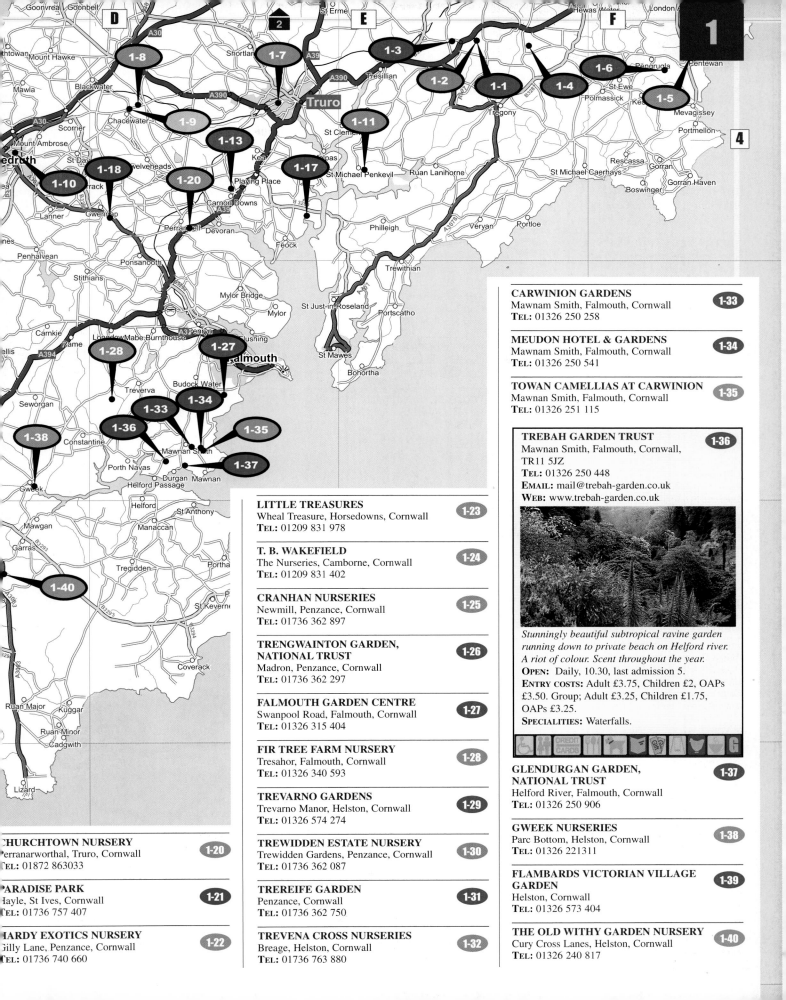

Map markers

1-8, 1-7, 1-3, 1-6, 1-5, 1-2, 1-1, 1-4, 1-9, 1-13, 1-11, 1-18, 1-20, 1-17, 1-10, 1-28, 1-27, 1-33, 1-34, 1-36, 1-38, 1-35, 1-37, 1-40

Map labels: Goonvrea, Goonbell, St Erme, Hewas Water, London, Shortlar, Tresillian, Pengrugla, Pentewan, Mount Hawke, Blackwater, Mawla, St Day, Twelveheads, Chacewater, Truro, St Clement, St Ewe, Polmassick, Kes, Scorrier, Kea, Tregony, Mevagissey, Mount Ambrose, Redruth, Carrack, Playing Place, St Michael Penkevil, Ruan Lanihorne, St Michael Caerhays, Portmellon, Lanner, Gwennap, Carnon Downs, Rescassa, Gorran, Perranwell, Devoran, Philleigh, Veryan, Boswinger, Gorran Haven, Stithians, Feock, Portloe, Penhallick, Ponsanooth, Trewithian, Mylor Bridge, St Just-in-Roseland, Portscatho, Carnkie, Rame, Longdowns, Mabe Burnthouse, Penryn, Flushing, Falmouth, St Mawes, Bohortha, Treverva, Budock Water, Sewogan, Mawnan Smith, Porth Navas, Durgan, Mawnan, Constantine, Gweek, Helford Passage, Helford, St Anthony, Mawgan, Manaccan, Garras, Tregidden, Portha, St Keverne, Ruan Major, Kuggar, Coverack, Ruan Minor, Cadgwith, Lizard

---

Listings

LITTLE TREASURES 1-23
Wheal Treasure, Horsedowns, Cornwall
Tel: 01209 831 978

T. B. WAKEFIELD 1-24
The Nurseries, Camborne, Cornwall
Tel: 01209 831 402

CRANHAN NURSERIES 1-25
Newmill, Penzance, Cornwall
Tel: 01736 362 897

TRENGWAINTON GARDEN, NATIONAL TRUST 1-26
Madron, Penzance, Cornwall
Tel: 01736 362 297

FALMOUTH GARDEN CENTRE 1-27
Swanpool Road, Falmouth, Cornwall
Tel: 01326 315 404

FIR TREE FARM NURSERY 1-28
Tresahor, Falmouth, Cornwall
Tel: 01326 340 593

TREVARNO GARDENS 1-29
Trevarno Manor, Helston, Cornwall
Tel: 01326 574 274

TREWIDDEN ESTATE NURSERY 1-30
Trewidden Gardens, Penzance, Cornwall
Tel: 01736 362 087

TREREIFE GARDEN 1-31
Penzance, Cornwall
Tel: 01736 362 750

TREVENA CROSS NURSERIES 1-32
Breage, Helston, Cornwall
Tel: 01736 763 880

CHURCHTOWN NURSERY 1-20
Perranarworthal, Truro, Cornwall
Tel: 01872 863033

PARADISE PARK 1-21
Hayle, St Ives, Cornwall
Tel: 01736 757 407

HARDY EXOTICS NURSERY 1-22
Gilly Lane, Penzance, Cornwall
Tel: 01736 740 660

CARWINION GARDENS 1-33
Mawnam Smith, Falmouth, Cornwall
Tel: 01326 250 258

MEUDON HOTEL & GARDENS 1-34
Mawnam Smith, Falmouth, Cornwall
Tel: 01326 250 541

TOWAN CAMELLIAS AT CARWINION 1-35
Mawnan Smith, Falmouth, Cornwall
Tel: 01326 251 115

TREBAH GARDEN TRUST 1-36
Mawnan Smith, Falmouth, Cornwall,
TR11 5JZ
Tel: 01326 250 448
Email: mail@trebah-garden.co.uk
Web: www.trebah-garden.co.uk

Stunningly beautiful subtropical ravine garden running down to private beach on Helford river. A riot of colour. Scent throughout the year.
Open: Daily, 10.30, last admission 5.
Entry costs: Adult £3.75, Children £2, OAPs £3.50. Group; Adult £3.25, Children £1.75, OAPs £3.25.
Specialities: Waterfalls.

GLENDURGAN GARDEN, NATIONAL TRUST 1-37
Helford River, Falmouth, Cornwall
Tel: 01326 250 906

GWEEK NURSERIES 1-38
Parc Bottom, Helston, Cornwall
Tel: 01326 221311

FLAMBARDS VICTORIAN VILLAGE GARDEN 1-39
Helston, Cornwall
Tel: 01326 573 404

THE OLD WITHY GARDEN NURSERY 1-40
Cury Cross Lanes, Helston, Cornwall
Tel: 01326 240 817

CORNWALL · DEVON

BRUALLEN NURSERY `2-1`
Trewennen Lane, Bodmin, Cornwall
TEL: 01208 850 650

LONG CROSS VICTORIAN GARDENS `2-2`
Trelights, Port Isaac, Cornwall
TEL: 01208 880 243

THE OLD MILL HERBARY `2-3`
Helland Bridge, Bodmin, Cornwall
TEL: 01208 841 206

TRELAWNEY GARDEN LEISURE `2-4`
Sladesbridge, Wadebridge, Cornwall
TEL: 01208 812 966

PENCARROW `2-5`
Washaway, Bodmin, Cornwall
TEL: 01208 841 369

JAPANESE GARDEN & BONSAI NURSERY `2-6`
Penpont Cottages, Newquay, Cornwall
TEL: 01637 860 116

BODMIN PLANT & HERB NURSERY `2-7`
Laveddon Mill, Bodmin, Cornwall
TEL: 01208 72 837

GOLDENBANK NURSERY & GARDEN CENTRE `2-8`
Plymouth Road, Liskeard, Cornwall
TEL: 01579 348 622

LANHYDROCK, NATIONAL TRUST `2-9`
Lanhydrock, Bodmin, Cornwall
TEL: 01208 733 20

PORTH VEOR FUSCHIAS `2-10`
54 Arundel Way, Newquay, Cornwall
TEL: 01637 877 208

MERLIN GARDEN SUPPLIES `2-11`
3 St. Georges Road, Newquay, Cornwall
TEL: 01637 879100

DUCHY OF CORNWALL NURSERY `2-12`
Cott Road, Lostwithiel, Cornwall
TEL: 01208 872 668

NEWQUAY GARDEN CENTRE `2-13`
Little Trethiggey, Newquay, Cornwall
TEL: 01637 872 199

CATCHFRENCH MANOR GARDENS `2-14`
St Germans, Saltash, Cornwall
TEL: 01503 240 759

TRERICE, NATIONAL TRUST `2-15`
Kestle Mill, Newquay, Cornwall
TEL: 01637 875 404

EDEN PROJECT `2-16`
Bodelva, St Austell, Cornwall
TEL: 01726 222 900

THE AZALEA CENTRE `2-17`
Cherrywood, Looe, Cornwall
TEL: 01503 220 750

PINE LODGE GARDEN & NURSERY `2-18`
Cuddra, St Austell, Cornwall
TEL: 01726 735 00

WYEVALE GARDEN CENTRE `2-19`
Par Moor Road, Plymouth, Devon
TEL: 01726 814 854

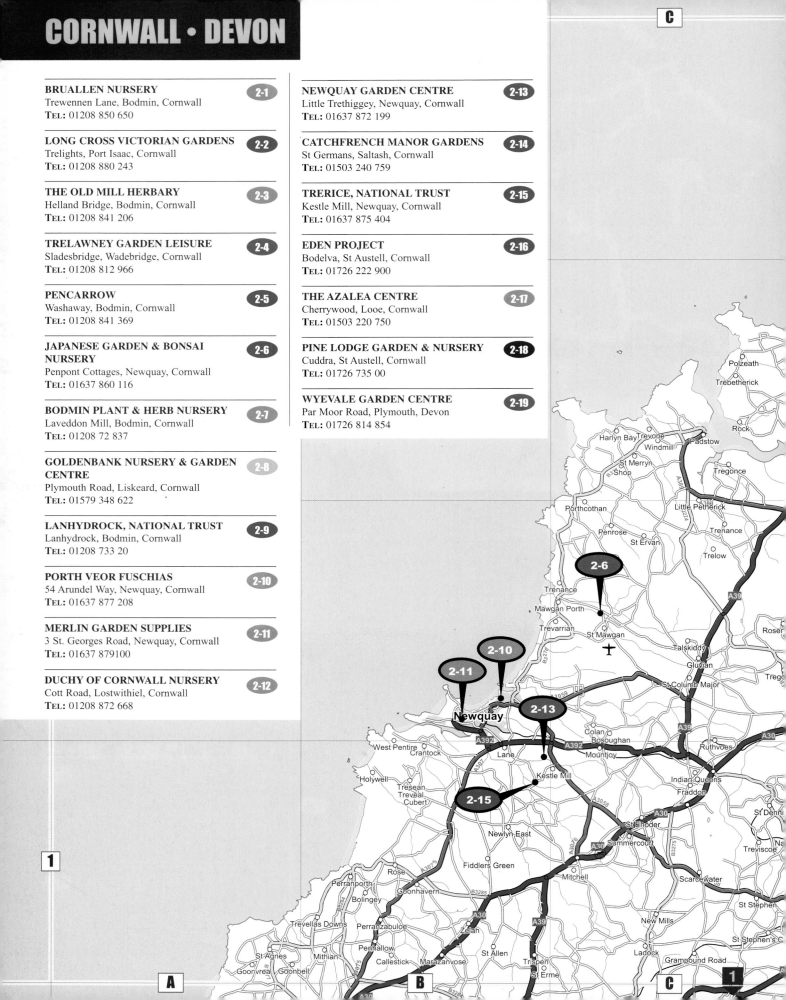

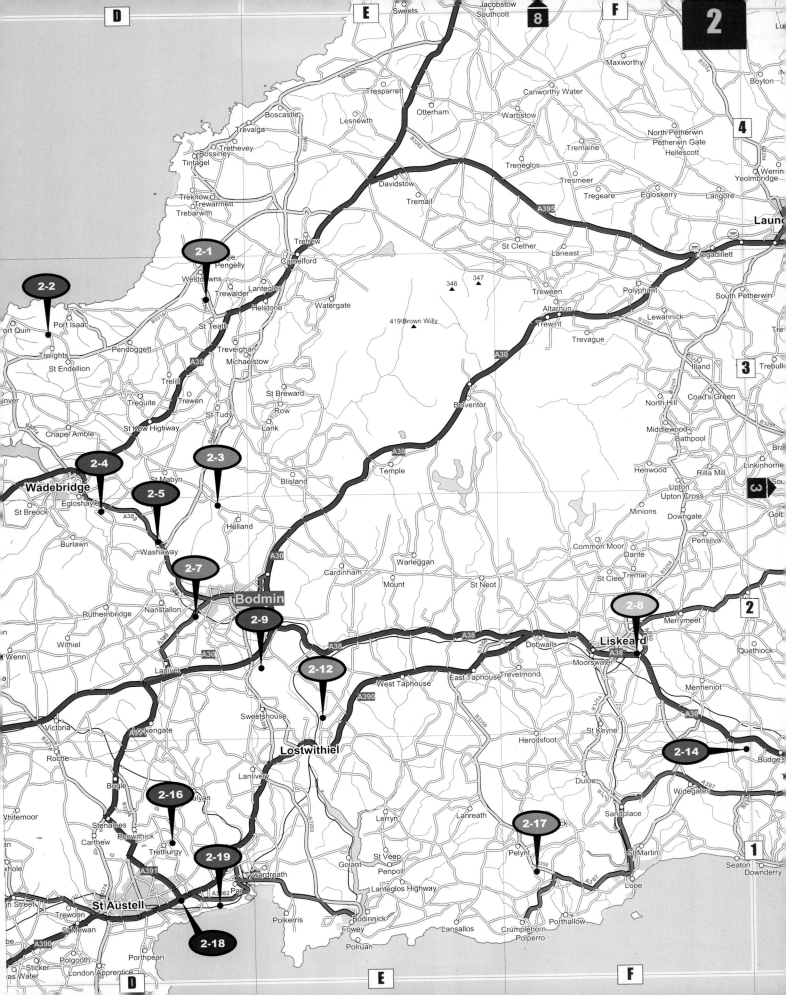

HIGURASHI BONSAI `3-1`
Henford, Ashwater, Devon
TEL: 01409 211 137

THORNDON CROSS NURSERY `3-2`
Whincote, Okehampton, Devon
TEL: 01837 861 347

CASTLE DROGO, NATIONAL TRUST `3-3`
Drewsteignton, Exeter, Devon
TEL: 01647 433 306

THE PLANTSMAN NURSERY `3-4`
North Wonson Farm, Okehampton, Devon
TEL: 01647 231 699

THE MYTHIC GARDEN `3-5`
Stone Farm, Newton Abbot, Devon
TEL: 01647 231 311

LYDFORD ALPINE NURSERY `3-6`
2 Southern Cottages, Okehampton, Devon
TEL: 01822 820 398

BOYTON NURSERY & GARDEN CENTRE `3-7`
Braggs Hill, Launceston, Cornwall
TEL: 01566 776 474

ROWDEN GARDENS `3-8`
Rowden, Tavistock, Cornwall
TEL: 01822 810 275

ENDSLEIGH GARDENS NURSERY `3-9`
Milton Abbot, Tavistock, Devon
TEL: 01822 870 235

ENDSLEIGH HOUSE AND GARDENS `3-10`
Milton Abbot, Devon
TEL: 01822 870 248

KAMINSKI HOME & GARDEN CENTRE `3-11`
17b Parkwood Road, Tavistock, Cornwall
TEL: 01822 613 311

COCKINGTON NURSERY `3-12`
Callington, Cornwall
TEL: 01579 370 977

COTEHELE, NATIONAL TRUST `3-13`
St Dominick, Saltash, Cornwall
TEL: 01579 351 346

THE GARDEN HOUSE `3-14`
Buckland Monachorum, Yelverton, Cornwall
TEL: 01822 854 769

MARISTOW NURSERY GARDENS `3-15`
Roborough, Plymouth, Cornwall
TEL: 01752 736779

DEVON VIOLET NURSERY `3-16`
Rattery, South Brent, Devon
TEL: 01364 643 033

PLYMOUTH GARDEN CENTRE `3-17`
Fort Austin Avenue, Plymouth, Cornwall
TEL: 01752 771 820

MEADOW COTTAGE PLANTS `3-18`
Pitt Hill, Ivybridge, Devon
TEL: 01752 894 532

NARKURS NURSERY `3-19`
The Cottage, Torpoint, Cornwall
TEL: 01503 250 379

ANTONY WOODLAND GARDEN, NATIONAL TRUST `3-20`
Near Antony House, Torpoint, Cornwall
TEL: 01752 812 364

ENDSLEIGH GARDEN & LEISURE `3-21`
Ivybridge, Ivybridge, Devon
TEL: 01752 898 989

SALTRAM, NATIONAL TRUST `3-22`
Plymton, Plymouth, Devon
TEL: 01752 336 546

STANBOROUGH GARDEN CENTRE `3-23`
Haye Road, Plymouth, Cornwall
TEL: 01752 403240

MOUNT EDGCUMBE HOUSE & GARDENS `3-24`
Cremyll, Torpoint, Cornwall
TEL: 01752 822 236

SUNRIDGE NURSERIES `3-25`
Worston, Plymouth, Cornwall
TEL: 01752 880 438

OTTER NURSERIES OF PLYMOUTH `3-26`
Chittleburn Hill, Plymouth, Devon
TEL: 01752 405 422

POUNSLEY PLANTS `3-27`
Poundsley Combe, Plymouth, Devon
TEL: 01752 402 873

RIVERFORD PLANT CENTRE `3-28`
Riverford at Kitley, Plymouth, Devon
TEL: 01752 880 925

M. G. M. NURSERIES `3-29`
Brent Road, Kingsbridge, Devon
TEL: 01548 550 754

Ranunculus

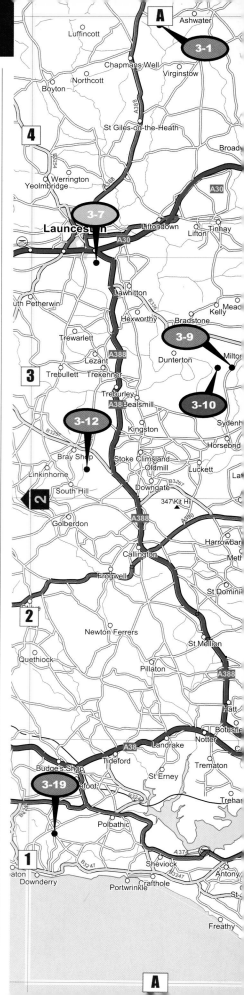

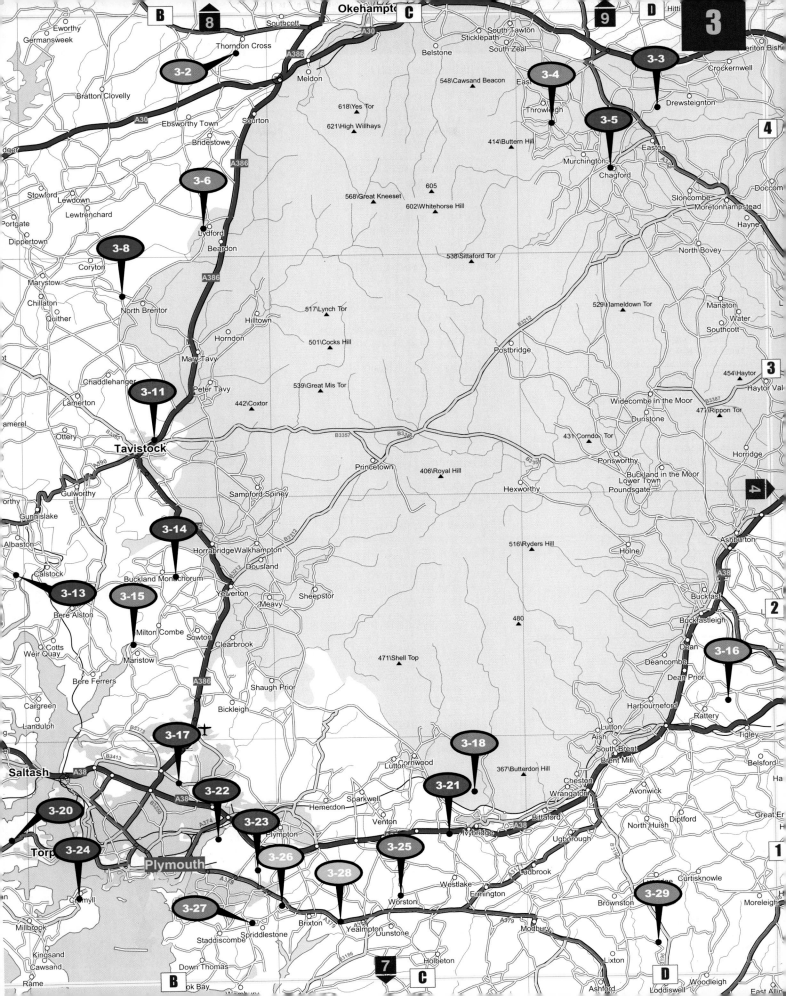

DEVON

● GARDEN CENTRE   ● NURSERY & GARDEN CENTRE
● NURSERY   ● GARDEN & NURSERY
● GARDEN   ● WATER GARDEN SPECIALIST

MARSHBROAD MOOR NURSERY
Daisymount, Ottery St Mary, Devon
TEL: 01404 822 738

EXETER UNIVERSITY GARDENS
Streatham Farm, Exeter, Devon
TEL: 01392 263 059

ST. BRIDGET NURSERIES & GARDEN CENTRE
Sidmouth Road, Exeter, Devon
TEL: 01392 876 281

SPRINGWELL NURSERY
Old Ide Lane, Exeter, Devon
TEL: 01392 410 545

ST. BRIDGET NURSERIES & GARDEN CENTRE
Old Rydon Lane, Exeter, Devon
TEL: 01392 873 672

SEABROOK GARDEN CENTRE
Topsham Road, Exeter, Devon
TEL: 01392 875070

SIDMOUTH GARDEN CENTRE
Stowford Cross, Sidmouth, Devon
TEL: 01395 516 142

STRAWBERRY HILL NURSERY
Dunsford, Exeter, Devon
TEL: 01647 253 297

TEIGN VALLEY NURSERY
Bridford Mills, Exeter, Devon
TEL: 01647 252 654

BICTON PARK BOTANICAL GARDENS
East Budleigh, Budleigh Salterton, Devon, EX9 7BJ
TEL: 01395 568 465
EMAIL: lister@bictongardens.co.uk
WEB: www.bictongardens.co.uk
Grade 1 Listed Historic Gardens, unique Palm

House, extensive museum, indoor & outdoor children's play areas, 1.5 miles of railway, garden centre, shop and Orangery restaurant together make Bicton Park Gardens the perfect place to visit.
OPEN: Daily all year, Summer 10-6. Winter 10-5, closed Christmas Day only.
ENTRY COSTS: Adult £4.75, Child £2.75, Concession £3.75, Family £12.75 (2 adults, up to 4 children)
SPECIALITIES: Arboretum, Formal garden, Herbaceous borders, Pinetum, Seasonal bedding plants.

PEVERIL CLEMATIS NURSERY
Christow, Exeter, Devon
TEL: 01647 252 937

LUXTON GARDEN CENTRE
Higher Hulham Road, Exmouth, Devon
TEL: 01395 271 911

POWDERHAM CASTLE
Powderham, Exeter, Devon
TEL: 01626 890 243

BROAD OAK NURSERIES
Mowlish Lane, Exeter, Devon
TEL: 01626 890 034

SALTERTON GARDEN CENTRE
Budleigh Salterton, Devon
TEL: 01395 445 085

THE ROCK NURSERY
Station Hill, Newton Abbot, Devon
TEL: 01626 852 134

BLYTH'S DEVON NURSERIES
Exeter Road, Dawlish, Devon
TEL: 01626 863 131

ORCHID PARADISE
Burnham Nurseries, Newton Abbot, Devon
TEL: 01626 352 233

JACK'S PATCH GARDEN CENTRE
Bishopsteignton, Teignmouth, Devon
TEL: 01626 776 996

BUCKFAST NURSERY
Unit 29, Newton Abbot, Devon
TEL: 01626 201 009

PLEASANT VIEW NURSERY AND GARDEN
Two Mile Oak, Newton Abbot, Devon
TEL: 01803 813 388

TORBAY PALM FARM
St Marychurch Road, Newton Abbot, Devon
TEL: 01803 872 800

TORBAY AQUATIC CENTRE
St Marychurch Road, Newton Abbot, Devon
TEL: 01803 873 663

BRAMLEY LODGE GARDEN NURSERY
Beech Tree Lane, Newton Abbot, Devon
TEL: 01803 813 265

PLANT WORLD GARDENS & NURSERY
St Marychurch Road, Newton Abbot, Devon
TEL: 01803 872 939

FERMOY'S GARDEN CENTRE & FARM SHOP
Totnes Road, Newton Abbot, Devon
TEL: 01803 813 504

HILL HOUSE NURSERY AND GARDEN
Landscove, Newton Abbot, Devon
TEL: 01803 762 273

KERSWELL GARDEN CENTRE
Newton Road, Torquay, Devon
TEL: 01803 872 124

GILBERTS PET & GARDEN CENTRE
40 Fore Street, Torquay, Devon
TEL: 01803 329 149

OTTER NURSERIES & GARDEN CENTRE
250 Babbacombe Road, Torquay, Devon
TEL: 01803 214 294

STAVERTON BRIDGE NURSERY
Staverton, Totnes, Devon
TEL: 01803 762 678

DARTINGTON HALL
Dartington, Totnes, Devon
TEL: 01803 862 367

CIDER PRESS PLANT CENTRE
Shinners Bridge, Totnes, Devon
TEL: 01803 864 171
LONGCOMBE NURSERY & GARDEN

PAIGNTON ZOO & BOTANICAL GARDENS
Totnes Road, Paignton, Devon, TQ4 7EU
TEL: 01803 697 500
EMAIL: info@paigntonzoo.org.uk
WEB: www.paigntonzoo.org.uk
Paignton Zoo's redevelopment programme has transformed the zoo into a unique environmental park, featuring the plants and animals of some of the world's threatened habitats.
OPEN: All year: daily Apr-Oct: 10-6, Nov-Mar 10-5. Closed 25 Dec.
ENTRY COSTS: Adult £7.70, Children £5.50, Family £23.70, OAPs £6.20, Other Students: £6.20 Discounts for groups +15
SPECIALITIES: Aviary, Exotic plants, Fruit & fruit trees, Gifts.

CENTRE
Longcombe Cross, Totnes, Devon
TEL: 01803 863 098

TORBAY GARDEN CENTRE
Brixham Road, Paignton, Devon
TEL: 01803 559 768

SAMUEL DOBIE & SON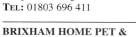
Long Road, Paignton, Devon
TEL: 01803 696 411

BRIXHAM HOME PET & GARDEN SUPPLIES
10 Greenswood Road, Brixham, Devon
TEL: 01803 854 410

GREENWAY HOUSE & GARDENS, NATIONAL TRUST
Churston Ferrers, Brixham, Devon
TEL: 01803 842 382/843 235

COLETON FISHACRE HOUSE & GARDEN, NATIONAL TRUST
Coleton, Dartmouth, Devon
TEL: 01803 752 466

Water Lily

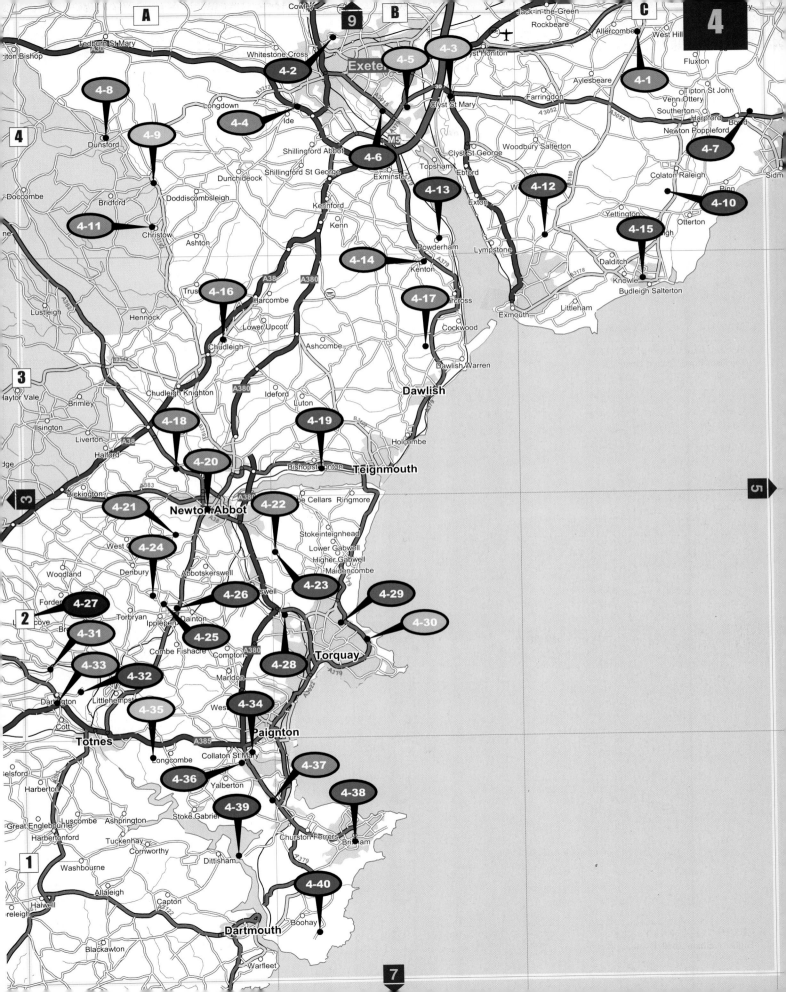

DORSET

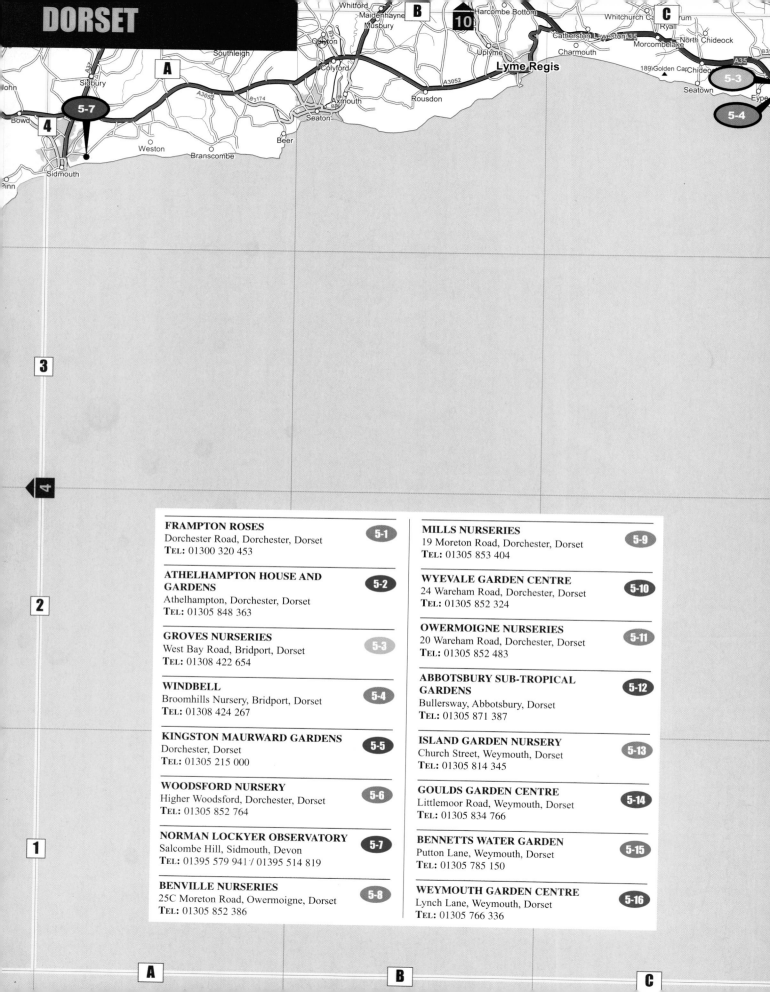

FRAMPTON ROSES 5-1
Dorchester Road, Dorchester, Dorset
Tel: 01300 320 453

ATHELHAMPTON HOUSE AND GARDENS 5-2
Athelhampton, Dorchester, Dorset
Tel: 01305 848 363

GROVES NURSERIES 5-3
West Bay Road, Bridport, Dorset
Tel: 01308 422 654

WINDBELL 5-4
Broomhills Nursery, Bridport, Dorset
Tel: 01308 424 267

KINGSTON MAURWARD GARDENS 5-5
Dorchester, Dorset
Tel: 01305 215 000

WOODSFORD NURSERY 5-6
Higher Woodsford, Dorchester, Dorset
Tel: 01305 852 764

NORMAN LOCKYER OBSERVATORY 5-7
Salcombe Hill, Sidmouth, Devon
Tel: 01395 579 941 / 01395 514 819

BENVILLE NURSERIES 5-8
25C Moreton Road, Owermoigne, Dorset
Tel: 01305 852 386

MILLS NURSERIES 5-9
19 Moreton Road, Dorchester, Dorset
Tel: 01305 853 404

WYEVALE GARDEN CENTRE 5-10
24 Wareham Road, Dorchester, Dorset
Tel: 01305 852 324

OWERMOIGNE NURSERIES 5-11
20 Wareham Road, Dorchester, Dorset
Tel: 01305 852 483

ABBOTSBURY SUB-TROPICAL GARDENS 5-12
Bullersway, Abbotsbury, Dorset
Tel: 01305 871 387

ISLAND GARDEN NURSERY 5-13
Church Street, Weymouth, Dorset
Tel: 01305 814 345

GOULDS GARDEN CENTRE 5-14
Littlemoor Road, Weymouth, Dorset
Tel: 01305 834 766

BENNETTS WATER GARDEN 5-15
Putton Lane, Weymouth, Dorset
Tel: 01305 785 150

WEYMOUTH GARDEN CENTRE 5-16
Lynch Lane, Weymouth, Dorset
Tel: 01305 766 336

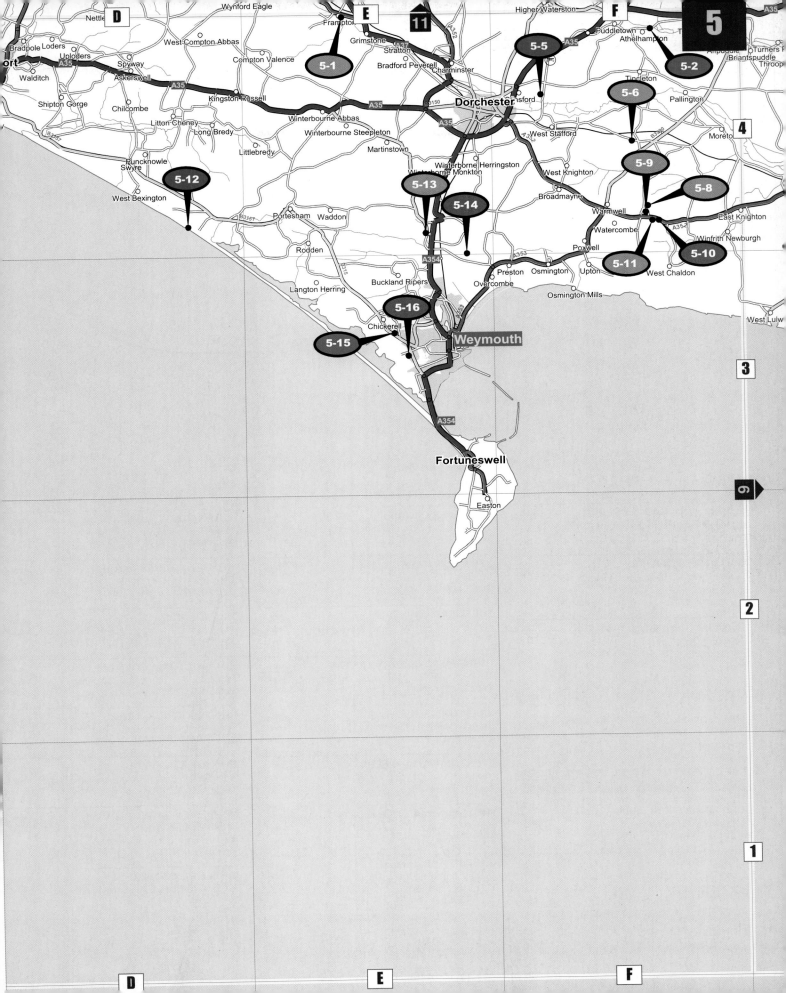

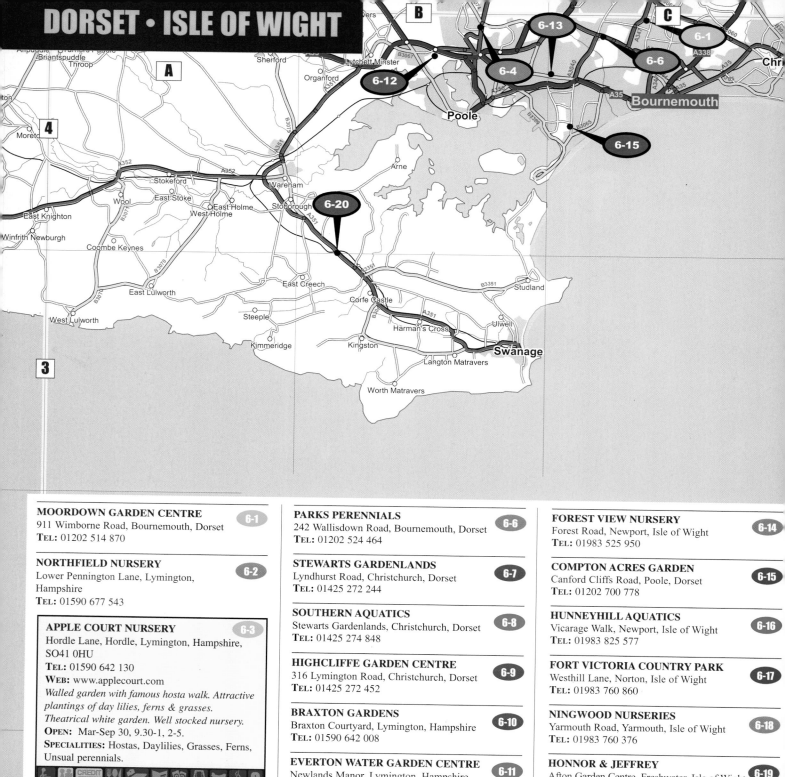

MOORDOWN GARDEN CENTRE 6-1
911 Wimborne Road, Bournemouth, Dorset
TEL: 01202 514 870

NORTHFIELD NURSERY 6-2
Lower Pennington Lane, Lymington,
Hampshire
TEL: 01590 677 543

APPLE COURT NURSERY 6-3
Hordle Lane, Hordle, Lymington, Hampshire,
SO41 0HU
TEL: 01590 642 130
WEB: www.applecourt.com
Walled garden with famous hosta walk. Attractive
plantings of day lilies, ferns & grasses.
Theatrical white garden. Well stocked nursery.
OPEN: Mar-Sep 30, 9.30-1, 2-5.
SPECIALITIES: Hostas, Daylilies, Grasses, Ferns,
Unusual perennials.

COLD HARBOUR NURSERY 6-4
19 Hilary Road, Poole, Dorset
TEL: 01202 696 875

EVERTON NURSERIES 6-5
Farmers Walk, Lymington, Hampshire
TEL: 01590 642 155

PARKS PERENNIALS 6-6
242 Wallisdown Road, Bournemouth, Dorset
TEL: 01202 524 464

STEWARTS GARDENLANDS 6-7
Lyndhurst Road, Christchurch, Dorset
TEL: 01425 272 244

SOUTHERN AQUATICS 6-8
Stewarts Gardenlands, Christchurch, Dorset
TEL: 01425 274 848

HIGHCLIFFE GARDEN CENTRE 6-9
316 Lymington Road, Christchurch, Dorset
TEL: 01425 272 452

BRAXTON GARDENS 6-10
Braxton Courtyard, Lymington, Hampshire
TEL: 01590 642 008

EVERTON WATER GARDEN CENTRE 6-11
Newlands Manor, Lymington, Hampshire
TEL: 01590 644 405

SOUTHERN AQUATICS & PETS 6-12
North Mead Drive, Poole, Dorset
TEL: 01202 602 060

CHUBB'S NURSERY 6-13
25 Churchill Road, Poole, Dorset
TEL: 01202 741 893

FOREST VIEW NURSERY 6-14
Forest Road, Newport, Isle of Wight
TEL: 01983 525 950

COMPTON ACRES GARDEN 6-15
Canford Cliffs Road, Poole, Dorset
TEL: 01202 700 778

HUNNEYHILL AQUATICS 6-16
Vicarage Walk, Newport, Isle of Wight
TEL: 01983 825 577

FORT VICTORIA COUNTRY PARK 6-17
Westhill Lane, Norton, Isle of Wight
TEL: 01983 760 860

NINGWOOD NURSERIES 6-18
Yarmouth Road, Yarmouth, Isle of Wight
TEL: 01983 760 376

HONNOR & JEFFREY 6-19
Afton Garden Centre, Freshwater, Isle of Wight
TEL: 01983 752 870

**NORDEN FARM SHOP & MINI
GARDEN CENTRE** 6-20
Norden Farm, Wareham, Dorset
TEL: 01929 480 098

LITTLE HERMITAGE 6-21
St Catherines Down, Ventnor, Isle of Wight
TEL: 01983 730 512

OSBORNE HOUSE, ENGLISH HERITAGE 7-1
York Avenue, East Cowes, Isle of Wight
TEL: 01983 200 022

RYDE HOUSE NURSERY 7-2
Binstead Road, Ryde, Isle of Wight
TEL: 01983ñ565 650

LUSHINGTON GARDEN CENTRE 7-3
Lushington Hill, Wootton , Isle of Wight
TEL: 01983 882 216

LYNWOOD GARDEN CENTRE 7-4
Fairlee Road, Newport, Isle of Wight
TEL: 01983 526 618

MEDINA GARDEN CENTRE 7-5
Staplers Road, Wootton, Isle of Wight
TEL: 01983 883 430

BUSY BEE PLANT CENTRE 7-6
Tesco Roundabout, Ryde, Isle of Wight
TEL: 01983 811 096

THE OASIS 7-7
Carpenters Road, Brading, Isle of Wight
TEL: 01983 613 760

MORTON MANOR 7-8
Brading, sandown, Isle of Wight
TEL: 01983 406 168

BRADING ROMAN VILLA 7-9
Oglander Roman Trust, Brading, Isle of Wight
TEL: 01983 406 223

HASELEY MANOR 7-10
Arreton, Newport, Isle of Wight
TEL: 01983 865 420

THOMPSON'S PLANT & GARDEN CENTRE 7-11
Watery Lane, Sandown, Isle of Wight
TEL: 01983 865 292

STONE & WATERSCAPES 7-12
Watery Lane, Sandown, Isle of Wight
TEL: 01983 867 249

HIGHWOOD NURSERIES 7-13
Newport Road, Rookley, Isle of Wight
TEL: 01983 721 011

HONNOR & JEFFREY 7-14
Dalverton Garden Centre, Sandown, Isle of Wight
TEL: 01983 868 602

NEWCHURCH NURSERIES 7-15
Springbank Nursery, Sandown, Isle of Wight
TEL: 01983 865 444

JUBILEE NURSERIES & GARDEN CENTRE 7-16
Newport Road, Sandown, Isle of Wight
TEL: 01983 865 562

DEACONS NURSERY 7-17
Moor View, Godshill, Isle of Wight
TEL: 01983 840 750

AQUASCAPE 7-18
1 Merryl Lane, Godshill, Isle of Wight
TEL: 01983 840 268

APPULDURCOMBE HOUSE, ENGLISH HERITAGE 7-19
Wroxall, Ventnor, Isle of Wight
TEL: 01983 852 484

STENBURY NURSERY 7-20
Smarts Cross, Southford, Isle of Wight
TEL: 01983 840 115

VENTNOR BOTANIC GARDEN 7-21
Undercliff Drive, Ventnor, Isle of Wight
TEL: 01983 855 397

HIGH GARDEN 7-22
Courtwood, Newton Ferrers, Devon
TEL: 01752 872 528

OVERBECKS MUSEUM & GARDEN, NATIONAL TRUST 7-23
Sharpitor, Salcombe, Devon
TEL: 01548 842 893

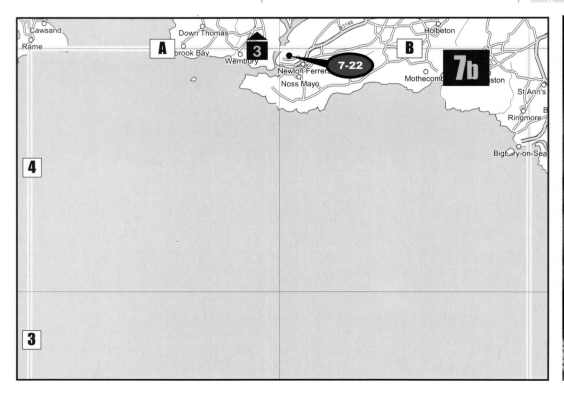

Aster

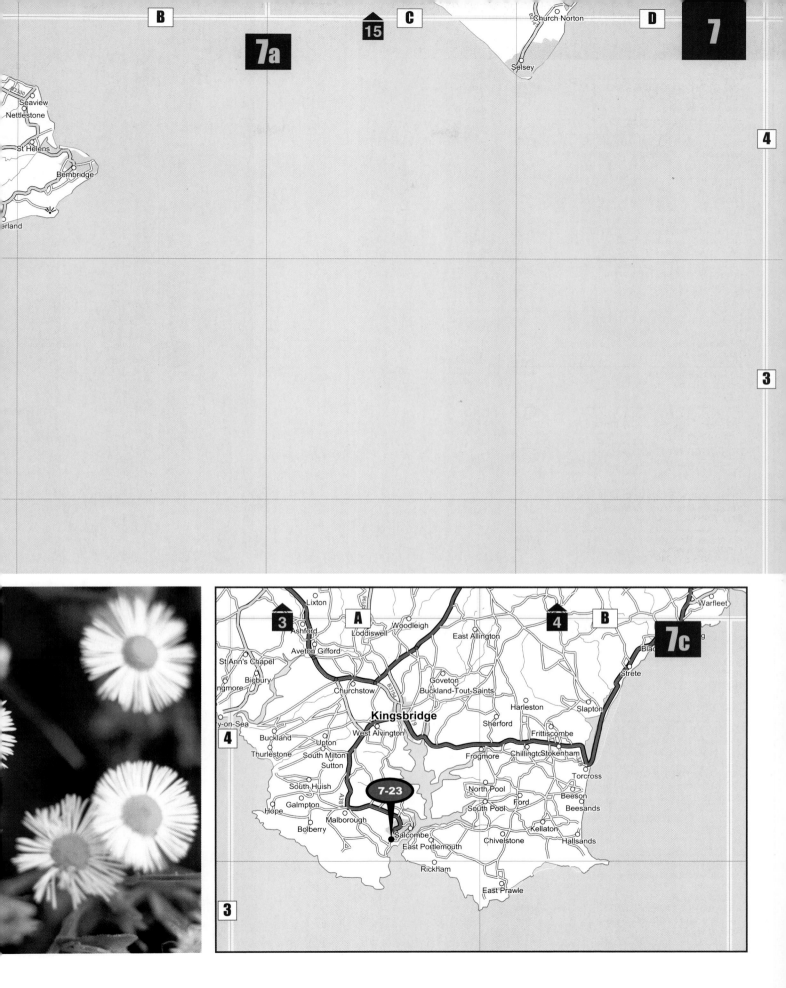

B

C

D

7

7a

15

4

3

Seaview
Nettlestone

St Helens

Bembridge

erland

Church Norton

Selsey

3

Lixton

A

Woodleigh

East Allington

4

B

Warfleet

7c

Ashford

Aveton Gifford

Loddiswell

St Ann's Chapel

Bigbury

ngmore

Churchstow

Goveton
Buckland-Tout-Saints

Blac

Strete

Kingsbridge

Harleston

Slapton

y-on-Sea

4

Buckland

Upton

West Alvington

Sherford

Frittiscombe

Thurlestone

South Milton

Sutton

Frogmore

Chillingto Stokenham

Torcross

South Huish

North Pool

Beeson

Galmpton

7-23

South Pool

Ford

Beesands

Hope

Malborough

Salcombe

Kellaton

Hallsands

Bolberry

East Portlemouth

Chivelstone

Rickham

3

East Prawle

DEVON · CORNWALL

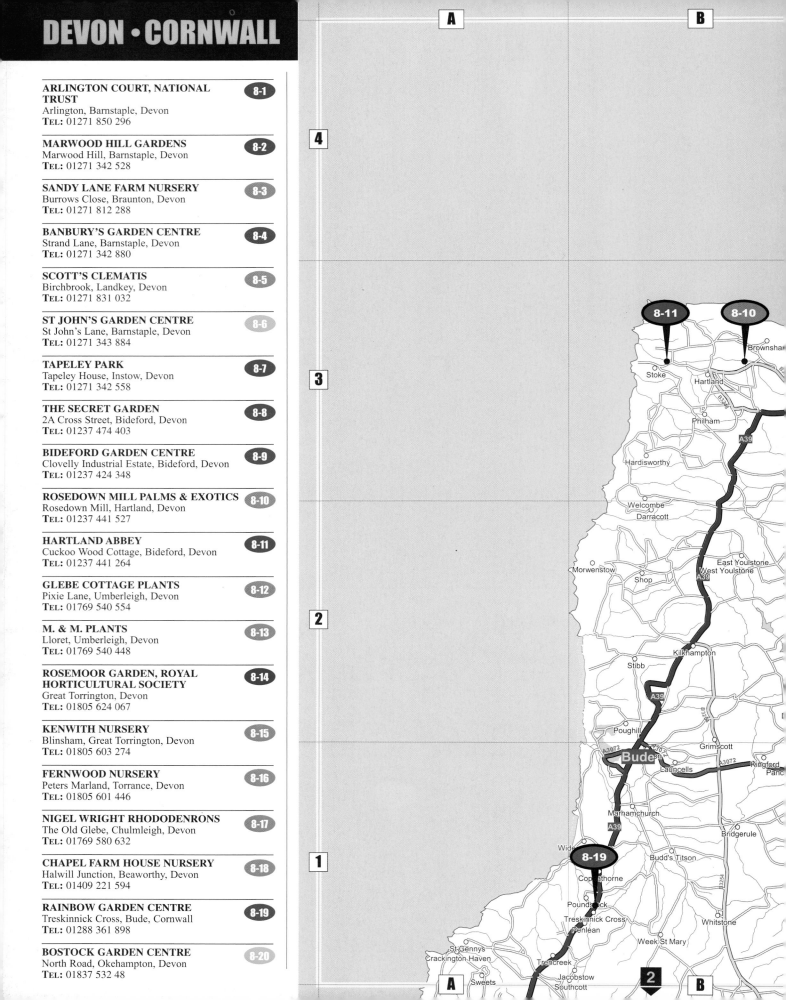

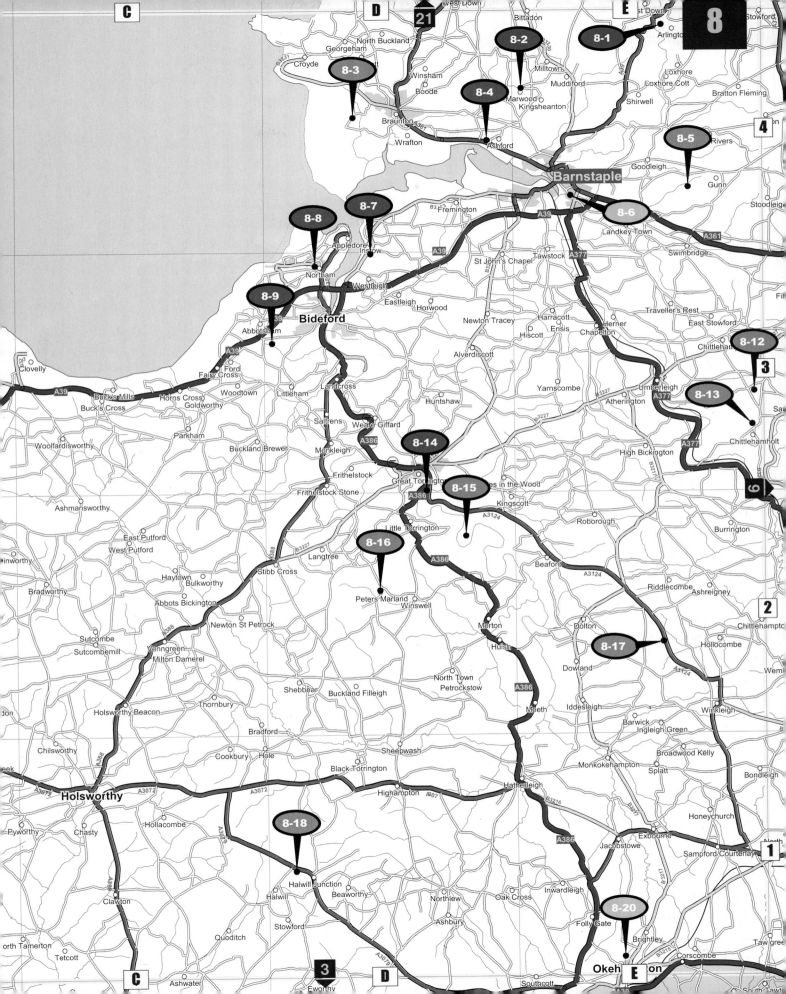

CAMFORD NURSERIES `9-1`
Woodford, Taunton, Somerset
TEL: 01984 640 522

ELWORTHY COTTAGE PLANTS `9-2`
Elworthy, Taunton, Somerset
TEL: 01984 656 427

NORTH STREET GARDEN CENTRE `9-3`
6 North Street, Taunton, Somerset
TEL: 01984 623 256

ASH MOOR NURSERY `9-4`
Rose Ash, South Molton, Devon
TEL: 01884 860 355

KNIGHTSHAYES COURT, NATIONAL TRUST `9-5`
Bolham, Tiverton, Devon
TEL: 01884 254 665

SAMPFORD SHRUBS `9-6`
Sampford Peverell, Tiverton, Devon
TEL: 01884 821 164

SOUTH WEST CARNIVOROUS PLANTS `9-7`
2 Rose Cottages, Cullompton, Devon
TEL: 01884 841 549

TURNPIKE NURSERIES `9-8`
Leonard Moor Cross, Cullompton, Devon
TEL: 01884 840 980

WITHLEIGH NURSERIES `9-9`
Withleigh, Tiverton, Devon
TEL: 01884 253 351

EGGESFORD GARDENS `9-10`
Eggesford, Chulmleigh, Devon
TEL: 01769 580 250

WATER GARDENS `9-11`
Highcroft, Chulmleigh, Devon
TEL: 01837 83 566

DULFORD NURSERIES `9-12`
Cullompton, Devon
TEL: 01884 266 361

THORNHAYES NUSERY `9-13`
St Andrews Wood, Cullompton, Devon
TEL: 01884 266 746

BOW AQUATIC CENTRE `9-14`
Burston, Crediton, Devon
TEL: 01363 824 38

EDWIN TUCKER & SONS `9-15`
Commercial Road, Crediton, Devon
TEL: 01363 772 202

KILLERTON HOUSE, NATIONAL TRUST `9-16`
Broadclyst, Exeter, Devon
TEL: 01392 881 345

FEEBERS HARDY PLANTS `9-17`
1 Feeber Cottage, Exeter, Devon
TEL: 01404 822 118

BOW AQUATIC CENTRE `9-16`
Bernaville Nurseries, Exeter, Devon
TEL: 01392 851 823

BERNAVILLE NURSERIES `9-19`
Three Horse Shoes, Exeter, Devon
TEL: 01392 851 326

OTTER NURSERIES GARDEN CENTRE `9-20`
Gosford Road, Ottery St Mary, Devon
TEL: 01404 815 815

California Poppies

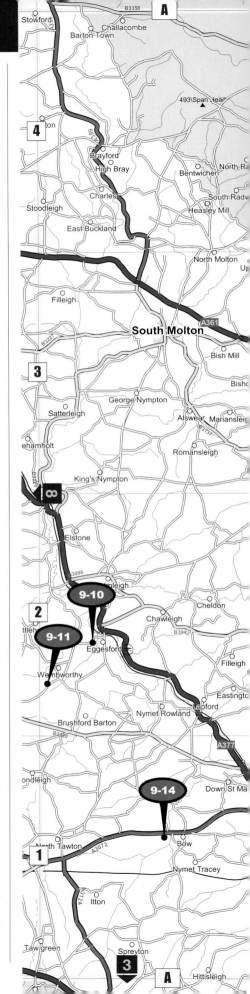

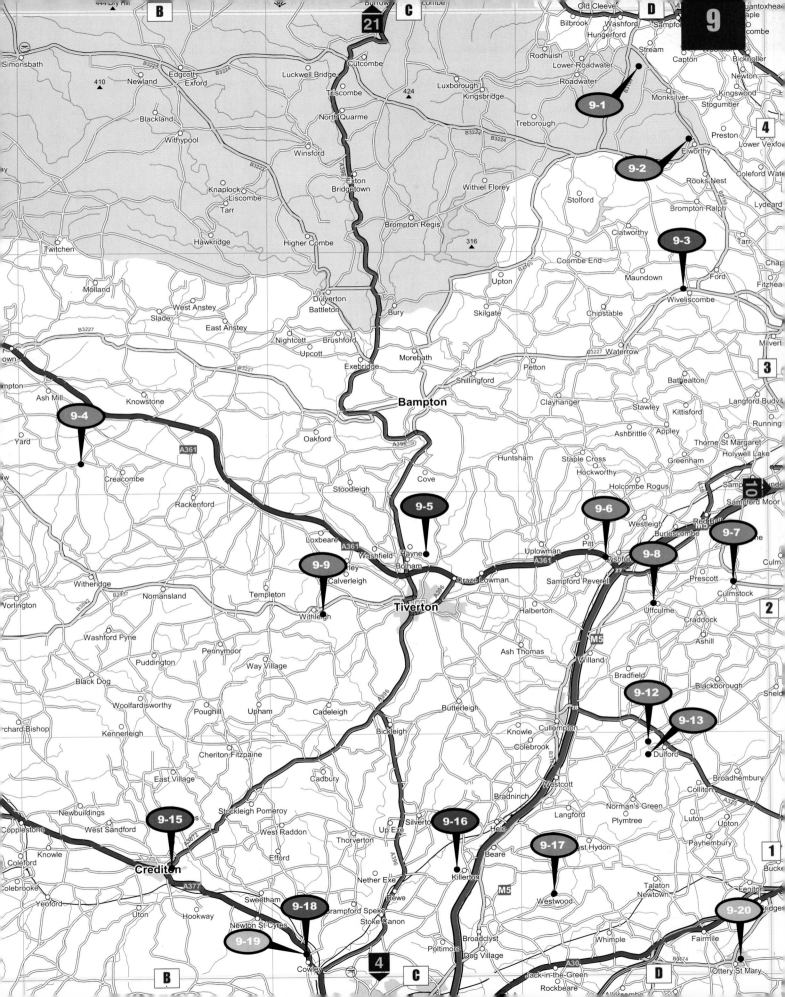

DEVON · SOMERSET

○ GARDEN CENTRE   ○ NURSERY & GARDEN CENTRE
○ NURSERY   ○ GARDEN & NURSERY
○ GARDEN   ○ WATER GARDEN SPECIALIST

CANNINGTON COLLEGE HERITAGE GARDENS
Cannington, Bridgwater, Somerset
TEL: 01278 655 000

HALSWAY NURSERIES
Crowcombe, Taunton, Somerset
TEL: 01984 618 243

TRINITY NURSERIES
Broadway, Bridgewater, Somerset
TEL: 01278 422 897

TRISCOMBE NURSERIES
West Bagborough, Taunton, Somerset
TEL: 01984 618 267

ASHFIELD COURT NURSERIES
Farringdon, North Petherton, Somerset
TEL: 01278 663 438

HESTERCOMBE GARDENS
Cheddon Fitzpaine, Taunton, Somerset
TEL: 01823 413 923

GREENWAY NURSERY
Mount Fancy, Taunton, Somerset
TEL: 01823 412 681

MONKTON ELM GARDEN & PET CENTRE
Monkton Elm, Taunton, Somerset
TEL: 01823 414 104

WYEVALE GARDEN CENTRE
Pen Elm, Taunton, Somerset
TEL: 01823 323 777

HIGH ELMS NURSERIES
Broad Lane, Taunton, Somerset
TEL: 01823 490 306

AVERY PLANT CENTRE
Silk Mills Road, Taunton, Somerset
TEL: 01823 288 324

ST JOHN'S GARDEN CENTRE
Priory Way, Barnstaple, Devon
TEL: 01823 336 279

BROADLEIGH GARDENS NURSERY
Bishops Hull, Taunton, Somerset
TEL: 01823 286 231

BROOKFIELD FARM SHOP & NURSERY
Brookfield Farm, Taunton, Somerset
TEL: 01823 443 333

DEANE GARDEN SHOPS
29 North Street, Taunton, Somerset
TEL: 01823 337 768

BARN CLOSE NURSERIES
Barn Close, Taunton, Somerset
TEL: 01823 443 507

GREENSHUTTERS NURSERIES
Milehill, Taunton, Somerset
TEL: 01460 281 265

MALLET COURT NURSERY
Curry Mallet, Taunton, Somerset
TEL: 01823 480 748

Nemesia

BLACKDOWN NURSERIES & GARDEN CENTRE
2 Hockholler, Wellington, Somerset
TEL: 01823 661 699

CHELSTON NURSERIES
Chelston, Wellington, Somerset
TEL: 01823 662 007

FOXMOOR FLOWER TOWER
Foxmoor Nurseries, Wellington, Somerset
TEL: 01823 661 662

HATCH COURT
Hatch Beauchamp, Taunton, Somerset
TEL: 01823 480 120

WELLINGTON PET, GARDEN & FARM STORE
10-10A High Street, Wellington, Somerset
TEL: 01823 662 914

EAST LAMBROOK MANOR GARDENS
East Lambrook, South Petherton, Somerset
TEL: 01460 240 328

BARRINGTON COURT & GARDEN, NATIONAL TRUST
Barrington, Ilminster, Somerset
TEL: 01460 241 938

LYNASH NURSERIES
Wall Ditch Lane, Merriott, Somerset
TEL: 01460 777 64

STREET ASH NURSERY & PLANT CENTRE
Street Ash, Chard, Somerset
TEL: 01460 234 582

SCOTTS NURSERIES
Higher Street, Merriott, Somerset
TEL: 01460 723 06

GRANVILLES NURSERY
Hazlebury Road, Crewkerne, Somerset
TEL: 01460 77844

LOWER SEVERALLS GARDEN & NURSERY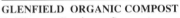
Crewkerne, Somerset
TEL: 01460 732 34

GLENFIELD ORGANIC COMPOST
Puddletown, Crewkerne, Somerset
TEL: 01460 73251

CHARD GARDEN CENTRE
Cuttifords Door, Chard, Somerset
TEL: 01460 63 088

KINGSFIELD CONSERVATION NURSERY
Broadenham Lane, Chard, Somerset
TEL: 01460 300 70

FORDE ABBEY
Chard, Somerset
TEL: 01460 221 290

NICKY'S ROCK GARDEN NURSERY
Broadhayes, Honiton , Devon
TEL: 01404 881 213

NURSERY OF MINIATURES
Hutgate Road, Honiton , Devon
TEL: 01404 42617

HALE LANE NURSERY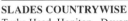
Honiton , Devon
TEL: 01404 427 11

BURROW FARM GARDENS
Dalwood, Axminster, Devon
TEL: 01404 831 285

SLADES COUNTRYWISE
Turks Head, Honiton , Devon
TEL: 01404 427 20

HUNTERS CROFT NURSERY
Raymonds Hill, Axminster, Devon
TEL: 01297 333 66

SINCLAIR GARDEN NURSERY
Maes- y- Haf, Lyme Regis, Dorset
TEL: 01297 443 079

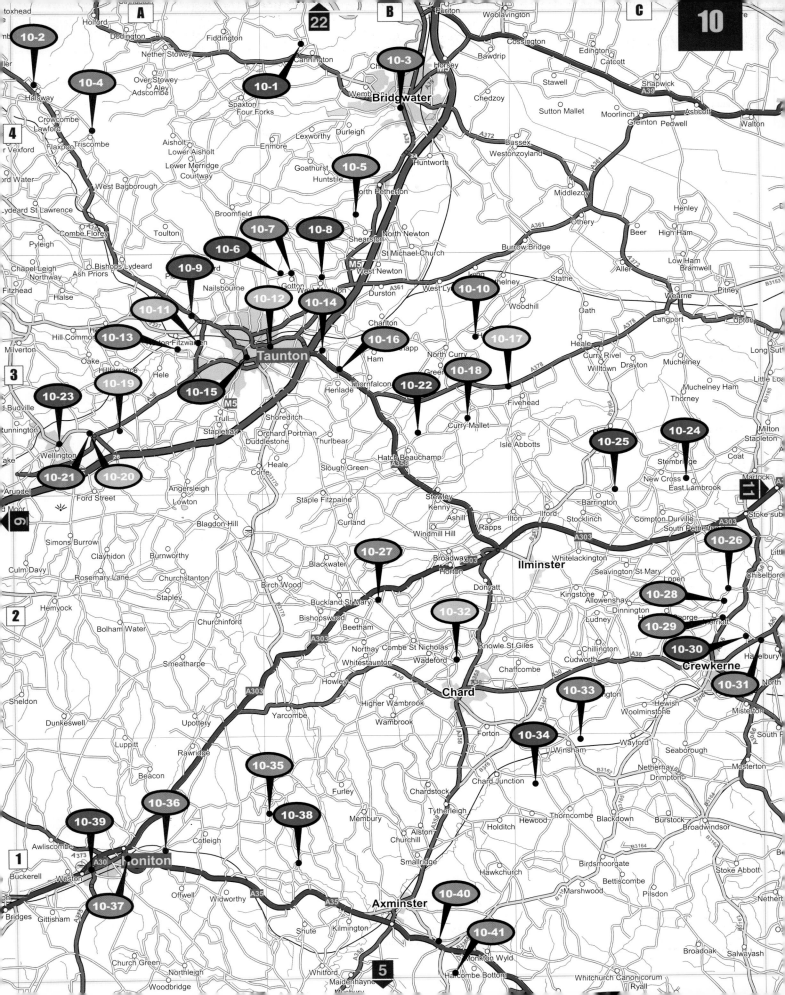

PEAR TREE COTTAGE PLANTS 11-1
Pear Tree Cottage, Shepton Mallet, Somerset
TEL: 01749 831 487

SWEET ACRE NURSERY 11-2
Godney Road, Glastonbury, Somerset
TEL: 01458 834 602

ST ANNE'S NURSERY 11-3
Havyatt, Glastonbury, Somerset
TEL: 01458 832 720

STOURHEAD, NATIONAL TRUST 11-4
Stourton, Warminster, Wiltshire
TEL: 09001 335 205

STOURTON HOUSE 11-5
Stourton, Warminster, Wiltshire
TEL: 01747 840 417

HADSPEN GARDEN & NURSERY 11-6
Hadspen House, Castle Cary, Somerset
TEL: 01749 813 707

LITTLETON MONOCOT NURSERY 11-7
St. Michaels, Somerton, Somerset
TEL: 01458 272 356

ABBEY PLANTS 11-8
Chiffchaffs, Gillingham, Dorset
TEL: 01747 840 841

MILTON GARDEN PLANTS 11-9
Milton on Stour, Gillingham, Dorset
TEL: 01747 822 484

PLANTWORLD NURSERY 11-10
Kendalls Lane, Gillingham, Dorset
TEL: 01747 824 015

DAYSPRING NURSERY 11-11
Quarr, Gillingham, Devon
TEL: 01747 823 030

SCATS COUNTRY STORE 11-12
Station Road, Gillingham, Dorset
TEL: 01747 824 933

HARDY ORCHIDS 11-13
New Gate Farm, Gillingham, Dorset
TEL: 01747 838 368

WILLIAMS NURSERY 11-14
L. A. Williams & Son, Stalbridge, Dorset
TEL: 01963 362 355

BRINSMORE GARDENS 11-15
Tintinhull Road, Yeovil, Somerset
TEL: 01935 411 000

MONTACUTE HOUSE, NATIONAL TRUST 11-16
Montacute, Yeovil, Somerset
TEL: 01935 823 289

CASTLE GARDENS PLANT CENTRE 11-17
Castleton, Sherborne, Dorset
TEL: 01935 814 633

SHERBORNE CASTLE 11-18
Sherborne, Dorset
TEL: 01935 813 182

GOLDEN ACRES NURSERY 11-19
Alvington Lane, Yeovil, Somerset
TEL: 01935 475 613

TINTINHULL HOUSE GARDEN, NATIONAL TRUST 11-20
Farm Street, Yeovil, Somerset
TEL: 01935 822 545

NORTH PERROTT GARDEN CENTRE 11-21
North Perrott, Crewkerne, Somerset
TEL: 01460 77090

DORSET WATER LILY CO. 11-22
Yeovil Road, Yeovil, Somerset
TEL: 01935 891 668

DIGWELL NURSERY 11-23
The Villa, Blandford Forum, Dorset
TEL: 01258 454 714

MINTERNE HOUSE 11-24
Minterne Magna, Dorchester, Dorset
TEL: 01300 341 370

PARNHAM HOUSE 11-25
Beaminster, Dorset
TEL: 01308 862 204

Liatris

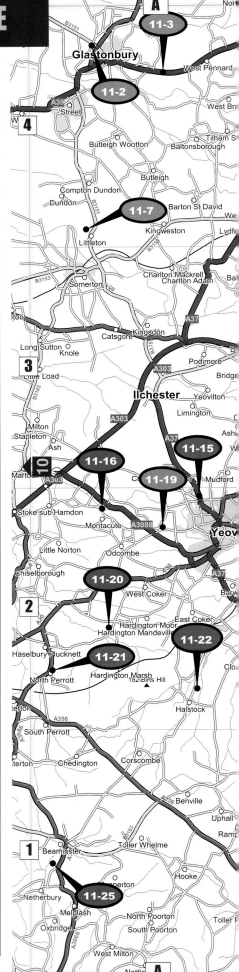

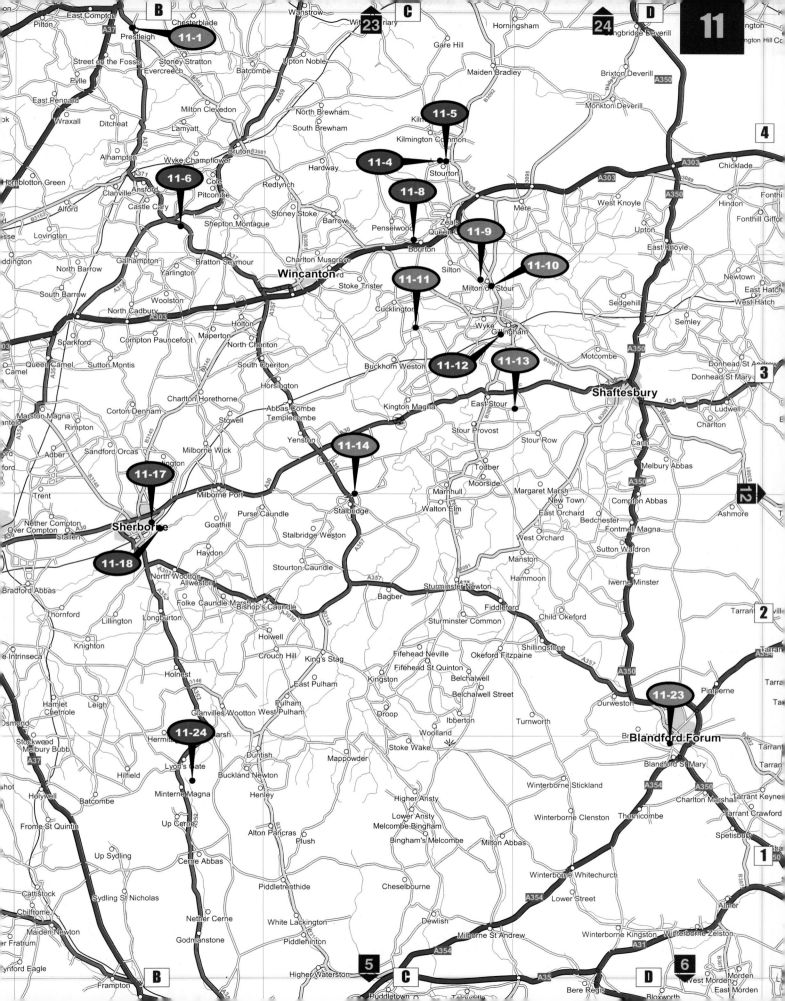

DORSET · HAMPSHIRE · WILTS

● GARDEN CENTRE
● NURSERY
● GARDEN

◐ NURSERY & GARDEN CENTRE
GARDEN & NURSERY
◑ WATER GARDEN SPECIALIST

LONGHALL NURSERY 12-1
Stockton, Warminster, Wiltshire
TEL: 01985 850 914

HEALE GARDENS 12-2
Heale House, Salisbury, Wiltshire
TEL: 01722 782 504

WILTON HOUSE 12-3
Wilton, Salisbury, Wiltshire
TEL: 01722 746 720

SCATS COUNTRY STORE 12-4
Churchfields Road, Salisbury, Wiltshire
TEL: 01722 336 886

MOMPESSON HOUSE 12-5
The Close, Salisbury, Wiltshire
TEL: 01722 335 659

SOUCHEZ NURSERIES 12-6
86 Britford Lane, Salisbury, Wiltshire
TEL: 01722 336 777

OLD WARDOUR CASTLE 12-7
Tisbury, Salisbury, Wiltshire
TEL: 01747 870 487

COURTENS GARDEN CENTRE 12-8
Romsey Road, Salisbury, Wiltshire
TEL: 01794 884 489

LANDFORD TREES 12-9
Landford Lodge, Salisbury, Wiltshire
TEL: 01794 390 808

GOLDEN ACRES NURSERY 12-10
Southampton Road, Salisbury, Wiltshire
TEL: 01794 390 319

LARMER TREE GARDENS 12-11
Tollard Royal, Salisbury, Wiltshire
TEL: 01725 516 228

DRYSDALE NURSERY 12-12
Bowerwood Road, Fordingbridge, Hampshire
TEL: 01425 653 010

WOLVERCROFT WORLD OF PLANTS 12-13
Fordingbridge Road, Fordingbridge, Hamps.
TEL: 01425 652 437

CHETTLE HOUSE 12-14
Chettle, Blandford Forum, Dorset
TEL: 01258 830 209

POPS PLANTS 12-15
Greenfield Farm, Fordingbridge, Hampshire
TEL: 01725 511 421

HORTON VALE NURSERY 12-16
Horton Heath, Wimborne, Dorset
TEL: 01202 813 473

GLOBAL ORANGE GROVES UK 12-17
Horton Road, Wimborne, Dorset
TEL: 01202 826 244

GUYS NURSERY & GARDEN CENTRE 12-18
Forest Corner, Ringwood, Hampshire
TEL: 01425 473 113

BRACKENDALE NURSERIES 12-19
Horton Road, Wimborne, Dorset
TEL: 01202 822 349

THREE LEGGED CROSS GARDEN CENTRE 12-20
Ringwood Road, Wimborne, Dorset
TEL: 01202 822 203

KOI SHOP AQUATIC CENTRE 12-21
Within John Brown Garden Centre, Wimborne, Dorset
TEL: 01202 823 042

LITTLEBANKS NURSERY 12-22
Green Lane, Ringwood, Hampshire
TEL: 01425 461 658

STEWARTS COUNTRY GARDEN CENTRE 12-23
God's Blessing Lane, Wimborne, Dorset
TEL: 01202 882 462

SHELLEY NURSERIES 12-24
77 Pinehurst Road, Ferndown, Dorset
TEL: 01202 873 283

KINGSTON LACY, NATIONAL TRUST 12-25
Wimborne Minster, Dorset
TEL: 01202 883 402

WYEVALE GARDEN CENTRE 12-26
Wimbourne Road West, Wimborne, Dorset
TEL: 01908 281 161

STAPEHILL ABBEY CRAFTS & GARDENS 12-27
276 Wimborne Road West, Ferndown, Dorset
TEL: 01202 861 686

KNOLL GARDENS & NURSERY 12-28
Hampreston, Wimborne, Dorset
TEL: 01202 873 931

TREHANE CAMELLIA NURSERY 12-29
Stapehill Road, Wimborne, Dorset
TEL: 01202 873 490

HASKINS GARDEN CENTRE 12-30
Longham, Ferndown, Dorset
TEL: 01202 591 919

GOLDEN ACRES NURSERY 12-31
359 Christchurch Road, Ferndown, Dorset
TEL: 01202 570 033

PLOWMANS GARDEN NURSERY & PLANT CENTRE 12-32
392 Christchurch Road, Ferndown, Dorset
TEL: 01202 582 169

MACPENNYS NURSERIES 12-33
154 Burley Road, Christchurch, Hampshire
TEL: 01425 672 348

COPPINS PLANT CENTRE 12-34
Christchurch Road, Ferndown, Dorset
TEL: 01202 574 665

OAKS GARDEN CENTRE 12-35
Queen Anne Drive, Wimborne, Dorset
TEL: 01202 603 322

BEECROFT NURSERIES 12-36
Queen Anne Drive, Wimborne, Dorset
TEL: 01202 693 705

WOODLANDS THE SPECIALIST PLANT CENTRE 12-37
Blandford Road, Poole, Dorset
TEL: 01258 857 163

CANFORD PARK GARDEN CENTRE 12-38
Magna Road, Wimborne, Dorset
TEL: 01202 577 770

BASHLEY PLANT CENTRE 12-39
Bashley Common Road, New Milton, Hamps
TEL: 01425 612 442

REDCLIFFE GARDEN CENTRE 12-40
Bashley Road, New Milton, Hampshire
TEL: 01425 614 210

GARDEN COTTAGE NURSERY 12-41
New Lane, New Milton, Hampshire
TEL: 01425 613 029

CHERRY TREE NURSERY 12-42
Off New Road Roundabout, Bournemouth, Dorset
TEL: 01202 593 537

NAKED CROSS NURSERIES 12-43
Waterloo Road, Wimborne, Dorset
TEL: 01202 693 256

Ice Plant

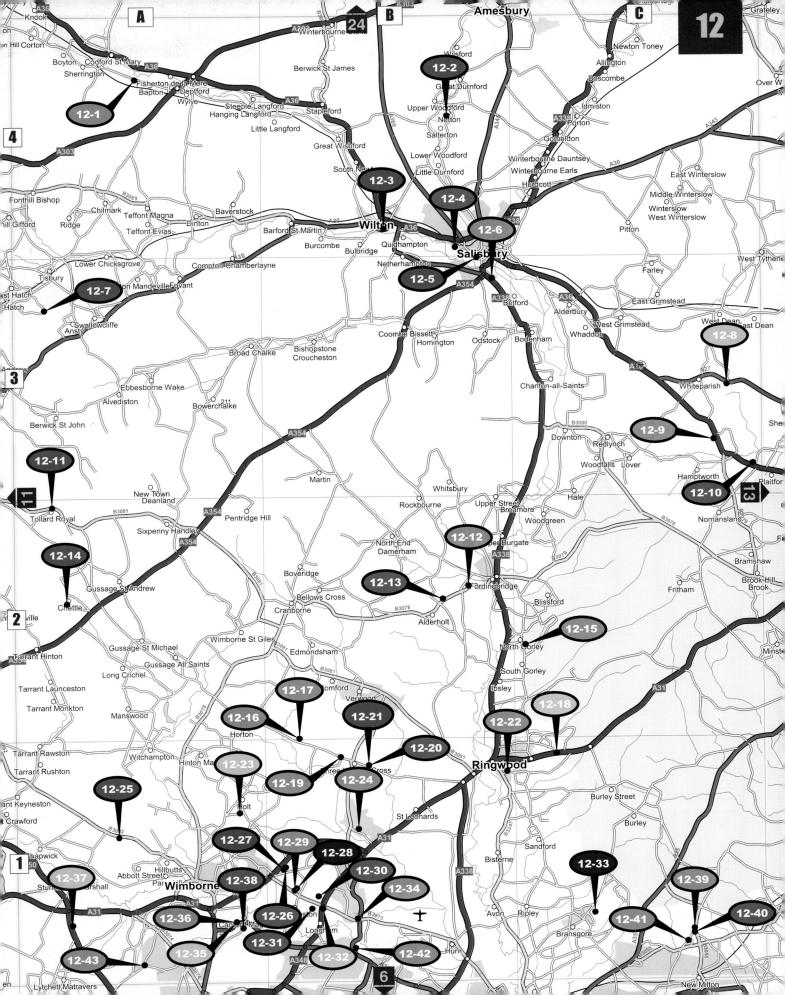

LONGSTOCK PARK NURSERY 13-1
Longstock, Stockbridge, Hampshire
TEL: 01264 810 894

HOUGHTON LODGE GARDENS 13-2
Hampshire Hydroponicum, Stockbridge, Hants
TEL: 01264 810 912

HOOKER'S GARDEN CENTRE 13-3
Main Road, Winchester, Hampshire
TEL: 01962 880 292

SCATS COUNTRY STORE 13-4
Easton Lane, Winchester, Hampshire
TEL: 01962 863 007

GREAT HALL 13-5
Castle Avenue, Winchester, Hampshire
TEL: 01962 846 476

 HILLIER GARDEN 13-6
CENTRE
Romsey Road, Winchester,
Hampshire, SO22 5DN
TEL: 01962 842 288
WEB: www.hillier.co.uk

A very individual garden centre in the heart of the historic city of Winchester. Excellent selection of garden plants and sundries. Top quality advice.
OPEN: Daily 9-5.30, Sun 10-4.
SPECIALITIES: Furniture, Gifts, Hardy plants, Shrubs, Trees.

WINCHESTER PET & AQUATIC CENTRE 13-7
Hillier Garden Centre, Winchester, Hampshire
TEL: 01962 856 753

MOTTISFONT ABBEY & GARDEN, NT 13-8
Mottisfont, Romsey, Hampshire
TEL: 01794 340 757

TEST VALLEY NURSERY 13-9
Stockbridge Road, Romsey, Hampshire
TEL: 01794 368 881

GEORGE BECKETT NURSERIES 13-10
Compton Nursery, Winchester, Hampshire
TEL: 01962 713 732

MACGREGORS PLANTS FOR SHADE 13-11
Carters Clay Road, Romsey, Hampshire
TEL: 01794 340 256

SIR HAROLD HILLIER GARDENS & 13-13
ARBORETUM
Jermyns Lane, Romsey, Hampshire
TEL: 01794 368 787

CHOICE PLANTS 13-14
Stockbridge Road, Romsey, Hampshire
TEL: 01794 368 895

CEDAR NURSERIES 13-15
Sandy Lane, Romsey, Hampshire
TEL: 01794 368 375

 HILLIER PLANT 13-12
CENTRE
Jermyns Lane, Braishfield,
Romsey, SO51 0QA
TEL: 01794 368 407
EMAIL: braishfieldgc@hillier.co.uk
WEB: www.hillier.co.uk

On the site of The Sir Harold Hillier Gardens & Arboretum. Large and varied selection of nursery stock and other plants. Good gardening book and gift selection.
OPEN: Daily 9-5.30, Sun 10.30-4.30.
SPECIALITIES: Ornaments, Shrubs, Trees, Hardy plants, Gifts.

POCOCKS ROSES 13-16
Jermyns Lane, Romsey, Hampshire
TEL: 01794 367 500

GANGER FARM 13-17
Jermyn's Lane, Romsey,
Hampshire, SO51 0QA
TEL: 01794 513 345
Family-run PYO for strawberries, raspberries, currants, gooseberries and a wide selection of fresh vegetables.
OPEN: Daily, Jun-Sep, 10-6, closed Mon after strawberry season has finished.

MILLWATER GARDENS 13-18
Mill Lane, Romsey, Hampshire
TEL: 01794 513 444

BRAMBRIDGE PARK GARDEN 13-19
CENTRE
Kiln Lane, Eastleigh, Hampshire
TEL: 01962 713 707

GREENACRES NURSERY 13-20
Green Lane, Romsey, Hampshire
TEL: 01794 512 409

WORLD OF WATER 13-21
Stockbridge Road, Romsey, Hampshire,
SO51 0HB
TEL: 01794 515 923
WEB: www.worldofwater.com
Everything for the pond and tropical fish enthusiast. Extensive showgardens. Expert advice.
OPEN: 9-5.30 Mon-Sat, Sun 10.30-4.30.
SPECIALITIES: Aquatic plants, Waterfalls, Water features, Shrubs, Terracotta pots.

SANDYFIELDS NURSERIES 13-22
Main Road, Winchester, Hampshire
TEL: 01962 712 218

DANDY'S NURSERY 13-23
Dandy's Ford Lane, Romsey, Hampshire
TEL: 01794 324 398

 HILLIER GARDEN 13-24
CENTRE
Botley Road, Romsey,
Hampshire, SO51 8ZL
TEL: 01794 513 459
WEB: www.hillier.co.uk
A gardener's delight in the middle of the picturesque market town of Romsey. Easy access and an extensive range of gardening products from paving to furniture.
OPEN: Daily 9-5.30, Sun 10.30-4.30.
SPECIALITIES: Furniture, Gifts, Greenhouses & sheds, Hardy plants, Shrubs.

BROADLANDS 13-2
Broadlands Park, Romsey, Hampshire
TEL: 01794 505 010

WYEVALE GARDEN CENTRE 13-2
Winchester Road, Eastleigh, Hampshire
TEL: 023 8060 0392

FIELDFARE OF FARE OAK 13-2
Winchester Road, Eastleigh, Hampshire
TEL: 023 8060 0541

B. & W. NURSERIES 13-2
Salisbury Road, Romsey, Hampshire
TEL: 01794 232 28

CONIGER NURSERIES 13-2
Bishopstoke Road, Eastleigh, Hampshire
TEL: 023 8061 2385

ALLINGTON NURSERY 13-3
Allington Lane, Eastleigh, Hampshire
TEL: 023 8060 0182

TREETOPS NURSERY 13-3
Allington Lane, Eastleigh, Hampshire
TEL: 023 8060 0782

ARTURI'S GARDEN CENTRE 13-3
Allington Lane, Eastleigh, Hampshire
TEL: 02380 602 234

PAULTONS NURSERY & PLANT CENTRE 13-3
Romsey Road, Southampton, Hampshire
TEL: 023 8081 3776

SPENCER COTTAGE NURSERY 13-3
Nursling Street, Southampton, Hampshire
TEL: 023 8073 9352

WEST END NURSERY 13-3
Burnetts Lane, Southampton, Hampshire
TEL: 023 8047 0595

HASKINS GARDEN CENTRE 13-3
Gaters Hill, Southampton, Hampshire
TEL: 023 8047 2324

ABBEY GARDEN CENTRE 13-3
Southampton Road, Southampton, Hampshire
TEL: 023 8081 2240

HILLIER GARDEN CENTRE 13-37

Woodhouse Lane, Botley, Southampton, Hampshire, SO30 2EZ

TEL: 01489 782 306
WEB: www.hillier.co.uk

A large garden centre with a comprehensive range of everything you could want for the garden. Easy access and friendly expert advice are sure to impress.

OPEN: Daily 9-5.30, Sun 10.30-4.30.
SPECIALITIES: Furniture, Gifts, Greenhouses & sheds, Hardy plants, Shrubs.

TUDOR HOUSE MUSEUM GARDEN 13-39
Cultural Services, Southampton, Hampshire
TEL: 023 8063 5904

FURZEY GARDENS NURSERY 13-40
Minstead Lodge, Lyndhurst, Hampshire
TEL: 023 8081 2464

FURZEY GARDENS 13-41
Minstead, Lyndhurst, Hampshire
TEL: 023 8081 2464

MEDINA NURSERIES 13-42
46 Brook Lane, Southampton, Hampshire
TEL: 0802 902 200

FAIRWEATHER'S GARDEN CENTRE 13-43
High street, Brockenhurst, Hampshire
TEL: 01590 612 307

HOLLY BUSH GARDEN CENTRE 13-44
Setley, Brockenhurst, Hampshire
TEL: 01590 622 839

EXBURY GARDENS 13-45
Exbury, Southampton, Hampshire
TEL: 023 8089 8625

SPINNERS GARDEN 13-46
School Lane, Lymington, Hampshire
TEL: 01590 673 347

BECKHEATH NURSERIES 13-47
East End, Lymington, Hampshire
TEL: 01590 626 620

SCATS COUNTRY STORE 13-48
Sway Road, Lymington, Hampshire
TEL: 01590 676 633

LYMINGTON PLANT CENTRE 13-49
Pitmore Lane, Lymington, Hampshire
TEL: 01590 682 611

AGARS NURSERY 13-50
Agars Lane, Lymington, Hampshire
TEL: 01590 683 703

STEVEN BAILEY 13-51
Silver Street, Lymington, Hampshire
TEL: 01590 682 227

FAIRWINDS GARDEN CENTRE 13-52
126 High Street, Lymington, Hampshire
TEL: 01590 677 022

SADLERS GARDENS 13-53
31 Rawley Road, Lymington, Hampshire
TEL: 01590 672 728

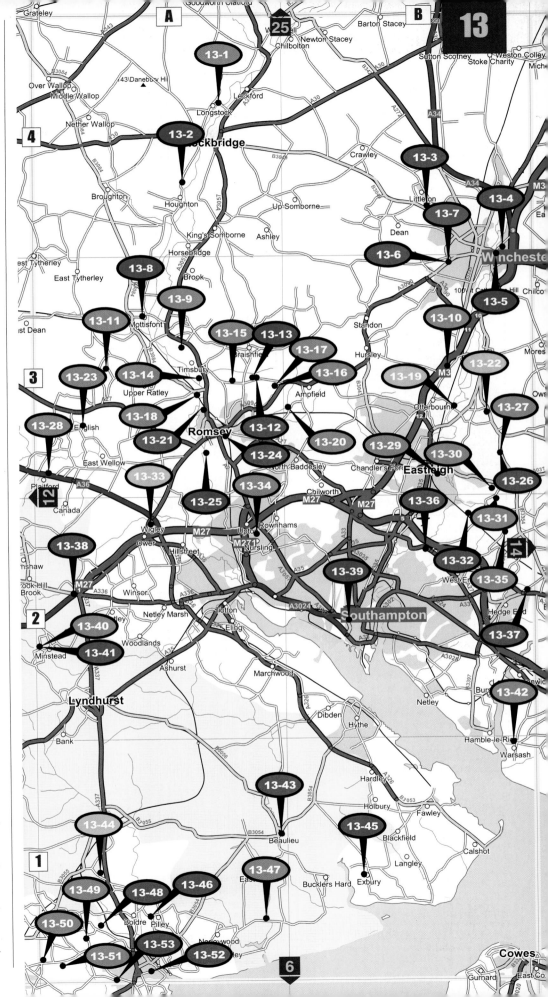

HAMPSHIRE

○ **GARDEN CENTRE**
○ **NURSERY**
○ **GARDEN**

● **NURSERY & GARDEN CENTR**
● **GARDEN & NURSERY**
● **WATER GARDEN SPECIALIS**

VALLEY NURSERIES
Basingstoke Road, Alton, Hampshire
TEL: 01420 549 700

EASTFIELD PLANT CENTRE
Paice Lane, Alton, Hampshire
TEL: 01420 563 640

GARTHOWEN GARDEN CENTRE
Alton Lane, Alton, Hampshire
TEL: 01962 773 225

OAKLEIGH NURSERIES
Petersfield Road, Alresford, Hampshire
TEL: 01962 773 344

WATER MEADOW NURSERY & HERB FARM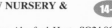
Water Meadows, Cheriton, Alresford, Hants, SO24 0QB
TEL: 01962 771 895
EMAIL: watermeadowplants@msn.com
WEB: www.plantaholic.co.uk

Award-winning nursery, specialising in water plants, unusual perennials, herbs and wild flowers, all in a garden setting. NCCPG holders, Papaver Orientale group of poppies.
OPEN: Mar-Jul, Wed-Sat, 10-5. Jul-Oct by appt. only.
SPECIALITIES: Aquatic, Garden design & landscaping, Herbaceous, Perennials, National Collection.

WATER MEADOW NURSERY & HERB FARM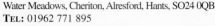
Water Meadows, Cheriton, Alresford, Hants, SO24 0QB
TEL: 01962 771 895
EMAIL: watermeadowplants@msn.com
WEB: www.plantaholic.co.uk
Huge selection of both native and decorative water plants and lilies and plants for both wet and dry pond borders, all in a garden setting.
OPEN: Mar-Jul, Wed-Sat, 10-5. Jul-Oct by appt. only.
SPECIALITIES: Aquatic, Bamboos, Ferns, Perennials, National Collection.

BLACKTHORN NURSERY
Kilmeston, Arlesford, Hampshire
TEL: 01962 771 796

QUEEN ELIZABETH COUNTRY PARK
Gravel Hill, Waterlooville, Hampshire
TEL: 023 9259 5040

ORCHARDLEIGH NURSERIES
Botley Road, Southampton, Hampshire
TEL: 01489 892 687

JOBS COTTAGE NURSERIES
Durley Hall Lane, Southampton, Hampshire
TEL: 01489 860 456

RUMSEY GARDENS NURSERIES 14-11
117 Drift Road, Waterlooville, Hampshire
TEL: 023 9259 3367

MEON VALLEY NURSERIES 14-12
Soberton Heath, Southampton, Hampshire
TEL: 01329 832 266

FAMILY TREES 14-13
The Tree Nursery, Shedfield, Hampshire
TEL: 01329 834 812

RUSTLINGS NURSERIES 14-14
104 Catherington Lane, Waterlooville, Hamps.
TEL: 023 9259 4832

UPLANDS NURSERIES 14-15
Winchester Street, Southampton, Hampshire
TEL: 01489 782 069

KEYDELL NURSERIES 14-16
Havant Road, Waterlooville, Hampshire
TEL: 023 9259 3839

LODGE HILL NURSERY 14-17
Lodge Hill, Fareham, Hampshire
TEL: 01329 834 753

PARK PLACE FARM NURSERY 14-18
Titchfield Lane, Wickham, Hampshire
TEL: 01329ñ834 991

MUD ISLAND NURSERIES 14-19
Southwick Road, Fareham, Hampshire
TEL: 01329 834 407

MOUNT FOLLY NURSERIES 14-20
Southwick Road, Wickham, Hampshire
TEL: 01329 832 294

STAUNTON COUNTRY PARK 14-21
Middle Park Way, Havant, Hampshire
TEL: 023 9245 3405

GARSONS 14-25
Fontley Road, Titchfield, Fareham,
Hampshire, PO15 6QX
TEL: 01329 844336
EMAIL: mail@garsonfarm.co.uk
WEB: www.garson-farm.co.uk

A modern garden centre with restaurant, gift shop, farm shop and comprehensive choice of plants and garden furniture. Excellent Pet Shop and Camping Centre.
OPEN: Daily, summer 9-6, winter 9-5. Sun 10-4, closed Christmas & Boxing Day.
SPECIALITIES: Bedding plants, Climbers, Shrubs, Pot plants.

SILVER SPRINGS NURSERIES
Fontley Road, Fareham, Hampshire
TEL: 01329 842 114

WYEVALE GARDEN CENTRE 14-23
Bartons Road, Havant, Hampshire
TEL: 023 9245 6200

HAYWARDS CARNATIONS 14-24
The Chace Gardens, Waterlooville, Hampshire
TEL: 023 9226 3047

HAMBROOKS GARDEN CENTRE 14-26
135 Southampton Road, Fareham, Hampshire
TEL: 01489 572 285

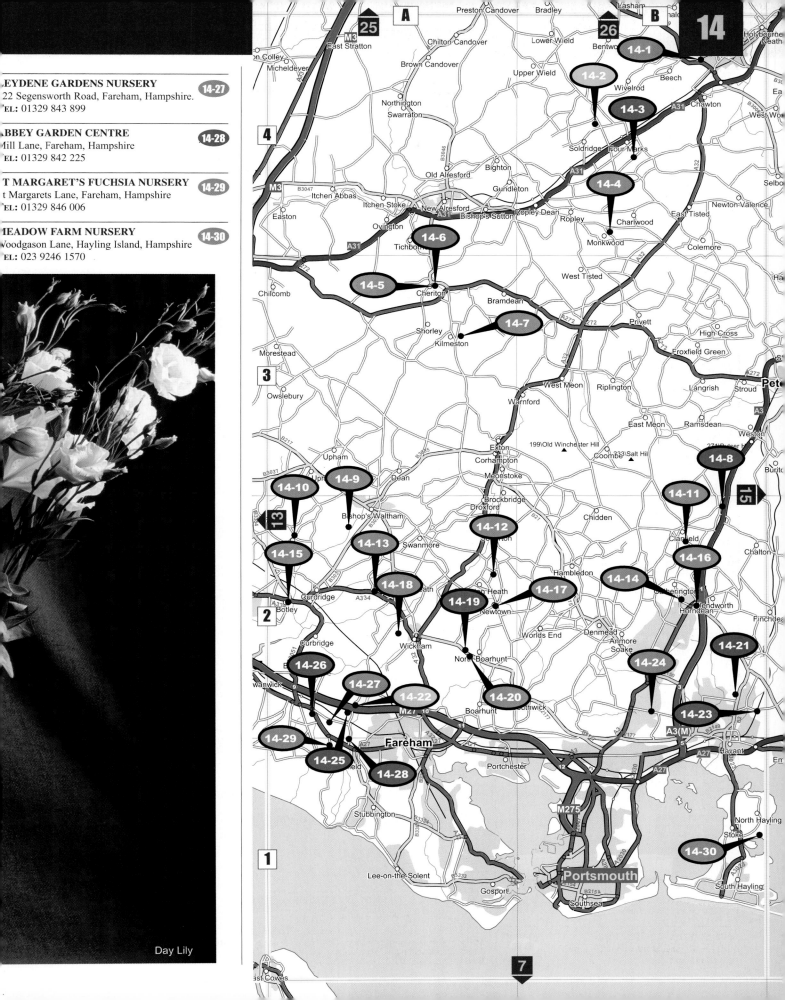

EYDENE GARDENS NURSERY `14-27`
22 Segensworth Road, Fareham, Hampshire.
TEL: 01329 843 899

ABBEY GARDEN CENTRE `14-28`
Mill Lane, Fareham, Hampshire
TEL: 01329 842 225

ST MARGARET'S FUCHSIA NURSERY `14-29`
St Margarets Lane, Fareham, Hampshire
TEL: 01329 846 006

MEADOW FARM NURSERY `14-30`
Woodgason Lane, Hayling Island, Hampshire
TEL: 023 9246 1570

Day Lily

WHEELER STREET NURSERY 15-1
Wheeler Lane, Godalming, Surrey
TEL: 01428 682 638

MILLAIS NURSERIES 15-2
Crosswater Farm, Farnham, Surrey
TEL: 01252 792 698

SWEETWATER NURSERY 15-3
Sweetwater Farm, Godalming, Surrey
TEL: 01428 682 211

ROSE COTTAGE NURSERY 15-4
Rose Cottage, Bordon, Hampshire
TEL: 01420 489 071

OAKLANDSCAPES 15-5
Main Street, Bordon, Hampshire
TEL: 01420 474 718

GARDENING WORLD 15-6
Haslemere Road, Brook, Godalming,
Surrey, GU8 5LB
TEL: 01293 883 237
EMAIL: worldofwater@ukonline.co.uk
WEB: www.worldofwater.com
Huge range of specimen shrubs, terracotta pots and garden furniture, as well as compost, chemicals, tools, seeds and all garden sundries. Large selection of aquatic plants, pond equipment and self contained water features. Experienced, helpful staff.
OPEN: 9-5.30 Mon-Sat, Sun 10.30-4.30. Closed Easter Sun.
SPECIALITIES: Aquatic plants, Water features, Garden & conservatory furniture, Shrubs, Terracotta pots.

GREEN STOP GARDEN CENTRE 15-7
Haslemere Road, Godalming, Surrey
TEL: 01428 682 913

BLACKMOOR NURSERY 15-8
Blackmoor, Liss, Hampshire
TEL: 01420 473 141

GILBERT WHITE'S HOUSE & GARDEN 15-9
The Wakes, Selborne, Hampshire
TEL: 01420 511 275

RAMSTER GARDENS 15-10
Ramster, Chiddingfold, Surrey
TEL: 01428 654 167

STRIKERS NURSERIES 15-11
2 New Building, Godalming, Surrey
TEL: 01428 708 167

LANGLEY BOXWOOD NURSERY 15-12
Rake, Liss, Hampshire, GU33 7JL
TEL: 01730 894 467
EMAIL: langbox@msn.com
WEB: www.boxwood.co.uk
Specialist nursery for box and yew hedging and topiary. Many varieties of box, with a national collection of Buxus.
OPEN: 6 days, Mon-Fri 9-4.30, Sat 10-4.
SPECIALITIES: Hardy plants, Pot plants, Shrubs.

PRINCES GARDEN CENTRE 15-13
The Steps, Liss, Hampshire
TEL: 01730 894 011

LISS PET & AQUATIC CENTRE 15-14
Hillier Garden Centre, Liss, Hampshire
TEL: 01730 894 135

HILLIER GARDEN CENTRE 15-15
Farnham Road, Liss,
Petersfield, Hants, GU33 6LJ
TEL: 01730 892 196
EMAIL: lissgc@hillier.co.uk
WEB: www.hillier.co.uk
Set in beautiful Hampshire countryside the centre specialises in nursery stock and trees. A large garden shop is dedicated to sundries, furniture and giftware.

OPEN: Daily 9-5.30, Sun 10.30-4.30.
SPECIALITIES: Furniture, Gifts, Hardy plants, Shrubs, Trees.

PETERSFIELD PHYSIC GARDEN 15-16
16 High Street, Petersfield, Hampshire
TEL: 01730 233 371

ROTHERHILL NURSERIES 15-17
Stedham, Midhurst, West Sussex
TEL: 01370 813 687

AYLINGS GARDEN CENTRE 15-18
Trotton Rogate, Petersfield,
Hampshire, GU31 5ES
TEL: 01730 813 621
EMAIL: sales@aylingsgardencentre.co.uk
Very large range of trees, shrubs, conifers, specimen plants, herbaceous plants, pot plants, pots and compost.
OPEN: Daily. Mon-Sat, 8-5, Sun 10.30-4.30.
SPECIALITIES: Alpines, Bedding plants, Fruit & ornamental trees, Climbers, Hardy plants.

FITZHALL 15-19
Iping, Midhurst, West Sussex
TEL: 01730 813 634

UPPARK, NATIONAL TRUST 15-20
South Harting, Petersfield, West Sussex
TEL: 01730 825 415

WEALD & DOWNLAND OPEN AIR MUSEUM 15-21
Singleton, Chichester, W. Sussex
TEL: 01243 811 363

GARDEN IN MIND 15-23
Stansted Park, Rowland's Castle, Hampshire
TEL: 023 9241 3149

STANSTED PARK GARDEN CENTRE 15-24
Stansted Park, Rowland's Castle, Hampshire
TEL: 023 9241 3090

PUMPKIN COTTAGE 15-25
The Lodge, Arundel, West Sussex
TEL: 01243 814 219

EAST ASHLING NURSERIES 15-26
Lye Lane, Chichester, West Sussex
TEL: 01243 575 523

ALDINGBOURNE COUNTRY CENTRE 15-27
Blackmill Lane, Chichester, West Sussex
TEL: 01243 542 075

DENMANS GARDEN 15-28
Clock House, Arundel, West Sussex
TEL: 01243 542 808

WEST DEAN GARDENS 15-22
West Dean, Chichester, W. Sussex, PO18 0QZ
TEL: 01243 818 210
EMAIL: gardens@westdean.org.uk
WEB: www.westdean.org.uk
Highly acclaimed restored Victorian walled Kitchen Garden. Sixteen Victorian Glasshouses and cold-frames. Herbaceous borders, specimen trees and 300' Harold Peto designed pergola hosting climbers.
OPEN: Open daily 1 Mar-31 Oct, 11-5. Mar, Apr & Oct, 10.30-5.
ENTRY COSTS: Adult £4.50, Children £2.00, Family £11.00, OAPs £4.
SPECIALITIES: Climbers, Fruit & fruit trees, Greenhouses & sheds, Hardy plants, Shrubs.

MAUDLIN NURSERY 15-2
Westhampnett, Chichester, West Sussex
TEL: 01243 773 024

BEACHLANDS NURSERY 15-3
Newells Lane, West Ashling, West Sussex
TEL: 01243 573 117

BARRY'S BLOOMING BASKETS 15-3
Gosden Green Nurseries, Emsworth, Hamps
TEL: 01243 379 929

GREEN ACRE NURSERY 15-32
Main Road, Chidham,
Chichester,
West Sussex PO18 8TP
TEL: 01243 572 441
Growing bedding, fuchsias, geraniums, hanging baskets and tubs, shrubs, climbers and shop.
OPEN: 9.30-5.
SPECIALITIES: Fuchsia.

SHOPWHYKE NURSERIES & SUPPLIES 15-3
Shopwhyke Road, Chichester, West Sussex
TEL: 01243 783 123

THE GARDEN PLACE 15-3
Main Road, Chichester, West Sussex
TEL: 01243 573 696

FISHBOURNE ROMAN PALACE & GARDENS 15-3
Salthill Road, Chichester, West Sussex
TEL: 01243 785 859

HIGHFIELD & SUNNYSIDE NURSERIES 15-3
Yapton Road, Bognor Regis, West Sussex
TEL: 01243 553 062

LILLIES NURSERY & CARAVAN PARK 15-3
Yapton Road, Bognor Regis, West Sussex
TEL: 01243 552 081

ARCHITECTURAL PLANTS 0-00
Lidsey Road Nursery, Woodgate, Chichester,
West Sussex, PO20 6SU
TEL: 01243 545 008
EMAIL: architectural-plants@chichester.intelynx.net
WEB: www.architecturalplants.com
Nursery specialising in hardy exotics and seaside plants. Phone for free catalogue.
OPEN: Sun-Fri, 10-4.
SPECIALITIES: Exotic-looking hardy plants.

BRICK KILN NURSERY 15-3
Bognor Road, Chichester, West Sussex
TEL: 01243 531 700

WYEVALE GARDEN CENTRE
15-40
Bognor Road, Chichester, West Sussex
TEL: 01243 789 276

APULDRAM ROSES
15-41
Apuldram Lane, Chichester, West Sussex
TEL: 01243 785 769

CEDAR NURSERY
15-42
Birdham Road, Chichester, West Sussex,
PO20 7EQ
TEL: 01243 782 666

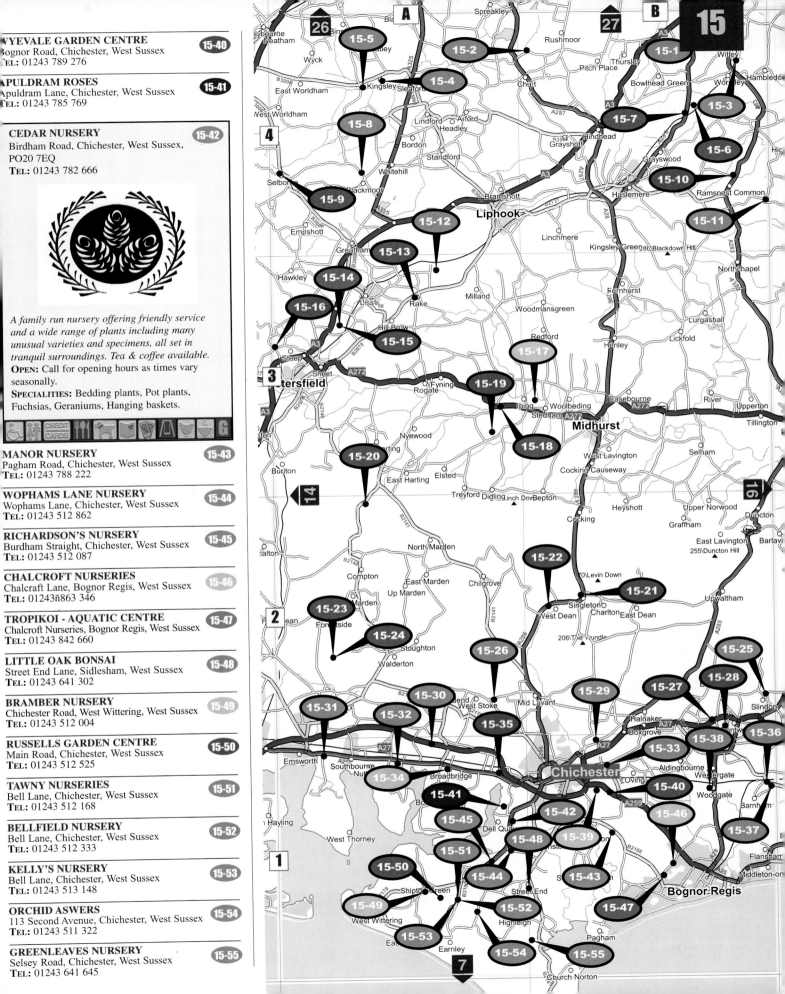

*A family run nursery offering friendly service
and a wide range of plants including many
unusual varieties and specimens, all set in
tranquil surroundings. Tea & coffee available.*
OPEN: Call for opening hours as times vary
seasonally.
SPECIALITIES: Bedding plants, Pot plants,
Fuchsias, Geraniums, Hanging baskets.

MANOR NURSERY
15-43
Pagham Road, Chichester, West Sussex
TEL: 01243 788 222

WOPHAMS LANE NURSERY
15-44
Wophams Lane, Chichester, West Sussex
TEL: 01243 512 862

RICHARDSON'S NURSERY
15-45
Burdham Straight, Chichester, West Sussex
TEL: 01243 512 087

CHALCROFT NURSERIES
15-46
Chalcraft Lane, Bognor Regis, West Sussex
TEL: 01243ñ863 346

TROPIKOI - AQUATIC CENTRE
15-47
Chalcroft Nurseries, Bognor Regis, West Sussex
TEL: 01243 842 660

LITTLE OAK BONSAI
15-48
Street End Lane, Sidlesham, West Sussex
TEL: 01243 641 302

BRAMBER NURSERY
15-49
Chichester Road, West Wittering, West Sussex
TEL: 01243 512 004

RUSSELLS GARDEN CENTRE
15-50
Main Road, Chichester, West Sussex
TEL: 01243 512 525

TAWNY NURSERIES
15-51
Bell Lane, Chichester, West Sussex
TEL: 01243 512 168

BELLFIELD NURSERY
15-52
Bell Lane, Chichester, West Sussex
TEL: 01243 512 333

KELLY'S NURSERY
15-53
Bell Lane, Chichester, West Sussex
TEL: 01243 513 148

ORCHID ASWERS
15-54
113 Second Avenue, Chichester, West Sussex
TEL: 01243 511 322

GREENLEAVES NURSERY
15-55
Selsey Road, Chichester, West Sussex
TEL: 01243 641 645

WINKWORTH ARBORETUM, NT 16-1
Hascombe Road, Godalming, Surrey
TEL: 01483 208 477

HYDON NURSERIES 16-2
Clock Barn Lane, Godalming, Surrey
TEL: 01483 860 252

OCKLEY COURT FARM 16-3
Ockley Court, Dorking, Surrey
TEL: 01306 711 160

NOTCUTTS GARDEN CENTRE 16-4
Guildford Road, Cranleigh, Surrey
TEL: 01483 274 222

WYEVALE GARDEN CENTRE 16-5
Horsham Road, Cranleigh, Surrey
TEL: 01403 752 359

KINGSFOLD NURSERY PLANT CENTRE 16-6
Dorking Road, Horsham, West Sussex
TEL: 01306 627 614

BROOKSIDE CACTUS NURSERY 16-7
Elderberry Farm, Horsham, West Sussex
TEL: 01403 790 996

LOXWOOD CONIFER NURSERIES 16-8
Guildford Road, Loxwood, West Sussex
TEL: 01403 753 389

NEWBRIDGE NURSERIES 16-9
Billingshurst Road, Horsham, West Sussex
TEL: 01403 272 686

**CAMELIA BOTNAR GARDEN
& CRAFT CENTRE** 16-10
Littleworth Lane, Horsham, West Sussex
TEL: 01403 864 773

HORSHAM WATER GARDEN CENTRE 16-11
Hillier Garden Centre, Horsham, West Sussex
TEL: 01403 268 152

HILLIER GARDEN CENTRE 16-12
Brighton Road, Horsham, West Sussex, RH13 6QA
TEL: 01403 210 113
EMAIL: horshamgc@hillier.co.uk
WEB: www.hillier.co.uk

A large garden centre with a comprehensive range of everything you could want for the garden. Easy access and friendly expert advice make a visit a pleasure.
OPEN: Daily 9-5.30, Sun 10.30-4.30.
SPECIALITIES: Shrubs, Furniture, Garden machinery, Gifts, Hardy plants.

OAKDEAN NURSERY 16-13
Sedgwick Lane, Horsham, West Sussex
TEL: 01403 252 897

MAYFIELD NURSERY 16-16
West Chiltington Lane, Billingshurst, West Sussex
TEL: 01403 741 224

ARCHITECTURAL PLANTS 16-14
Nuthurst, Horsham, West Sussex
RH13 6LH
TEL: 01403 891 772
EMAIL: architectural-plants@horsham.intelynx.net
WEB: www.architecturalplants.com
Nursery specialising in unusual and hardy exotics. Phone for free catalogue.
OPEN: Mon-Sat, 9-5.
SPECIALITIES: Exotic-looking hardy plants.

SCATS COUNTRYSTORES 16-15
Wildmoor Lane, Sherfield-on-Loddon, Basingstoke, Hampshire, RG27 0HA
TEL: 08451 30 40 30
EMAIL: basingstoke.countrystore@scats.co.uk
WEB: www.scatscountrystores.co.uk
Scats Countrystores offer a comprehensive range of products covering country clothing and footwear, horse feed and equestrian sundries, garden furniture and equipment, DIY, animal feeds, pet foods and accessories and farm supplies.
OPEN: Mon-Sat 8.30-5.30, Sun 10-4
SPECIALITIES: Christmas trees, Garden & Conservatory furniture, Garden machinery, Gifts, Sundries.

A. ARCHER-WILLS 16-17
Broadford Bridge Road, Pulborough, West Sussex
TEL: 01798 813 204

MURRELLS NURSERY 16-18
Broomers Hill Lane, Pulborough, West Sussex, RH20 2DU
TEL: 01798 875 508

Extensive range (including unusual varieties) of shrubs, herbaceous, bedding plants, trees and fruit trees. Bonsai.
OPEN: Daily, summer 9-5.30, Sun 10-4, winter, Mon-Sat 9-5, closed Christmas, Boxing, New Year's Day & Easter Sun.
SPECIALITIES: Bedding plants, Climbers, Fruit & fruit trees, Shrubs, Bonsai.

THE CITRUS CENTRE 16-20
Marehill Nursery, Pulborough, West Sussex
TEL: 01798 872 786

OLD BARN NURSERIES 16-19
Dial Post, Horsham, West Sussex, RH13 8NR
TEL: 01403 710 000
EMAIL: oldbarn@globalnet.co.uk,
WEB: www.oldbarnnurseries.co.uk

Attractive garden centre. Large house plant and outdoor areas. Garden and conservatory furniture. Sundries/gifts. Lunch/snack in Old Barn Restaurant.
OPEN: Barn open daily 9-6, Sun closed 4.30.
SPECIALITIES: House plants, Shrubs, Everything for Christmas.

WYEVALE GARDEN CENTRE 16-21
Stopham Road, Pulborough, West Sussex
TEL: 01798 872 981

THE VILLAGE NURSERIES 16-22
Sinnocks, West Chiltington, Pulborough, West Sussex, RH20 2JX
TEL: 01798 813 040
EMAIL: plants@village-nurseries.co.uk
WEB: www.village-nurseries.co.uk
Exceptional range of nursery grown hardy perennials, grasses and shrubs including many new varieties. Bedding and patio plants in season.
OPEN: Mon-Fri 9-6, closed at dusk in winter.
SPECIALITIES: Grasses, Hardy plants, Shrubs, Perennials.

CHURCHFIELD FARM 16-23
West Chiltington, Pulborough, West Sussex
TEL: 0800 783 3879

BLACKGATE LANE NURSERY 16-24
Blackgate Lane, Pulborough, West Sussex
TEL: 01798 872 923

HOLLY GATE CACTUS NURSERY & GARDEN 16-25
Billingshurst Road, Ashington, West Sussex
TEL: 01903 892 930

CHANCTONBURY NURSERIES 16-26
Rectory Lane, Pulborough, West Sussex
TEL: 01903 892 870

LANCASTERS NURSERY 16-27
West End Lane, Henfield, West Sussex
TEL: 01273 493 913

HOLE STREET NURSERIES 16-28
Hole Street, Ashington, West Sussex
TEL: 01903 892 897

SPITHANDLE NURSERY 16-29
Spithandle Lane, Steyning, West Sussex
TEL: 01903 816 299

THE PARADISE GARDEN 16-30
The Courtyard, Pulborough, West Sussex
TEL: 01903 740 540

PARHAM ELIZABETHAN HOUSE AND GARDENS 16-31
Parham Park, Pulborough, West Sussex
TEL: 01903 744 888

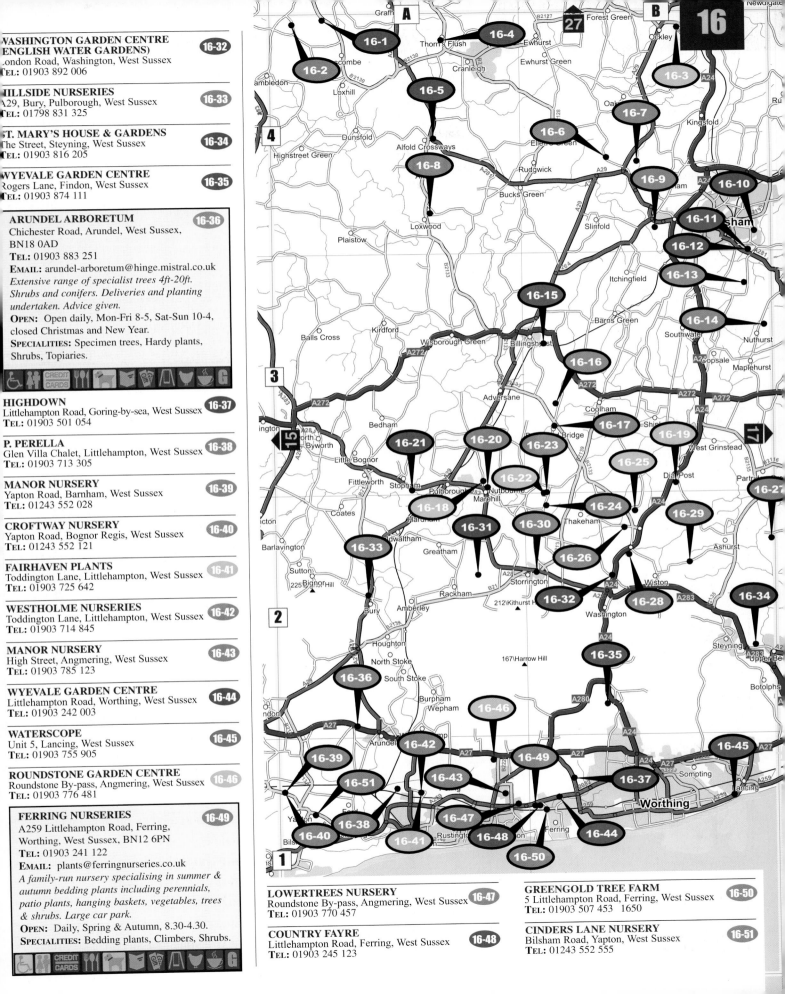

WASHINGTON GARDEN CENTRE (ENGLISH WATER GARDENS) — 16-32
London Road, Washington, West Sussex
TEL: 01903 892 006

HILLSIDE NURSERIES — 16-33
A29, Bury, Pulborough, West Sussex
TEL: 01798 831 325

ST. MARY'S HOUSE & GARDENS — 16-34
The Street, Steyning, West Sussex
TEL: 01903 816 205

WYEVALE GARDEN CENTRE — 16-35
Rogers Lane, Findon, West Sussex
TEL: 01903 874 111

ARUNDEL ARBORETUM — 16-36
Chichester Road, Arundel, West Sussex,
BN18 0AD
TEL: 01903 883 251
EMAIL: arundel-arboretum@hinge.mistral.co.uk
*Extensive range of specialist trees 4ft-20ft.
Shrubs and conifers. Deliveries and planting
undertaken. Advice given.*
OPEN: Open daily, Mon-Fri 8-5, Sat-Sun 10-4,
closed Christmas and New Year.
SPECIALITIES: Specimen trees, Hardy plants,
Shrubs, Topiaries.

HIGHDOWN — 16-37
Littlehampton Road, Goring-by-sea, West Sussex
TEL: 01903 501 054

P. PERELLA — 16-38
Glen Villa Chalet, Littlehampton, West Sussex
TEL: 01903 713 305

MANOR NURSERY — 16-39
Yapton Road, Barnham, West Sussex
TEL: 01243 552 028

CROFTWAY NURSERY — 16-40
Yapton Road, Bognor Regis, West Sussex
TEL: 01243 552 121

FAIRHAVEN PLANTS — 16-41
Toddington Lane, Littlehampton, West Sussex
TEL: 01903 725 642

WESTHOLME NURSERIES — 16-42
Toddington Lane, Littlehampton, West Sussex
TEL: 01903 714 845

MANOR NURSERY — 16-43
High Street, Angmering, West Sussex
TEL: 01903 785 123

WYEVALE GARDEN CENTRE — 16-44
Littlehampton Road, Worthing, West Sussex
TEL: 01903 242 003

WATERSCOPE — 16-45
Unit 5, Lancing, West Sussex
TEL: 01903 755 905

ROUNDSTONE GARDEN CENTRE — 16-46
Roundstone By-pass, Angmering, West Sussex
TEL: 01903 776 481

FERRING NURSERIES — 16-49
A259 Littlehampton Road, Ferring,
Worthing, West Sussex, BN12 6PN
TEL: 01903 241 122
EMAIL: plants@ferringnurseries.co.uk
*A family-run nursery specialising in summer &
autumn bedding plants including perennials,
patio plants, hanging baskets, vegetables, trees
& shrubs. Large car park.*
OPEN: Daily, Spring & Autumn, 8.30-4.30.
SPECIALITIES: Bedding plants, Climbers, Shrubs.

LOWERTREES NURSERY — 16-47
Roundstone By-pass, Angmering, West Sussex
TEL: 01903 770 457

COUNTRY FAYRE — 16-48
Littlehampton Road, Ferring, West Sussex
TEL: 01903 245 123

GREENGOLD TREE FARM — 16-50
5 Littlehampton Road, Ferring, West Sussex
TEL: 01903 507 453   1650

CINDERS LANE NURSERY — 16-51
Bilsham Road, Yapton, West Sussex
TEL: 01243 552 555

SNOWHILL PLANT & GARDEN CENTRE 17-3

Snow Hill Lane, Copthorne, Crawley, West Sussex, RH10 3EY
TEL: 01342 712 545
EMAIL: info@snowhill.co.uk
WEB: www.snowhill.co.uk
Independently run garden centre. Huge range of outdoor plants, garden sundries, machinery, gifts and house plants. Licensed restaurant. Ample parking.
OPEN: Daily, 9-5.30 Mon-Sat, 10.30-4.30 Sun, closed Christmas & Boxing Day.
SPECIALITIES: Garden & conservatory furniture, Hardy plants, Paving, gates, railings & fencing, Stone ornaments, Sundries.

IMBERHORNE LANE NURSERY 17-9

Imberhorne Lane, East Grinstead, West Sussex, RH19 1TZ
TEL: 01342 321 175
EMAIL: gardenexpert@btinternet.com
WEB: www.imberhornelanenursery.co.uk
Retail nursery growing herbaceous plants, shrubs and bedding plants. Suppliers of eco composts and mulches.
OPEN: Daily, Mar-Nov 9-5, Dec-Feb 10-4.
SPECIALITIES: Alpines, Bedding plants, Climbers, Hardy plants, Herbaceous, Shrubs.

WORLD OF WATER 17-10

Turners Hill Road, Worth, Crawley, West Sussex, RH10 4PE
TEL: 01293 883 237
EMAIL: worldofwater@ukonline.co.uk
WEB: www.worldofwater.com
Everything for the pond and tropical fish enthusiast. Extensive showgardens. Expert advice.
OPEN: 9-5.30 Mon-Sat, Sun 10.30-4.30. Closed Easter Sun.
SPECIALITIES: Aquatic plants, Shrubs, Terracotta pots, Water features, Waterfalls.

GARDEN PRIDE GARDEN CENTRE 17-36

Common Lane, Ditchling, BN6 8TP
TEL: 01273 846 844
EMAIL: info@gardenpridegc.co.uk
WEB: www.gardenpridegc.com

Large garden centre stocking quality plants, furniture and unusual gifts. Pet, aquatic and craft shops together with popular coffee shop.
OPEN: Daily, Mon-Sat 9-6, Sun 10.30-4.30, closed Christmas & Boxing day.
SPECIALITIES: Gifts, Furniture, Pet centre, Fish.

POTS AND PITHOI 17-11

The Barns, East Street, Turners Hill, West Sussex, RH10 4QQ
TEL: 01342 714 793
EMAIL: info@pots-and-pithoi.co.uk
WEB: www.pots-and-pithoi.co.uk

Largest selection in the world of handmade terracotta pots from Crete. For garden, terrace, patio, conservatory & water features. Prices from £10-£750.
OPEN: Daily, summer 10-5, winter 10-4, closed Christmas-New Year & Jan weekends.
SPECIALITIES: Terracotta pots.

PLANTS 'N' GARDENS 17-12

World of Water, Turners Hill Road, Worth, Crawley, West Sussex, RH10 4PE
TEL: 01293 882 992
EMAIL: paul@plantsandgardens.freeserve.co.uk
WEB: www.plantsandgardens.org.uk

Picturesque woodland setting with extensive display gardens. Wide range of perennials, shrubs and climbers. Ability to source unusual, rare plants.
OPEN: Daily, summer Mon-Sat 9-6, winter 9-5. Sun 10.30-4.30.
SPECIALITIES: Japanese maples, Hardy ferns, Tree ferns, Ornamental grasses.

SQUIRE'S GARDEN CENTRE CHEALS 17-13

Horsham Road, Crawley, W. Sussex, RH11 8PL
TEL: 01293 522 101
EMAIL: admin@squiresgardencentres.co.uk
WEB: www.squiresgardencentres.co.uk
Long established centre recently acquired by Squire's offering choice and quality.
OPEN: Daily, 9-6 Mon-Sat, 10.30-4.30 Sun.
SPECIALITIES: Bedding plants, Climbers, Roses, Bulbs, Shrubs.

BIRCH FARM HARDY PLANT NURSERY 17-15

Gravetye Estate, East Grinstead, West Sussex, RH19 4LE
TEL: 01342 810 236

Award-winning hardy plant nursery: alpines, rock plants, dwarf shrubs and conifers.
OPEN: Mar-Sept: 6 days a week, Mon-Sat 9-1 & 1.30-4, Closed Sun & Bank holidays.
SPECIALITIES: Alpines, Rock plants.

WYCH CROSS NURSERIES 17-18

Wych Cross, Forest Row, East Sussex, RH18 5JW
TEL: 01342 822 705
EMAIL: roses@wychcross.co.uk
WEB: www.wychcross.co.uk

Independent garden centre with Britain's biggest selection of roses - 1400 varieties. Larger than average selection of shrubs and other plants. Excellent refreshments at The Hybrid Tea Room.
OPEN: Mon-Sat 9-5.30. Closed Sun, Christmas, Boxing day & New Year's Day.
SPECIALITIES: Roses, Shrubs, Garden & conservatory furniture.

BORDE HILL GARDEN

17-26

Balcombe Road, Haywards Heath,
West Sussex, RH16 1XP

TEL: 01444 450 326
EMAIL: info@bordehill.co.uk
WEB: www.bordehill.co.uk

A garden of colour and contrasts, created in the 19th century. Containing a unique botanical collection set in 200 acres of parkland.
OPEN: Daily all year 10-6.
ENTRY COSTS: Adult £5.00, Children £2.50, Family £13, OAPs £4.50, Group visit to House & Garden (min 30) £7.50, guided tour by request.
SPECIALITIES: Rhododendrons and azaleas, Roses, Herbaceous & Water Plants, Greenhouses & 'Champion' Trees.

LEONARDSLEE GARDENS

17-28

Brighton Road, Lower Beeding, Horsham, West Sussex, RH13 6PP

TEL: 01403 891 212
EMAIL: leonardslee.gardens@virgin.net
WEB: www.leonardslee.com

Peaceful 240-acre valley with 7 beautiful lakes. Spectacular rhododendrons and azaleas in spring, fine trees, summer wildflowers and autumn tints. Wallabies, deer and wildlife. Rock garden, fascinating bonsai, Victorian Motorcar collection and Dolls House exhibition.
OPEN: Daily, 1 Apr-31 Oct, 9.30-6.
ENTRY COSTS: Adult, May weekends £7, May weekdays £6. Other times £5. Children £3.
SPECIALITIES: Rhododendrons and azaleas, Bonsai, Camellias, Magnolias, Water features.

WARRENORTH NURSERY

17-32

East Grinstead Road, North Chailey, East Sussex, BN8 4JD

TEL: 01825 723 266
Fuchsia & non-hardy geranium specialist. Breeders & suppliers of quality plants.
OPEN: Tue-Sun, 9.30-5. Closed Mon except for Bank holidays.
SPECIALITIES: Fuchsias, Geraniums.

WINDMILL NURSERY TEL: 01273 834 696 **17-33**

ALLWOOD BROS TEL: 01273 844 229 **17-34**

CHUBBS NURSERY TEL: 01273 400 218 **17-35**

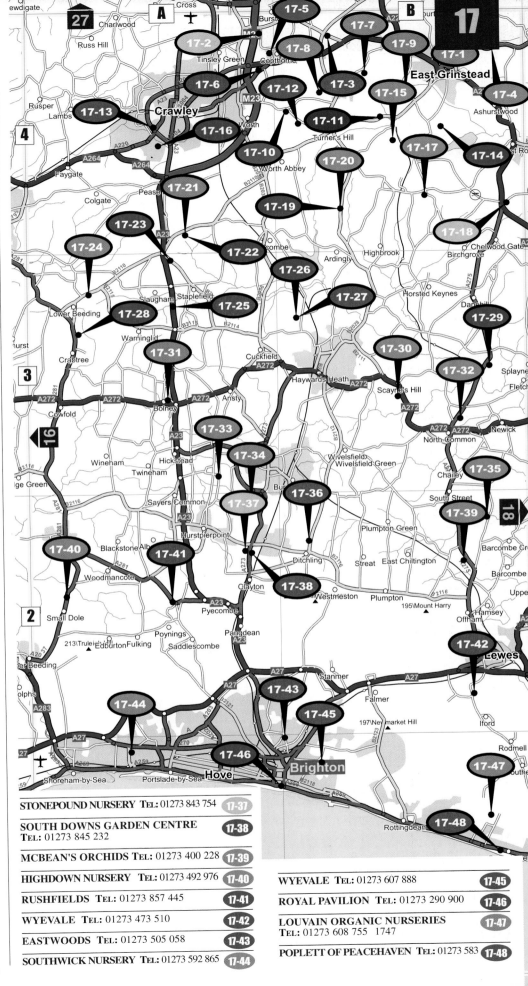

STONEPOUND NURSERY TEL: 01273 843 754 **17-37**

SOUTH DOWNS GARDEN CENTRE **17-38**
TEL: 01273 845 232

MCBEAN'S ORCHIDS TEL: 01273 400 228 **17-39**

HIGHDOWN NURSERY TEL: 01273 492 976 **17-40**

RUSHFIELDS TEL: 01273 857 445 **17-41**

WYEVALE TEL: 01273 473 510 **17-42**

EASTWOODS TEL: 01273 505 058 **17-43**

SOUTHWICK NURSERY TEL: 01273 592 865 **17-44**

WYEVALE TEL: 01273 607 888 **17-45**

ROYAL PAVILION TEL: 01273 290 900 **17-46**

LOUVAIN ORGANIC NURSERIES **17-47**
TEL: 01273 608 755 1747

POPLETT OF PEACEHAVEN TEL: 01273 583 **17-48**

NOTCUTTS GARDEN CENTRE
Tonbridge Road, Tunbridge Wells, Kent
TEL: 01892 822 636

KINGS TOLL NURSERY
Maidstone Road, Tonbridge, Kent
TEL: 01892 824 474

PLANTBASE
Charcott Holm Farm, Tonbridge, Kent
TEL: 01892 891 453

WYEVALE GARDEN CENTRE
Eridge Road, Tunbridge Wells, Kent
TEL: 01892 515 234

BROADWATER PLANTS
Fair View Lane, Langton Green, Tunbridge
Wells, Kent, TN3 9JP
TEL: 01892 534 760
EMAIL: broadwater@coblands.co.uk
WEB: www.broadwaterplants.co.uk
*Specialist working nursery, growing ericaceous
plants, rhododendrons (to specimen sizes), pieris
plus other rare and unusual plants that should be
more widely grown.*
OPEN: Mon-Fri, 9-4 all year. Sat from 1 Oct-30
Jun, 9-4.
SPECIALITIES: Rhododendrons and azaleas,
Camellias, Japanese maples, Magnolias, Shrubs

GROOMBRIDGE PLACE GARDENS
Groombridge, Tunbridge Wells, Kent
TEL: 01892 863 999

PERRYHILL NURSERIES
Hartfield, East Sussex,
TN7 4JP
TEL: 01892 770 377
EMAIL: sales@perryhillnurseries.co.uk
WEB: www.perryhillnurseries.co.uk

*Over 5000 varieties of plants, we believe we
have the widest range in the South-East,
including the rare and unusual.*
OPEN: Daily, Mar-Oct 9-5, Nov-Feb 9-4.30.
SPECIALITIES: Alpines, Bedding plants, Hardy
plants, House plants, Pot plants.

FLOWER POWER
The Nursery, Tunbridge Wells, Kent
TEL: 01892 510 190

GREENCAP NURSERY
Sleepers Stile Road, Wadhurst, East Sussex
TEL: 01892 782 685

GEMA NURSERY
Lye Green, Crowborough, East Sussex
TEL: 01892 864 682

ROYAL MIRES NURSERY
London Road, Crowborough, East Sussex
TEL: 01892ñ668 850

MOORLANDS 18-12
Friar's Gate, Crowborough, East Sussex
TEL: 01892 652 474

OAKHURST NURSERY 18-13
Oakhurst, Crowborough, East Sussex
TEL: 01892 653 273

SUSSEX COUNTRY GARDENS
Eastbourne Road, Mark Cross,
Crowborough, East Sussex, TN6 3PJ
TEL: 01892 852 828
*Extensive ranges of plants, terracotta, stoneware
and garden sundries. Hardwood and conservatory furniture. Statuary. Fish and aquatics centre.
Expert and friendly advice.*
OPEN: Daily, Mon-Sat 9-5.30, Sun 10-5, closed
Christmas and Boxing Day, and Easter Sunday.
SPECIALITIES: Alpines, Bedding plants,
Climbers, Fruit & fruit trees, Garden & conservatory furniture.

ROCKINGTON NURSERY 18-15
Blackness Road, Crowborough, East Sussex
TEL: 01892 654 083

THE MILLBROOK GARDEN COMPANY 18-16
Rotherfield Road , Crowborough, East Sussex
TEL: 01474 331135

NUTLIN NURSERY 18-17
Crowborough Road, Uckfield, East Sussex
TEL: 01825 712 670

ASHDOWN FOREST GARDEN CENTRE 18-18
Streeters Farm, Uckfield, East Sussex
TEL: 01825 712 300

MOYSES NURSERIES 18-19
Five Ashes, Mayfield, East Sussex
TEL: 01435 872 375

WILDERNESS WOOD
Hadlow Down, Uckfield, E. Sussex TN22 4HJ
TEL: 01825 830 509
EMAIL: enquiries@wildernesswood.co.uk
WEB: www.wildernesswood.co.uk
*Garden furniture and wood products direct from
the grower/maker, at a fascinating family-run
working woodland with trails, bluebell walks
and picnic and play areas.*
OPEN: All year; daily, 10-dusk.
ENTRY COSTS TO WOODLAND: Adult £2.50,
Children £1.50, Family £7, OAPs £2, Disabled £2.
SPECIALITIES: Bluebells, Christmas trees,
Garden & conservatory furniture, Gates, railings
& fencing, Trellis.

OAST FARM 18-21
Lephams Bridge, Uckfield, East Sussex
TEL: 01825 733 446

OLD ORCHARD NURSERY 18-23
Burwash Common, Burwash, East Sussex
TEL: 01435 882 060

CABBAGES & KINGS 18-24
Wilderness Farm, Uckfield, East Sussex
TEL: 01825 830 552

BROAD OAK GARDEN CENTRE 18-25
Broad Oak, Heathfield, East Sussex
TEL: 01435 865 045

BLACKBOYS NURSERY 18-26
Lankhurst Oak, Uckfield, East Sussex
TEL: 01825 890 858

THORPE GARDENS 18-27
Little London Road, Heathfield, East Sussex
TEL: 01435 812 455

OAKDENE ALPINE NURSERY 18-22
Street End Lane, Broad Oak, Heathfield,
East Sussex, TN21 8TU
TEL: 01435 864 382

*Oakdene Alpine Nursery offers a wide range of
alpines and woodland plants for the experienced
and non-experienced enthusiast. The nursery is
situated in an area of outstanding natural beauty.*
OPEN: Wed-Sat, 9-5 all year, Sun by appt.
SPECIALITIES: Woodland plants.

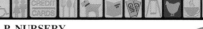

A. P. NURSERY 18-28
Vines Cross, Heathfield, East Sussex
TEL: 01435 812 965

STAVERTON NURSERY 18-29
Eastbourne Road, Halland, East Sussex
TEL: 01825 840 249

**BENTLEY WILDFOWL &
MOTOR MUSEUM & GARDENS** 18-30
Halland, Lewes, East Sussex
TEL: 01825 840 573

CLAYHILL NURSERIES 18-31
Uckfield Road, Lewes, East Sussex
TEL: 01273 812 409

GOLDCLIFF NURSERIES 18-32
The Holdings, Lewes, East Sussex
TEL: 01273 814 949

ROSSLOW ROSES 18-33
North Street Farm, Hellingly, East Sussex
TEL: 01323 440 888

WALLACE PLANTS 18-34
Lewes Road Nursery, Laughton, East Sussex
TEL: 01323 811 729

LIME CROSS NURSERY 18-35
Herstmonceux, Hailsham, East Sussex
TEL: 01323 833 229

COOPERS CROFT NURSERIES 18-36
New Road, Hailsham, East Sussex
TEL: 01323 832 151

NEW ROAD NURSERIES 18-37
New Road, Hailsham, East Sussex
TEL: 01323 846 577

WYEVALE GARDEN CENTRE 18-38
Lower Dicker, Hailsham, East Sussex
TEL: 01323 844 834

USUAL & UNUSUAL PLANTS 18-39
Onslow House, Hailsham, East Sussex
TEL: 01323 840 967

COLDHARBOUR NURSERY 18-40
Coldharbour Road, Hailsham, East Sussex
TEL: 01323 846 753

**HERSTMONCEUX CASTLE
GARDENS & GROUNDS** 18-41
Hailsham, East Sussex
TEL: 01323 833 816

ROBINS NURSERY 18-42
Coldharbour Road, Hailsham, East Sussex
TEL: 01323 844 734

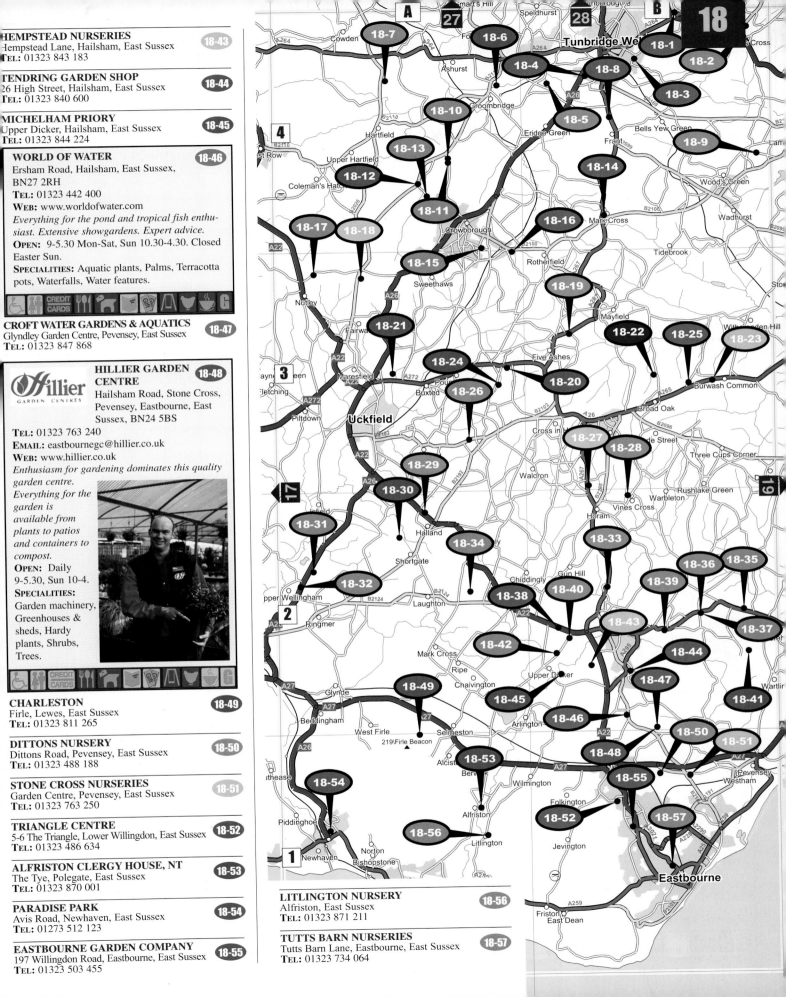

HEMPSTEAD NURSERIES `18-43`
Hempstead Lane, Hailsham, East Sussex
TEL: 01323 843 183

TENDRING GARDEN SHOP `18-44`
26 High Street, Hailsham, East Sussex
TEL: 01323 840 600

MICHELHAM PRIORY `18-45`
Upper Dicker, Hailsham, East Sussex
TEL: 01323 844 224

WORLD OF WATER `18-46`
Ersham Road, Hailsham, East Sussex,
BN27 2RH
TEL: 01323 442 400
WEB: www.worldofwater.com
Everything for the pond and tropical fish enthusiast. Extensive showgardens. Expert advice.
OPEN: 9-5.30 Mon-Sat, Sun 10.30-4.30. Closed Easter Sun.
SPECIALITIES: Aquatic plants, Palms, Terracotta pots, Waterfalls, Water features.

CROFT WATER GARDENS & AQUATICS `18-47`
Glyndley Garden Centre, Pevensey, East Sussex
TEL: 01323 847 868

HILLIER GARDEN CENTRE `18-48`
Hailsham Road, Stone Cross, Pevensey, Eastbourne, East Sussex, BN24 5BS
TEL: 01323 763 240
EMAIL: eastbournegc@hillier.co.uk
WEB: www.hillier.co.uk
Enthusiasm for gardening dominates this quality garden centre. Everything for the garden is available from plants to patios and containers to compost.
OPEN: Daily 9-5.30, Sun 10-4.
SPECIALITIES: Garden machinery, Greenhouses & sheds, Hardy plants, Shrubs, Trees.

CHARLESTON `18-49`
Firle, Lewes, East Sussex
TEL: 01323 811 265

DITTONS NURSERY `18-50`
Dittons Road, Pevensey, East Sussex
TEL: 01323 488 188

STONE CROSS NURSERIES `18-51`
Garden Centre, Pevensey, East Sussex
TEL: 01323 763 250

TRIANGLE CENTRE `18-52`
5-6 The Triangle, Lower Willingdon, East Sussex
TEL: 01323 486 634

ALFRISTON CLERGY HOUSE, NT `18-53`
The Tye, Polegate, East Sussex
TEL: 01323 870 001

PARADISE PARK `18-54`
Avis Road, Newhaven, East Sussex
TEL: 01273 512 123

EASTBOURNE GARDEN COMPANY `18-55`
197 Willingdon Road, Eastbourne, East Sussex
TEL: 01323 503 455

LITLINGTON NURSERY `18-56`
Alfriston, East Sussex
TEL: 01323 871 211

TUTTS BARN NURSERIES `18-57`
Tutts Barn Lane, Eastbourne, East Sussex
TEL: 01323 734 064

BUMBLES NURSERY
Tolehurst Farm, Cranbrook, Kent
TEL: 01580 715 319

MARLE PLACE GARDENS
Brenchley, Tonbridge, Kent
TEL: 01892 722 304

BIDDENDEN NURSERIES
Sissinghurst Road, Biddenden, Kent
TEL: 01580 292 100

1580 GARDEN CENTRE
Sissinghurst Road, Ashford, Kent
TEL: 01580 292 600

SISSINGHURST CASTLE GARDEN, NATIONAL TRUST
Sissinghurst, Cranbrook, Kent
TEL: 01580 715 330

OWL HOUSE GARDENS
Mount Pleasant, Tunbridge Wells, Kent
TEL: 01892 891 290

FINCHCOCKS
Goudhurst, Kent
TEL: 01580 211 702

SCOTNEY CASTLE GARDEN, NATIONAL TRUST
Lamberhurst, Tunbridge Wells, Kent
TEL: 01892 891 081

BEDGEBURY NATIONAL PINETUM
Goudhurst, Cranbrook, Kent
TEL: 01580 211 044

ASHENDEN NURSERY
Cranbrook Road, Cranbrook, Kent
TEL: 01580 241 792

HOPES GROVE NURSERIES
Hope Grove Farm, Tenterden, Kent
TEL: 01580 765 600

LAURELS NURSERY
Dingleden, Benenden, Kent
TEL: 01580 240 463

THE WALLED NURSERY
St Ronans, Cranbrook, Kent
TEL: 01580 752425

WORLD OF WATER
Hastings Road (A28), Rolvenden,
Cranbrook, Kent, TN17 4PL
TEL: 01580 241 771
WEB: www.worldofwater.com
Everything for the pond and tropical fish enthusiast. Extensive showgardens. Expert advice.
OPEN: 9-5.30 Mon-Sat, Sun 10.30-4.30. Closed Easter Sun.
SPECIALITIES: Aquatic plants, Shrubs, Terracotta pots, Waterfalls, Water features.

TILE BARN NURSERY
Standen Street, Benenden, Kent
TEL: 01580 240 221

PASHLEY MANOR GARDENS
Ticehurst, Wadhurst, East Sussex
TEL: 01580 200 888

THE NISHIKIGOI CENTRE
Hawkhurst Fish Farm, Hawkhurst, Kent
TEL: 01580 754 030

KING JOHN'S LODGE
Sheepstreet Lane, Etchingham, East Sussex
TEL: 01580 819 232

MERRIMENTS GARDENS & NURSERY
Hawkhurst Road, Hurst Green, East Sussex, TN19 7RA
TEL: 01580 860 666
EMAIL: markbuchele@beeb.net
WEB: www.merriments.co.uk

This is a garden of extraordinary intensity. The colour composition is remarkable for its imaginative flair and daring. The visitor will experience four acres of sheer delight that will remain in the mind forever.
OPEN: Nursery, open daily. Garden, 1 Apr-30 Oct.
ENTRY COSTS: Adult £3.50, Children £2.00, OAPs £3.50.
SPECIALITIES: Garden & conservatory furniture, Alpines, Hardy plants, Roses, Ornamental grasses.

GREAT DIXTER GARDENS
Northiam, Rye, East Sussex
TEL: 01797 252 878

JUST ROSES
Beales Lane, Rye, East Sussex
TEL: 01797 252 355

BODIAM NURSERY
Ockham House, Robertsbridge, East Sussex
TEL: 01580 830 649

BODIAM BONSAI
Ewhurst Green, Robertsbridge, East Sussex
TEL: 01580 830 644

BRICKWALL HOUSE AND GARDENS
Northiam, Rye, East Sussex
TEL: 01797 253 388

BATEMAN'S, NATIONAL TRUST
Burwash, Etchingham, East Sussex
TEL: 01435 882 302

ED'S NURSERY
Sunflower Gardens, Staplecross, East Sussex
TEL: 01580 830 701

STAPLECROSS SHRUB CENTRE
Brambles Cripps Corner, Robertsbridge, E. Sussex
TEL: 01580 830 678

BLACKBROOKS GARDEN CENTRE
Main A21, Sedlescombe, Hastings, East Sussex, TN33 0RJ
TEL: 01424 870 710
Indoor & outdoor plants, shrubs, trees, fish, ponds, fountains & ornaments. Cafe.
OPEN: 8-5.30.
SPECIALITIES: Shrubs, Trees, Water plants, House plants.

SUNNY RISE NURSERIES
North Trade Road, Battle, East Sussex
TEL: 01424 772 685

KENT STREET NURSERIES
Kent Street , Battle, East Sussex
TEL: 01424 751 134

LODGE NURSERY
Cottage Lane, Hastings, East Sussex
TEL: 01424 870 186

UCKHAM LANE NURSERY
Caldbec Hill, Battle, East Sussex
TEL: 01424 772 919

Daisy

ROTHERVIEW NURSERY

19-33

Ivyhouse Lane, Three Oaks, Hastings,
East Sussex, TN35 4NP
Tel: 01424 756 228
Email: rotherview@btinternet.com

A wide range of alpines available. We sell handmade hypertufa troughs empty and planted. An extensive Camellia range including autumn flowering Sasanquas.

Open: 7 days, 9.30-4.30. Winter 10-3.
Specialities: Alpines, Hardy plants, Camellias, Ferns, Grasses.

HARBOROUGH NURSERIES

19-34

The Thorne (Rye Road), Hastings, East Sussex
Tel: 0142 814 220

UPLANDS FUCHSIA NURSERY

19-35

Hooe, Battle, East Sussex
Tel: 01424 844 846

WYEVALE GARDEN CENTRE

19-36

Bexhill Road, Hastings, East Sussex
Tel: 01424 443 414

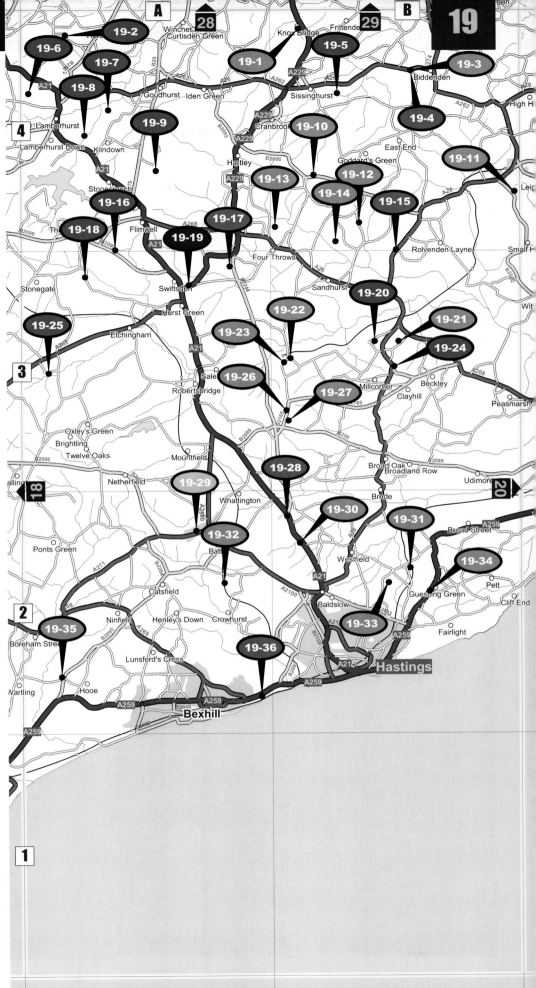

KENT

BRIDGE FARM FLOWERS `20-1`
Bridge Farm, Folkestone, Kent
TEL: 01303 863 625

LEE'S NURSERY `20-2`
Pot Kilne Lane, Ashford, Kent
TEL: 01233 850 456

OLDBURY NURSERIES `20-3`
Brissenden Green, Ashford, Kent
TEL: 01233 820 416

GREENWAYS GARDEN CENTRE `20-4`
Ashford Road, Bethersden, Kent
TEL: 01233 820 526

STONE OAK NURSERY `20-5`
Flood Street, Ashford, Kent
TEL: 01233 720 925

NEWINGREEN NURSERIES `20-6`
Ashford Road, Hythe, Kent
TEL: 01303 260 863

WYEVALE GARDEN CENTRE `20-7`
Ingles Meadow, Folkestone, Kent
TEL: 01303 258 100

PORT LYMPNE WILD ANIMAL PARK `20-8`
Lympne, Hythe, Kent
TEL: 01303 264 647

LONGACRE NURSERIES `20-9`
St Mary's Road, Hythe, Kent
TEL: 01303 265 444

WYEVALE GARDEN CENTRE `20-10`
Hamstreet, Ashford, Kent
TEL: 01233 732 988

PINECOVE NURSERIES `20-11`
Appledore Road, Tenterden, Kent
TEL: 01580 765 429

COUNTRY FLOWERS WILDFLOWER NURSERY `20-12`
62 Lower Sands, Romney Marsh, Kent
TEL: 01303 873 052

TENDERDEN GARDEN CENTRE `20-13`
Appledore Road, Tenterden, Kent
TEL: 01233 758 510

SOUTHCOTT NURSERY `20-14`
Southcott, Romney Marsh, Kent
TEL: 01797 321 848

Tristania

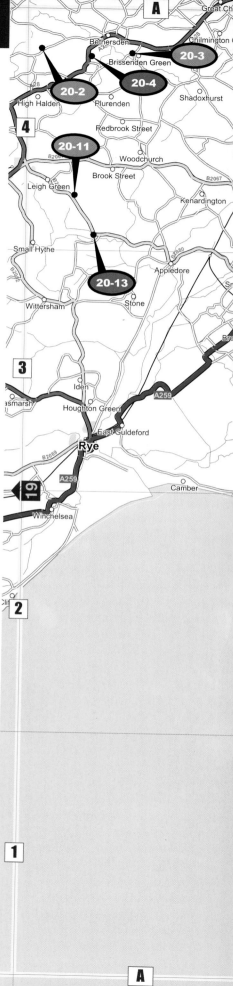

BRYNCETHIN NURSERY `21-1`
Mount Pleasant, Bridgend, Flintshire
TEL: 01656 862 379

THE GARDEN OUTLET `21-2`
Units 32-33, Bridgend, South Wales
TEL: 01656 651 413

WYEVALE GARDEN CENTRE `21-3`
2 Heol Mostyn, Bridgend, South Wales
TEL: 01656 741 443

CROSSROADS GARDEN CENTRE `21-4`
Junction 35, M4, Bridgend, South Wales
TEL: 01656 861 100 214

SINGLETON GARDEN CENTRE `21-5`
Greenknowe, Bridgend, South Wales
TEL: 01656 658201

HURRANS GARDEN CENTRE `21-6`
High Street, Cowbridge,
Vale of Glam., South Wales, CF71 7YP
TEL: 01446 775 053
EMAIL: info@hurrans.co.uk
WEB: www.hurrans.co.uk

HURRANS GardenCentres
Where great gardens don't cost the earth!

A family business established in 1909. This pretty market town site has plenty of free parking and features a garden machinery centre, pet shop and aquatic centre with excellent customer care, quality and value.
OPEN: 9-5.30 Mon-Sat; 10-5 Sun.

THE GARDEN CENTRE `21-7`
Boverton Road, Llantwit Major, South Wales
TEL: 01446 792 105

PLATNWISE NURSERIES `21-8`
Kibsworthy Farm, Lynton, Devon
TEL: 01598 753 766

HELE BAY GARDEN CENTRE `21-9`
25 Watermouth Road, Ilfracombe, Devon
TEL: 01271 862 873

SILVER DALE NURSERIES `21-10`
Shute Lane, Ilfracombe, Devon
TEL: 01271 882 539

WEST SOMERSET GARDEN CENTRE `21-11`
Mart Road, Minehead,
Somerset, TA24 5BJ
TEL: 01643 703 612
WEB: www.westsomersetgardencentre.co.uk
Friendly atmosphere with a good selection of shrubs and bedding grown in our own nursery. You will be pleasantly surprised.
OPEN: Daily, Mon-Sat 8-5, Sun 10-4.
SPECIALITIES: Alpines, Bedding plants, Climbers, Fruit & fruit trees, Garden & conservatory furniture.

DUNSTER CASTLE, NATIONAL TRUST `21-12`
Dunster, Minehead, Somerset
TEL: 01643 821 314

CAERPHILLY GARDEN CENTRE & COFFEE SHOP
Penrhos, Cardiff, South Wales
TEL: 029 2086 1511

TREDEGAR HOUSE & PARK
Newport, South Wales
TEL: 01633 815 880

WYEVALE GARDEN CENTRE
Newport Road, Cardiff, South Wales
TEL: 01633 680 002

J. DEEN & SONS
Dutch Nursery in Wales, Cardiff Gate, South Wales
TEL: 029 2077 7050

JARDINERIE
Newport Road, Cardiff, South Wales
TEL: 029 2077 7977

PUGHS GARDEN CENTRE
Tynant Nursery, Cardiff, South Wales
TEL: 02920 842 017

CEFN ONN PARK
Lisvane, Cardiff, South Wales
TEL: 029 2087 2000

ST. FAGANS CASTLE GARDENS
St Fagans, Cardiff, South Wales
TEL: 029 2057 3500

BORDERVALE PLANTS
Nantyderi, Cowbridge, South Wales
TEL: 01446 774 036

BRACKENWOOD GARDEN CENTRE
131 Nore Road, Bristol, Somerset
TEL: 01275 843 484

ALL SEASONS GARDEN CENTRE
99 Clive Street, Cardiff, South Wales
TEL: 029 2025 5337

P. WHELAN
Cae'r Delyn, Cowbridge, South Wales
TEL: 01446 772 888

BRYNHEULOG NURSERIES
St Andrews Road, Cardiff, South Wales
TEL: 029 2059 3375

DYFFRYN BOTANIC GARDEN
St Nicholas, Cardiff, South Wales
TEL: 029 2059 3328

GLEN BROOK BONSAI NURSERY
Tickenham, Clevedon, Somerset
TEL: 01275 858 596

BRYNAWEL GARDEN CENTRE
Cross Common Road, Penarth, South Wales
TEL: 029 2070 2660

ALEXANDRA PARK
Beach Road, Penarth, South Wales
TEL: 029 2070 4617

BROAD STREET GARDEN CENTRE
Barry Town Station Site, Barry, South Wales
TEL: 01446 720 333

Daisy

NATIONAL COLLECTION OF PASSIFLORA
Greenholm Nurseries Ltd, Clevedon, Somerset
TEL: 01934 833 350

CADBURY GARDEN & LEISURE 22-20
Smallway, Bristol, Somerset
TEL: 01934 876 464

ROUND TREES GARDEN CENTRE 22-21
Smallway, Congresbury, Somerset
TEL: 01934 838 237

WESTON WATERSCAPES 22-22
21 Rendcomb Close, Weston-Super-Mare, Somerset
TEL: 01934 620 129

MANSFIELD NURSERIES 22-23
Mansfield Avenue, Weston-Super-Mare, Somerset
TEL: 01934 627 916

GROVE NURSERIES 22-24
Lower Langford, Bristol, Somerset
TEL: 01934 862848

LITTLE CREEK NURSERY 22-25
39 Moor Road, Weston-Super-Mare, Somerset
TEL: 01934 823 739

HUTTON GARDEN CENTRE 22-26
Banwell Road, Weston-Super-Mare, Somerset
TEL: 01934 822 795

BANWELL GARDEN CENTRE 22-27
Castle Hill, Banwell, Somerset
TEL: 01934 822 246

BURNHAM GARDEN CENTRE 22-28
Pier Street, Burnham-on-sea, Somerset
TEL: 01278 792 262

THE FLOWER BOWER 22-29
Woodlands, Bridgwater, Somerset
TEL: 01278 732 134

COTSWOLD HARDY PLANTS 22-30
Wibble Farm, Taunton, Somerset
TEL: 01984 632 303

WILLOWS GARDEN CENTRE 22-31
Shapwick Road, Glastonbury, Somerset
TEL: 01458 860 060

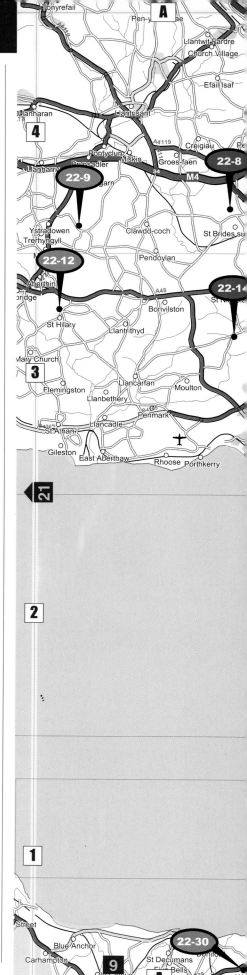

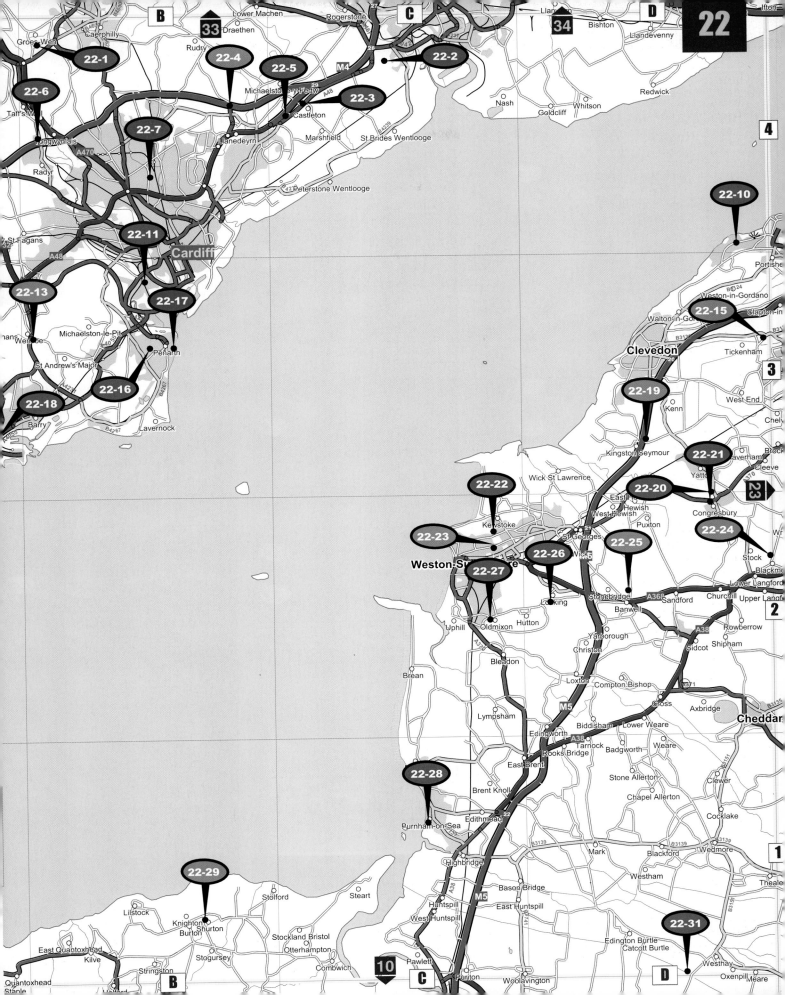

HORTHAM NURSERIES `23-1`
Hortham Lane, Bristol, Somerset
TEL: 01454 613 468

PARKERS GARDEN & AQUATIC CENTRE `23-2`
Lamb Leaze, Bristol, Somerset
TEL: 01454 228 761

ALMONDSBURY AQUATIC CENTRE `23-3`
Almondsbury Garden Centre, Bristol, Somerset
TEL: 01454 201 118

ALMONDSBURY GARDEN CENTRE `23-4`
Over Lane, Bristol, Avon
TEL: 01454 457 300

SANDAY'S NURSERY `23-5`
Over Lane, Almondsbury, Gloucestershire
TEL: 01454 615 076

C. S. LOCKYER (FUCHSIAS) `23-6`
Lansbury, Bristol, Somerset
TEL: 01454 772 219

ELMWOOD FARM NURSERIES `23-7`
The Hollows, Bristol, Somerset
TEL: 0117 956 1495

BLAISE CASTLE HOUSE `23-8`
Henbury, Bristol, Somerset
TEL: 0117 950 6789

AQUA STORE `23-9`
542 Filton Avenue, Bristol, Somerset
TEL: 0117 969 2345

POUND HILL GARDEN `23-10`
West Kington, Chippenham, Wiltshire
TEL: 01249 782 822

POUND HILL PLANTS `23-11`
West Kington, Chippenham, Wiltshire
TEL: 01249 782 822

HENLEAZE GARDEN SHOP `23-12`
146-148 Henleaze Road, Bristol, Somerset
TEL: 01179 620 418

MOORES PET & GARDEN STORES `23-13`
72 Shirehampton Road, Bristol, Somerset
TEL: 0117 987 2738

DYRHAM PARK, NATIONAL TRUST `23-14`
Chippenham, Wiltshire
TEL: 0117 937 2501

BRACKENWOOD PLANT CENTRE `23-15`
Leigh Court Estate, Bristol, Somerset
TEL: 01275 375 292

GARAWAYS GARDEN CENTRE `23-16`
Chantry Road, Bristol, Somerset
TEL: 0117 973 3402

BRECKLANDS NURSERY `23-17`
Syston Lane, Bristol, Somerset
TEL: 0117 961 0554

BRISTOL ZOO GARDENS `23-18`
Clifton, Bristol, Somerset
TEL: 0117 970 6176

UNIVERSITY OF BRISTOL BOTANIC GARDEN `23-19`
Bracken Hill, Bristol, Somerset
TEL: 0117 973 3682

SPECIAL PLANTS `23-20`
Greenways Lane, Chippenham, Wiltshire
TEL: 01225 891 686

RIVERSIDE GARDEN CENTRE `23-21`
Clift House Road, Bristol, Somerset
TEL: 0117 966 7535

ASHTON COURT ESTATE `23-22`
Long Ashton, Bristol, Somerset
TEL: 0117 963 9174

ALAN PHIPPS CACTI `23-23`
62 Samuel White Road, Bristol, Somerset
TEL: 0117 960 7591

JARRETT NURSERY `23-24`
Barry Road, Bristol, Somerset
TEL: 0117 9323112

BONSAI IN BRISTOL `23-25`
47 Bedminster Down Road, Bristol, Somerset
TEL: 0117 902 5641

AVON AQUATICS `23-26`
Jarretts Garden Centre, Bristol, Somerset
TEL: 0117 932 7659

WYEVALE GARDEN CENTRE `23-27`
Hicks Gate, Bristol, Somerset
TEL: 01179 778 945

WHITEGATE NURSERIES `23-28`
The Secret Garden Centre, Bristol, Somerset
TEL: 0117 986 2653

BATHFORD NURSERIES `23-29`
Box Road, Bath, Somerset
TEL: 01225 858 188

BATH AQUATICS `23-30`
14 Brookside House, Bath, Somerset
TEL: 01225 426 878

NORTON NURSERY & GARDEN CENTRE `23-31`
Norton Lane, Bristol, Somerset
TEL: 01275 832 296

HILLSIDE COTTAGE PLANTS `23-32`
Hilllside, Whitchurch, Somerset
TEL: 01275 837 505

GEORGIAN GARDEN `23-33`
Gravel Walk, Bath, Somerset
TEL: 01225 477 752

BATH BOTANIC GARDENS / ROYAL VICTORIA PARK `23-34`
Royal Victoria Park, Bath, Somerset
TEL: 01225 482 624

CLAVERTON MANOR `23-35`
Claverton, Bath, Somerset
TEL: 01225 460 503

ARNE HERBS `23-36`
Limeburn Nurseries, Chew Magna, Somerset
TEL: 01275 333 399

PRIOR PARK GARDEN CENTRE `23-37`
Prior Park Road, Widcombe, Somerset
TEL: 01225 427 175

BLACKMORE & LANGDON `23-38`
Stanton Nursery, Bristol, Somerset
TEL: 01275 332 300

CHEW VALLEY TREES `23-40`
Winford Road, Bristol, Somerset
TEL: 01275 333 752

PRIOR PARK LANDSCAPE GARDEN, NATIONAL TRUST `23-41`
Ralph Allen Drive, Bath, Somerset
TEL: 01225 833 422

DOWNSIDE NURSERIES `23-42`
Upper Westwood, Bradford on Avon, Wiltshire
TEL: 01225 862 392

IFORD MANOR `23-43`
Bradford on Avon, Wiltshire
TEL: 01225 863 146

BURRINGTON COOMBE GARDEN CENTRE `23-44`
Burrington Coombe, Bristol, Somerset
TEL: 01761 462 570

BLAGDON WATER GARDENS `23-45`
Bath Road, Upper Langford, Somerset
TEL: 01934 852 973

MEADGATE FARM NURSERIES `23-46`
Weekesley Lane, Bath, Somerset
TEL: 01761 470 344

WEST HARPTREE NURSERY `23-47`
Bristol Road, West Harptree, Somerset
TEL: 01761 221 370

RODE TROPICAL BIRD GARDENS `23-48`
Rode, Bath, Somerset
TEL: 01373 830 326

NORTON GREEN GARDEN CENTRE `23-49`
Norton Green Farm, Bath, Somerset
TEL: 01761 232 137

BRICKHOUSE FARM NURSERY `23-50`
Brickhouse Farm, Bath, Somerset
TEL: 01761 232 558

MEADOWS NURSERY `23-51`
5 Rectory Cottages, Frome, Somerset
TEL: 01373 813 025

SLIPPS GARDEN CENTRE `23-52`
Butts Hill, Frome, Somerset
TEL: 01373 467 013

ROCKY MOUNTAIN NURSERY `23-53`
Masbury, Wells, Somerset
TEL: 01749 841 014

SOMERSET COUNTY ENTERPRISES GARDEN CENTRE `23-54`
Manor Road, Frome, Somerset
TEL: 01373 453 094

MILL COTTAGE PLANTS `23-55`
The Mill, Wookey, Somerset
TEL: 01749 676 966

BROWNE'S GARDEN CENTRE `23-56`
Woodford Lane, Wells, Somerset
TEL: 01749 673 050

LONGLEAT `23-57`
Warminster, Wiltshire
TEL: 01985 844 400

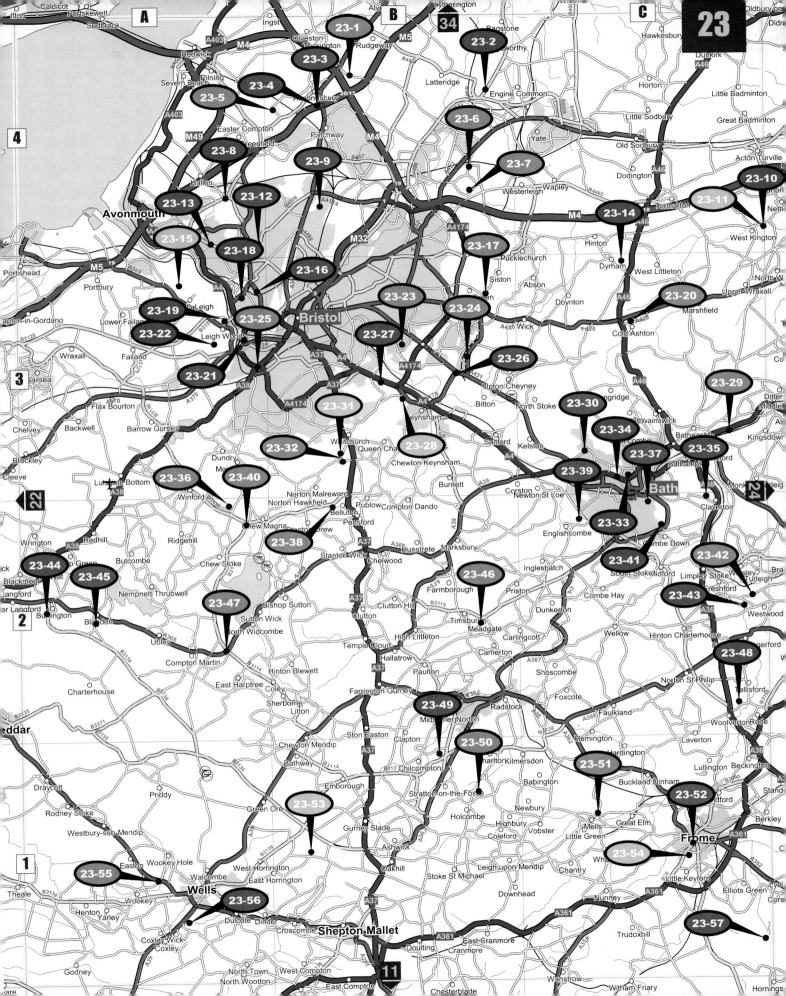

ABBEY HOUSE GARDENS `24-1`
Market Cross, Malmesbury, Wiltshire
TEL: 01666 822 212

FOXLEY ROAD NURSERIES `24-2`
Foxley Road, Malmesbury, Wiltshire
TEL: 01666 822 171

TOOMERS' STONE LANE GARDEN CENTRE `24-3`
Stone Lane, Swindon, Wiltshire
TEL: 01793 771 766

SHERSTON PARVA NURSERY `24-4`
Malmesbury Road, Malmesbury, Wiltshire
TEL: 01666 841 066

GREENHILL FARM NURSERIES `24-5`
Greenhill, Swindon, Wiltshire
TEL: 01793 770 224

NORTHERN ROAD NURSERIES `24-6`
1A Northern Road, Swindon, Wiltshire
TEL: 01793 535 580

THE GARDEN OUTLET `24-7`
Phase 2, Swindon, Wiltshire
TEL: 01793 531 106

JARDINERIE `24-8`
Hay Lane, Swindon, Wiltshire
TEL: 01793 852 736

WORLD OF WATER `24-9`
Jardinerie Garden Centre, Hay Lane,
Swindon, Wiltshire, SN4 9QT
TEL: 01793 853 097
WEB: www.worldofwater.com
Everything for the pond and tropical fish enthusiast. Extensive showgardens. Expert advice.
OPEN: 9-5.30 Mon-Sat, Sun 10.30-4.30. Closed Easter Sun.
SPECIALITIES: Aquatic plants, Water features, Waterfalls.

BREACH LANE NURSERY `24-10`
Upper Green Hill, Swindon, Wiltshire
TEL: 01793 854 660

BENCROFT GARDENS `24-11`
Bremhill, Calne, Wiltshire
TEL: 01249 740 324

BLOUNTS COURT NURSERIES `24-12`
Blounts Court, Calne, Wiltshire
TEL: 01249 812 103

CORSHAM COURT `24-13`
Corsham, Wiltshire
TEL: 01249 701 610

BOWOOD HOUSE AND GARDENS `24-14`
Bowood House, Calne, Wiltshire
TEL: 01249 812 102

AVEBURY MANOR & GARDEN, NATIONAL TRUST `24-15`
Marlborough, Wiltshire
TEL: 01672 539 250

WHITEHALL GARDEN CENTRE `24-16`
Corsham Road, Chippenham, Wiltshire
TEL: 01249 730 204

LACOCK ABBEY `24-17`
Lacock, Chippenham, Wiltshire
TEL: 01249 730 227

BOTANIC NURSERY `24-18`
Bath Road, Melksham, Wiltshire
TEL: 01225 706 597

PINE TREE NURSERY `24-19`
Conscience Lane, Devizes, Wiltshire
TEL: 01380 722 899

ROWDE MILL NURSERY `24-20`
Rowde, Devizes, Wiltshire
TEL: 01380 723 016

COURTS GARDEN, NATIONAL TRUST `24-21`
Holt, Trowbridge, Wiltshire
TEL: 01225 782 340

TOWNSENDS GARDEN CENTRE `24-22`
Bath Road, Devizes, Wiltshire
TEL: 01380 723 722

WESTDALE NURSERIES `24-23`
Holt Road, Bradford on Avon, Wiltshire
TEL: 01225 863 258

WOODBOROUGH GARDEN CENTRE `24-24`
Nursery Farm, Pewsey, Wiltshire
TEL: 01672 851 249

TROWBRIDGE GARDEN CENTRE `24-25`
288 Frome Road, Trowbridge, Somerset
TEL: 01225 763 927

VICARAGE LANE NURSERIES `24-26`
The Sands, Devizes, Wiltshire
TEL: 01380 812 332

HEATHER BANK NURSERY `24-27`
Woodlands, Devizes, Wiltshire
TEL: 01380 812 739

MEAD NURSERY `24-28`
Brokerswood, Westbury, Wiltshire
TEL: 01373 859 990

GRANBY GARDEN CENTRE `24-29`
32 Astor Crescent, Andover, Hampshire
TEL: 01264 790 275

BARTERS PLANT CENTRE `24-30`
Barters Farm Nurseries, Westbury, Wiltshire
TEL: 01373 832 694

LAKESIDE GARDEN CENTRE `24-31`
Crockerton Shopping Centre, Warminster, Wiltshire
TEL: 01985 217 413

Rose

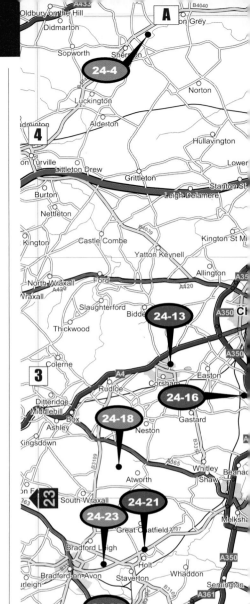

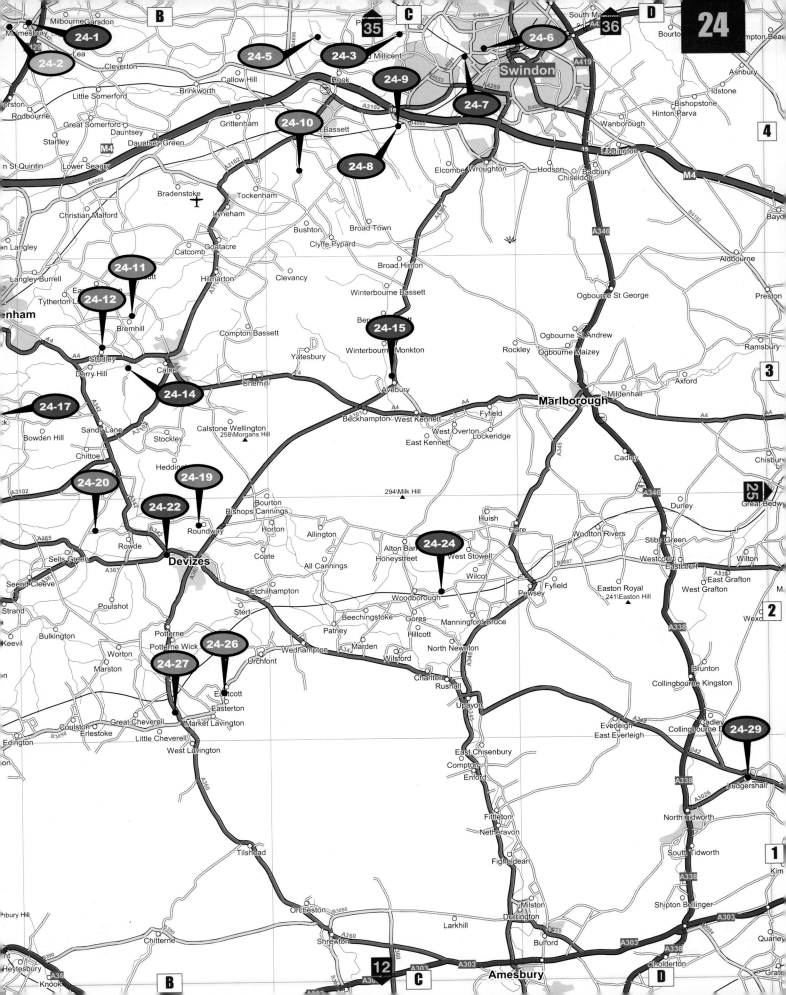

WYEVALE GARDEN CENTRE `25-1`
Newbury Road, Didcot, Oxfordshire
TEL: 01235 833 900

ASHDOWN HOUSE, NATIONAL TRUST `25-2`
Lambourn, Oxfordshire
TEL: 01488 725 84

GATEHAMPTON FUCHSIAS `25-3`
Gatehampton Farm, Reading, Berkshire
TEL: 01491 872 894

BEALE PARK `25-4`
Lower Basildon, Reading, Berkshire
TEL: 01734 845 172

BASILDON PARK, NATIONAL TRUST `25-5`
Lower Basildon, Reading, Berkshire
TEL: 0118 984 3040

THE LIVING RAINFOREST `25-6`
Wyld Court Hall, Newbury, Berkshire
TEL: 01635 202 444

AQUASCAPE `25-7`
Hillier Garden Centre, Hermitage, Berkshire
TEL: 01635 202 300

WOODSIDE FARM NURSERY `25-8`
Priors Court Road, Thatcham, Berkshire
TEL: 01635 201 561

DAI-ICHI BONSAI `25-9`
Priors Court Road, Thatcham, Berkshire
TEL: 01635 200 667

 HILLIER GARDEN CENTRE `25-10`
Priors Court Road, Hermitage,
Thatcham, Berks, RG18 9TG
TEL: 01635 200 442
WEB: www.hillier.co.uk

A large garden centre with a comprehensive range of everything you could want for the garden. Easy access and friendly expert advice make shopping a pleasure.
OPEN: Daily 9-5.30, Sun 10.30-4.30.
SPECIALITIES: Furniture, Gifts, Hardy plants, Trees, Shrubs.

WYEVALE GARDEN CENTRE `25-12`
4a Bath Road, Hungerford, Berkshire
TEL: 01488 682 916

COTTAGE GARDEN PLANTS `25-14`
9 Buckingham Road, Newbury, Berkshire
TEL: 01635 319 41

GLENVALE NURSERIES `25-11`
Hungerford Lane, Southend Bradfield,
Reading, Berkshire, RG7 6JH
TEL: 0118 974 4006
EMAIL: eric@glenvalesagehost.co.uk,
Open seven days a week for a full range of plants.
OPEN: Summer Mon-Sat 9-5.30, Sun, 10-5;
winter Mon-Sat 9-5, Sun 10-4.
SPECIALITIES: Alpines, Bedding plants,
Climbers, Fruit & fruit trees, House plants.

HAMSTEAD GROWERS `25-13`
Newbury, Berkshire, RG20 0JG
TEL: 01635 254 091
P.Y.O. soft fruit and vegetables, pot plants and farm shop.
OPEN: Mon-Fri 8.30-5.30, Sat 8.30-5, Oct-May closed Sun. May-Sep 8.30-5 Sun.
SPECIALITIES: Bedding plants, Pot plants, Vegetables.

WHITE TOWER NURSERY `25-15`
Aldermaston Village, Reading,
Berkshire, RG7 4LD
TEL: 0118 971 2123
Family nursery growing herbaceous, tender and hardy plants, shrubs, winter & summer baskets. Bonsai, up to 2.5m. Floral work.
OPEN: Daily, 9-6 or dusk if earlier, closed Christmas & Boxing day.
SPECIALITIES: Bedding plants, Hardy plants.

FOXGROVE PLANTS `25-16`
Foxgrove Farm, Newbury, Berkshire
TEL: 01635 405 54

YEW TREE GARDEN CENTRE `25-1`
Ball Hill, Newbury, Berkshire
TEL: 01635 255 250

DARLING BUDS OF MAY `25-18`
Newbury Road, Thatcham, Berkshire
TEL: 01635 269 308

LAKESIDE GARDEN CENTRE `25-19`
Brimpton Common Road, Tadley, Berkshire
TEL: 01189 814 138

PENWOOD NURSERIES `25-2`
The Drove, Newbury, Berkshire
TEL: 01635 254 366

THE COTTAGE GARDEN CENTRE `25-2`
Cottismore Park, Newbury, Berkshire
TEL: 01635 297 979

GREENACRES NURSERY `25-2`
Aldermaston Road, Basingstoke, Hampshire
TEL: 01256 850 470

HIGHCLERE CASTLE AND GARDENS `25-2`
Highclere, Newbury, Berkshire
TEL: 01635 253 210

ELM PARK GARDEN CENTRE `25-2`
Aldermaston Road, Basingstoke, Hampshire
TEL: 01256 850 587

HARDY'S COTTAGE GARDEN PLANTS `25-2`
Priory Lane, Whitchurch, Hampshire
TEL: 01256 896 533

WYEVALE GARDEN CENTRE `25-2`
Winchester Road, Basingstoke, Hampshire
TEL: 01256 397 155

WYEVALE GARDEN CENTRE `25-2`
Salisbury Road, Andover, Hampshire
TEL: 01264 710 551

Alstroemeria

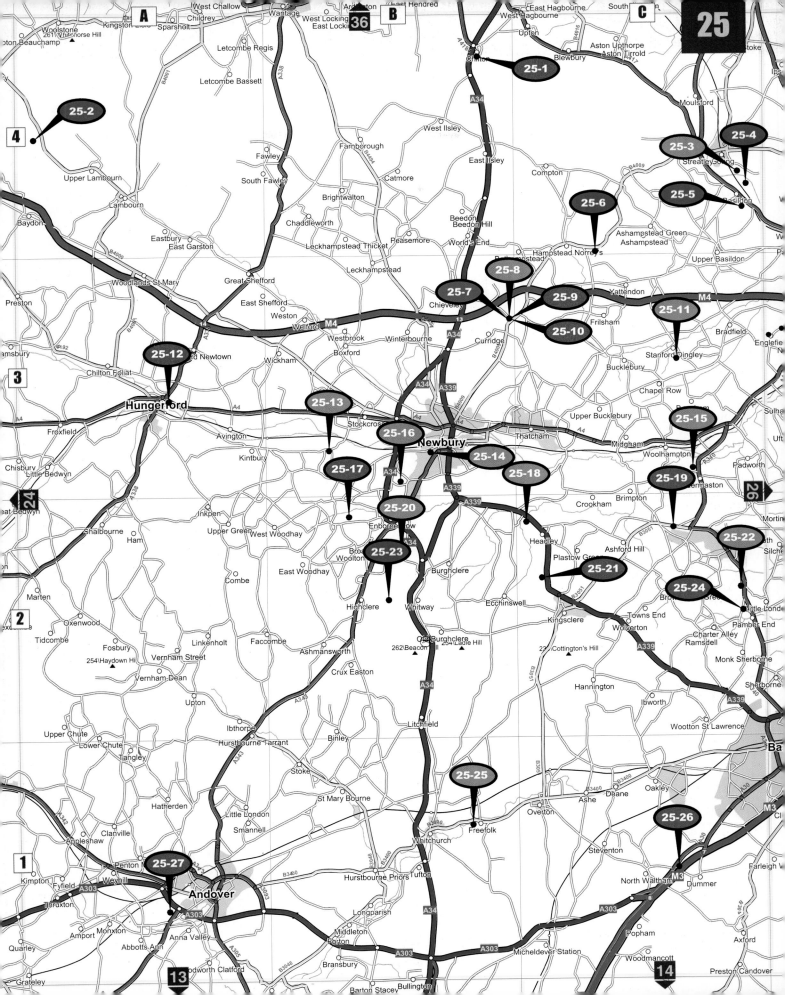

HAYDEN NURSERIES
Bishop Lane, Marlow, Berkshire
TEL: 01628 484 855

TOAD HALL GARDEN CENTRE
Marlow Road, Henley on Thames, Oxfordshire
TEL: 01491 574 615

GREYS COURT, NATIONAL TRUST
Rotherfield Greys, Henley on Thames, Oxfordshire
TEL: 01491 628 529

WOODCOTE GARDEN CENTRE
Reading Road, Reading, Berkshire
TEL: 01491 680 335

BERKSHIRE COLLEGE OF AGRICULTURE PLANT CENTRE
Hall Place, Maidenhead, Berkshire
TEL: 01628 824 444

ENGBERS NURSERY & GARDEN CENTRE
Harpsden Woods, Henley on Thames, Oxfordshire
TEL: 0118 940 3078

WATERFIELD NURSERY
Market Garden, Reading, Berkshire
TEL: 01491 681 541

LADD'S GARDEN VILLAGE
Bath Road, Reading, Berkshire
TEL: 01189 404 794

WYEVALE GARDEN CENTRE
Floral Mile, Reading, Berkshire
TEL: 01189 403 933

BERRY BROOK GARDEN CENTRE
Henley Road, Reading, Berkshire
TEL: 0118 948 4794

H. W. HYDE & SON
The Nursery, Reading, Berkshire
TEL: 0118 934 0011

PRIMROSE NURSERY
London Road, Reading, Berkshire
TEL: 0118 9404 288

ROTHERSTONE PLANTS
70 Long Lane, Reading, Berkshire
TEL: 0118 961 5889

BARN FARM NURSERIES
Wokingham Road, Hurst, Berkshire
TEL: 01734 321 008

ENGLEFIELD GARDEN CENTRE
The Street, Theale, Berkshire
TEL: 0118 930 4898

ENGLEFIELD HOUSE
Englefield Estate Office, Reading, Berkshire
TEL: 0118 930 2221 (0118 930 2504 - office)

D. & S. NURSERY & GARDEN CENTRE
Reading Road, Wokingham, Berkshire
TEL: 0118 977 2141

WYEVALE GARDEN CENTRE
Forrest Road, Bracknell, Berkshire
TEL: 01344 869 456

RURAL CRAFTS
374 Reading Road, Wokingham, Berkshire
TEL: 01734 790 000

LAURELS PLANT CENTRE
29 Hyde End Lane, Reading, Berkshire
TEL: 0118 988 3792

PUDDING LANE NURSERY
Reading Road, Reading, Berkshire
TEL: 0118 976 1048

GROVELANDS GARDEN CENTRE
166 Hyde End Road, Reading, Berkshire
TEL: 0800 074 7195

CHANDLERS FARM NURSERY
Grazeley Green, Reading, Berkshire
TEL: 01734 832 015

WORLD OF WATER
166 Hyde End, Shinfield, Reading, Berkshire, RG2 9ER
TEL: 0118 988 5492
WEB: www.worldofwater.com
Everything for the pond and tropical fish enthusiast. Extensive showgardens. Expert advice.
OPEN: 9-5.30 Mon-Sat, Sun 10.30-4.30. Closed Easter Sun.
SPECIALITIES: Aquatic plants, Waterfalls, Water features.

HENRY STREET GARDEN CENTRE
Swallowfield Road, Reading, Berkshire
TEL: 0118 976 1223

WYEVALE GARDEN CENTRE
Heathlands Road, Wokingham, Berkshire
TEL: 0118 977 3055

BROOKSIDE NURSERY
Church Road, Reading, Berkshire
TEL: 0118 988 4122

STRATFIELD SAYE HOUSE
Stratfield Saye, Reading, Berkshire
TEL: 01256 882 882

CHOBHAM NURSERIES
Bagshot Road, Chobham, Surrey
TEL: 01276 858 252

SOUTHVIEW NURSERIES
Chequers Lane, Hook, Hampshire
TEL: 0118 973 2206

SANDHURST GARDEN CENTRE
Yorktown Road, Sandhurst, Berkshire
TEL: 01252 872 294

PETER TRENEAR NURSERIES
Chequers Lane, Hook, Hampshire
TEL: 0118 973 2300

WHITEWATER NURSERY
Hound Green, Hook, Hampshire
TEL: 01189 326 487

WYEVALE GARDEN CENTRE
Wildmoor Lane, Sherfield on Loddon, Hampshire
TEL: 01256 882 239

VICARAGE HILL NURSERY
Hartley Wintney, Basingstoke, Hampshire
TEL: 01252 842 523

SCATS COUNTRYSTORES
Wildmoor Lane, Sherfield-on-Loddon, Basingstoke, Hampshire, RG27 0HA
TEL: 08451 304 030
EMAIL: basingstoke.countrystore@scats.co.uk
WEB: www.scatscountrystores.co.uk

Scats Countrystores offer a comprehensive range of products covering country clothing and footwear, horse feed and equestrian sundries, garden furniture and equipment, DIY, animal feeds, pet foods and accessories and farm supplies.
OPEN: Mon-Sat 8.30-5.30, Sun 10-4.
SPECIALITIES: Christmas trees, Garden & Conservatory furniture, Garden machinery, Gifts, Sundries.

D. H. WATER GARDENS
Wyevale Garden Centre, Wildmoor Lane, Sherfield-on-Loddon, Basingstoke, Hampshire, RG27 0HA
TEL: 01256 882 019

Hampshire aquatic superstore for every indoor/outdoor need. Maintenance, installation, landscaping available.
OPEN: Daily, 9.30-5.30 Mon-Sat. 10.30-4.30 Sun, closed Christmas day & Easter Sun.

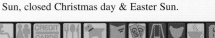

HOOK GARDEN CENTRE & NURSERY
Reading Road, Hook, Berkshire
TEL: 01256 762 739

VYNE
Sherborne St John, Basingstoke, Hampshire
TEL: 01256 881 337

CONKERS GARDEN CENTRE
London Road, Basingstoke, Hampshire
TEL: 01256 840 515

REDFIELDS GARDEN CENTRE
Ewshot Lane, Fleet, Hampshire
TEL: 01252 624 444

WYCHWOOD WATERLILY FARM
Farnham Road, Hook, Hampshire
TEL: 01256 702 800

COACH HOUSE GARDEN CENTRE 26-38

London Road, Hartley Wintney, Hook,
Hampshire, RG27 8HY
TEL: 01252 842 400
EMAIL: coach_house@hotmail.com
WEB: www.thecoachhousegardencentre.co.uk

*Good value family run centre with wide and
unusual range of plants and shrubs. Everything
from pots to swimming pools!*
OPEN: Every day except Christmas, Boxing &
Easter day, Mon-Fri 8.30-6, Sat 9-6, Sun 10.30-4.30.
SPECIALITIES: Garden and conservatory furniture,
Garden machinery, Palms, Topiary, Water features.

ODIHAM WATERLILY COLLECTION 26-44

At Wychwood, Hook, Hampshire
TEL: 01256 702 800

BOURNE BUILDINGS 26-45

39-43 Guildford Road, Farnham, Surrey
TEL: 01252 718 481

GREEN FARM PLANTS 26-46

Bury Court, Farnham, Surrey
TEL: 01420 232 02

GARDEN STYLE 26-47

Wrecclesham Hill, Farnham, Surrey
TEL: 01252 735 331

BIRDWORLD 26-48

Forest Lodge Garden Centre, Farnham, Surrey
TEL: 01420 221 40

FOREST LODGE GARDEN CENTRE 26-49

Holt Pound, Farnham, Surrey
TEL: 01420 232 75

AVENUE NURSERIES GARDEN CENTRE 26-50

The Avenue, Lasham, Alton,
Hampshire, GU34 5RX
TEL: 01256 381 648
*Large garden centre
with a wide selection of
plants, gifts, garden
furniture, aquatics and
sheds. Large restaurant.
A garden centre in a
woodland setting ideal
for a pleasant browse
followed by a cream tea,
snack or meal in the
restaurant.*
OPEN: Daily, Mon-
Sat, 9-6. Sun 10.30-
4.30, closed Christmas & Boxing day.

LONDON &
HOME COUNTIES

SEE PAGES
138-147
FOR DETAIL

GARDEN CENTRE
NURSERY
GARDEN

NURSERY & GARDEN CENTRE
GARDEN & NURSERY
WATER GARDEN SPECIALIST

GROVELAND NURSERY
Clay Tye Road, Upminster, Essex
TEL: 01708 222 528

HIGH HOUSE GARDEN CENTRE
Ockendon Road, Upminster, Essex
TEL: 01708 222 181

NORTHWICK GARDEN CENTRE
Canvey Road, Canvey Island, Essex
TEL: 01268 692 595

CORNELL'S GARDEN CENTRE
36a Fobbing Road, Stanford le Hope, Essex
TEL: 01375 642 118

THURROCK GARDEN CENTRE
South Road, South Ockendon, Essex
TEL: 01708 851 991

SMITHS ORCHARD GARDEN CENTRE
70 Chadwell Road, Grays, Essex
TEL: 01375 372 195

SWALLOW AQUATICS
Millbrook Garden Centre, Gravesend, Kent
TEL: 01474 561 123

THE MILLBROOK GARDEN COMPANY
Station Road, Gravesend, Kent
TEL: 01474 331 135

HAWLEY GARDEN CENTRE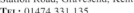
Hawley Road, Hawley, Dartford,
Kent, DA2 7RB
TEL: 01322 224 108
EMAIL: HawleyGardenCtr@aol.com
WEB:

Family run centre with large range of bedding plants, shrubs, garden sundries and much more! Aquatic centre also on site.
OPEN: Daily, Mon-Sat, 8-6, Sun 10.30-4.30, closed Christmas Day & Easter Sunday.
SPECIALITIES: Bedding plants, Climbers, Rhododendrons and azaleas, Roses, Shrubs.

WATERLAND
Dillywood Lane, Rochester, Kent
TEL: 01634 719 889

SCALERS HILL NURSERY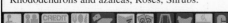
Scalers Hill, Gravesend, Kent
TEL: 01474 822 856

WALNUT HILL NURSERIES
Walnut Hill Road, Gravesend, Kent
TEL: 01474 704 859

RIVERSIDE FUCHSIAS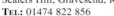
Gravel Road, Sutton at Hone, Dartford, Kent, DA4 9HQ
TEL: 01322 863 891
National Collection and 5,000 varieties of fuchsias. 1,000 varieties of geraniums, hardy & erodiums. Penstemons.
OPEN: 6 days a week, 9-5, closed Mon, Christmas & Boxing Day.

WOODLAND NURSERIES & GARDEN CENTRE
Ash Lane, Sevenoaks, Kent
TEL: 01474 852 788

ROSIE'S GARDEN PLANTS
Rochester Road, Aylesford, Kent
TEL: 01622 715 777

MILLYARD NURSERIES
The Garden Shop Millyard, West Malling, Kent
TEL: 01732 875 545

IGHTHAM PLANT CENTRE
Borough Green Road, Ightham,
Kent, TN15 9JA
TEL: 01732 884 726
WEB: www.hedging.uk.com
Fully stocked plant centre specialising in specimens and hedging and lilies.

WILLIAM T. DYSON
Great Comp Nursery, Borough Green, Kent
TEL: 01732 886 154

GREAT COMP GARDEN & NURSERY
Comp Lane, Platt, Borough Green,
Kent, TN15 8QS
TEL: 01732 882 669 / 886 154
EMAIL: william.dyson@ukgateway.net
WEB: www.greatcomp.co.uk

Seven-acre 'plantsman's paradise' surrounding 17th century manor. Enormous collection of choice and unusual plants from all over the globe, many of which are available at the nursery.
OPEN: 1 Apr-31 Oct, 11-6.
ENTRY COSTS: Adult £3.50, Children £1.00, OAPs £3.50
SPECIALITIES: Perennials, esp. Salvias.

G. REUTHE NURSERIES
Sevenoaks Road, Sevenoaks, Kent
TEL: 01732 810 694

CROMAR NURSERY
North Pole, Maidstone, Kent
TEL: 01622 812 380

DESIGNER PLANTS
Back Lane, Ightham, Sevenoaks, Kent,
TN15 9AU
TEL: 01732 885 700
EMAIL: dp@coblands.co.uk
WEB: www.coblands.co.uk
Specialist herbaceous nursery with other plants which will tempt designers and plant hunters. Select from our vast range of perennials both the usual and the unusual.
OPEN: Mon-Fri all year. Sat a.m. in Spring, other times please phone to confirm opening times.
SPECIALITIES: Alpines, Ferns, Geraniums, Ornamental grasses, Perennials.

WINDMILL NURSERY
The Street, Maidstone, Kent
TEL: 01622 813 330

BIJOU NURSERIES
Tonbridge Road, Maidstone, Kent
TEL: 01622 812 278

PLAXTOL NURSERIES
The Spoute, Sevenoaks, Kent
TEL: 01732 810 550

IGHTHAM MOTE, NATIONAL TRUST
Ivy Hatch, Sevenoaks, Kent
TEL: 01732 810 378

DOWNDERRY NURSERY
Pillar Box Lane, Tonbridge, Kent
TEL: 01732 810 081

OLD WALLED GARDEN
Oxonhoath, Hadlow, Kent
TEL: 01732 810 012

RIVERHILL HOUSE GARDENS
Riverhill House, Sevenoaks, Kent
TEL: 01732 452 557

RALPH'S NURSERY & FARM SHOP
Marlpit Farm, Maidstone, Kent
TEL: 01622 743 851

BROOKSIDE GARDEN CENTRE
Seven Mile Lane, East Peckham,
Tonbridge, Kent, TN12 5JG
TEL: 01622 871 250
EMAIL: brooksidegckent@ukonline.co.uk
WEB: www.gardenaquatics.co.uk and www.brooksidegardencentre.co.uk
Large independent centre est. 1968. A wide range of trees, shrubs, conifers, perennials, alpines, bedding & house plants. Aquatics.
OPEN: Daily, weekday hours 8.30-5.30, closed Christmas & Boxing Day.
SPECIALITIES: Aquatic plants, Fish, Pet centre, Shrubs.

G. & S. SMALLHOLDINGS 28-32
Wheelers Lane, Maidstone, Kent
TEL: 01622ñ744 273

HADLOW COLLEGE 28-33
Hadlow, Kent
TEL: 01732 850 551

HADLOW COLLEGE PLANT CENTRE 28-34
Hadlow College, Tonbridge, Kent
TEL: 01732 853 211

YALDING ORGANIC GARDENS 28-35
Benover Road, Yalding, Maidstone,
Kent, ME18 6EX
TEL: 01622 814 650
EMAIL: enquiry@hdra.org.uk
WEB: www.hdra.org.uk
*Take a fascinating
trip through the
history of garden-
ing. Beautiful dis-
plays, all organic.
Guided tours avail-
able. Organic cafe.
Gift shop. Full
programme of
events.*
OPEN: Daily,
May-Sep, Wed-Sun
10-5 and weekends
in Apr & Oct.
ENTRY COSTS:
Adult £3, Children
under 16 and
HDRA/RHS members free.
SPECIALITIES: Showcase of organic growing.

GATE HOUSE FARM NURSERY 28-36
Gate House Farm, Tonbridge, Kent
TEL: 01732 832 180

**FOUR SEASONS BONSAI NURSERY
& RHINO ROCK GARDENS** 28-37
Snoll Hatch Road, East Peckham, Kent
TEL: 01622 872 403

DE JAGER & SONS 28-38
The Nurseries, Marden, Kent
TEL: 01622 831 235

WYEVALE GARDEN CENTRE 28-39
Maidstone Road, Tonbridge, Kent
TEL: 01892 835 777

HAYESDEN HERB & HONEY FARM 28-40
Upper Hayesden Lane, Tonbridge, Kent
TEL: 01732 353 421

SPELDHURST NURSERIES 28-41
Langton Road, Tunbridge Wells, Kent
TEL: 01892 862 682

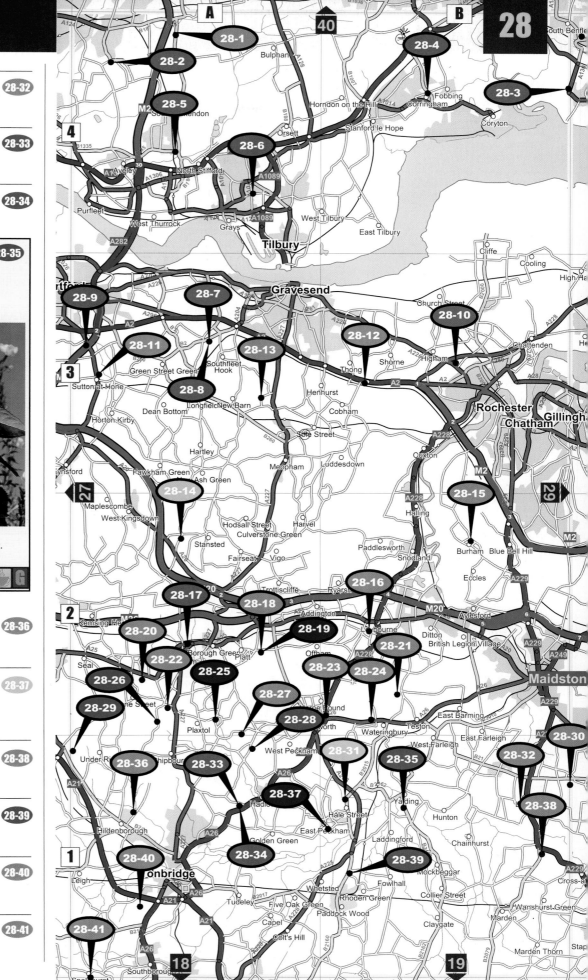

● GARDEN CENTRE
● NURSERY
● GARDEN
● NURSERY & GARDEN CENTRE
● GARDEN & NURSERY
● WATER GARDEN SPECIALIST

OASIS `29-1`
42 Greenwood Avenue, South Benfleet, Essex
TEL: 01268 757 666

LEIGH GARDEN & TIMBER SUPPLIES `29-2`
1 Ligham Court Drive, Leigh on Sea, Essex
TEL: 01702 474376

HOMELEIGH NURSERY `29-3`
Ratcliffe Highway, Rochester, Kent
TEL: 01634 250 235

STONES NURSERY `29-4`
Halfway Road, Sheerness, Kent
TEL: 01795 580 411

BRAMBLEDOWN GARDEN CENTRE `29-5`
Lower Road, Sheerness, Kent
TEL: 01795 877 977

WAVERLEY NURSERIES `29-6`
622 Lower Rainham Road, Gillingham, Kent
TEL: 01634 232 520

HOLYWELL LANE NURSERIES `29-7`
Holywell Lane, Sittingbourne, Kent
TEL: 01795 842 335

KNOWLER NURSERY `29-8`
143 Berengrave Lane, Gillingham, Kent
TEL: 01634 361 631

BERENGRAVE NURSERIES `29-9`
61 Berengrave Lane, Gillingham, Kent
TEL: 01634 363 412

GORE HOUSE NURSERY `29-10`
London Road, Sittingbourne, Kent
TEL: 01795 842 365

W. H. CARTER & SON `29-11`
34 Borstal Hill, Whitstable, Kent
TEL: 01227 272 903

OAKLANDS NURSERIES `29-12`
24 London Road, Sittingbourne, Kent
TEL: 01795 842 173

ULTIMATE KOI `29-13`
Colourpack Plant Centre, Sittingbourne, Kent
TEL: 01795 841 300

BREDHURST NURSERY `29-14`
Dunn Street, Gillingham, Kent
TEL: 01634 386 444

MERESBOROUGH NURSERY `29-15`
Meresborough Road, Rainham,
Gillingham, Kent ME8 8PP
TEL: 01634 231 639
Specialist growers of geraniums & fuchsias.
OPEN: Daily, 1 Apr-end Jun, 8-5. Sep-Christmas,
Mon-Fri 8-5, Sat & Sun 9-12.
SPECIALITIES: Cut flowers, Fuchsias, Geraniums.

WYEVALE GARDEN CENTRE `29-16`
Elm Court, Gillingham, Kent
TEL: 01634 813 778

MEADOW GRANGE NURSERY `29-17`
Honey Hill, Whitstable, Kent
TEL: 01227 471 205

WYEVALE GARDEN CENTRE `29-18`
Norton Crossroads, Faversham, Kent
TEL: 01795 521 549

THE BONSAI SHOP `29-19`
Country Gardens Faversham, Sittingbourne, Kent
TEL: 01795 522 466

SHILLINGHURST NURSERY `29-20`
Oad Street, Sittingbourne, Kent
TEL: 01795 842 446

VALE NURSERY `29-21`
Heath Cottage, Sittingbourne, Kent
TEL: 01795 844 004

MACKNADE GARDEN CENTRE `29-22`
Canterbury Road, Faversham, Kent
TEL: 01795 531 213

BROGDALE HORTICULTURAL TRUST `29-23`
Brogdale Road, Faversham, Kent
TEL: 01795 535 286

COPTON ASH SPECIALIST NURSERY `29-24`
105 Ashford Road, Faversham, Kent
TEL: 01795 535 919

MOUNT EPHRAIM GARDENS `29-25`
Staple Street, Faversham, Kent
TEL: 01227 751 496

WYEVALE GARDEN CENTRE `29-26`
Upper Harbledown, Canterbury, Kent
TEL: 01227 454 264

DODDINGTON PLACE GARDENS `29-27`
Doddington, Sittingbourne, Kent
TEL: 01795 886 101

NOTCUTTS GARDEN CENTRE `29-28`
Newnham Court , Maidstone, Kent
TEL: 01622 739 944

LONGACRE NURSERY `29-29`
Perrywood, Faversham, Kent
TEL: 01227 752 254

POTTED GARDEN NURSERY `29-30`
Ashford Road, Maidstone, Kent
TEL: 01622 737 801

PILGRIM HOUSE HERBS `29-31`
Pilgrim House, Maidstone, Kent
TEL: 01622 859 371

LEEDS CASTLE `29-32`
, Maidstone, Kent
TEL: 01622 765 400

RUMWOOD NURSERIES & GARDEN CENTRE `29-33`
Sutton Road, Maidstone, Kent
TEL: 01628 614 77

COOKOO BOX NURSERY `29-34`
Longfield, Maidstone, Kent
TEL: 01622 844 866

PLEASANT VIEW GARDEN CENTRE `29-35`
Plough Wents Road, Maidstone, Kent
TEL: 01622 844 872

BEECH COURT GARDENS `29-36`
Canterbury Road, Ashford, Kent
TEL: 01233 740 735

VICTORIANA NURSERY GARDENS `29-37`
Challock, Ashford, Kent
TEL: 01233 740 480

WARMLAKE NURSERY & FARM SHOP `29-38`
North Street, Maidstone, Kent
TEL: 01622 844 000

CROFTERS NURSERY `29-39`
Church Hill, Ashford, Kent
TEL: 01233 712 798

CHURCH HILL COTTAGE GARDENS AND NURSERY `29-40`
Church Hill, Ashford, Kent
TEL: 01233 712 522

OLANTIGH GARDEN NURSERIES `29-41`
Olantigh Gardens, Ashford, Kent
TEL: 01233 812 248

GRAFTY GARDEN CENTRE `29-42`
Crumps Corner, Maidstone, Kent
TEL: 01622 858 800

HEADCORN FLOWER CENTRE & VINEYARD `29-43`
Grigg Lane, Headcorn, Kent
TEL: 01622 890 250

BYBROOK BARN GARDEN CENTRE `29-44`
Canterbury Road, Ashford, Kent
TEL: 01233 631 959

IDEN CROFT HERBS `29-45`
Frittenden Road, Staplehurst, Kent
TEL: 01580 891 432

MADRONA NURSERY `29-46`
Pluckley Road, Bethersden, Ashford,
Kent, TN26 3DD
Tel: 01233 820 100
Unusual, rare and new plant varieties displayed on a spectacular and unique nursery site. Catalogue available.
Open: Mid Mar-end Oct, Sat-Tue 10-5, closed Wed-Fri.
Specialities: Hardy plants, Shrubs, Trees, Perennials, Grasses, Ferns, Roses and Climbers.

THE COTTAGE GARDEN `29-47`
Cranbrook Road, Staplehurst, Kent
TEL: 01580 891 312

WYEVALE GARDEN CENTRE `29-48`
Hythe Road, Ashford, Kent
TEL: 01233 502 136

BEAN PLACE NURSERY `29-49`
52 Gladstone Road, Ashford, Kent
TEL: 01233 631 550

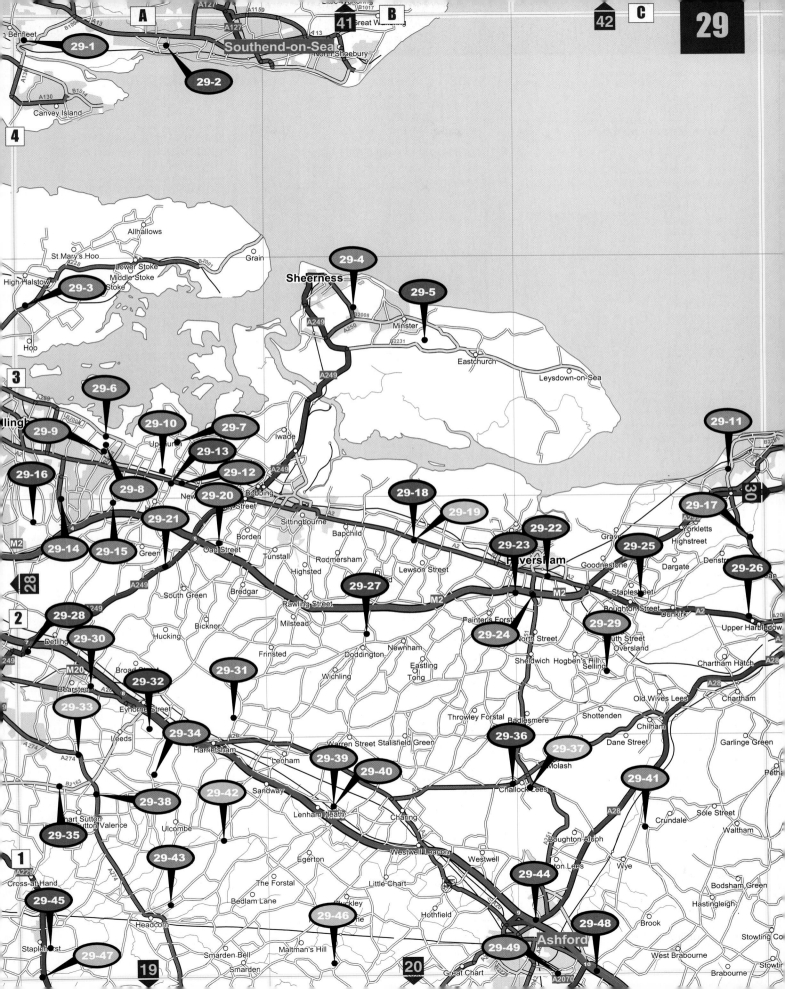

● GARDEN CENTRE   ● NURSERY & GARDEN CENTRE
● NURSERY   ● GARDEN & NURSERY
● GARDEN   ● WATER GARDEN SPECIALIST

KINGSGATE & KENVER NURSERIES `30-1`
George Hill Road, Broadstairs, Kent
TEL: 01843 604 407

EAST NORTHDOWN FARM & GARDENS `30-2`
Margate, Kent, T9 3TS
TEL: 01843 862 060 FAX: 01843 860 206
EMAIL: friend.northdown@ukonline.co.uk
WEB: www.botanyplants.co.uk

Family nursery specialising in plants for coastal and chalky areas, farmhouse gardens with many unusual plants suited to local conditions.
OPEN: Daily 10-5.
ENTRY COSTS: Free.
SPECIALITIES: Bamboos, Conservatory plants, Perennials, Shrubs, Trees.

CROFTERS GARDENING STORE `30-3`
42 Station Road, Westgate-on-sea, Kent
TEL: 01843 836 286

NICKY'S NURSERY `30-4`
33 Fairfield Road, Broadstairs, Kent
TEL: 01843 601 897

ROSEMARY NURSERY `30-5`
Manston Road, Margate, Kent
TEL: 01843 823 282

VINCENT NURSERIES `30-6`
47 Eddington Lane, Herne Bay, Kent
TEL: 01227 375 806

JOHNSONS NURSERY `30-7`
Thanet Way, Whitstable, Kent
TEL: 01227 793 763

WYEVALE GARDEN CENTRE `30-8`
Hereson Road, Ramsgate, Kent
TEL: 01843 592 393

BUSHEYFIELDS NURSERY `30-9`
Herne Common, Herne Bay, Kent
TEL: 01227 375 415

FOXHILL NURSERY `30-10`
Foxhill, Canterbury, Kent
TEL: 01227 713 012

ROSEWOOD DAYLILIES `30-11`
70 Deansway Avenue, Canterbury, Kent
TEL: 01227 711 071

SAUNDERS HOUSE NURSERY `30-13`
Saunders Lane, Canterbury, Kent
TEL: 01304 812 092

WYEVALE GARDEN CENTRE `30-15`
Stour Valley Business Park, Canterbury, Kent
TEL: 01227 731 033

PRESTON NURSERY `30-12`
The Street, Preston next Wingham,
Canterbury, Kent, CT3 1ED
TEL: Freephone 0800 035 1169 or 01227 722 250
EMAIL: tim-offord@supanet.com

An attractive family run nursery, specialising in trees and specimen palms, bamboos, topiary, tree ferns, large pots etc.
OPEN: Daily 10-5.
SPECIALITIES: Large trees, Palms, Bamboos, Box and Yew Topiary, Specimen shrubs.

ARCHERS LOW NURSERY `30-14`
Ash Road, Sandwich, Kent, CT13 9JB
TEL: 01304 613 150
WEB: www.archerslow.co.uk
Old-established garden centre growing shrubs, trees and border perennials. Full nursery stock.
OPEN: 7 day opening, 9-5.30.

MERRYFIELD NURSERIES `30-16`
Stodmarsh Road, Canterbury, Kent
TEL: 01227 462 602

PICKARD'S MAGNOLIA GARDENS `30-17`
Stodmarsh Road, Canterbury, Kent
TEL: 01227 463 951

LAYHAM GARDEN CENTRE `30-18`
Lower Road, Staple, Canterbury,
Kent, CT3 1LH
TEL: 01304 813 267
EMAIL: layham@gcstaple.fnet.co.uk
Specialist rose growers as well as offering a wide selection of shrubs, trees, conifers and herbaceous plants.
OPEN: Daily 9-5, closed 25-26 Dec and 1-2 Jan.
SPECIALITIES: Garden & conservatory furniture, Roses, Shrubs, Trees, Herbaceous plants.

TREVORS NURSERY `30-19`
Dover Road, Sandwich, Kent
TEL: 01304 614 377

SOUTH EAST WATER GARDENS `30-20`
Dover Road, Sandwich, Kent
TEL: 01304 614 963

SUMMERFIELD NURSERIES `30-21`
Barnsole Road, Staple, Kent
TEL: 01304 812 549

MARTINS NURSERY `30-22`
Poison Cross Nursery, Sandwich, Kent
TEL: 01304 611 262

HIGHAM PARK & GARDENS `30-23`
Higham Park, Canterbury, Kent
TEL: 01227 830 830

GOODNESTONE PARK GARDENS `30-24`
Goodnestone, Canterbury, Kent
TEL: 01304 840 107

WALMER NURSERY `30-25`
19-21 Dover Road, Deal, Kent
TEL: 01304 375 277

THOMPSON'S PLANT & GARDEN CENTRE `30-26`
Stone Street, Canterbury, Kent
TEL: 01227 700 449

WALMER CASTLE & GARDENS, ENGLISH HERITAGE `30-27`
Kingsdown Road, Deal, Kent
TEL: 01304 364 288

ORCHARD NURSERIES `30-28`
Stone Street, Canterbury, Kent
TEL: 01227 700 375

RINGWOULD ALPINES `30-29`
Dover Road, Deal, Kent
TEL: 01304 360 034

BLAKENEY HOUSE NURSERIES `30-30`
Osier Grounds, Canterbury, Kent
TEL: 01227 831 800

GARDEN PLANTS `30-31`
Windy Ridge, Dover, Kent
TEL: 01304 853 225

PINES GARDEN `30-32`
Beach Road, Dover, Kent
TEL: 01304 852 764

KERSNEY ABBEY & RUSSELL GARDENS `30-33`
Alkham Valley Road, Dover, Kent
TEL: 01304 872 434

ELWIN F. END `30-34`
32 Lower Road, Dover, Kent
TEL: 01304 822 541

FARTHING COMMON PLANT CENTRE `30-35`
Stone Street, Folkestone, Kent
TEL: 01303 863 438

MACFARLANES NURSERY & GARDEN CENTRE `30-36`
Swingfield, Folkestone, Kent
TEL: 01303 844 244

DOUR GARDENS & AQUATIC CENTRE `30-37`
Charlton Green, Dover, Kent
TEL: 01304 201 101

ALKHAM VALLEY GARDEN CENTRE `30-38`
Alkham Valley Road, Dover, Kent
TEL: 01303 893 351

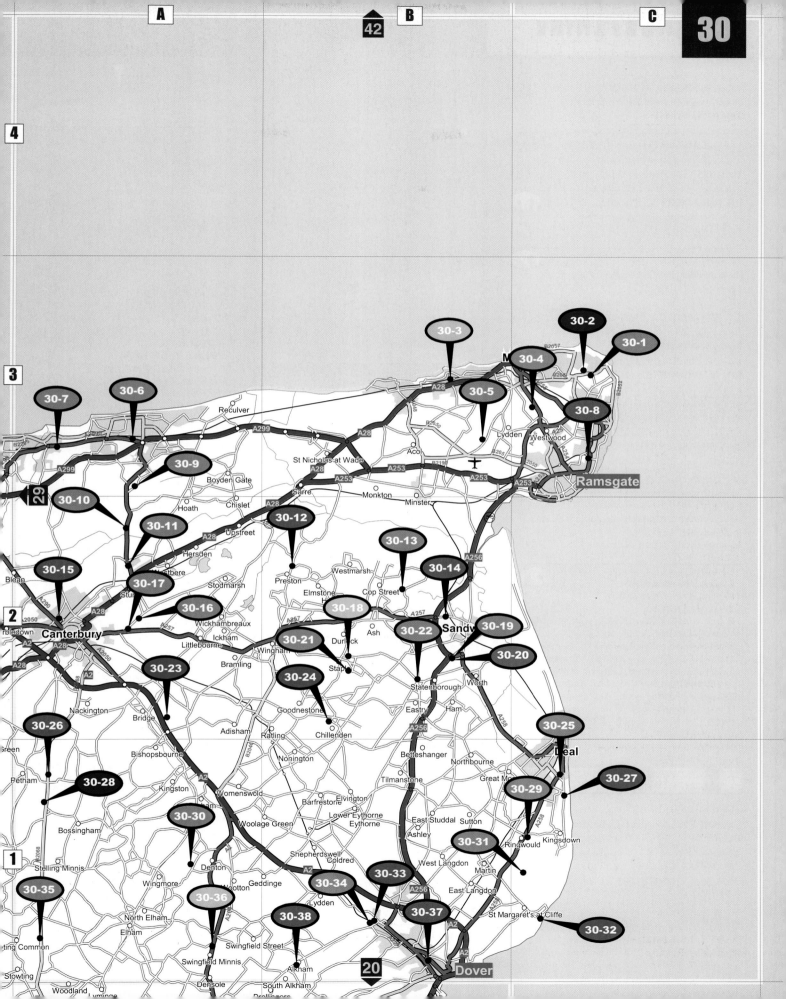

PEMBROKESHIRE

THE PERENNIAL NURSERY `31-1`
St. Davids, Haverfordwest, Pembrokeshire
TEL: 01437 721 954

LITTLE RHYNDASTON NURSERIES `31-2`
Hayscastle, Haverfordwest, Pembrokeshire
TEL: 01437 710 656

HILTON COURT `31-3`
Roch, Haverfordwest, Pembrokeshire
TEL: 01437 710 262

PICTON CASTLE `31-4`
Haverfordwest, Pembrokeshire
TEL: 01437 751 326

TAVERNSPITE GARDEN CENTRE `31-5`
Tavernspite, Whitland, Pembrokeshire
TEL: 01834 831 671

COLBY WOODLAND GARDEN, `31-6`
NATIONAL TRUST
Amroth, Narberth, Pembrokeshire
TEL: 01834 811 885

ST. ISHMAEL'S NURSERIES `31-7`
Haverfordwest, Pembrokeshire
TEL: 01646 636 343

HONEYBOROUGH GARDEN CENTRE `31-8`
Honeyborough Industrial Estate, Milford Haven,
Pembrokeshire
TEL: 01646 601 943

UPTON CASTLE GARDENS `31-9`
Cosheton, Pembroke Dock,
Pembrokeshire, SA72 4SE
TEL: 01646 651 782
EMAIL: enquiries@carewcastle-pembrokeshirecoast.org.uk
WEB: www.pembrokeshire.org.uk
37 acre garden set among wooded slopes over-
looking Milford Haven waterway. Particularly
noted for rhododendrons, camelias, magnolias,
250 different species of trees and shrubs, formal
terraces, herbaceous borders and rose gardens.
OPEN: 2 Apr-end Oct 10-5 Sun-Fri.
ENTRY COSTS: Adult £1.20, Children 60p, Family
£3.00, OAPs £1.20.
SPECIALITIES: Rhododendrons and azaleas,
Roses, Shrubs, Trees.

STAMMERS GARDENS `31-10`
Stammers Road, Saundersfoot, Pembrokeshire
TEL: 01834 813 766

PEMBROKE GARDEN CENTRE `31-11`
Slade Cross, Pembroke Dock, Pembrokeshire
TEL: 01646 622 488

BUSH SCHOOL CASH & CARRY NURSERY `31-12`
Bush Hill, Pembroke, Pembrokeshire
TEL: 01646 681 780

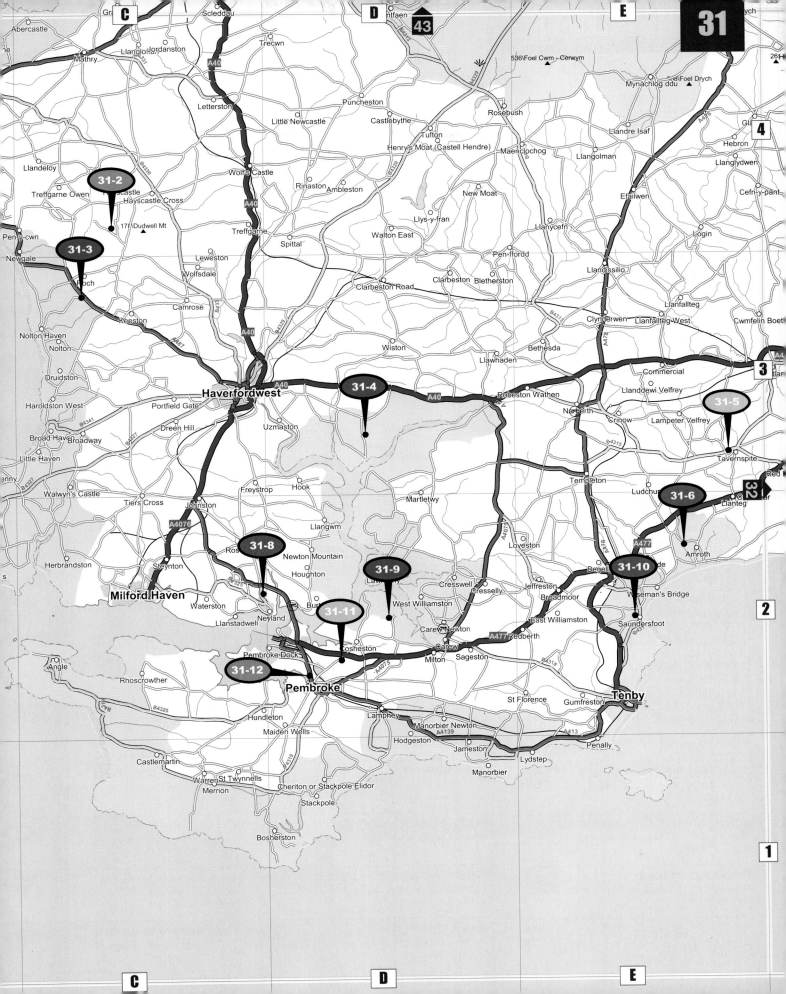

SOUTH WALES

CILWERN PLANTS 32-1
Cilwern, Llandeilo, Carmarthenshire
Tel: 01558 685 526

BEACONS' BOTANICALS 32-2
Bancyfelin, Llangadog, Carmarthenshire
Tel: 01550 777 992

ALLTYFERIN NURSERY 32-3
Nantgaredig, Carmarthen, Carmarthenshire
Tel: 01267 290 367

ABERGLASNEY GARDENS 32-4
Llangathen, Carmarthenshire, SA32 8QH
Tel: 01558 668 998
Email: director@aberglasney.org.uk
Web: www.aberglasney.org.uk

Set in the beautiful Tywi Valley, the gardens have first class horticultural qualities and a mysterious history. Although still under restoration, it is destined to become one of the most fascinating gardens in the U.K.
Open: 1 Apr-31 Oct, daily 10-6 (last admission 5). Nov 2001-Apr 2002, Mon-Fri, & 1st Sun in month, 10.30-3.
Entry costs: Adult £3.95, Children 5 -16 £1.95, Under 5s Free, Family £9.85, OAPs £3.45, Disabled £1.45, Group Rates 10+: Adults £3.45, OAPs £2.95, Children £1.45, Under 5s 95p.
Specialities: Walled garden, Water features, Woodland plants, Exotic plants, Hardy plants.

WYEVALE GARDEN CENTRE 32-5
Myrtle Hill, Carmarthen, Carmarthenshire
Tel: 01267 221 363

NATIONAL BOTANIC GARDENS OF WALES 32-6
Middleton Hall, Llanarthne, Carmarthenshire
Tel: 01558 668 768

SINGLETON BOTANIC GARDENS 32-7
Singleton Park, Swansea, South Wales
Tel: 01792 302 420

PONTARDDULAIS GARDEN CENTRE 32-8
Alltygraban Road, Swansea, South Wales
Tel: 01792 882 561

ROSE VILLA NURSERY 32-9
43 Cwmrhydyceirw Road, Swansea, South Wales
Tel: 01792 772 602

WYEVALE GARDEN CENTRE 32-10
Bynea, Llanelli, Carmarthenshire
Tel: 01554 772 189

BETTS NURSERIES 32-11
Cadoxton Road, Neath, South Wales
Tel: 01639 632 746

WYEVALE GARDEN CENTRE 32-12
Siemans Way, Swansea, South Wales
Tel: 01792 310 052

FFORESTMILL GARDEN CENTRE 32-13
Pontardulais Road, Swansea, South Wales
Tel: 01792 580 005

SWANSEA PLANTASIA 32-14
Parc Tawe, Swansea, South Wales
Tel: 01792 474 555

BLACKHILLS NURSERIES 32-15
Blackhills Lane, Swansea, South Wales
Tel: 01792 280 520

CLYNE GARDENS 32-16
Mill Lane, Swansea, South Wales
Tel: 01792 401 737

GOWER GARDEN CENTRE 32-17
Parsonage Farm, Swansea, South Wales
Tel: 01792 371 615

CASH HARDWARE STORES 32-18
13-15 Newton Road, Swansea, South Wales
Tel: 01792 368 187

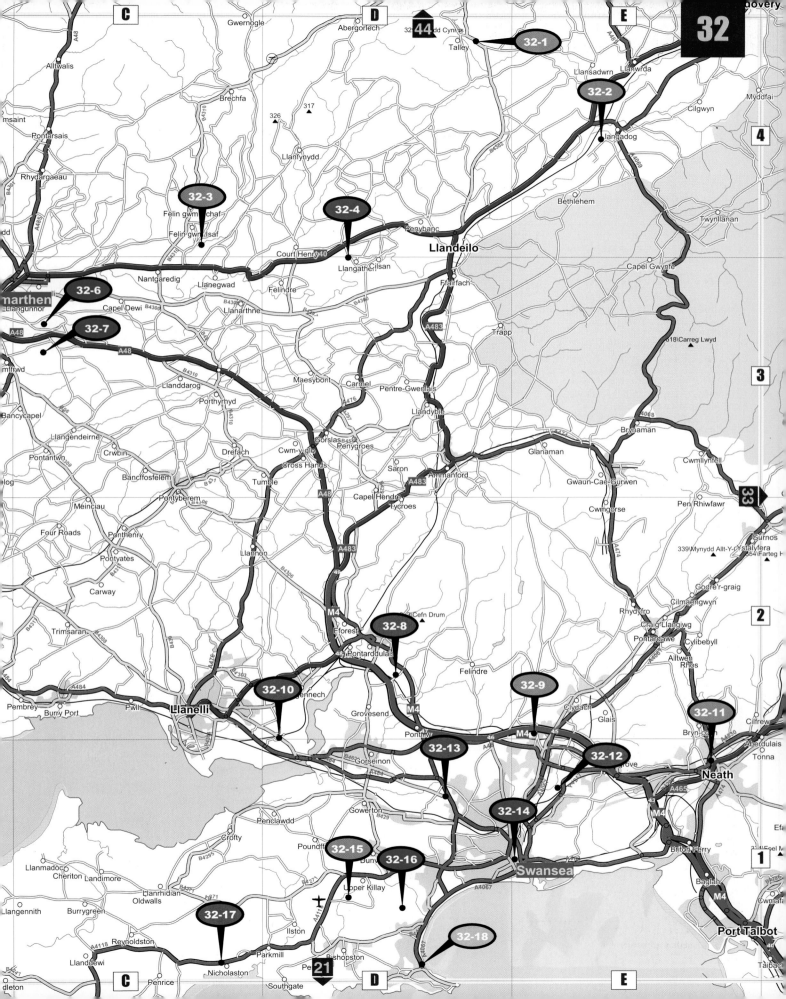

WALES

HERBS AT MYDDFAI
Beiliglas, Llandovery, Carmarthenshire
TEL: 01550 720 494

THE GARDEN CENTRE
53 High Street, Brecon, Powys
TEL: 01874 625 913

TRETOWER COURT
Tretower, Crickhowell, Powys
TEL: 01874 730 279

EVESHAM GARDENS
Llanfoist, Abergavenny, Monmouthshire
TEL: 01873 853 839

CORNER SHOP GARDEN CENTRE
1 Church Crescent, Ebbw Vale, South Wales
TEL: 01495 303 951

PENPERGWM PLANTS
Penpergwm Lodge, Abergavenny, Monmouthshire
TEL: 01873 840 422

WILLOWS GARDEN CENTRE
The Willows, Merthyr Tydfil, South Wales
TEL: 01685 384 415

THE SECRET GARDEN
Pentwyn Farm, Pontypool, Pembrokeshire
TEL: 01495 785 237

GORDON'S NURSERY
1 Cefnpennar Cottages, Mountain Ash, South Wales
TEL: 01443 474 593

SUNNINGDALE GARDEN CENTRE 33-10
St. Davids Wood, Blackwood, Carmarthenshire
TEL: 01495 228 015

PUGHS GARDEN CENTRE 33-11
Treherbert Road Nursery, Cwmbran, South Wales
TEL: 01633 484 004

WOODFIELDS PLANT & NURSERY CENTRE
Derwen Deg, Hengoed, Powys
TEL: 01443 812 773   33-12

Japanese Iris

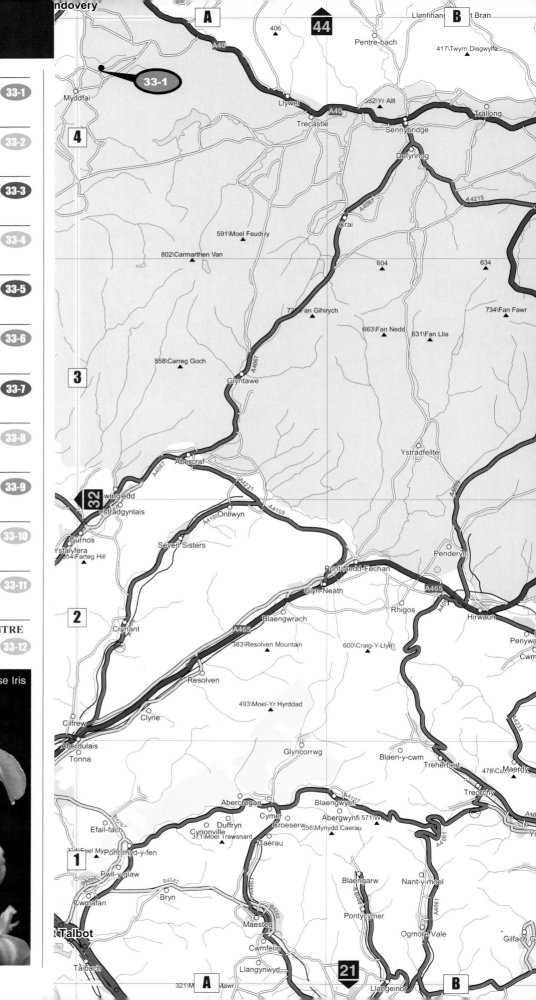

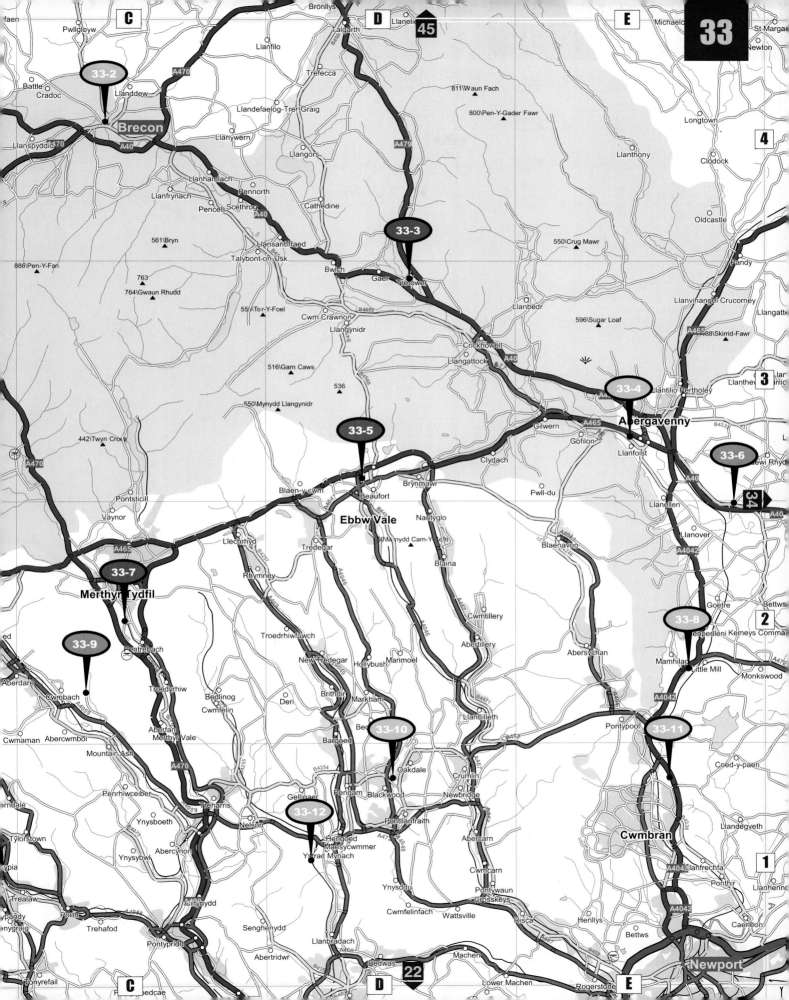

ABBEY DORE COURT GARDEN
Abbey Dore, Hereford, Herefordshire
TEL: 01981 240 419

HOW CAPLE COURT GARDENS
How Caple, Hereford, Herefordshire
TEL: 01989 740 626

SUNNYBANK VINE NURSERY
Sunnybank, Pontrilas, Herefordshire
TEL: 01981 240 256

ROSES COUNTRY FAYRE
52 Ledbury Road, Newent, Gloucestershire
TEL: 01531 821 242

THUYA ALPINE NURSERY
Glebelands, Hartpury, Gloucestershire
TEL: 01452 700 548

BROOK FARM PLANTS
Boulsdon Lane, Newent, Gloucestershire
TEL: 01531 822 534

KINGSTONE COTTAGES
Weston-under-Penyard, Ross on Wye, Herefordshire
TEL: 01989 565 267

GREEN'S LEAVES
Leba Orchard, Ross on Wye, Herefordshire
TEL: 01989 750 303

THE COUNTRY GARDEN CENTRE
Ross Road, Gloucester, Gloucestershire
TEL: 01452 830 229

SPLENDOUR OF THE ORIENT
Jubilee Park, Symonds Yat West, Herefordshire
TEL: 01600 890 668

39 STEPS
Grove Cottage, Lydbrook, Gloucestershire
TEL: 01594 860 544

QUEDGELEY GARDEN CENTRE
73 Bristol Road, Quedgeley, Gloucestershire
TEL: 01452 500 576

WESTBURY COURT GARDEN, NATIONAL TRUST
Westbury Court, Westbury-on-Severn, Gloucestershire
TEL: 01452 760 461

PYGMY PINETUM NURSERIES
Cannop Cross Roads, Coleford, Gloucestershire
TEL: 01594 833 398

JARDINERIE
Bath Road, Gloucester, Gloucestershire
TEL: 01452 721 081

COLEFORD GARDEN CENTRE
Lambsquay Road, Coleford, Gloucestershire
TEL: 01594 832 700

RAGLAN GARDEN CENTRE
Old Abergavenny Road, Usk, South Wales
TEL: 01291 690 751

HIGHFIELD NURSERIES
School Lane, Whitminster, Gloucestershire
TEL: 01452 741 444

WORLD OF WATER
Highfield Garden Centre, Whitminster, Gloucestershire, GL2 7PB
TEL: 01452 741 414
WEB: www.worldofwater.com
Everything for the pond and tropical fish enthusiast. Extensive showgardens. Expert advice.
OPEN: 9-5.30 Mon-Sat, Sun 10.30-4.30. Closed Easter Sun.
SPECIALITIES: Aquatic plants, Waterfalls, Water features.

COINROS NURSERY
Clements End, Coleford, Gloucestershire
TEL: 01594 562 610

UNUSUAL PLANTS
Mork Road, Lydney, Gloucestershire
TEL: 01594 530 561

W. G. GEISSLER
Winsford, Slimbridge, Gloucestershire
TEL: 01453 890 340

LYDNEY GARDEN & AQUATIC CENTRE
15 High Street, Lydney, Gloucestershire
TEL: 01594 842 121

WYE VALLEY PLANTS
The Nurtons, Chepstow, South Wales
TEL: 01291 689 253

USK LEIRE
The Nurseries, Usk, South Wales
TEL: 01291 673 603

WATERWHEEL NURSERY
Bully Hole Bottom, Chepstow, Monmouthshire
TEL: 01291 641 577

HUNTS COURT
North Nibley, Dursley, Gloucestershire
TEL: 01453 547 440

MOUNT PLEASANT NURSERY
Mount Pleasant Farm, Berkeley, Gloucestershire
TEL: 01454 260 348

EASTWOOD GARDEN PLANT CENTRE
The Gardens, Wotton under Edge, Gloucestershire
TEL: 01454 260288

PARKWALL GARDEN CENTRE
Crick, Caldicot, South Wales
TEL: 01291 424 585

PENHOW NURSERIES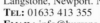
St Brides Netherwent, Penhow, South Wales
TEL: 01633 400 419

SUNNTYSIDE NURSERIES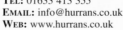
Chepstow Road, Newport, Pembrokeshire
TEL: 01633 412 411

THORNBURY GARDEN SHOP
The Courtyard, Bristol, Somerset
TEL: 01454 419 350

AQUAJARDIN
Hurrans Garden Centre, Newport, Pembrokeshire
TEL: 01633 413 587

HURRANS GARDEN CENTRE
Catsash Road
Langstone, Newport. NP18 2LZ
TEL: 01633 413 355
EMAIL: info@hurrans.co.uk
WEB: www.hurrans.co.uk

Where great gardens don't cost the earth!

A family business established in 1909.
A spacious store featuring an extensive gift shop, patio and garden buildings centre, inviting gallery tea shop and aquatic centre. Excellent customer care, quality and value.
OPEN: 9-6 Mon-Sat; 11-5 Sun.

WYEVALE GARDEN CENTRE
Milbury Heath, Wotton under Edge, Gloucestershire
TEL: 01454 412 247

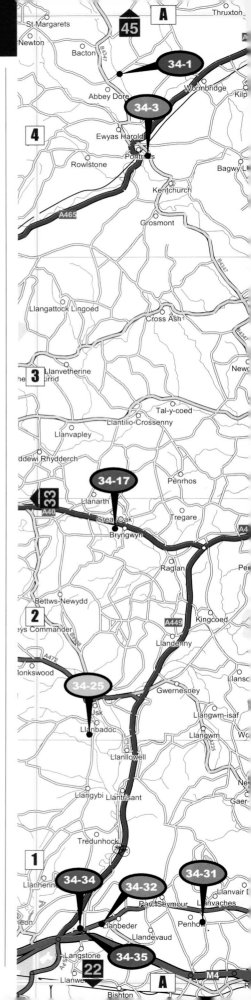

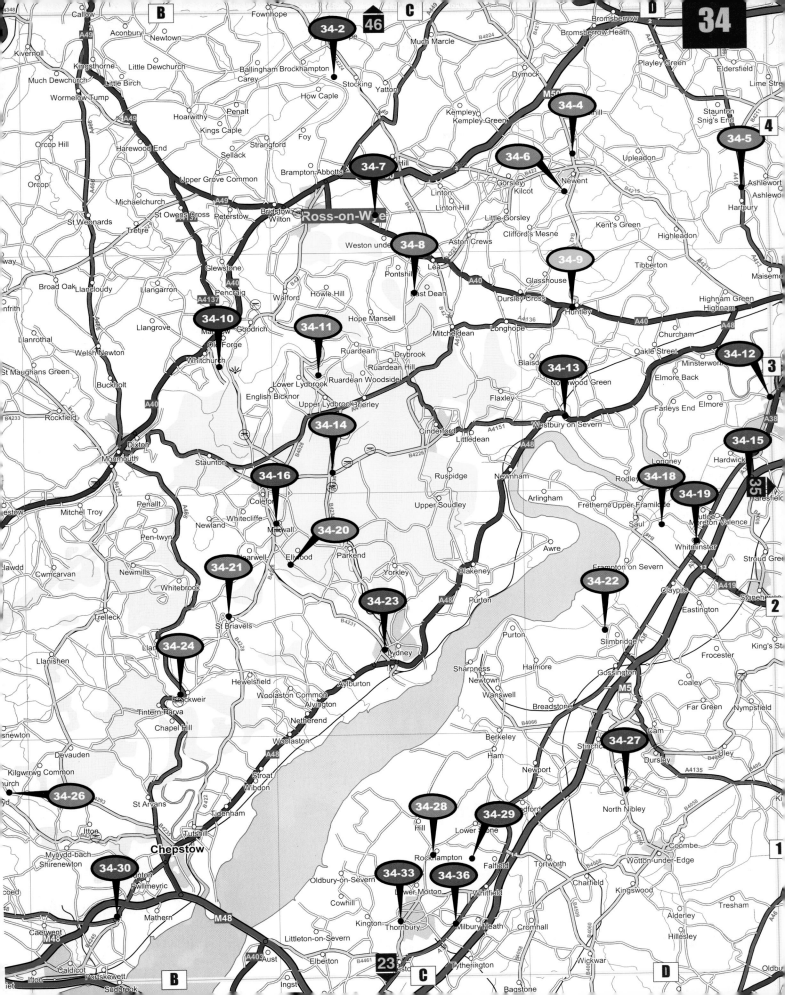

TODDINGTON GARDEN CENTRE `35-1`
Toddington Railway Yard, Cheltenham, Gloucestershire
TEL: 01242 621 314

TINPENNY PLANTS `35-2`
Tinpenny Farm, Tewkesbury, Gloucestershire
TEL: 01684 292 668

NOMADS FUSCHAIS & PELARGONIUM SPECIALISTS `35-3`
West Warren Farm, Cheltenham, Gloucestershire
TEL: 01242 604 304

GOTHERINGTON NURSERIES `35-4`
Gretton Road, Cheltenham, Gloucestershire
TEL: 01242 676 722

HOO HOUSE NURSERY `35-5`
Hoo House, Tewkesbury, Gloucestershire
TEL: 01684 293 389

THE GARDEN NURSERY `35-6`
Evesham Road, Cheltenham, Gloucestershire
TEL: 01242 674 695

SUDELEY CASTLE & GARDENS `35-7`
Winchcombe, Cheltenham, Gloucestershire
TEL: 01242 602 308

BONSAI WORLD OF CHELTENHAM `35-8`
Two Hedges Road, Cheltenham, Gloucestershire
TEL: 01242 674 389

JARDINERIE `35-9`
Evesham Road, Cheltenham, Gloucestershire
TEL: 01242 672 560

BEDDING PLANT CENTRE `35-10`
Chelt Nurseries, Cheltenham, Gloucestershire
TEL: 01242 680 366

BARBRIDGE NURSERIES `35-11`
Tewksbury Road, Cheltenham, Gloucestershire
TEL: 01242 680 277

HURRANS GARDEN CENTRE `48-20`
Cheltenham Road East, Churchdown, nr. Glos., Gloucestershire, GL3 1AB
TEL: 01452 712 232
EMAIL: info@hurrans.co.uk
WEB: www.hurrans.co.uk

A family business established in 1909. This homely Centre has an attractive gallery coffee shop and plenty of free parking. Features patio, garden buildings and aquatic centres. Excellent customer care, quality and value
OPEN: 9-6 Mon-Sat; 11-5 Sun.

TELLING & COATES `35-13`
64a Church Street, Cheltenham, Gloucestershire
TEL: 01242 514 472

VALLEY ROUNDABOUT NURSERIES `35-14`
Badgeworth Road, Cheltenham, Gloucestershire
TEL: 01452 713 102

CHELTENHAM POT & PLANT CENTRE `35-15`
Kidnappers Lane, Cheltenham, Gloucestershire
TEL: 01242 513 401

GLEBE GARDEN NURSERY `35-16`
Kidnappers Lane, Cheltenham, Gloucestershire
TEL: 01242 521 001

DAWN NURSERIES `35-17`
Main Road, Cheltenham, Gloucestershire
TEL: 01242 862 877

BARTON HARDWARE & GARDEN SHOP `35-18`
217 Barton Street, Gloucester, Gloucestershire
TEL: 01452 524 601

WYEVALE GARDEN CENTRE `35-19`
Shurdington Road, Brockworth, Gloucestershire
TEL: 01452 862 334

SHURDINGTON NURSERIES `35-20`
Whitelands Lane, Cheltenham, Gloucestershire
TEL: 01242 863 738

PAINSWICK ROCOCO GARDEN `35-21`
Painswick House, PAINSWICK, Gloucestershire
TEL: 01452 813 204

MISERDEN NURSERY `35-22`
Miserden, Stroud, Gloucestershire
TEL: 01285 821 638

MISARDEN PARK GARDENS `35-23`
Stroud, Gloucestershire
TEL: 01285 821 303

CERNEY HOUSE GARDENS `35-24`
North Cerney, Cirencester, Gloucestershire, GL7 7BX
TEL: 01285 831 300
EMAIL: cerneygardens@email.com
WEB: cerneygardens.com

Romantic secret garden in the Cotswolds. Walled garden, old-fashioned roses, herbaceous borders, herb garden, kitchen garden, important plant collections.
OPEN: Apr-Sep, Tues, Wed, Fri, 10-5, or by appointment.
ENTRY COSTS: Adult £3, Children £1.
SPECIALITIES: Labelled plant collections.

A. G. O. AQUATICS `35-25`
Unit 3, Cirencester, Gloucestershire
TEL: 01285 750 307

WYEVALE GARDEN CENTRE `35-26`
Ebley Road, Stroud, Gloucestershire
TEL: 01453 823 846

BARNSLEY HOUSE GARDEN `35-37`
Barnsley House, Barnsley, Cirencester, Gloucestershire, GL7 5EE
TEL: 01285 740 561
WEB: www.opengarden.co.uk

A popular choice; this family business welcomes you to Rosemary Verey's internationally famous garden in the Cotswolds.
OPEN: Feb-Dec, Mon, Wed, Thurs, Fri & Sat 10-5.30.
ENTRY COSTS: Adult £3.75, Children Free, OAPs £3.
SPECIALITIES: Bedding plants, Climbers, Garden & conservatory furniture, Hardy plants, Seeds.

SPINNYWELL NURSERY `35-28`
Waterlane, Bisley, Gloucestershire
TEL: 01452 770 092

SELSLEY HERB FARM `35-29`
Waterlane, Stroud, Gloucestershire
TEL: 01453 766 682

WYEVALE GARDEN CENTRE `35-30`
Waterside Garden Centre, Nailsworth, Gloucs.
TEL: 01453 833 989

MARSHALL'S MALMAISON `35-31`
4 The Damsells, Tetbury, Gloucestershire
TEL: 01666 502 589

WESTONBIRT ARBORETUM PLANT CENTRE `35-32`
Westonbirt Arboretum, Tetbury, Gloucs.
TEL: 01666 880 544

NURDENS GARDEN CENTRE `35-33`
Crudwell Road, Malmesbury, Wiltshire
TEL: 01666 822 809

Anemone

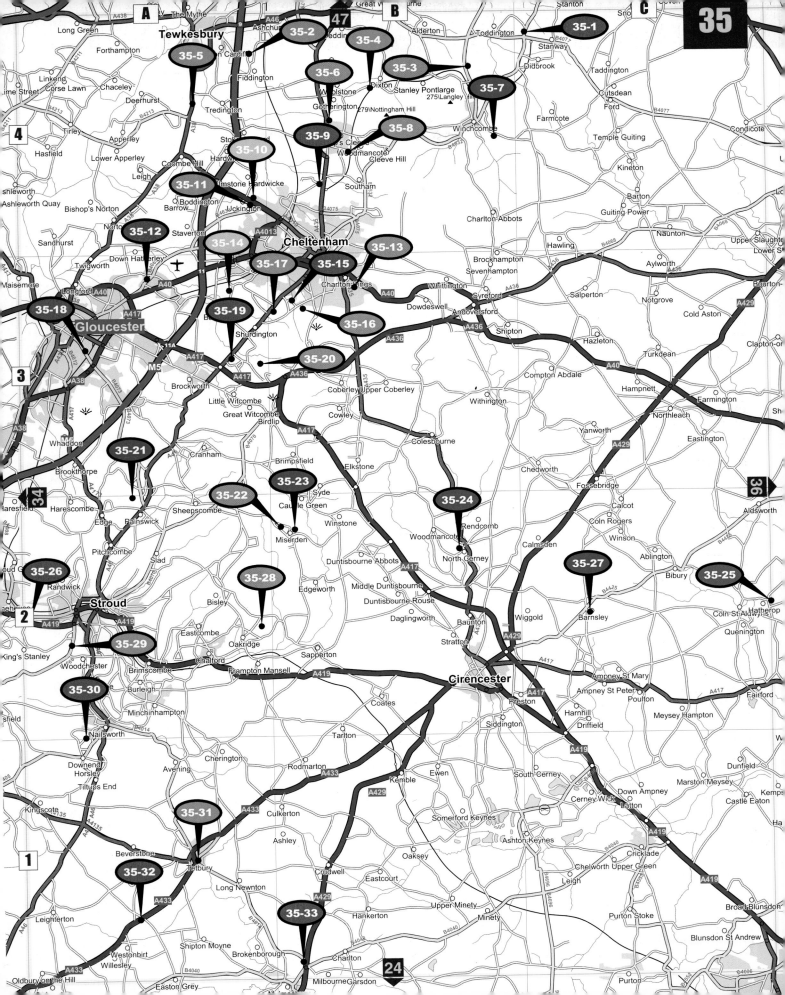

BATSFORD GARDEN CENTRE `36-1`
Batsford, Moreton in Marsh, Gloucestershire
TEL: 01386 700 409

FOSSEWAY FARM NURSERY `36-2`
Stow Road, Moreton in Marsh, Gloucs.
TEL: 01608 651 757

COMPTON LANE NURSERIES `36-3`
Little Compton, Moreton in Marsh, Gloucs.
TEL: 01608 674 578

APPLEGARTH NURSERIES `36-4`
Hardy Plant Centre, Chipping Norton, Oxon.
TEL: 01608 641 642

ROUSHAM HOUSE `36-5`
Steeple Aston, Bicester, Oxfordshire
TEL: 01869 347 110

PEBBLY HILL FARM NURSERY `36-6`
Icomb Road, Chipping Norton, Oxfordshire
TEL: 01608 659 851

COTSWOLD GARDEN CENTRE & FARMSHOP `36-7`
Wyck Hill, Stow-on-the-Wold, Gloucestershire
TEL: 01451 830 216

Q GARDEN COMPANY `36-8`
Wyck Hill, Stow-on-the-Wold, Gloucs.
TEL: 01451 830 216

BLOOMS OF BICESTER `36-9`
Oxford Road, Bicester, Oxfordshire
TEL: 01869 242248

BICESTER GARDEN & PET CENTRE `36-10`
Oxford Road, Bicester, Oxfordshire
TEL: 01869 242 248

PLANTASIA `36-11`
Bicester Garden Centre, Bicester, Oxfordshire
TEL: 01869 325 455

WORLD OF WATER `36-12`
Bicester Garden Centre, Oxford Road,
Bicester, Oxfordshire, OX6 8NY
TEL: 01869 322 489
WEB: www.worldofwater.com
Everything for the pond and tropical fish enthusiast. Extensive showgardens. Expert advice.
OPEN: 9-5.30 Mon-Sat, Sun 10.30-4.30. Closed Easter Sun.
SPECIALITIES: Aquatic plants, Waterfalls, Water features.

BLENHEIM PALACE `36-13`
Woodstock, Oxford, Oxfordshire
TEL: 01993 811 325

HILLTOP GARDEN CENTRE `36-14`
Witney Road, Chipping Norton, Oxfordshire
TEL: 01993 868 403

FIELDFARE NURSERIES & GARDEN CENTRE `36-15`
Church Road, Church Hanborough, Oxfordshire
TEL: 01993 882 663

FREELAND NURSERIES `36-16`
Wroslyn Road, Witney, Oxfordshire
TEL: 01993 881 430

THE BURFORD GARDEN COMPANY `36-17`
Shilton Road, Burford, Oxfordshire
TEL: 01993 823 117

WHITEHILL FARM NURSERY `36-18`
Whitehill Farm, Burford, Oxfordshire
TEL: 01993 823 218

CASSSINGTON NURSERIES `36-19`
Yarnton Road, Witney, Oxfordshire
TEL: 01865 882 550

SUMMERTOWN GARDEN CENTRE `36-20`
200-202 Banbury Road, Oxford, Oxfordshire
TEL: 01865 554 956

OXFORD BOTANIC GARDENS `36-21`
Rose Lane, Oxford, Oxfordshire
TEL: 01865 276 920

WYEVALE GARDEN CENTRE `36-22`
57 London Road, Oxford, Oxfordshire
TEL: 01865 873 057

MILL VIEW NURSERY `36-23`
Ladder Hill, Oxford, Oxfordshire
TEL: 01865 873 488

WYEVALE GARDEN CENTRE `36-24`
Southern by-pass, Oxford, Oxfordshire
TEL: 01865 326 066

BOUNDRY FARM SHOP AND NURSERY `36-25`
Wheatley Road, Oxford, Oxfordshire
TEL: 01865 361 311

LECHLADE GARDEN CENTRE `36-26`
Fairford Road, Lechlade, Gloucestershire
TEL: 01367 252 372

NOTCUTTS GARDEN CENTRE `36-27`
Mattocks Roses, Nuneham Courtenay, Oxon
TEL: 01865 343 454

HARCOURT ARBORETUM `36-28`
Oxford Lodge, Nuneham Courtenay, Oxon
TEL: 01865 343 501

NEWINGTON NURSERIES `36-29`
Newington, Wallingford, Oxfordshire
TEL: 01865 400 533

FROSTS MILLETS FARM `36-30`
Milletts Farm Garden Centre, Abingdon, Oxon
TEL: 01865 391 923

MARCHAM PLANTS `36-31`
Hyde Farm Nurseries, Abingdon, Oxon
TEL: 01865 391 054   3631

BUSCOT PARK `36-32`
Faringdon, Oxfordshire
TEL: 01367 240 786   3632

STEVENTON ROAD NURSERY `36-33`
Steventon Road, Wantage, Oxfordshire
TEL: 01235 868 828

SEVEN ACRES NURSERY `36-34`
Faringdon Road, Faringdon, Oxfordshire
TEL: 01367 718 266

BROADSTONE NURSERIES `36-35`
13 The Nursery, Abingdon, Oxfordshire
TEL: 01235 847 557

SHEARDS GARDEN CENTRE `36-36`
High Road, Wallingford, Oxfordshire
TEL: 01491 836 277

WYEVALE GARDEN CENTRE `36-37`
Hyde Road, Swindon, Wiltshire
TEL: 01793 822 224

CHARLTON PARK GARDEN CENTRE `36-38`
Charlton Road, Wantage, Oxfordshire
TEL: 01235 772 700

OLD CHURCH HOUSE `36-39`
2 Priory Road, Wantage, Berkshire
TEL: 01235 762 785

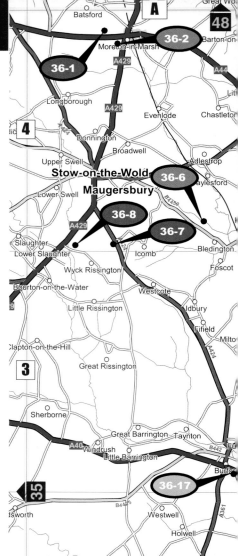

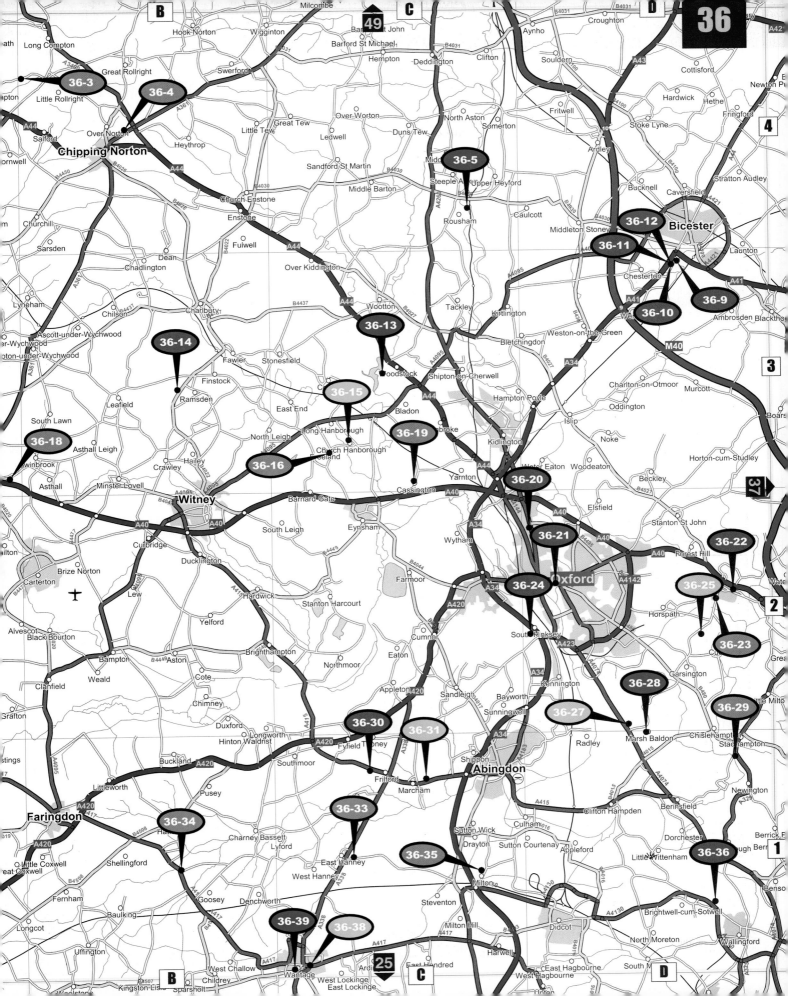

BEDS · BUCKS · HERTS · OXON

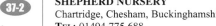

GARDEN CENTRE
NURSERY
GARDEN

NURSERY & GARDEN CENTR
GARDEN & NURSERY
WATER GARDEN SPECIALIST

BARR'S NURSERIES 37-1
Bletchley Road, Buckingham, Bucks
TEL: 01280 816 855

PRESTON BISSETT NURSERIES & COUNTRY SHOP 37-2
Bushey Lane, Preston Bissett, Buckinghamshire
TEL: 01280 848 038

FOUR ACRE NURSERY 37-3
Station Road, Milton Keynes, Bucks
TEL: 01296 720 791

LEIGHTON BUZZARD GARDEN CENTRE 37-4
Hickliffe Road, Leighton Buzzard, Bedfordshire
TEL: 01525 850 100

RYE NURSERIES 37-5
The Rye, Dunstable, Bedfordshire
TEL: 01525 220 104

WADDESDON MANOR, NT 37-6
Aylesbury, Buckinghamshire
TEL: 01296 651 226

WYEVALE GARDEN CENTRE 37-7
Bulbourne Road, Tring, Hertfordshire
TEL: 01442 891 393

BERNWODE PLANTS 37-8
Kingswood Lane, Aylesbury, Buckinghamshire
TEL: 01844 237 415

EMERALD VALLEY NURSERY 37-9
Thrift Cottage, Tring, Hertfordshire
TEL: 01442 891 213

WYEVALE GARDEN CENTRE 37-10
World's End Garden Centre, Aylesbury, Buckinghamshire
TEL: 01296 623 116

WATERPERRY GARDENS 37-11
Wheatley, Oxford, Oxfordshire
TEL: 01844 339 226

LOWER ICKNIELD FARM NURSERIES 37-12
Lower Icknield Way, Great Kimble, Aylesbury, Buckinghamshire, HP17 9TX
TEL: 01844 343 436

Family nursery specialising in argyranthemum (National Collection) hardy and tender perennials. Basket and patio plants. 2 acre display garden.
OPEN: Daily, 9-5.30, closed Christmas to New Year.
SPECIALITIES: Annuals, Conservatory plants, Grasses, National Collection, Perennials.

TUNFIELD NURSERY 37-13
Hogg Lane, Chesham, Buckinghamshire
TEL: 01442 865 552

SHEPHERD NURSERY 37-14
Chartridge, Chesham, Buckinghamshire
TEL: 01494 775 688

LASHLAKE NURSERIES 37-15
Chinnor Road, Thame, Oxfordshire
TEL: 01844 212 392

SOUTH HEATH GARDEN CENTRE & NURSERY LTD (B N SPENCER) 37-16
Meadow Lane, Great Missenden, Buckinghamshire
TEL: 01494 863 269

Q GARDEN COMPANY 37-17
Thame Road, Chinnor, Oxfordshire
TEL: 01844 353 540

THE CONIFER NURSERY 37-18
Hare Lane Nursery, Great Missenden, Buckinghamshire
TEL: 01494 862 086

THE WALLED GARDEN 37-19
2 Castle Road, Watlington, Oxfordshire
TEL: 01491 612 882

HUGHENDEN MANOR, NT 37-20
High Wycombe, Buckinghamshire
TEL: 01494 755 573

JARDINERIE 37-21
Studley Green, High Wycombe, Bucks.
TEL: 01494 483 761

WEST WYCOMBE GARDEN CENTRE 37-22
Chorley Road, High Wycombe, Bucks.
TEL: 01494 438 635

WEST WYCOMBE PARK, NT 37-23
West Wycombe, Buckinghamshire
TEL: 01628 488 675

FIELD GROVE NURSERY 37-24
Hammersley Lane, High Wycombe, Buckinghamshire
TEL: 01494 816 754

NOTCUTTS BOOKER GARDEN CENTRE 37-25
Clay Lane, Marlow, Buckinghamshire
TEL: 01494 532 532

WYEVALE GARDEN CENTRE 37-26
London Road, Beaconsfield, Buckinghamshire
TEL: 01494 672 522

WYEVALE GARDEN CENTRE 37-27
Pump Lane South, Marlow, Buckinghamshire
TEL: 01628 482 716

SPRINGLEA NURSERY 37-28
Springlea, Marlow, Buckinghamshire
TEL: 01628 473 366

Gerber Daisy with Butterfly

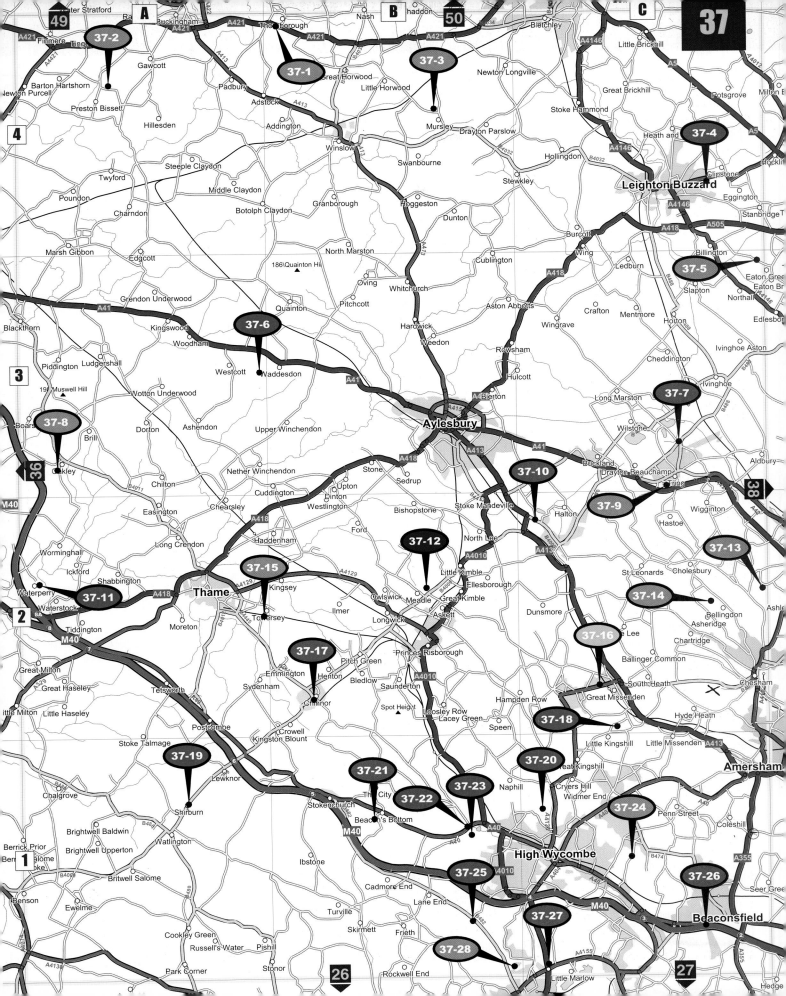

FLITTVALE GARDEN CENTRE & NURSERY 38-1
Flitwich Road, Westoning, Bedfordshire
TEL: 01525 712 484

HILLCREST NURSERY 38-2
Bedford Road, Hitchin, Hertfordshire
TEL: 01462 712 636

BRIDGESIDE NURSERIES & GARDEN CENTRE 38-3
Westoning Road, Harlington, Bedfordshire
TEL: 01525 873 070

POPLARS NURSERY GARDEN CENTRE 38-4
Harlington Road, Dunstable, Bedfordshire
TEL: 01525 872 017

GROVE ROAD GARDEN CENTRE 38-5
20 Grove Road, Hitchin, Hertfordshire
TEL: 01462 451 519

PAUL BROMFIELD AQUATICS 38-6
Maydencroft Lane, Hitchin, Hertfordshire
TEL: 01462 457 399

PUTTERIDGE BURY 38-7
Putteridge, Luton, Bedfordshire
TEL: 01582 489 069

STOCKWOOD NURSERIES 38-8
Town Hall, Luton, Bedfordshire
TEL: 01582 730 237

STOCKWOOD PARK 38-9
Stockwood Craft Museum, Luton, Bedfordshire
TEL: 01582 738 714

WYEVALE GARDEN CENTRE 38-10
Dunstable Road, Luton, Bedfordshire
TEL: 01582 457 313

SHAW'S CORNER, NATIONAL TRUST 38-11
Ayot St Lawrence, Welwyn, Hertfordshire
TEL: 01438 820 307

L. W. PLANTS 38-12
23 Wroxham Way, Harpenden, Hertfordshire
TEL: 01582 768 467

STUDHAM NURSERY 38-13
Clements End Road, Dunstable, Bedfordshire
TEL: 01582 872 958

TOWNSEND NURSERY 38-14
96 Townsend Lane, Harpenden, Hertfordshire
TEL: 01582 713 083

HARPENDEN GARDEN CENTRE 38-15
9 Amenbury Lane, Harpenden, Hertfordshire
TEL: 01582 764 679

GODLY'S ROSES 38-16
Redding Lane, St Albans, Hertfordshire
TEL: 01582 792 255

FOUR ACRES NURSERY 38-17
Hemel Hempstead Road, Berkhamsted, Hertfs
TEL: 01442 842 838

WYEVALE GARDEN CENTRE 38-18
Broadwater Garden Centre, Hemel Hempstead, Hertfordshire
TEL: 01442 231 284

CARPENTER'S NURSERY 38-19
106 St Albans Road, St Albans, Hertfordshire
TEL: 01727 853 340

 HILLIER GARDEN CENTRE 38-20
Leighton Buzzard Road, Piccotts End, Hemel Hempstead, Herts, HP1 3BA
TEL: 01442 242 637
WEB: www.hillier.co.uk

Pretty much everything you could want for the garden including landscape products and garden buildings. Friendly expert advice.
OPEN: Daily 9-5.30, Sun 10.30-4.30.
SPECIALITIES: Furniture, Gifts, Hardy plants, Shrubs, Trees.

LITTLE HEATH FARM NURSERY 38-21
Little Heath Lane, Berkhamsted, Hertfordshire
TEL: 01442 864 951

CAPITAL GARDENS LTD 38-22
The Old Iron Works, Berkhamsted, Herts
TEL: 01442 863 159

NOTCUTTS GARDEN CENTRE 38-23
Hatfield Road, St Albans, Hertfordshire
TEL: 01727 853 224

SEEDS BY SIZE 38-24
45 Crouchfield, Hemel Hempstead, Hertfs.
TEL: 01442 251 458

WYEVALE GARDEN CENTRE 38-25
North Orbital Road, St Albans, Hertfordshire
TEL: 01727 825 815

AYLETT NURSERIES 38-26
North Orbital Road, St Albans, Hertfordshire
TEL: 01727 822 255

THE GARDENS OF THE ROSE 38-27
Royal National Rose Society, Chiswell Green, St Albans, Hertfordshire, AL2 3NR
TEL: 01727 850 46
EMAIL: mail@rnrs.org.uk
WEB: www.roses.co.uk
Famous rose garden with an additional iris and clematis garden.
OPEN: 2 Jun-30 Sep, daily Mon-Sat 10-5; Sun &Bank hols 10-6.
ENTRY COSTS: Adult £4, Child £1.50, OAPs £3.50.
SPECIALITIES: Clematis, Iris, Roses, Garden & craft fairs, Open-air concerts.

HERTFORDSHIRE FISHERIES 38-29
Burston Nurseries, St Albans, Hertfordshire
TEL: 01727 833 960

BURSTON ROSE & GARDEN CENTRE 38-28
North Orbital Road, Chiswell Green, St Albans, Hertfordshire, AL2 2DS
TEL: 01727 832 444
EMAIL: enquiries@burstongardencentre.co.uk
WEB: www.burstongardencentre.co.uk

Long established family business. Attractive air-conditioned shop and large outdoor area. Reputation for high quality plants. Helpful, expert staff.
OPEN: Mar-Oct, Mon-Sat 8.30-6. Sun 10-4.30; Nov-Feb, Mon-Sat 8.30-5. Sun 10-4.30.
SPECIALITIES: Bedding plants, Garden & conservatory furniture, Hardy plants, Roses, Shrubs.

WYEVALE GARDEN CENTRE 38-30
Tower Hill, Chipperfield, Hertfordshire
TEL: 01442 834 364

HYRONS TREES 38-31
The Green, Rickmansworth, Hertfordshire
TEL: 01923 263 000

CHESLYN HOUSE 38-32
54 Nascot Wood Road, Watford, Hertfordshire
TEL: 01923 235 946

PLANTS DIRECT 38-33
Roundbush, Watford, Hertfordshire
TEL: 01923 850 809

CHANDLERS CROSS GARDEN CENTRE 38-34
Firtree Hill, Rickmansworth, Hertfordshire
TEL: 01923 261 219

BLACKETTS NURSERIES 38-35
Rousebarn Lane, Rickmansworth, Hertfordshire
TEL: 01923 265 743

CHENIES AQUATICS 38-36
The Van Hage Garden Company, Rickmansworth, Hertfordshire
TEL: 01494 764 549

THE VAN HAGE GARDEN COMPANY AT CHENIES 38-37
Rickmansworth, Hertfordshire
TEL: 01494 764 545

D. & J. NURSERIES 38-38
The Green, Rickmansworth, Hertfordshire
TEL: 01923 779 799

ROWAN NURSERIES GARDEN CENTRE 38-39
Gorelands Lane, Chalfont St Giles, Bucks
TEL: 01494 872 335

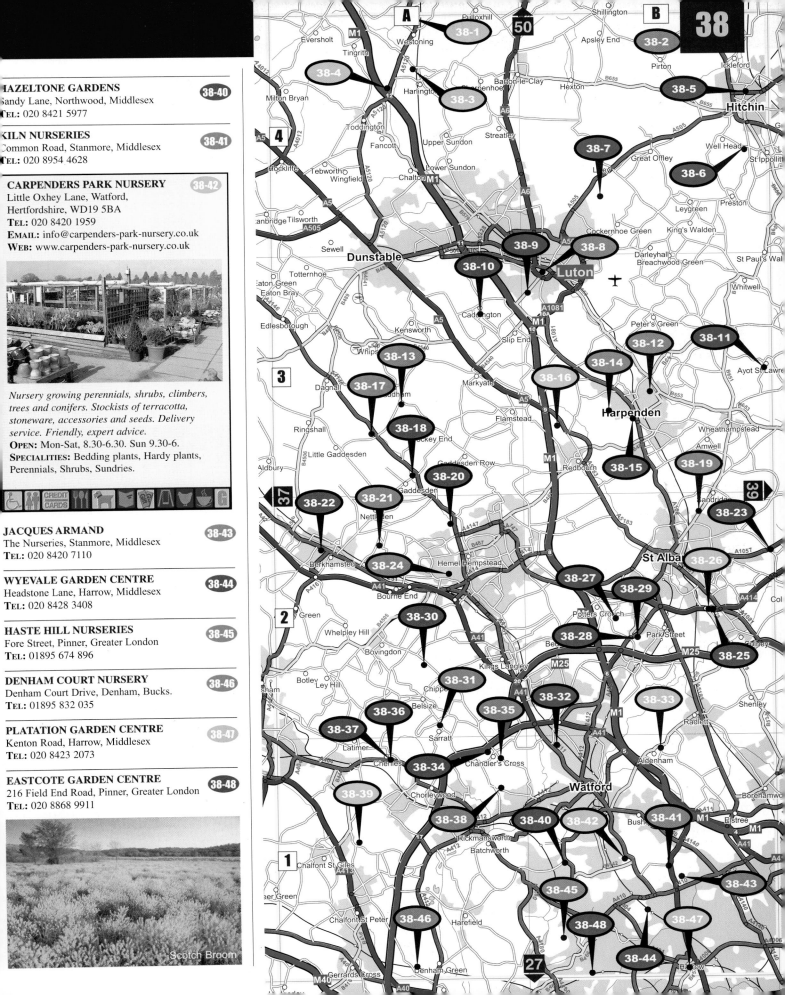

HAZELTONE GARDENS 38-40
Sandy Lane, Northwood, Middlesex
TEL: 020 8421 5977

KILN NURSERIES 38-41
Common Road, Stanmore, Middlesex
TEL: 020 8954 4628

CARPENDERS PARK NURSERY 38-42
Little Oxhey Lane, Watford,
Hertfordshire, WD19 5BA
TEL: 020 8420 1959
EMAIL: info@carpenders-park-nursery.co.uk
WEB: www.carpenders-park-nursery.co.uk

Nursery growing perennials, shrubs, climbers, trees and conifers. Stockists of terracotta, stoneware, accessories and seeds. Delivery service. Friendly, expert advice.
OPEN: Mon-Sat, 8.30-6.30. Sun 9.30-6.
SPECIALITIES: Bedding plants, Hardy plants, Perennials, Shrubs, Sundries.

JACQUES ARMAND 38-43
The Nurseries, Stanmore, Middlesex
TEL: 020 8420 7110

WYEVALE GARDEN CENTRE 38-44
Headstone Lane, Harrow, Middlesex
TEL: 020 8428 3408

HASTE HILL NURSERIES 38-45
Fore Street, Pinner, Greater London
TEL: 01895 674 896

DENHAM COURT NURSERY 38-46
Denham Court Drive, Denham, Bucks.
TEL: 01895 832 035

PLATATION GARDEN CENTRE 38-47
Kenton Road, Harrow, Middlesex
TEL: 020 8423 2073

EASTCOTE GARDEN CENTRE 38-48
216 Field End Road, Pinner, Greater London
TEL: 020 8868 9911

Scotch Broom

MILL END NURSERY
Mill End, Buntingford, Hertfordshire
TEL: 01763 288 434

WYEVALE GARDEN CENTRE
Cambridge Road, Hitchin, Hertfordshire
TEL: 01462 434 027

PIONEER NURSERY
Baldock Lane, Letchworth, Hertfordshire
TEL: 01462 675 858

STEVENAGE GARDEN CENTRE
North Road, Stevenage, Hertfordshire
TEL: 01438 312 660

KNEBWORTH HOUSE AND COUNTRY PARK
Knebworth Park, Knebworth, Hertfordshire
TEL: 01438 813 825

THE VAN HAGE GARDEN COMPANY
Bragbury Lane, Stevenage, Hertfordshire
TEL: 01438 811 777

VANSTONE PARK GARDEN CENTRE
B656 Hitchin Road, Hitchin, Hertfordshire
TEL: 01438 820 412

HOPLEYS PLANTS
High Street, Much Hadham, Hertfordshire
TEL: 01279 842 509

WYEVALE GARDEN CENTRE
High Street, Codicote, Hertfordshire
TEL: 01438 820 433

PRIORSWOOD CLEMATIS NURSERY
Priorswood, Ware, Hertfordshire
TEL: 01920 461 543

THE PET AND GARDEN CENTRE
5 Howardsgate, Welwyn Garden City, Herts.
TEL: 01707 320 577

RIVERSIDE GARDEN CENTRE
Lower Hatfield Road, Hertford, Hertfordshire
TEL: 01992 501 502

THE GARDEN OUTLET
Unit 50 (Level 1), Hatfield, Hertfordshire
TEL: 01707 272 932

HATFIELD HOUSE
Hatfield Park, Hatfield, Hertfordshire
TEL: 01707 262 823

BONNIES OAK GARDEN CENTRE
Bonnies Oak, Harlow, Essex
TEL: 01279 792 231

ROYDON HAMLET WATER GARDENS
Tylers Road, Harlow, Essex
TEL: 01279 792 235

KINGLEA PLANT CENTRE
Sedge Green, Waltham Abbey, Essex
TEL: 01992 470 460

RHODES & ROCKLIFFE
2 Nursery Road, Nazing, Essex
TEL: 01992 463 693

KINGFISHER NURSERIES & GARDEN CENTRE
Kingfishers, Hertford, Hertfordshire
TEL: 01992 511 611

HOE LANE NURSERY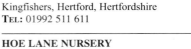
Hoe Lane, Waltham Abbey, Essex
TEL: 01992 892 181

BRYNFIELD NURSERY
610 Goffs Lane, Waltham Cross, Hertfordshire
TEL: 01707 873 311

WYEVALE GARDEN CENTRE
Cattlegate Road, Enfield, Middlesex
TEL: 020 8367 0422

POTTERS BAR NURSERY
The Ridgeway, Potters Bar, Hertfordshire
TEL: 01707 658 444

THE CHELSEA GARDENER
Cattlegate Road, Enfield, Middlesex
TEL: 020 8367 3377

ST. SIMON'S NURSERY
Cattlegate Road, Enfield, Middlesex
TEL: 020 8366 4404

WOLDENS NURSERIES AND GARDEN CENTRE
Cattlegate Road, Enfield, Middlesex
TEL: 020 8363 7003

SPRINGTIME NURSERIES ENFIELD
Cattlegate Road, Enfield, Middlesex
TEL: 020 83679 326

CULVER GARDEN CENTRE
Cattlegate Road, Enfield, Middlesex
TEL: 020 8366 0701

BROWN'S GARDEN CENTRE
Theobalds Park Road, Enfield, Middlesex
TEL: 020 8367 1741

CAPEL MANOR
Bullsmoor Lane, Enfield, Middlesex
TEL: 020 8366 4442

MYDDELTON HOUSE GARDENS
Myddelton House, Enfield, Middlesex
TEL: 01992 717 711

A J MILLS
Clock House Nursery, Enfield, Middlesex
TEL: 020 8363 1016

NORTHFIELD NURSERIES
Sewardstone Road, London, Greater London
TEL: 020 8529 0367

WYEVALE GARDEN CENTRE
Duke O'York Garden Centre, Barnet, Hertfordshire
TEL: 020 8440 4734

SANTA MARIA NURSERIES
Daws Hill, London, Greater London
TEL: 020 8524 0385

FOREST NURSERIES
Nursery Road, Loughton, Essex
TEL: 020 8508 1377

COTTAGE GARDEN NURSERY  39-3
Barnet Road, Barnet, Hertfordshire
TEL: 020 8441 8829

FINCHLEY NURSERIES 39-38
Burton Hole Lane, London, Greater London
TEL: 020 8959 2124

HURRANS NURSERY 39-39
175 New Road, London, E4 9EZ
TEL: 020 8529 1898

WYEVALE GARDEN CENTRE 39-40
Daws Lane, London, Greater London
TEL: 020 8906 4255

REDBRIDGE GARDEN CENTRE 39-41
152 Snakes Lane East, Woodford Green, Essex
TEL: 020 8532 9000

ALEXANDRA PALACE GARDEN CENTRE 39-42
Alexandra Palace, London, Greater London
TEL: 020 8444 2555

Water Lily

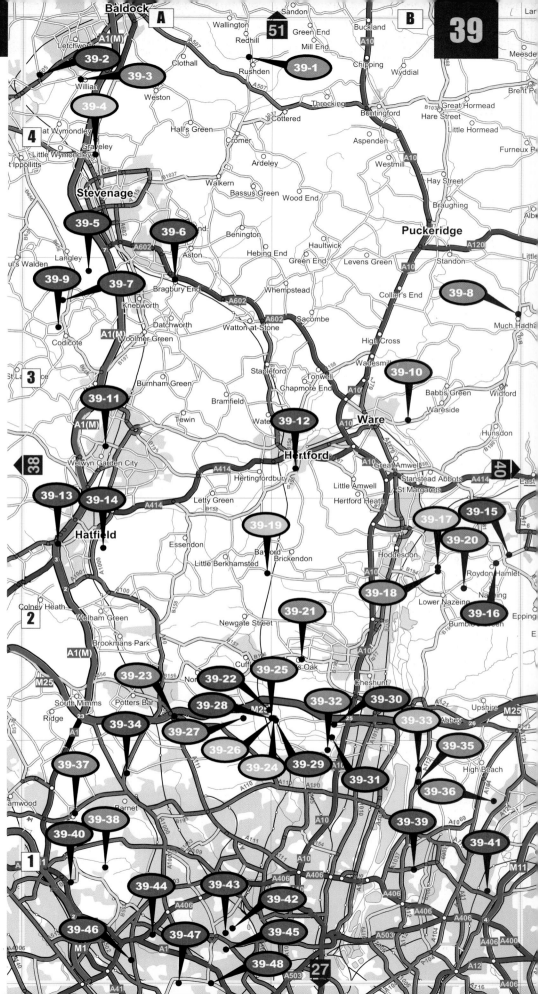

CAMBS · ESSEX · HERTS

● GARDEN CENTRE   ● NURSERY & GARDEN CENTRE
● NURSERY   ● GARDEN & NURSERY
● GARDEN   ● WATER GARDEN SPECIALIST

F.W. WHYMAN
Hill Crest, Saffron Walden, Cambridgeshire
TEL: 01799 550 568

BARDFIELD TREES
Great Lodge, Braintree, Essex
TEL: 01371 810 776

SNOWHILL NURSERY
Snow Hill, Dunmow, Essex
TEL: 01371 870 030

BROOKSIDE GARDEN CENTRE
Bran End, Dunmow, Essex
TEL: 01371 856 999

CHAPEL END NURSERY
Chapel End, Dunmow, Essex
TEL: 01279 850 771

EASTON LODGE, THE FORGOTTEN GARDENS
Little Easton, Great Dunmow, Essex
TEL: 01371 876 979

G. MARIS & SON
Garden Centre, Bishop's Stortford, Hertfordshire
TEL: 01279 870 472

LANGTHORNS PLANTERY
Little Canfield, Dunmow,
Essex, CM6 1TD
TEL: 01371 872 611
World famous nursery with an eye for the rare and spectacular. A huge variety of interesting plants available all year round. Under new management.
OPEN: 10-5 (or dusk if earlier) 7 days a week. Closed Christmas fortnight & Easter Sun.
SPECIALITIES: Bamboos, Conservatory plants, Shrubs, Trees, Herbaceous plants.

RHODES MUSEUM GARDEN
Rhodes Museum, Bishop's Stortford, Hertfordshire
TEL: 01279 651 746

ROBIN SAVILL CLEMATIS SPECIALIST
2 Bury Cottages, Chelmsford, Essex
TEL: 01245 237 380

OAKRIDGE NURSERY
Redricks Lane, Sawbridgeworth, Hertfordshire
TEL: 01279 641 078

WOODHOUSE NURSERY
Main Road, Chelmsford, Essex
TEL: 01245 381 781

JEWELS GARDEN CENTRE
Hodges Cottage, Chelmsford, Essex
TEL: 01245 460 878

WYEVALE GARDEN CENTRE
Homelands Retail Park, Chelmsford, Essex
TEL: 01245 466 466

AUSFERN UK
Sedge Green, Nazing, Essex
TEL: 01992 465 074

HARLOW GARDEN CENTRE
Canes Lane, Harlow, Essex
TEL: 01279 419 039

HANGING GARDENS NURSERIES
15 Further Meadow, Chelmsford, Essex
TEL: 01245 421 020

WRITTLE ROAD NURSERY
7 Writtle Road, Chelmsford, Essex
TEL: 01245 265 655

REDRICKS NURSERY
Vicarage Lane, Epping, Essex
TEL: 01992 524 570

HAPPY GROW
High Road, Thornwood, Essex
TEL: 01992 575 387

GREENBROOK NURSERY
Wyses Road, Chelmsford, Essex
TEL: 01245 248 871

ABERCORN PLANT & GARDEN CENTRE
Beehive Lane, Chelmsford, Essex
TEL: 01245 257 398

C. J. SKILTON AQUARIST
Great Gibcracks Chase, Chelmsford, Essex
TEL: 01245 400 535

WYEVALE GARDEN CENTRE
Langford Bridge, Brentwood, Essex
TEL: 01277 365 485

STOCKBROOK FARM SHOP & NURSERY
Stock Road, Ingatestone, Essex
TEL: 01277 840 046

WAYSIDE AQUATICS
5 Blackmore Road, Brentwood, Essex
TEL: 01277 823 603

INGATESTONE GARDEN CENTRE
Roman Road, Ingatestone, Essex
TEL: 01277 353 268

INGATESTONE HALL
Hall Lane, Ingatestone, Essex
TEL: 01277 353 010

CROWTHER NURSERIES
160 Ongar Road, Romford, Essex
TEL: 01708 688 479

SHEILA CHAPMAN CLEMATIS
Crowther Nurseries, Romford, Essex
TEL: 01708 688 090

SOW & GROW NURSERY
Ongar Road, Brentwood, Essex
TEL: 01277 375 252

HUTTON GARDEN CENTRE
North Drive, Brentwood, Essex
TEL: 01277 633 515

HUNTERS CHASE GARDEN CENTRE 40-33
Rayleigh Road, Brentwood, Essex
TEL: 01277 623 793

BILLERICAY NURSERIES 40-34
London Road, Billericay, Essex
TEL: 01277 622 083

ALPHA GARDEN CENTRE 40-35
238 London Road, Wickford, Essex
TEL: 01268 766 093

TOMLINS NURSERY 40-36
Mascals Lane, Brentwood, Essex
TEL: 01277 214 883

JENNIKINGS GARDEN CENTRE 40-37
210-212 Manor Road, Chigwell, Essex
TEL: 020 8501 2328

CHIGWELL NURSERY 40-38
245 High Road, Chigwell, Essex
TEL: 020 8500 2690

ESSEX AQUASCAPES 40-39
Orchard House, Billericay, Essex
TEL: 01277 655 669

BRENTWOOD GARDEN CENTRE 40-40
Vicarage Close, Brentwood, Essex
TEL: 01277 262 303

HILLCREST NURSERIES 40-41
A128 Brentwood Road, Brentwood, Essex
TEL: 01277 810 385

GREENHOUSE WATERGARDENS 40-42
87 Chase Cross Road, Romford, Essex
TEL: 01708 726 726

SUMMERHILL NUSERY & GARDEN CENTRE 40-43
Pipps Hill Road North, Billericay, Essex
TEL: 01268 521 052

ALTONS GARDEN CENTRE 40-44
Arterial Road, Wickford, Essex
TEL: 01268 726 421

BASILDON GARDEN & MOWER CENTRE 40-45
Nevendon Road, Basildon, Essex
TEL: 01268 523 515

WYEVALE GARDEN CENTRE 40-46
Nags Head Lane, Upminster Common, Essex
TEL: 01708 342 469

NORTH STREET GARDEN CENTRE 40-47
North Street, Romford, Essex
TEL: 01708 737 585

COUNTY PARK NURSERY 40-48
Essex Gardens, Hornchurch, Essex
TEL: 01708 445 205

FUTURE GARDEN HYDROPONICS 40-49
26a Woodford Avenue, Ilford, Essex
TEL: 020 8550 7310

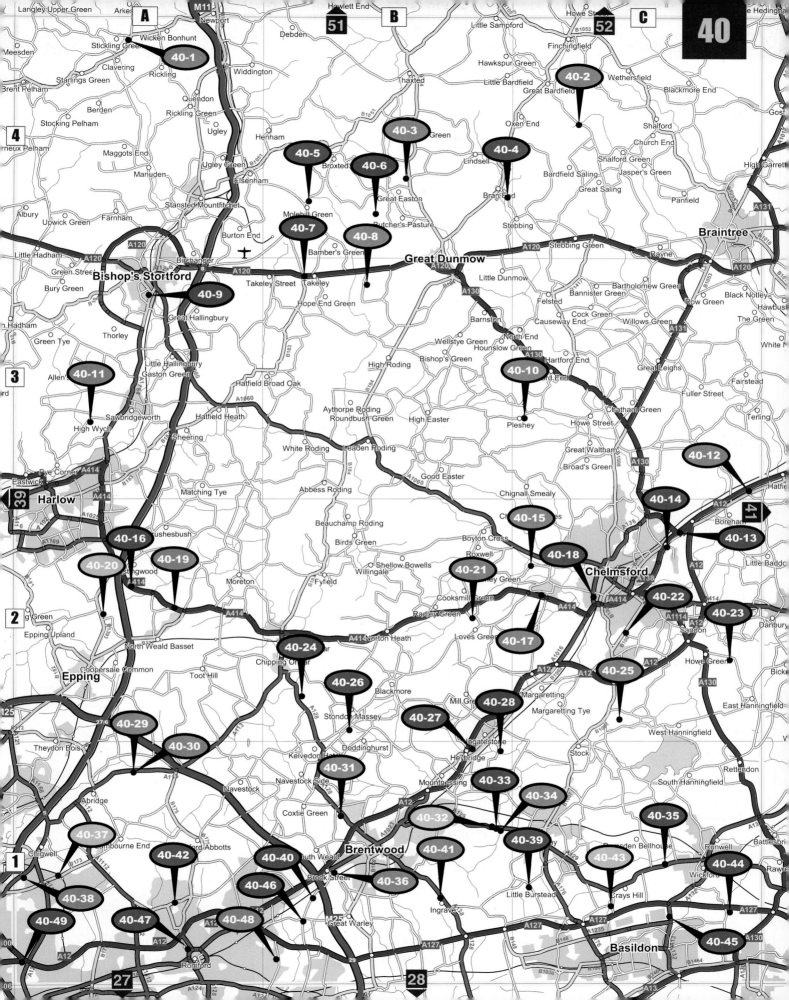

ESSEX

● GARDEN CENTRE ● NURSERY & GARDEN CENTR
● NURSERY GARDEN & NURSERY
● GARDEN ● WATER GARDEN SPECIALIST

THE COTTAGE GARDEN 41-1
Langham Road, Colchester, Essex
TEL: 01206 272 269

SOW & SOW NURSERIES 41-2
Horkesley Road, Colchester, Essex
TEL: 01206 273 300

CONSERVATORY PLANTLINE 41-3
Nayland Road, Colchester, Essex
TEL: 01206 242 533

ROBINSON BROS. 41-4
Sprintrees, Colchester, Essex
TEL: 01787 223 775

MILL RACE NURSERY 41-5
New Road, Colchester, Essex
TEL: 01206 242 521

BOURNE BROOK NURSERIES 41-6
Greenstead Green, Halstead, Essex
TEL: 01787 472 900

BARNPLANTS 41-7
Turkey Cock Lane, Colchester, Essex
TEL: 01206 210 486

WYEVALE GARDEN CENTRE 41-8
342 London Road, Colchester, Essex
TEL: 01206 213 050

POPLAR NURSERIES 41-9
Coggeshall Road, Colchester, Essex
TEL: 01206 210 374

PONDLIFE 41-10
Poplar Nurseries, Colchester, Essex
TEL: 01206 212 310

BAYTREE FARM SHOP & GARDEN CENTRE 41-11
Coggeshall Road, Braintree, Essex
TEL: 01376 344 301

MARKS HALL ARBORETUM 41-12
Marks Hall, Colchester, Essex
TEL: 01376 563 796

WORLD OF WATER 41-13
The Dutch Nursery, West Street,
Coggeshall, Essex, CO6 1NT
TEL: 01376 563 836
WEB: www.worldofwater.com
Everything for the pond enthusiast. Extensive
showgardens. Expert advice.
OPEN: 9-5.30 Mon-Sat, Sun 10.30-4.30. Closed
Easter Sun.
SPECIALITIES: Aquatic plants, Waterfalls, Water
features.

BLOOMFIELD GARDEN CENTRE 41-14
241 Berechurch Hall Road, Colchester, Essex
TEL: 01206 575 941

WYEVALE GARDEN CENTRE 41-15
Cressing Road, Braintree, Essex
TEL: 01376 553 043

CRESSING TEMPLE BARNS 41-16
Witham Road, Braintree, Essex
TEL: 01376 584 903

PERRYWOOD NURSERIES 41-17
Kelvedon Road, Inworth, Tiptree,
Essex, CO5 9SX
TEL: 01376 570 777
Large nursery and garden centre, outstanding
range of plants. Wide selection of gardening
products, rural setting, delightful coffee shop.
OPEN: Mon-Sat 8.30-5. Sun, Mar-Oct 9-5, Nov-
Feb 10-4.
SPECIALITIES: Alpines, Bedding plants,
Climbers, Fruit & fruit trees, Hardy plants.

OLD MILL HOUSE GARDEN NURSERY 41-18
Guithavon Valley, Witham, Essex
TEL: 01376 512 396

FOUR SEASONS 41-19
126 Newland Street, Witham, Essex
TEL: 01376 308 002

GLEN CHANTRY 41-20
Ishams Chase, Witham, Essex
TEL: 01621 891 342

MAYPOLE PET & GARDEN CENTRE 41-21
Maypole Road, Witham, Essex
TEL: 01621 892 411

HORSESHOE NURSERIES 41-22
White Elm Road, Chelmsford, Essex
TEL: 01245 223 789

MAYFLOWER NURSERY & GARDEN CENTRE 41-23
Mill Road, Chelmsford, Essex
TEL: 01621 740 269

WESTVIEW NURSERIES 41-24
Main Road, Chelmsford, Essex
TEL: 01245 324 171

HYDE HALL, THE ROYAL HORTICULTURAL SOCIETY 41-25
Rettendon, Chelmsford, Essex
TEL: 01245 400 256

PLANTOME NURSERIES & GARDEN CENTRE 41-26
Woodham Road, Wickford, Essex
TEL: 01245 320 263

BUSHUKAN BONSAI 41-27
Ricbra, Hockley, Essex
TEL: 01702 201 029

NEWHALL NURSERIES 41-28
Lower Road, Hockley, Essex
TEL: 01702 205 355

FAIRWAYS GARDEN CENTRE 41-29
Hullbridge Road, Rayleigh, Essex
TEL: 01702 230 795

VIEW GARDENS 41-30
Chelmsford Road, Wickford, Essex
TEL: 01268 761 337

READ'S NURSERY 41-31
99 Rawreth Lane, Rayleigh, Essex
TEL: 01268 785 893

Tulips

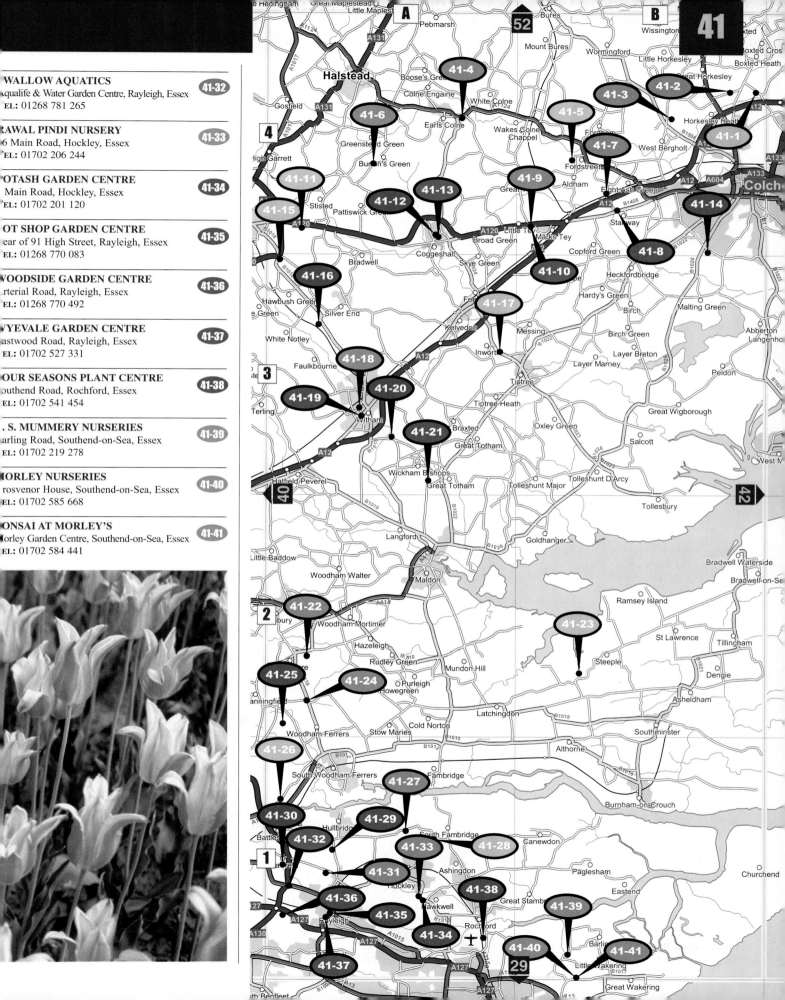

SWALLOW AQUATICS `41-32`
Aqualife & Water Garden Centre, Rayleigh, Essex
TEL: 01268 781 265

RAWAL PINDI NURSERY `41-33`
6 Main Road, Hockley, Essex
TEL: 01702 206 244

POTASH GARDEN CENTRE `41-34`
Main Road, Hockley, Essex
TEL: 01702 201 120

POT SHOP GARDEN CENTRE `41-35`
Rear of 91 High Street, Rayleigh, Essex
TEL: 01268 770 083

WOODSIDE GARDEN CENTRE `41-36`
Arterial Road, Rayleigh, Essex
TEL: 01268 770 492

WYEVALE GARDEN CENTRE `41-37`
Eastwood Road, Rayleigh, Essex
TEL: 01702 527 331

FOUR SEASONS PLANT CENTRE `41-38`
Southend Road, Rochford, Essex
TEL: 01702 541 454

J. S. MUMMERY NURSERIES `41-39`
Carling Road, Southend-on-Sea, Essex
TEL: 01702 219 278

MORLEY NURSERIES `41-40`
Grosvenor House, Southend-on-Sea, Essex
TEL: 01702 585 668

BONSAI AT MORLEY'S `41-41`
Morley Garden Centre, Southend-on-Sea, Essex
TEL: 01702 584 441

ESSEX

● GARDEN CENTRE   ● NURSERY & GARDEN CENTRE
● NURSERY   ● GARDEN & NURSERY
● GARDEN   ● WATER GARDEN SPECIALIST

Rhododendron

HEARTS DELIGHT NURSERY
Long Road, Manningtree, Essex
TEL: 01206 392 539
`42-1`

OAKVIEW NURSERIES
Dead Lane, Colchester, Essex
TEL: 01206 231 134
`42-2`

NOTCUTTS GARDEN CENTRE
Station Road, Ardleigh, Essex
TEL: 01206 230 271
`42-3`

HULL FARM NURSERY
Spring Valley, Colchester, Essex
TEL: 01206 230 045
`42-4`

SPRING VALLEY NURSERIES
Spring Valley Lane, Colchester, Essex
TEL: 01206 230 238
`42-5`

BLENHEIM NURSERIES
Bromley Road, Colchester, Essex
TEL: 01206 870 605
`42-6`

ROLTS NURSERY & GARDEN CENTRE
Clacton Road, Colchester, Essex
TEL: 01206 822 427
`42-7`

BETH CHATTO GARDENS
White Barn House, Colchester, Essex
TEL: 01206 822 007
`42-8`

HOMESTEAD NURSERIES
Thorpe Road, Clacton-on-sea, Essex
TEL: 01255 830 967
`42-9`

BLACKWELL NURSERY
Fingringhoe Road, Colchester, Essex
TEL: 01206 729 121
`42-1`

F. E. PAYNE & SON
Hilltop Nurseries, Clacton-on-sea, Essex
TEL: 01255 830 325
`42-1`

FRINTON ROAD NURSERY
158-164 Frinton Road, Frinton-on-sea, Essex
TEL: 01255 674 838
`42-1`

CHINA MAROC BONSAI
Five Oaks, Colchester, Essex
TEL: 01206 250 547
`42-1`

HONEYPOT FARM
Rectory Road, Clacton-on-sea, Essex
TEL: 01255 830 181
`42-1`

THE GARDEN OUTLET
Unit 1, Clacton-on-sea, Essex
TEL: 01924 827 065
`42-1`

GARDEN WORLD
6 High Street, Colchester, Essex
TEL: 01206 303 868
`42-1`

CLACTON GARDEN CENTRE
St Johns Road, Clacton-on-sea, Essex
TEL: 01255 425 711
`42-1`

WALES

LLANARTH GARDEN CENTRE **43-1**
Pontfaen, Llanarth, Ceredigion
TEL: 01545 580 271

THE WALLED GARDEN AT PIGEONSFORD **43-2**
Llangranog, Llandysul, Ceredigion
TEL: 01239 654 360

GWYNFOR GROWERS **43-3**
Gwynfor, Llandysul, Ceredigion
TEL: 01239 654 151

BRONDESBURY PARK GARDEN CENTRE **43-4**
Brondesbury Park, Cardigan, South Wales
TEL: 01239 615 300

PENRALLT FARM NURSERY **43-5**
Moylegrove, Cardigan, South Wales
TEL: 01239 881 295

PENLAN PERENNIALS **43-6**
Penlan Farm, Llandysul, Ceredigion
TEL: 01239 851 244

GWASTOD NURSERY **43-7**
Prengwyn, Llandysul, Powys
TEL: 01545 590 479

TREFHEDYN GARDEN CENTRE **43-8**
Bridge Street, Newcastle Emlyn, Carmarthenshire
TEL: 01239 710 292

FARMYARD NURSERIES **43-9**
Farmyard Farm, Carmarthen, Carmarthenshire
TEL: 01559 363 389

TY RHOS TREES **43-10**
Ty Rhos, Crymych, Pembrokeshire
TEL: 01239 820 701

NEW INN NURSERIES **43-11**
Blaenffos, Boncath, Pembrokeshire
TEL: 01239 841 215

PENLAN-UCHAF FARM GARDENS **43-12**
Gwaun Valley, Fishguard, Pembrokeshire
TEL: 01348 881 388

ANTHONY'S NURSERY **43-13**
Glasfryn Farm, Fishguard, Pembrokeshire
TEL: 01348 874 034

MOORLAND COTTAGE PLANTS **43-14**
Rhyd - y - Groes, Crymych, Pembrokeshire
TEL: 01239 891 363

Hanging Basket

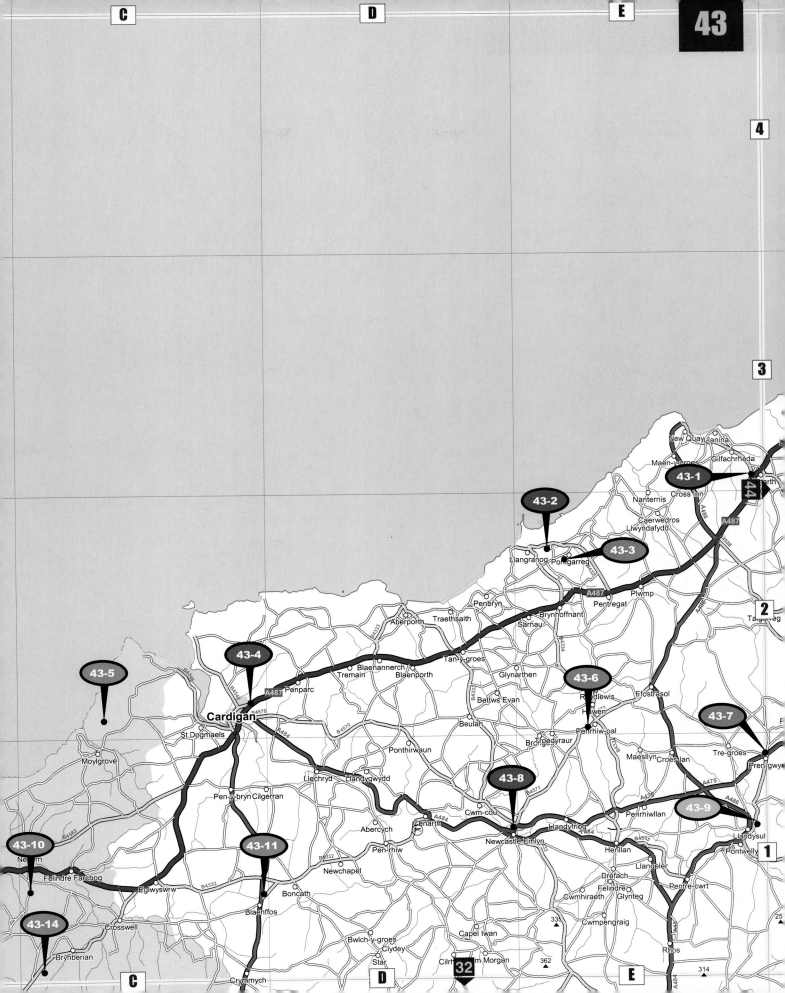

WALES

Ranunculus

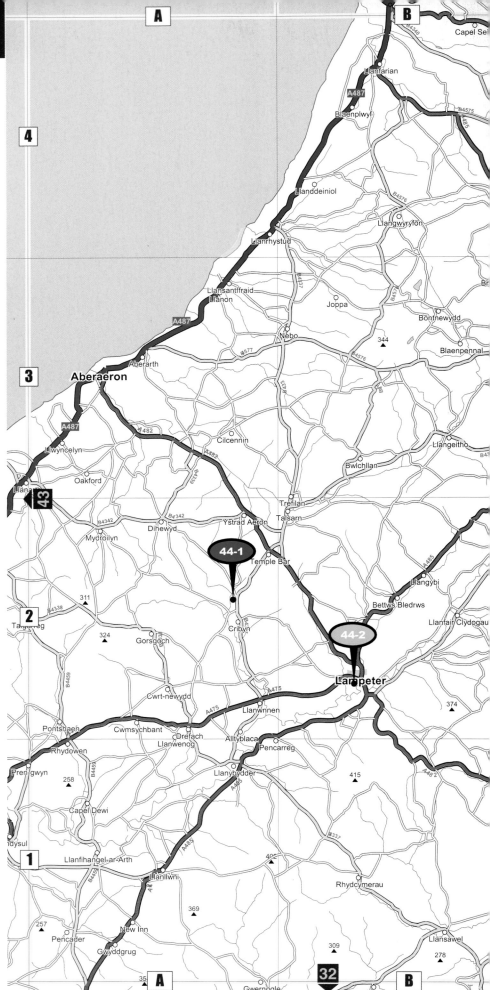

JOHN CLAYFIELD 45-1
Llanbrook Alpine Nursery, Clunton, Shropshire
TEL: 01547 530 298

BUCKNELL NURSERIES 45-2
The Nurseries, Bucknell, Shropshire
TEL: 01547 530 606

LINGEN NURSERY & GARDENS 45-3
Lingen, Bucknell, Shropshire
TEL: 01544 267 720

SWN Y GWYNT NURSERIES 45-4
Nantmel, Llandrindod Wells, Powys
TEL: 01597 823 798

THE OLD VICARAGE NURSERY 45-5
Lucton, Leominster, Herefordshire
TEL: 01568 780 538

BRYAN'S GROUND GARDENS 45-6
Letchmoor Lane, Presteigne, Powys
TEL: 01544 260 001

WHIMBLE NURSERY & GARDEN 45-7
Kinnerton, Presteigne, Powys
TEL: 01547 560 413

MIDWAY NURSERIES 45-8
Penybont, Llandrindod Wells, Powys
TEL: 01597 851 662

ORNAMENTAL TREE NURSERIES 45-9
Broomey Hill Gardens, Leominster, Herefordshire
TEL: 01568 708 016

HERGEST CROFT GARDENS 45-10
Kington, Herefordshire
TEL: 01544 230 160

LYONSHALL NURSERIES AND GARDEN CENTRE 45-11
Lyonshall, Kington, Herefordshire
TEL: 01544 340 214

IVY CROFT PLANTS 45-12
Ivington Green, Leominster, Herefordshire
TEL: 01568 720 344

AULDEN FARM 45-13
Aulden, Leominster, Herefordshire
TEL: 01568 720 129

CHENNELS GATE GARDENS & NURSERY 45-14
Chennels Gate, Eardisley, Herefordshire
TEL: 01544 327 288

BROBURY GARDENS 45-15
Brobury, Herefordshire
TEL: 01981 500 229

THE OLD RAILWAY LINE NURSERY 45-16
Three Cocks, Brecon, Powys, LD3 0SG
TEL: 01497 847 055
EMAIL: clearynursery@aol.com

Family established business of over 10 years for all your gardening requirements and floral tributes.
OPEN: Daily, Winter 8.30-5.30, Summer 8.30-6. Closed Christmas week.
SPECIALITIES: Alpines, Bedding plants, Climbers, Fruit & fruit trees, Hardy plants.

Dahlia

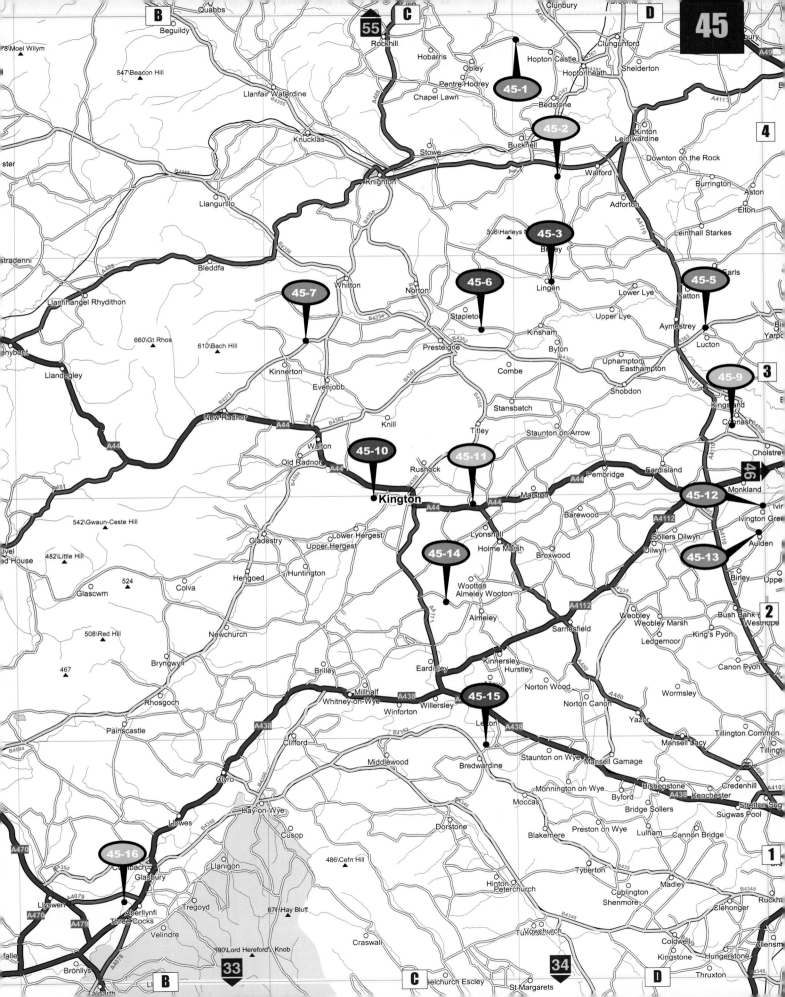

GARDEN CENTRE
NURSERY
GARDEN

NURSERY & GARDEN CENTRE
GARDEN & NURSERY
WATER GARDEN SPECIALIST

GARDEN THYME NURSERY 46-1
Blackmans Stitch, Bewdley, Worcestershire
TEL: 01299 400 658

EVERGREEN CONIFER CENTRE 46-2
Tenbury Road, Kidderminster, Worcestershire
TEL: 01299 266 581

BOURNEWOOD NURSERY 46-3
Lickhill Road North, Stourport on Severn,
Worcestershire
TEL: 01299 828 988

THE COTTAGE HERBARY 46-4
Mill House, Tenbury Wells, Worcestershire
TEL: 01584 781 575

BURFORD HOUSE GARDENS 46-5
Tenbury Wells, Tenbury Wells, Worcestershire
TEL: 01584 810 777

TREASURES OF TENBURY 46-6
Burford House, Tenbury Wells, Worcestershire
TEL: 01584 810 777

PERHILL NURSERIES 46-7
Worcester Road, Great Witley, Worcestershire
TEL: 01299 896 329

WITLEY COURT, ENGLISH HERITAGE 46-8
Worcester Road, Worcester, Worcestershire
TEL: 01299 896 636

EASTGROVE COTTAGE GARDEN NURSERY 46-9
Sankyns Green, Little Witley, Worcestershire
TEL: 01299 896 389

BERRINGTON HALL, NATIONAL TRUST 46-10
Leominster, Leominster, Herefordshire
TEL: 01568 615 721

KYRE PARK GARDENS 46-11
Kyre Park, Tenbury Wells, Worcestershire
TEL: 01885 410 247

RICKARD'S HARDY FERNS 46-12
Kyre Park Gardens, Tenbury Wells, Worcs.
TEL: 01885 410 282

STOCKTON BURY GARDENS 46-13
Stockton Bury, Leominster, Herefordshire
TEL: 01568 613 432

THE GARDEN AT THE ELMS NURSERY 46-14
Frenchlands Lane, Lower Broadheath,
Worcestershire
TEL: 01905 640 841

WINTERGREEN NURSERIES 46-15
Bringsty Common, Worcester, Worcestershire
TEL: 01886 821 858

LAYLOCKS NURSERIES 46-16
Bromyard Road, Worcester, Worcestershire
TEL: 01905 429 212

THE GARDEN AT THE BANNUT 46-17
Bringsty, Bringsty, Herefordshire
TEL: 01885 482 206

HAMPTON COURT 46-18
The Van Kampen Gardens, Leominster,
Herefordshire
TEL: 01568 797 777

QUEEN'S WOOD ARBORETUM 46-19
Dinmore Hill, Leominster, Herefordshire
TEL: 01568 797 052

WEIR GARDEN, NATIONAL TRUST 46-20
Swainshill, Hereford, Herefordshire
TEL: 01981 590 697

HURRANS GARDEN CENTRE 46-21
Hereford Road, Leigh Sinton,
Worcestershire, WR13 5ED
TEL: 01886 832 462
EMAIL: info@hurrans.co.uk
WEB: www.hurrans.co.uk

Where great gardens don't cost the earth!

*A family business established in 1909.
Features fishing lake, landscaped display
gardens, fencing & trellis specialists, and garden
buildings centre. Also equestrian
supplies available. You'll find excellent customer
care, quality and value.*
OPEN: 9-6 each day; (5.30 Winter).

ACTON BEAUCHAMP ROSES 46-22
The Tynnings, Worcester, Worcestershire
TEL: 01531 640 433

QUEENSWOOD GARDEN CENTRE 46-23
Wellington, Hereford, Herefordshire
TEL: 01432 830 880

MADRESFIELD NURSERY & GARDEN CENTRE 46-24
Jennet Tree Lane, Malvern, Worcestershire
TEL: 01684 574 066

OVERCOURT GARDEN NURSERY 46-25
Overcourt, Hereford, Herefordshire
TEL: 01432 880 845

GRANGE FARM NURSERY 46-26
Guarlford, Malvern, Worcestershire
TEL: 01684 562 544

THREE ACRE NURSERIES 46-27
Wyatt Road, Hereford, Herefordshire
TEL: 01432 820 471

KENCHESTER WATER GARDENS 46-28
Church Road, Hereford, Herefordshire
TEL: 01432 270 981

THE PICTON GARDEN AND THE OLD COURT NURSERIES 46-29
Walwyn Road, Malvern, Worcestershire
TEL: 01684 540 416

MEREBROOK WATER PLANTS 46-30
Merebrook Farm, Worcester, Worcestershire
TEL: 01684 310 950

OLD COURT NURSERIES 46-3
Walwyn Road, Malvern, Worcestershire
TEL: 01684 540 416

WYEVALE GARDEN CENTRE 46-3
Kings Acres Road, Hereford, Herefordshire
TEL: 01432 266 261

LEDBURY'S SECRET GARDEN CENTRE 46-3
58 The Homend, Ledbury, Herefordshire
TEL: 01531 636 087

RUSHFIELDS OF LEDBURY 46-3
Ross Road, Ledbury, Herefordshire
TEL: 01531 632 004

EASTNOR CASTLE 46-3
Eastnor, Ledbury, Herefordshire
TEL: 01531 633 160

EASTNOR GARDEN PLANTS 46-36
Eastnor, Ledbury,
Herefordshire, HR8 1RL
TEL: 01531 635 982
EMAIL: enquiries@knightsmaze.co.uk
WEB: www.knightsmaze.co.uk
*Plant Nursery. Yew maze in the shape of a castle
with trails to test all the family. Amazing puzzle
shop.*
OPEN: Tues-Sat 9.30-5.30, Sun 12-5.30. Closed
Nov-Feb.
SPECIALITIES: Climbers, Perennials, Shrubs,
Ornaments, Maze.

Dahlia

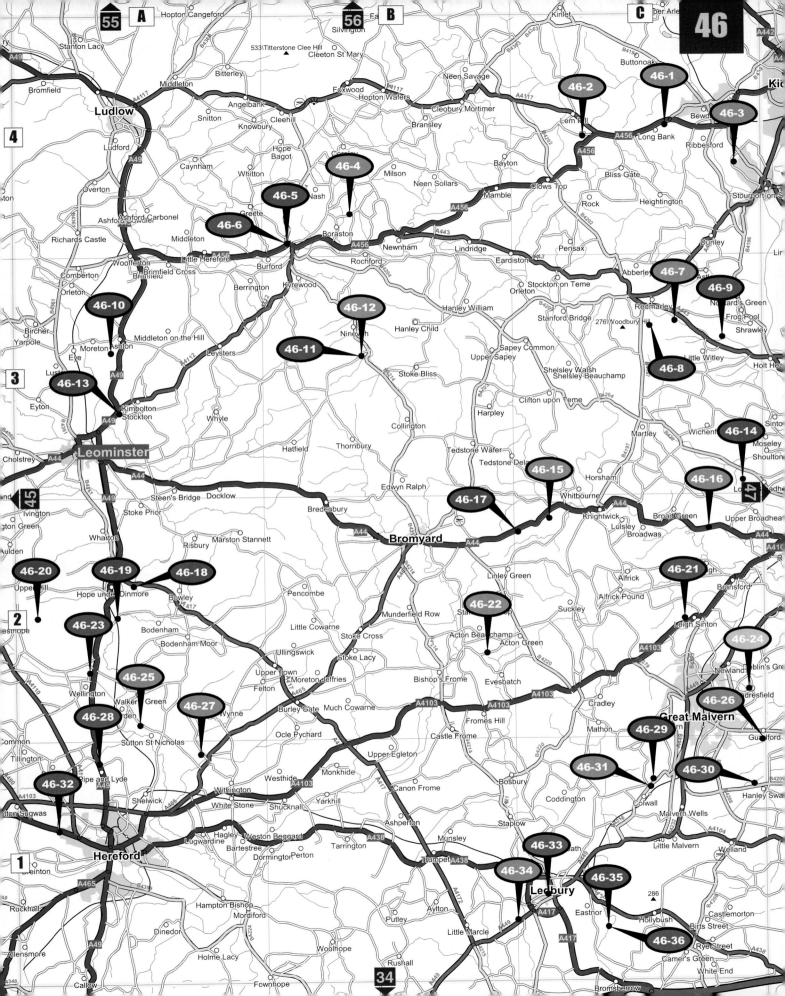

○ GARDEN CENTRE
○ NURSERY
○ GARDEN

● NURSERY & GARDEN CENTRE
○ GARDEN & NURSERY
● WATER GARDEN SPECIALIST

BODENHAM ARBORETUM & EARTH CENTRE `47-1`
Wolverley, Kidderminster, Worcestershire
TEL: 01562 850 382

HURRANS GARDEN CENTRE `47-2`
Kidderminster Road South,
West Hagley, Worcestershire, DY9 0JB
TEL: 01562 700 511
EMAIL: info@hurrans.co.uk
WEB: www.hurrans.co.uk

A family business established in 1909. Features aquatic and falconry centres with daily flying displays, landscaped show gardens, garden buildings and patio & stone centres. You'll find excellent customer care, quality and value.
OPEN: 9-6 Mon-Sat; 11-5 Sun.

SUNSET NURSERIES `47-3`
Waggon Lane, Kidderminster, Worcestershire
TEL: 01562 700 672

WOOLMANS GARDEN CENTRE `47-4`
72 Solihull Road, Solihull, West Midlands
TEL: 0121 744 3094

WASELEY HILLS COUNTRY PARK `47-5`
Gannow Green Lane, Birmingham, West Midlands
TEL: 01562 710 025

A. CALDICOTT & SON `47-6`
The Nursery, Solihull, West Midlands
TEL: 0121 705 747

NOTCUTTS GARDEN CENTRE `47-7`
Stratford Road, Solihull, West Midlands
TEL: 0121 744 4501

BEECHCROFT NURSERIES & GARDEN CENTRE `47-8`
Madeley Road, Stourbridge, West Midlands
TEL: 01562 710 358

HOLLYWOOD GARDENS & PETS `47-9`
73 May Lane, Birmingham, West Midlands
TEL: 01564 826 843

BARNET HILL GARDEN CENTRE `47-10`
Worcester Road, Stourbridge, West Midlands
TEL: 01562 700308

TREADMILL NURSERY `47-11`
Tythebarn Lane, Solihull, West Midlands
TEL: 0121 744 6954

FOUR ASHES NURSERIES `47-12`
Four Ashes Road, Solihull, West Midlands
TEL: 01564 773 019

STONE HOUSE COTTAGE NURSERIES `47-13`
Stone, Kidderminster, Worcestershire
TEL: 01562 699 02

AMBLESIDE GARDEN CENTRE `47-14`
Norton Lane, Solihull, West Midlands
TEL: 01564 703 553

HARVINGTON HALL `47-15`
Harvington, Kidderminster, Worcestershire
TEL: 01562 777 846

EARLSWOOD NURSERIES `47-16`
Forshaw Heath Road, Solihull, West Midlands
TEL: 01564 702 749

KINGFISHER NURSERIES `47-17`
Catshill, Bromsgrove, Worcestershire
TEL: 01527 835 084

LITTLE HEATH GARDEN CENTRE `47-18`
Little Heath Lane, Bromsgrove, Worcestershire
TEL: 01527 878 174

WYEVALE GARDEN CENTRE `47-19`
Alcester Road, Bromsgrove, Worcestershire
TEL: 01527 873 470

COOKS GARDEN CENTRE `47-20`
26 Worcester Road, Stourport on Severn, Worcestershire
TEL: 01299 826 169

BISHOPSWOOD NURSERY `47-21`
Bishopswood, Stourport on Severn, Worcestershire
TEL: 01299 251 208

HILLIER GARDEN CENTRE `47-22`
Woodhouse Lane, Botley, Southampton, Hampshire, SO30 2EZ
TEL: 01489 782 306
WEB: www.hillier.co.uk

A large garden centre with a comprehensive range of everything you could want for the garden. Easy access and friendly expert advice are sure to impress.
OPEN: Daily 9-5.30, Sun 10.30-4.30.
SPECIALITIES: Furniture, Gifts, Greenhouses & sheds, Hardy plants, Shrubs.

BADGER NURSERIES PLANT CENTRE `47-23`
Birmingham Road, Studley, West Midlands
TEL: 01527 852 631

WEBBS OF WYCHBOLD `47-24`
Wychbold, Droitwich, Worcestershire
TEL: 01527 861 777

BOTANY BAY NURSERIES `47-25`
Edgioake Lane, Redditch, Worcestershire
TEL: 01527 893 885

COUGHTON COURT `47-26`
, Alcester, Warwickshire
TEL: 01789 400 777

RIDGEWAY NURSERIES `47-27`
Evesham Road, Alcester, Warwickshire
TEL: 01527 894 111

WORCESTER GARDEN CENTRE `47-28`
Droitwich Road, Worcester, Worcestershire
TEL: 01905 451231

SPRINGRIDGE NURSERIES `47-29`
Springridge, Worcester, Worcestershire
TEL: 01905 381 451

HILLER GARDEN & PLANT CENTRE `47-30`
Dunnington Heath Farm, Alcester, Warwickshire
TEL: 01789 490 991

CRABTREE FARM NURSERIES `47-31`
3 Stratford Road, Alcester, Warwickshire
TEL: 01789 773 497

NEW INN LANE NURSERIES `47-32`
Pitchill, Evesham, Worcestershire
TEL: 01386 870 073

ST. PETERS GARDEN CENTRE `47-33`
Pear Tree Farm, Worcester, Worcestershire
TEL: 01905 357 595

MILL LANE NURSERIES `47-34`
Mill Lane, Evesham, Worcestershire
TEL: 01789 773231

MILL LANE NURSERIES `47-35`
Mill Lane, Pershore, Worcestershire
TEL: 01905 841 650

FIBREX NURSERIES `47-36`
Honeybourne Road, Stratford-upon-Avon, Warwickshire
TEL: 01789 720 788

THREE SPRINGS NURSERY `47-37`
Defford Road, Pershore, Worcestershire
TEL: 01386 555 476

SIDING NURSERIES `47-38`
Offenham Road, Evesham, Worcestershire
TEL: 01386 493 47

BIRLINGHAM NURSERIES `47-39`
Birlingham, Pershore, Worcestershire
TEL: 01386 750 668

COTSWOLD GARDEN FLOWERS `47-40`
Sands Lane, Evesham, Worcestershire
TEL: 01386 422 829

EARLS CROOME NURSERY & GARDEN CENTRE `47-41`
Worcester Road, Worcester, Worcestershire
TEL: 01684 592 143

BOWERS HILL NURSERY `47-42`
Willersley Road, Evesham, Worcestershire
TEL: 01386 832 124

BEACONS NURSERIES `47-43`
Tewkesbury Road, Pershore, Worcestershire
TEL: 01386 750 359

ORCHARD VIEW NURSERIES `47-44`
Orchard View, Broadway, Worcestershire
TEL: 01386 852 346

BARN HOUSE `47-45`
152 High Street, Broadway, Worcestershire
TEL: 01386 858 633

CHARLES F ELLIS `47-46`
Nursery Oak Piece, Stanston, Worcestershire
TEL: 01386 584 077

SNOWSHILL MANOR, NATIONAL TRUST `47-47`
Snowshill, Broadway, Worcestershire
TEL: 01386 852 410

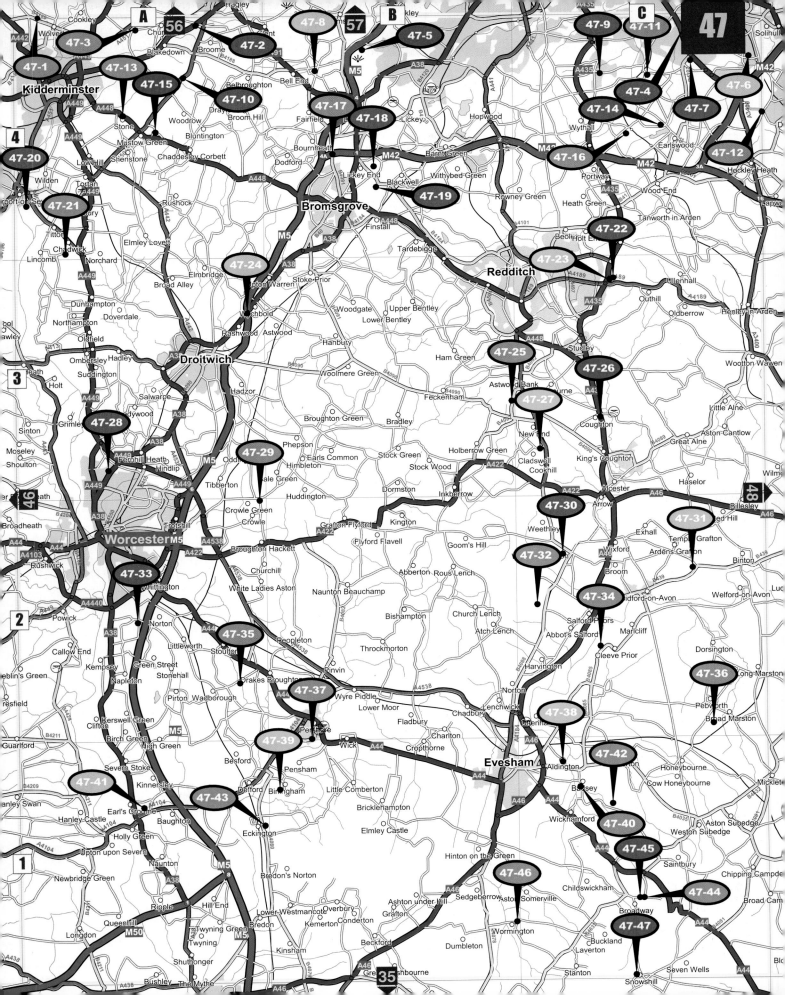

GARDEN CENTRE
NURSERY
GARDEN

NURSERY & GARDEN CENTR
GARDEN & NURSERY
WATER GARDEN SPECIALIST

JARDINERIE 48-1
Kenilworth Road, Solihull, West Midlands
Tel: 01675 442 866

COOMBE COUNTRY PARK 48-2
Brinklow Road, Coventry, West Midlands
Tel: 024 7645 3720

OAK FARM NURSERY 48-3
Brinklow Road, Coventry, West Midlands
Tel: 024 7645 4658

WYEVALE GARDEN CENTRE 48-4
Hampton Road, Solihull, West Midlands
Tel: 01675 442 031

AVONDALE COTTAGE PERENNIALS 48-5
3 Avondale Road, Coventry, West Midlands
Tel: 024 7667 3662

UNIVERSITY OF WARWICK GARDENS 48-6
Gibbet Hill Road, Coventry, West Midlands
Tel: 024 7652 3523

WYNDLEY GARDEN CENTRE 48-7
Warwick Road, Solihull, West Midlands
Tel: 01564 777 106

SMITH'S NURSERIES 48-8
Twelve Ash Lodge, Coventry, West Midlands
Tel: 024 7630 3382

OSCROFT'S DAHLIA'S 48-9
Woodside, Solihull, West Midlands
Tel: 01564 782 450

BADDESLEY CLINTON, NATIONAL TRUST 48-10
Rising Lane, Solihull, West Midlands
Tel: 01564 783 294

PACKWOOD HOUSE, NATIONAL TRUST 48-11
Lapworth, Solihull, West Midlands
Tel: 01564 782 024

JUST PLANTS 48-12
25 Talisman Square, Kenilworth, Warwickshire
Tel: 01926 853311

GUEST FOR PLANTS 48-13
Queens Road, Kenilworth, Warwickshire
Tel: 01926 852759

STONELEIGH GARDEN 48-14
, Kenilworth, Warwickshire
Tel: 01926 858 585

WAPPENBURY HALL ESTATE NURSERY 48-15
Wappenbury Hall, Leamington Spa, Warwickshire
Tel: 01926 633 251

BARNCLOSE NURSERY 48-16
Old Warwick Road, Warwick, Warwickshire
Tel: 01926 843 502

WARWICK NURSERIES 48-17
Woodloes Lane, Warwick, Warwickshire
Tel: 01926 492 273

HATTON PLANT CENTRE 48-18
Dark Lane, Warwick, Warwickshire
Tel: 01926 843 370

JEPHSON GARDENS 48-19
Leamington Spa, Warwickshire
Tel: 01926 450 000

HURRANS GARDEN CENTRE 48-20
Myton Road, Leamington Spa,
Warwickshire, CV31 3PB
Tel: 01926 881122
Email: info@hurrans.co.uk
Web: www.hurrans.co.uk

Where great gardens don't cost the earth!

A family business established in 1909. This bright, cheerful Centre is well worth a visit. Close to both Leamington and Warwick, it features the award-winning 'Four Seasons' coffee shop. Excellent customer care, quality and value.
Open: 9-6 Mon-Sat; 10.30-4.30 Sun.

WARWICK CASTLE 48-21
Castle Hill, Warwick, Warwickshire
Tel: 01926 406 600

THE MASTER'S GARDEN 48-22
Lord Leycester Hospital, 60 High Street,
Warwick, Warwickshire, CV34 4BH
Tel: 01926 491 422
A 1 acre walled town garden originating in the 16th century and re-planned in the 19th century. Important historical artefacts. Featured in BBC TV's "Gardeners' World".
Open: 18 Mar-30 Sep, Tues-Sun & Bank holidays, 10-4.30.
Entry costs: £1.
Specialities: Annuals, Box hedges, Camellias, Clematis, Roses.

WYEVALE GARDEN CENTRE 48-23
Warwick Road, Stratford-upon-Avon, Warwickshire
Tel: 01789 734 200

MARY ARDEN'S HOUSE 48-24
Station Road, Stratford-upon-Avon, Warwickshire
Tel: 01789 204 016

CHARLECOTE FRUIT & FLOWERS 48-25
Dog Kennel Close, Warwick, Warwickshire
Tel: 01789 842 674

CHARLECOTE PARK, NATIONAL TRUST 48-26
Charlecote, Warwick, Warwickshire
Tel: 01789 470 277

SHAKESPEARE BIRTHPLACE GARDEN 48-27
Henley Street, Stratford-upon-Avon, Warwickshire
Tel: 01789 204 016

BANCROFT GARDENS 48-28
Waterside, Stratford Upon Avon, Warwickshire
Tel: 01789 260 631

ANNE HATHAWAY'S COTTAGE & GARDEN SHOP 48-29
Cottage Lane, Stratford-upon-Avon, Warwickshire
Tel: 01789 204 016

NASH'S HOUSE & NEW PLACE 48-30
Chapel Street, Stratford-upon-Avon, Warwickshire
Tel: 01789 204 016

DUDFIELD'S PLANT CENTRE 48-31
Tavern Lane, Stratford-upon-Avon, Warwickshire
Tel: 01789 292 689

HALL'S CROFT 48-32
Old Town, Stratford-upon-Avon, Warwickshire
Tel: 01789 204 016 / 292 107

AVON VALLEY GARDEN CENTRE 48-33
Banbury Road, Stratford-upon-Avon, Warwickshire
Tel: 01789 414 383

WOODFIELD BROTHERS 48-34
Wood End, Stratford-upon-Avon, Warwickshire
Tel: 01789 205 618

WAYSIDE NURSERIES 48-35
Clifford Garden Centre, Stratford-upon-Avon, Warwickshire
Tel: 01789 205 745

AVON AQUATICS 48-36
Sweet Knowle Farm, Stratford-upon-Avon, Warwickshire
Tel: 01789 450 638

UPTON HOUSE, NATIONAL TRUST 48-37
Banbury, Oxfordshire
Tel: 01295 670 266

Tiger Lily

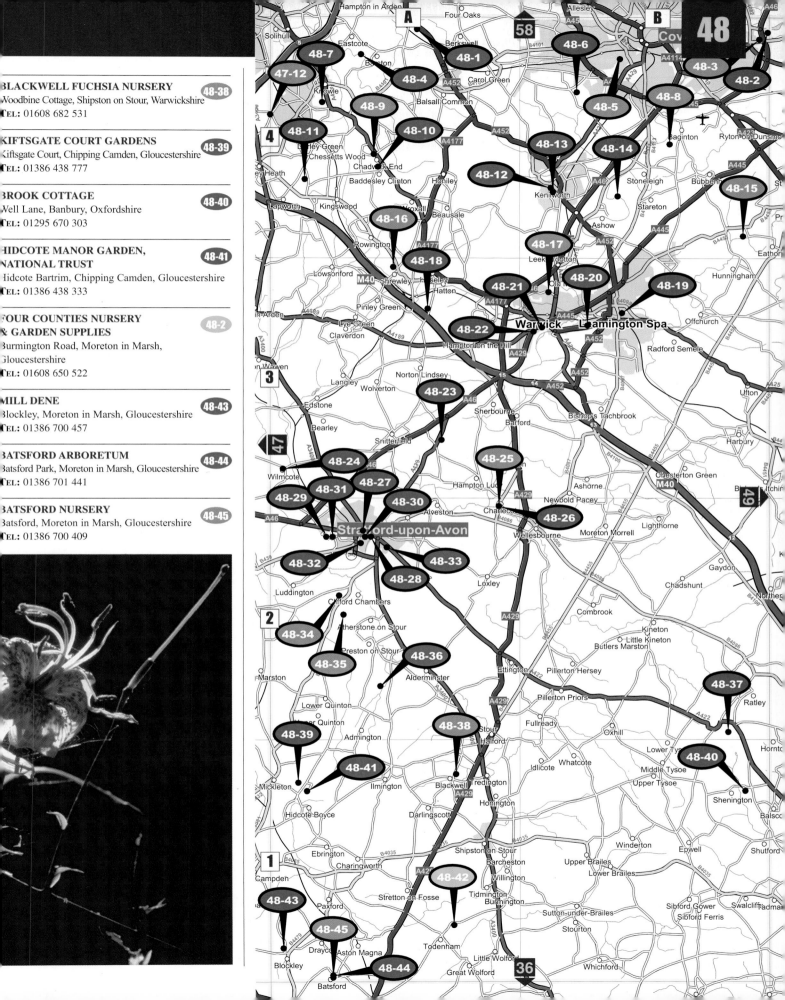

BLACKWELL FUCHSIA NURSERY 48-38
Woodbine Cottage, Shipston on Stour, Warwickshire
TEL: 01608 682 531

KIFTSGATE COURT GARDENS 48-39
Kiftsgate Court, Chipping Camden, Gloucestershire
TEL: 01386 438 777

BROOK COTTAGE 48-40
Well Lane, Banbury, Oxfordshire
TEL: 01295 670 303

HIDCOTE MANOR GARDEN,
NATIONAL TRUST 48-41
Hidcote Bartrim, Chipping Camden, Gloucestershire
TEL: 01386 438 333

FOUR COUNTIES NURSERY
& GARDEN SUPPLIES 48-2
Burmington Road, Moreton in Marsh,
Gloucestershire
TEL: 01608 650 522

MILL DENE 48-43
Blockley, Moreton in Marsh, Gloucestershire
TEL: 01386 700 457

BATSFORD ARBORETUM 48-44
Batsford Park, Moreton in Marsh, Gloucestershire
TEL: 01386 701 441

BATSFORD NURSERY 48-45
Batsford, Moreton in Marsh, Gloucestershire
TEL: 01386 700 409

BUCKS · OXON · NORTHANTS · WARWKS

- GARDEN CENTRE
- NURSERY
- GARDEN
- NURSERY & GARDEN CENTRE
- GARDEN & NURSERY
- WATER GARDEN SPECIALIST

OAKDALE ROSE & GARDEN CENTRE
Oakdale Nurseries, Coventry, West Midlands
TEL: 024 7654 2151

WYEVALE GARDEN CENTRE
Kings Newnham Road, Rugby, Warwickshire
TEL: 024 7654 2319

TEBBS GARDEN CENTRE
59-69 Hillmorton Road, Rugby, Warwickshire
TEL: 01788 542 997

BLOOMS OF RUGBY
Bernhards Garden Centre, Rugby, Warwickshire
TEL: 01788 522 345

RYTON ORGANIC GARDENS 49-5
Ryton on Dunsmore, Coventry, West
Midlands, CV8 3LG
TEL: 024 7630 3517
EMAIL: enquiry@hdra.org.uk
WEB: www.hdra.org.uk
Britain's premier organic gardens with wildflowers, roses, herbs, fruit and vegetables, and much more. Guided tours. Organic restaurant. Family friendly. Events throughout the year.
OPEN: Daily, 9-5.
ENTRY COSTS: Adult £3, Children under 16 and HDRA/RHS members free.
SPECIALITIES: Organic gardening.

BUNGALOW NURSERIES
65 London Road, Rugby, Warwickshire
TEL: 01788 810 505

COTTESBROOKE HALL & GARDENS 49-7
Cottesbrooke Hall, Northampton, Northamptonshire
TEL: 01604 505 808

TEBBS CRICK LODGE NURSERIES
West Haddon Road, Crick, Northamptonshire
TEL: 01788 824 154

COTON MANOR GARDENS 49-9
Guilsborough, Northampton, Northamptonshire
TEL: 01604 740 219

PLANTSMAN
West Haddon Nurseries, Northampton, Northamptonshire
TEL: 01788 510 206

BERNHARDS RUGBY NURSERIES
The Straight Mile, Rugby, Warwickshire
TEL: 01788 521 177

VILLAGE FARM NURSERIES
Onley Lane, Rugby, Warwickshire
TEL: 01788 891 608

HADDONSTONE SHOW GARDENS 49-13
The Forge House, Church Lane, East
Haddon, Northampton, Northamptonshire,
NN6 8DB
TEL: 01604 770 711
EMAIL: info@haddonstone.co.uk
WEB: www.haddonstone.co.uk
View Haddonstone's classic garden ornaments including urns, fountains, sundials, statuary, balustrading and follies.
OPEN: Daily, Mon-Fri 9-5.30, closed bank holidays & Christmas period.
SPECIALITIES: Fountains, Ornaments, Paving, gates, railings & fencing, Stone ornaments, Water features.

HOLDENBY HOUSE & GARDENS
Holdenby, Northampton, Northamptonshire
TEL: 01604 770 074

A. D. & N. WHEELER
Pye Court, Rugby, Warwickshire
TEL: 01788 890 341

BRIDGE NURSERY 49-16
Tomlow Road, Rugby, Warwickshire
TEL: 01926 812 737

WHILTON LOCKS GARDEN CENTRE
Whilton Locks, Daventry, Northamptonshire
TEL: 01327 842 727

WYEVALE GARDEN CENTRE
Harlestone Road, Northampton, Northamptonshire
TEL: 01604 751 346

BLISS LANE NURSERY
34 Bliss Lane, Northampton, Northamptonshire
TEL: 01327 340 918

CANONS ASHBY HOUSE, NATIONAL TRUST 49-20
Canons Ashby, Daventry, Northamptonshire
TEL: 01327 860 044

FARNBOROUGH GARDEN CENTRE
Southam Road, Banbury, Oxfordshire
TEL: 01295 690 479

BELL PLANTATION
Plantation House, Towcester, Northamptonshire
TEL: 01327 354 126

GREEN LANE NURSERIES
Brackley Road, Towcester, Northamptonshire
TEL: 01327 350 593

BARN FARM PLANTS
Wardington, Banbury, Oxfordshire
TEL: 01295 758 080

D. A. CHESTER HOME NURSERIES
Sulgrave Road, Banbury, Oxfordshire
TEL: 01295 768 141

PURELY PLANTS 49-26
Turnpike Hill, Middleton Cheney, Oxfordshire
TEL: 01295 812 735

WROXTON ABBEY
Wroxton, Banbury, Oxfordshire
TEL: 01295 730 551

HURRANS GARDEN CENTRE 49-28
Compton Road, Banbury,
Oxfordshire, OX16 8PR
TEL: 01295 266300
EMAIL: info@hurrans.co.uk
WEB: www.hurrans.co.uk

A family business established in 1909. This modern Centre is in the heart of town with attractive coffee shop and free parking. Features landscaped display gardens and aquatic centre. Excellent customer care, quality and value.
OPEN: 9-6 Mon-Sat; 10.30-4.30 Sun.

STOWE GARDENS, NATIONAL TRUST 49-29
Buckingham, Buckinghamshire
TEL: 01280 822 850

GREENFINGERS GARDEN CENTRE 49-30
Market House Courtyard, Brackley,
Northamptonshire
TEL: 01280 701 677

PURELY PLANTS 49-31
Mill Lane, Banbury, Oxfordshire
TEL: 01295 812 735

PLANTA EXOTICA 49-32
11 Heath Close, Banbury, Oxfordshire
TEL: 01295 721 989

SWALLOW'S NURSERY 49-33
Finmere Road, Brackley, Northamptonshire
TEL: 01280 847 721

BUCKINGHAM NURSERIES 49-34
Tingewick Road, Buckingham, Buckinghamshire
TEL: 01280 813 556

Geranium

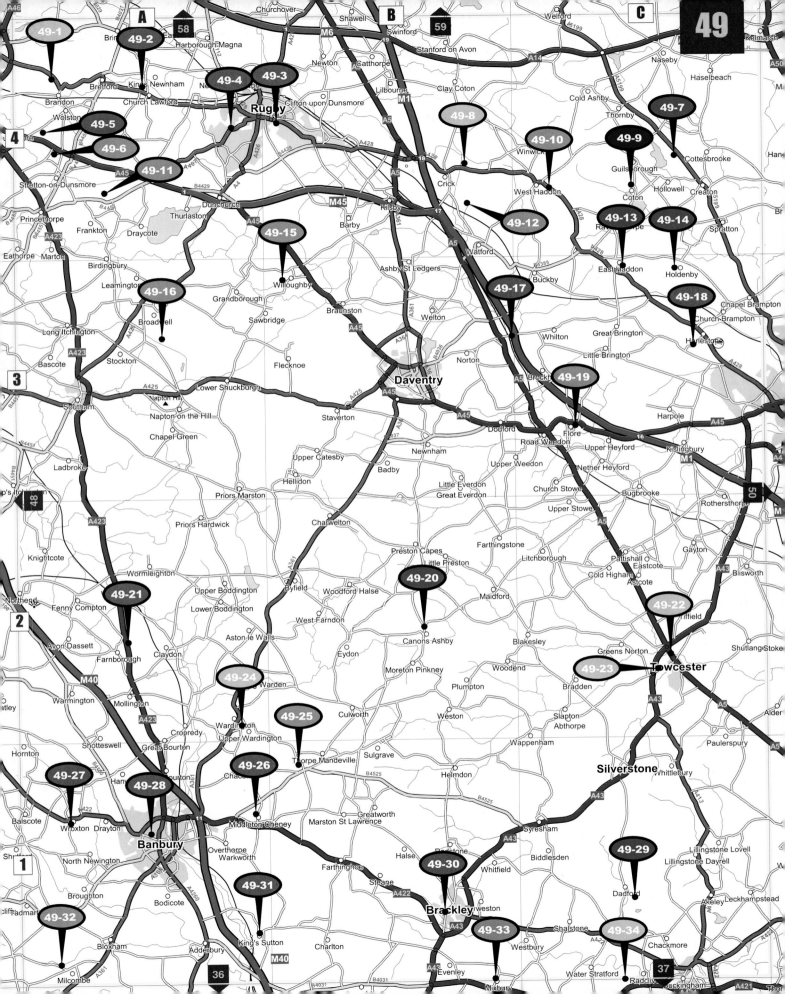

ISE GARDEN CENTRE `50-1`
Warkton Lane, Kettering, Northamptonshire
TEL: 01536 519 792

LAMPORT HALL GARDENS `50-2`
Lamport Hall, Northampton, Northamptonshire
TEL: 01604 686 272

BOSWORTH NURSERIES & GARDEN CENTRE `50-3`
110 Finedon Road, Kettering, Northamptonshire
TEL: 01536 722 635

HILLSIDE FARM NURSERIES `50-4`
Hillside Farm, Wellingborough, Northamptonshire
TEL: 01933 681 076

THE WATER GARDEN `50-5`
Greenacres, Wellingborough, Northamptonshire
TEL: 01933 271 870

GAGGINI'S PLANT CENTRE `50-6`
Glebe House, Northampton, Northamptonshire
TEL: 01604 812 371

THE PLANT NURSERY `50-7`
Sandy Hill Lane, Northampton, Northamptonshire
TEL: 01604 491 941

ROB'S NURSERY `50-8`
Castle Hill View, Northampton, Northamptonshire
TEL: 01604 495 073

WYEVALE GARDEN CENTRE `50-9`
Millers Lane, Wellingborough, Northamptonshire
TEL: 01933 273 728

BLOMS BULBS `50-10`
Primrose Nurseries, Melchbourne, Bedfordshire
TEL: 01234 709 099

CRAMDEN NURSERY `50-11`
Harborough Road North, Northampton,
Northamptonshire
TEL: 01604 846 246

RAVENSTHORPE NURSERY `50-12`
6 East Haddon Road, Ravensthorpe,
Northamptonshire
TEL: 01604 770 548

PODINGTON GARDEN CENTRE `50-13`
High Street, Wellingborough, Northamptonshire
TEL: 01933 353 656

GOLBY'S GARDEN CENTRE `50-14`
Tollgate Way, Northampton, Northamptonshire
TEL: 01604 752 155

CASTLE ASHBY GARDENS `50-15`
Castle Ashby, Northampton, Northamptonshire
TEL: 01604 696 696

BILLING GARDEN CENTRE `50-16`
The Causeway, Northampton, Northamptonshire
TEL: 01604 404 550

DELAPRE ABBEY `50-17`
London Road, Northampton, Northamptonshire
TEL: 01604 761 074

ROOKERY FARM NURSERIES `50-18`
5 Rookery Road, Bedford, Bedfordshire
TEL: 01480 213 506

WYEVALE GARDEN CENTRE `50-19`
Newport Pagnell Road, Northampton,
Northamptonshire
TEL: 01604 765 725

C. W. WARWICK `50-20`
Bedford Road East, Northampton, Northamptonshire
TEL: 01604 696 241

BLUEBELL NURSERIES `50-21`
Roxton Road, Bedford, Bedfordshire
TEL: 01480 216 934

MILTON ERNEST GARDEN CENTRE `50-22`
Radwell Road, Bedford, Bedfordshire
TEL: 01234 823 033

ROXTON GARDEN CENTRE `50-23`
Bedford Road, Roxton, Bedfordshire
TEL: 01480 212 701

SEDDINGTON NURSERIES `50-24`
Great North Road, Sandy, Bedfordshire
TEL: 01767 680 983

ASTERBY AND CHALKCROFT NURSERY `50-25`
The Ridgeway, Blunham, Bedfordshire
TEL: 01767 640 148

FROSTS WILLINGTON `50-26`
Willington Garden Centre, Bedford, Bedfordshire
TEL: 01234 838 777

WOODBURY NURSERY `50-27`
14 Box End Road, Kempston, Bedfordshire
TEL: 01234 856 232

RUSHEY FORD GARDEN CENTRE `50-28`
West End Road, Bedford, Bedfordshire
TEL: 01234 855 515

COTTAGE FARM NURSERIES `50-29`
312 Cople Road, Bedford, Bedfordshire
TEL: 01234 838 383

ALDERTON PLANT NURSERY `50-30`
Spring Lane, Towcester, Northamptonshire
TEL: 01327 811 253

SWISS GARDEN `50-31`
The Village, Biggleswade, Bedfordshire
TEL: 01767 627 666

FIR SCREEN NURSERIES `50-32`
Broom Road, Biggleswade, Bedfordshire
TEL: 01462 811 264

WOBURN ABBEY `50-33`
Woburn, Bedfordshire
TEL: 01525 290 666

LANGFORD NURSERIES & GARDEN CENTRE `50-34`
Henlow Road, Biggleswade, Bedfordshire
TEL: 01462 700791

WYEVALE GARDEN CENTRE `50-35`
Junction Avebury Boulevard & Secklow Gate,
Milton Keynes, Buckinghamshire
TEL: 01908 604 011

MCGRATH NURSERIES `50-36`
The A507, Maulden, Bedfordshire
TEL: 01525 862 124

STAPLES NURSERIES `50-37`
The Nurseries, Bedford, Bedfordshire
TEL: 01525 405 484

FROSTS WOBURN SANDS `50-38`
Newport Road, Milton Keynes, Buckinghamshire
TEL: 01908 583 511

WYEVALE GARDEN CENTRE `50-39`
Newport Road, Milton Keynes, Buckinghamshire
TEL: 01908 281 161

CUCKOO SPIT NURSERIES `50-40`
Walnut Tree Farm, Milton Keynes, Buckinghamshire
TEL: 01908 698 341

WREST PARK, ENGLISH HERITAGE `50-41`
Silsoe, Bedfordshire
TEL: 01234 228 337

STONDON MUSEUM & GARDEN CENTRE `50-42`
Station Road, Henlow, Bedfordshire
TEL: 01462 850 339

THE FISH HOUSE `50-43`
18 Watling Street, Milton Keynes, Buckinghamshire
TEL: 01908 377 336

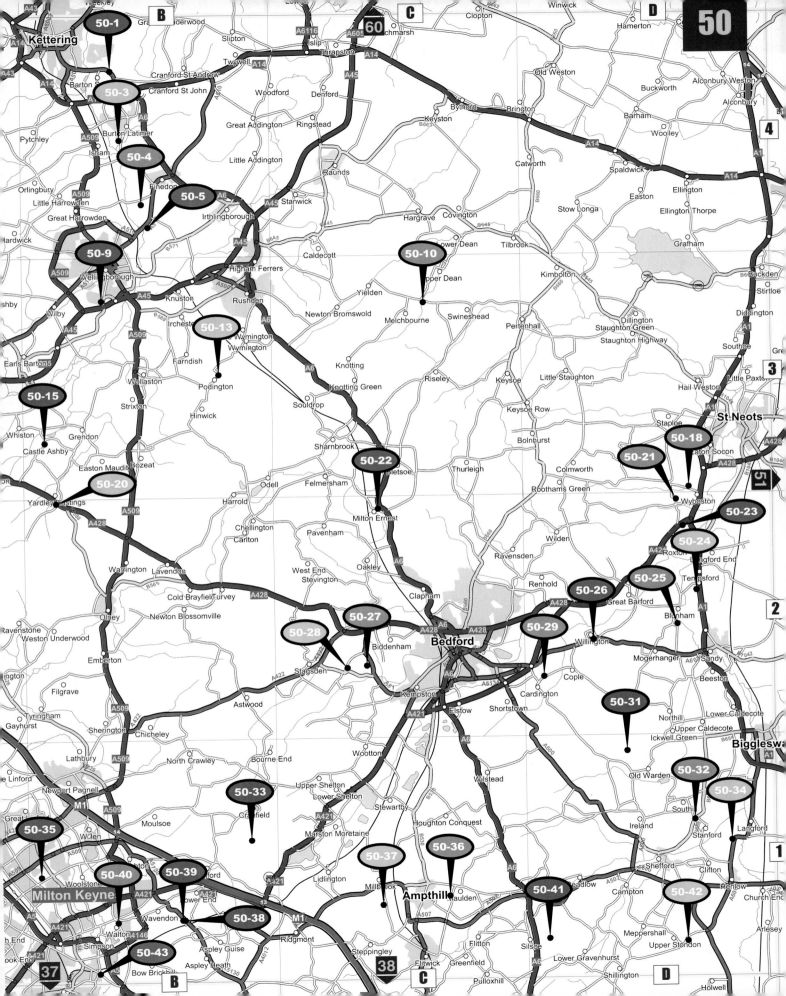

PARKHALL NURSERIES *51-1*
Parkhall Road, Huntingdon, Cambridgeshire
TEL: 01487 840 397

BARCHAM TREES *51-2*
Eye Hill Drove, Ely, Cambridgeshire
TEL: 01353 720 748

TWENTYPENCE GARDEN CENTRE *51-3*
Twentypence Road, Ely, Cambridgeshire
TEL: 01353 741 024

TRIANGLE FARM NURSERY *51-4*
Triangle Farm, Ely, Cambridgeshire
TEL: 01353 720 313

HUNTINGDON GARDEN & LEISURE *51-5*
Banks End, Huntingdon, Cambridgeshire
TEL: 01480 433 349

FORDHAM NURSERY *51-6*
Market Street, Ely, Cambridgeshire
TEL: 01638 720 455

BRAMPTON GARDEN CENTRE *51-7*
Buckden Road, Huntingdon, Cambridgeshire
TEL: 01480 453 048

THE PLANT PLACE *51-8*
2 Mill Road, Cambridge, Cambridgeshire
TEL: 01954 232 699

MONKSILVER NURSERY *51-9*
Oakington Road, Cottenham, Cambridgeshire
TEL: 01954 251 555

TURF MAZE *51-10*
The Green, Huntingdon, Cambridgeshire
TEL: 01480 830 137

OAKINGTON GARDEN CENTRE *51-11*
Dry Drayton Road, Cambridge, Cambridgeshire
TEL: 01223 234 818

CAMBRIDGE GARDEN PLANTS *51-12*
The Lodge, Cambridge, Cambridgeshire
TEL: 01223 861 370

ANSELLS GARDEN CENTRE *51-13*
High Street, Cambridge, Cambridgeshire
TEL: 01223 860 320

ANGLESEY ABBEY & GARDEN, NATIONAL TRUST *51-14*
Lode, Cambridge, Cambridgeshire
TEL: 01223 811 200

CLARE COLLEGE FELLOWS' GARDEN *51-15*
Trinity Lane, Cambridge, Cambridgeshire
TEL: 01223 333 200

CAMBRIDGE UNIVERSITY BOTANIC GARDEN *51-16*
Cory Lodge, Cambridge, Cambridgeshire
TEL: 01223 336 265

SAUNDERS NURSERIES *51-17*
11 West Street, Cambridge, Cambridgeshire
TEL: 01223 262 268

WARESLEY PARK GARDEN CENTRE & NURSERIES *51-18*
Gamlingay Road, Sandy, Bedfordshire
TEL: 01767 650 249

SCOTSDALE NURSERY & GARDEN CENTRE *51-19*
120 Cambridge Road, Cambridge, Cambridgeshire
TEL: 01223 842 777

PADLOCK CROFT *51-20*
Padlock Road, Cambridge, Cambridgeshire
TEL: 01223 290 383

ALL YEAR NURSERY *51-21*
51 North Road, Cambridge, Cambridgeshire
TEL: 01223 893 218

CROSSING HOUSE GARDEN *51-22*
78 Meldreth Road, Royston, Cambridgeshire
TEL: 01763 261 071

TYLERS GARDEN CENTRE *51-23*
Inglewood, Royston, Cambridgeshire
TEL: 01763 260 412

PHILLIMORE GARDEN CENTRE *51-24*
Cambridge Road, Royston, Cambridgeshire
TEL: 01763 260 537

ICKLETON GARDEN CENTRE & AQUATICS *51-25*
Frogge Street, Saffron Walden, Essex
TEL: 01799 530 911

GROWING CARPETS *51-26*
Christmas Tree House, Royston, Hertfordshire
TEL: 01763 852 705

MARDEN COTTAGE NURSERY *51-27*
1 Marden Cottage, Royston, Cambridgeshire
TEL: 01763 244 457

BEECHES NURSERY *51-28*
Village Centre, Saffron Walden, Essex
TEL: 01799 584 362

SPRINGWELL NURSERIES *51-29*
Walden Road, Saffron Walden, Essex
TEL: 01799 530 959

AUDLEY END HOUSE, ENGLISH HERITAGE *51-30*
Audley End, Saffron Walden, Essex
TEL: 01799 522 399

AUDLEY END ORGANIC KITCHEN GARDEN *51-31*
Audley End House, Saffron Walden, Essex, B11 4JF
TEL: 01799 522 842
EMAIL: enquiry@hdra.org.uk
WEB: www.hdra.org.uk
A beautiful restoration walled garden with extensive rows of herbaceous perennials plus fruit trees and vegetables. Superb glasshouses with ancient vines. A unique collaboration between HDRA and English Heritage.
OPEN: 1 Apr-28 Oct, Wed-Sun & Bank hols 11-6.
ENTRY COSTS (GARDEN ONLY): Adult £4, Children £2, Concessions £2, HDRA/Eng. Heritage. Free.
SPECIALITIES: Organic garden.

GARDEN CENTRE AT SAFFRON WALDEN *51-32*
Thaxted Road, Saffron Walden, Essex
TEL: 01799 527 536

MANOR NURSERIES *51-33*
Thaxted Road, Saffron Walden, Essex
TEL: 01799 513 481

BICKERDIKES GARDEN CENTRE *51-34*
Norton Road, Letchworth, Hertfordshire
TEL: 01462 673 333

R. & R. SAGGERS *51-35*
Waterloo House, Saffron Walden, Essex
TEL: 01799 540 858

TAPP'S GARDEN CENTRE *51-36*
Wallington Road, Baldock, Hertfordshire
TEL: 01462 896 302

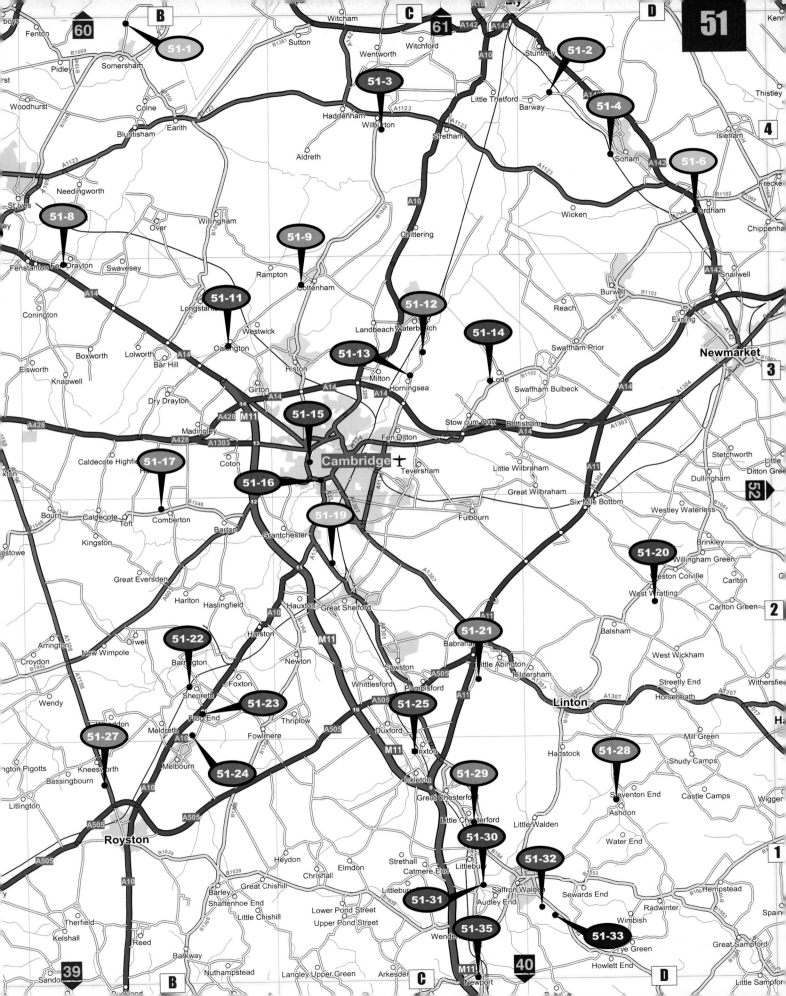

WAVENEY WATER GARDENS
Park Road, Diss, Norfolk
TEL: 01379 642 697

WOODHALLS NURSERY
Pearl Sulman, Bury St Edmunds, Suffolk
TEL: 01638 712 297

HILLCREST NURSERIES
Barnigham Road, Bury St Edmunds, Suffolk
TEL: 01359 250 327

FULLERS HOME & GARDEN CENTRE
Bell Lane, Bury St Edmunds, Suffolk
TEL: 01638 712 150

WYKEN HALL
Stanton, Bury St Edmunds, Suffolk
TEL: 01359 250 287

GARDINER'S HALL PLANTS
Braiseworth, Eye, Suffolk
TEL: 01379 678 285

RISBY GARDEN CENTRE
Antique Barns, Bury St Edmunds, Suffolk
TEL: 01284 811 055

POTASH NURSERY
Cow Green, Stowmarket, Suffolk
TEL: 01449 781 671

MARLOWS DIY & GARDEN CENTRE
Hollow Road, Bury St Edmunds, Suffolk
TEL: 01284 763 155

MILLS' FARM PLANTS & GARDENS
Norwich Road, Stowmarket, Suffolk
TEL: 01449 766 425

ABBEY GARDENS
Angel Hill, Bury St Edmunds, Suffolk
TEL: 01284 757 090

ANGLIA BONSAI
1 Raedwald Drive, Bury St Edmunds, Suffolk
TEL: 01284 750 710

ROUGHAM HALL NURSERIES
Ipswich Road, Bury St Edmunds, Suffolk
TEL: 01359 270 577

WYEVALE GARDEN CENTRE
Rougham Road, Bury St Edmunds, Suffolk
TEL: 01284 755 818

BEYTON NURSERIES
Tostock Road, Bury St Edmunds, Suffolk
TEL: 01359 270 800

PRESTIGE PLANTS
Calumbine Hall Nursery, Stowmarket, Suffolk
TEL: 01449 615 919

WOOLPIT NURSERIES
Woolpit, Bury St Edmunds, Suffolk
TEL: 01359 240 370

ICKWORTH PARK & GARDEN, NATIONAL TRUST
Ickworth, Bury St Edmunds, Suffolk
TEL: 01284 735 270

HARVEYS GARDEN PLANTS
Bradfield St George, Bury St Edmunds, Suffolk
TEL: 01284 386 777

MARTIN NURSERIES
Smallwood Green, Bury St Edmunds, Suffolk
TEL: 01449 737 698

LAVENHAM GUILDHALL OF CORPUS CHRISTI, NATIONAL TRUST
Market Place, Sudbury, Suffolk
TEL: 01787 247 646

PRIORY PLANTS
1 Covey Cottage, Ipswich, Suffolk
TEL: 01473 652 656

WYEVALE GARDEN CENTRE
Newton Road, Sudbury, Suffolk
TEL: 01787 373 628

ESSEX & SUFFOLK KOI
Bolton Garden Centre, Halstead, Essex
TEL: 01440 788 007

T. E. C. NURSERY
The Nursery, Sudbury, Suffolk
TEL: 01787 210 501

FRANCES MOUNT PERENNIAL PLANTS
1 Steps Farm, Colchester, Essex
TEL: 01206 262 811

PARADISE CENTRE
Twinstead Road, Bures, Essex
TEL: 01787 269 449

THE PLACE FOR PLANTS
East Bergholt Place, East Bergholt, Suffolk
TEL: 01206 299 224

SPAINS HALL FOREST NURSERY
Spains Hall Farmhouse, Braintree, Essex
TEL: 01371 810 156

Lotus

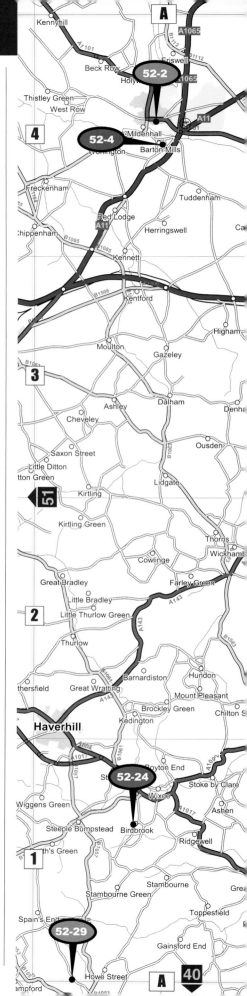

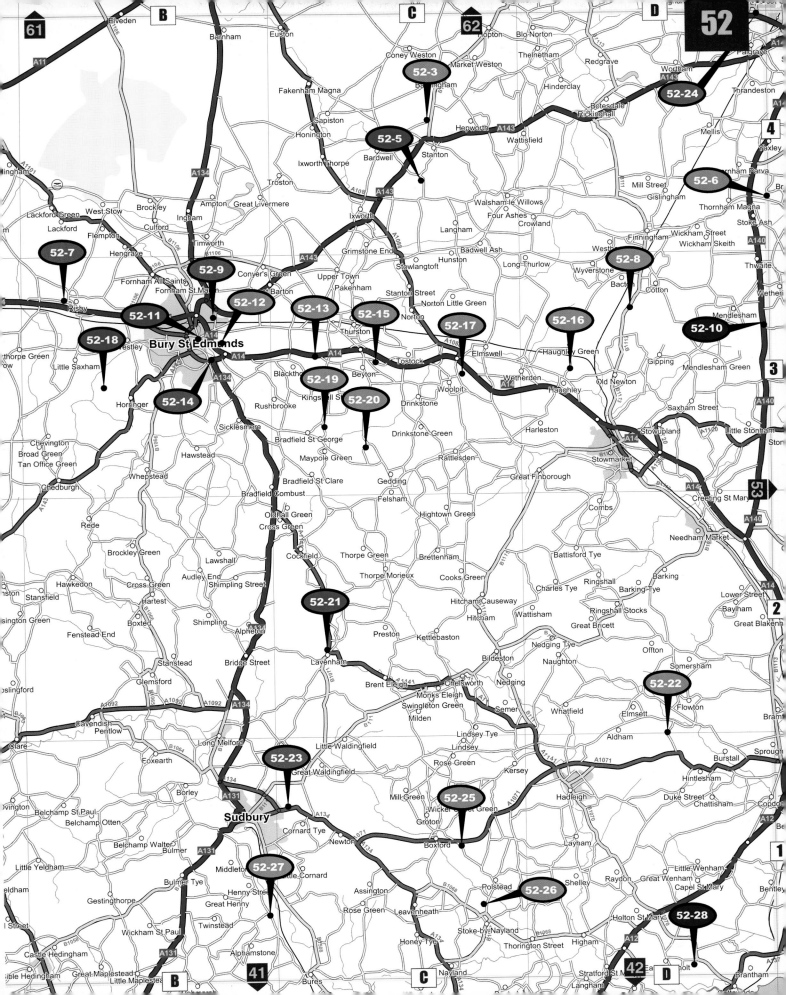

DISS GARDEN CENTRE `53-1`
Victoria Road, Diss, Norfolk
TEL: 01379 642 873

HOLTON ROAD GARDEN CENTRE `53-2`
36 Holton Road, Halesworth, Suffolk
TEL: 01986 872 761

GOLDBROOK PLANTS `53-3`
Hoxne, Eye, Suffolk
TEL: 01379 668 770

WOOTTENS PLANTS `53-4`
Blackheath, Halesworth, Suffolk
TEL: 01502 478 258

ETHERIDGE NURSERY `53-5`
Stradbroke, Eye, Suffolk
TEL: 01379 384 204

ASKERS HILL GARDEN CENTRE `53-6`
Little Street, Saxmundham, Suffolk
TEL: 01728 668 237

J. W. RICKEARD `53-7`
The Gables, Saxmundham, Suffolk
TEL: 01728 668 451

WHITE HALL PLANTS `53-8`
Southolt Road, Worlingworth, Suffolk
TEL: 01728 628 490

LAUREL FARM HERBS `53-9`
Main Road, Saxmundham, Suffolk
TEL: 01728 668 223

PARK GREEN NURSERIES `53-10`
Wetheringsett, Stowmarket, Suffolk
TEL: 01728 860 139

DEBEN VALLEY NURSERIES `53-11`
Thorpe Lane, Ashfield, Suffolk
TEL: 01728 860 559

MICKFIELD WATERGARDEN CENTRE `53-12`
Debenham Road, Stowmarket, Suffolk
TEL: 01449 711 336

THE WALLED GARDEN `53-13`
Park Road, Saxmundham, Suffolk
TEL: 01728 602 510

STONHAM BARNS GARDEN CENTRE `53-14`
Pettaugh Road, Stowmarket, Suffolk
TEL: 01449 711 103

LADYBIRD NURSERIES `53-15`
Gromford Lane, Saxmundham, Suffolk
TEL: 01728 688 289

HELMINGHAM HALL GARDENS `53-16`
Helmingham Hall, Stowmarket, Suffolk
TEL: 01473 890 363

SISKIN PLANTS `53-17`
Davey Lane, Woodbridge, Suffolk
TEL: 01473 737 567

OTLEY HALL `53-18`
Hall Lane, Ipswich, Suffolk
TEL: 01473 890 264

TENNYSON NURSERIES `53-19`
Chantry Farm, Wickham Market, Suffolk
TEL: 01728 747 113

CROWN NURSERY `53-20`
High Street, Woodbridge, Suffolk
TEL: 01394 460 755

N. J. SCOTT FARM SHOP AND NURSERY `53-21`
Glencoe, Ipswich, Suffolk
TEL: 01473 830 331

L. SWANN NURSERY `53-22`
Eyke Road, Woodbridge, Suffolk
TEL: 01394 382 698

WYEVALE GARDEN CENTRE `53-23`
Grundisburgh, Woodbridge, Suffolk
TEL: 01394 380 022

NOTCUTTS NURSERIES `53-24`
Ipswich Road, Woodbridge, Suffolk
TEL: 01394 445 400

REEDINGS NURSERY `53-25`
Main Road, Ipswich, Suffolk
TEL: 01473 251 066

LAUREL FARM GARDEN CENTRE `53-26`
Laurel Farm, Ipswich, Suffolk
TEL: 01473 215 984

HOME MEADOWS NURSERY `53-27`
Top Street, Woodbridge, Suffolk
TEL: 01394 382 419

VICTORIA NURSERIES `53-28`
Westerfield Road, Ipswich, Suffolk
TEL: 01473 253 980

CHRIS LING GARDEN SCENE `53-29`
9 Beardmoor Park, Ipswich, Suffolk
TEL: 01473 610 926

CHRIS LING GARDEN SCENE `53-30`
34-38 Tacket Street, Ipswich, Suffolk
TEL: 01473 250804

PALM VIEW PLANTS `53-31`
10 Milden Road, Ipswich, Suffolk
TEL: 01473 402 747

BOURNE GARDEN CENTRE `53-32`
Wherstead Road, Ipswich, Suffolk
TEL: 01473 691 567

STATION NURSERIES `53-33`
2 Cordys Lane, Felixstowe, Suffolk
TEL: 01394 283 518

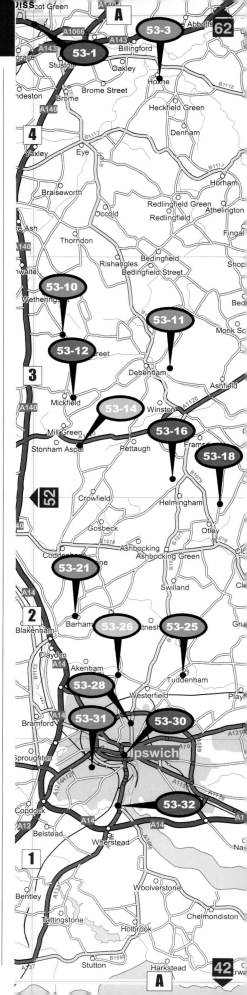

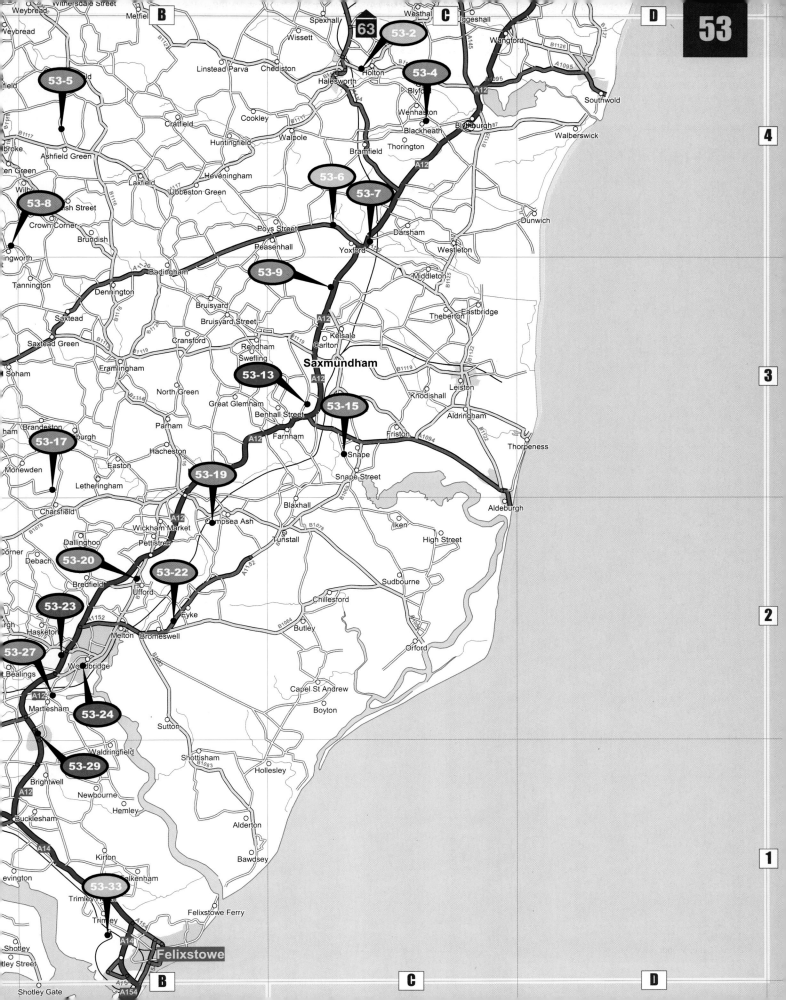

POWYS

Bugleweed

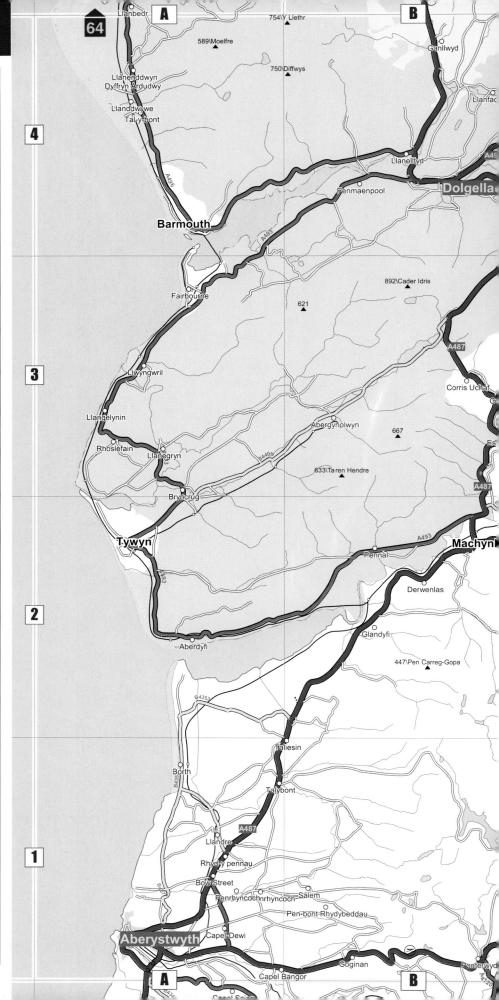

P. F. STUBBS
The Nursery, Shrewsbury, Shropshire
TEL: 01939 260 307

SHAWBURY GARDEN CENTRE & FRUIT FARM
Edgebolton, Shrewsbury, Shropshire
TEL: 01939 251 173

COUNTRY GARDEN PLANT CENTRE
Black Birches, Shrewsbury, Shropshire
TEL: 01939 210 380

HALL FARM NURSERY
Vicarage Lane, Oswestry, Shropshire
TEL: 01691 682 135

MERTON NURSERIES
Merton, Shrewsbury, Shropshire
TEL: 01743 850 773

OAK COTTAGE WALLED HERB GARDEN
Pimhill Organic Farm Shop, Harmer Hill, Shropshire
TEL: 01939 210 219

PERCY THROWER'S GARDENING CENTRE
Oteley Road, Shrewsbury, Shropshire
TEL: 01743 352 311

SUTTON GRANGE NURSERY
Oteley Road, Shrewsbury, Shropshire
TEL: 01743 355 201

EMSTREY GARDEN CENTRE
Shrewsbury, Shropshire
TEL: 01743 356 012

DOBBIES GARDEN WORLD
Shrewsbury, Shropshire
TEL: 01743 874 261

DINGLE NURSERIES & GARDEN
Frocas, Welshpool, Powys
TEL: 01938 555 145

SEVERNDALE NURSERIES
Wroxeter Lane, Shrewsbury, Shropshire
TEL: 01743 761 212

POWIS CASTLE GARDENS, NATIONAL TRUST
Welshpool, Powys
TEL: 01938 554 338

LOWER SPRING NURSERY
Kenley, Shrewsbury, Shropshire
TEL: 01952 510 589

GLANSEVERN HALL GARDENS
Glansevern, Welshpool, Powys
TEL: 01686 640 200

ABERMULE NURSERY GARDENS
Kerry Road, Montgomery, Powys
TEL: 01686 630 203

Bougainvillea

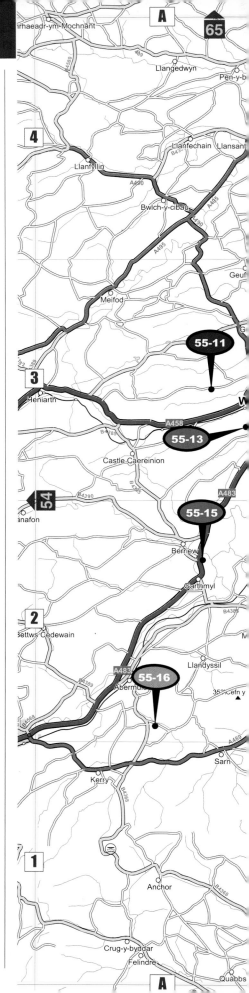

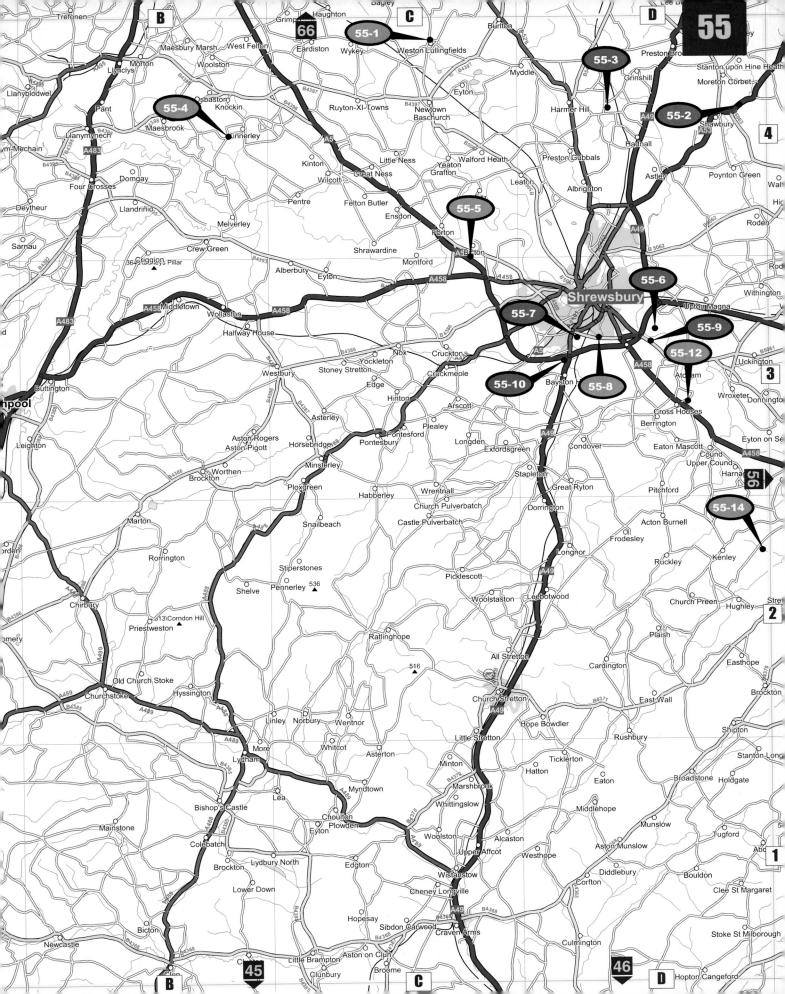

SHROPS • STAFFS • W.MIDS • WORCS

GARDEN CENTRE
NURSERY
GARDEN

NURSERY & GARDEN CENTRE
GARDEN & NURSERY
WATER GARDEN SPECIALIST

PRIORY GARDEN CENTRE
18-22 Corporation Street, Stafford, Staffordshire
TEL: 01785 246 363

BARLOW NURSERIES
Aylesland House, Newport, Shropshire
TEL: 01952 550 933

HERBERT ROAD NURSERIES
Herbert Road, Stafford, Staffordshire
TEL: 01785 257 268

SANDSTONES COTTAGE GARDEN PLANTS
58 Bolas Heath, Great Bolas, Shropshire
TEL: 01952 541 657

MILDENE NURSERY
Tibberton Road, Telford, Shropshire
TEL: 01952 541 314

PLOUGH FARM NURSERIES
Plough Farm, Newport, Shropshire
TEL: 01952 810 915

MILLINGTONS GARDEN CENTRE
101 High Street, Newport, Shropshire
TEL: 01952 811 190

FOSTER GARDEN CENTRE
Oak Lane, Stafford, Staffordshire
TEL: 01785 780 208

WYEVALE GARDEN CENTRE
Station Road, Telford, Shropshire
TEL: 01952 677 733

BLOOMSBURY NURSERY
Bloomsbury, Shifnal, Shropshire
TEL: 01952 691 203

STANELLI GARDEN CENTRE
Bungham Lane, Stafford, Staffordshire
TEL: 01785 712 387

WATKINS NURSERIES & GARDEN CENTRE
Apley Castle Gardens, Telford, Shropshire
TEL: 01952 242 393

WREKIN FARM & GARDEN CENTRE
Bridge Road, Telford, Shropshire
TEL: 01952 641 342

COTTAGE GARDEN ROSES
Woodlands House, Stafford, Staffordshire
TEL: 01785 840 217

TAFS (SALOP)
St Georges, Telford, Shropshire
TEL: 01952 620 184

DOBBIES GARDEN WORLD
Saxon Cross, Gailey, Staffordshire
TEL: 01902 791 555

BOSCOBEL HOUSE, ENGLISH HERITAGE
Boscobel Lane, Stafford, Shropshire
TEL: 01902 850 244

GRANGE FARM GARDEN CENTRE
Grange Farm, Telford, Shropshire
TEL: 01952 594 346

DAVID AUSTIN ROSES
Bowling Green Lane, Wolverhampton, Staffordshire
TEL: 01902 376 300

CLAIRE AUSTIN HARDY PLANTS
Bowling Green Lane, Wolverhampton, Staffordshire
TEL: 01902 376 333

WYEVALE GARDEN CENTRE
Newport Road, Wolverhampton, Staffordshire
TEL: 01902 374 200

R. P. P. ALPINES
6 Bentley Road, Wolverhampton, Staffordshire
TEL: 01902 784 508

OAKEN NURSERIES
Shop Lane, Wolverhampton, Staffordshire
TEL: 01902 842 200

BISHTONS NURSERY
Posenhall, Broseley, Shropshire
TEL: 01952 883 766

HARLEY NURSERY
Harley, Shropshire
TEL: 01952 510 241

WENLOCK PRIORY, ENGLLISH HERITAGE
6 The Bull Ring, Much Wenlock, Shropshire
TEL: 01952 727 466

RUDGE HEATH NURSERIES
Rudge Heath, Wolverhampton, Staffordshire
TEL: 01746 710 462

LEALAND NURSERIES & GARDEN CENTRE
Bridgnorth Road, Wolverhampton, Staffordshire
TEL: 01902 700 209

PAVILION GARDEN CENTRE
Garden Village Centre, Wolverhampton, Staffordshire
TEL: 01902 701 001

HILLVIEW HARDY PLANTS 56-30
Worfield, Bridgenorth, Shropshire
TEL: 01746 716 454

BEECHCROFT NURSERIES & GARDEN CENTRE 56-3
Orton Lane, Wolverhampton, Staffordshire
TEL: 01902 895 055

DIMMINGSDALE GARDEN CENTRE 56-3
Ebstree Road, Wolverhampton, Staffordshire
TEL: 01902 765 040

BEACON NURSERY & GARDEN CENTRE 56-3
Rowan Road, Dudley, Staffordshire
TEL: 01902 882 933

SANDIACRE FARM SHOP & NURSERIES 56-34
Himley Lane, Dudley, Staffordshire
TEL: 01902 893 542

ASHWOOD NURSERIES 56-3
Ashwood Lower Lane, Kingswinford, West Midlands
TEL: 01384 401 996

BEECHWOOD BONSAI NURSERY 56-3
Wolverhampton Road, Stourbridge, West Midlands
TEL: 01384 877 847

HANBURY NURSERIES 56-3
43 Worcester Street, Stourbridge, West Midlands
TEL: 01384 395 179

GOBBETT NURSERY 56-3
Farlow, Kidderminster, Worcestershire
TEL: 01746 718 276

Gerber Daisy

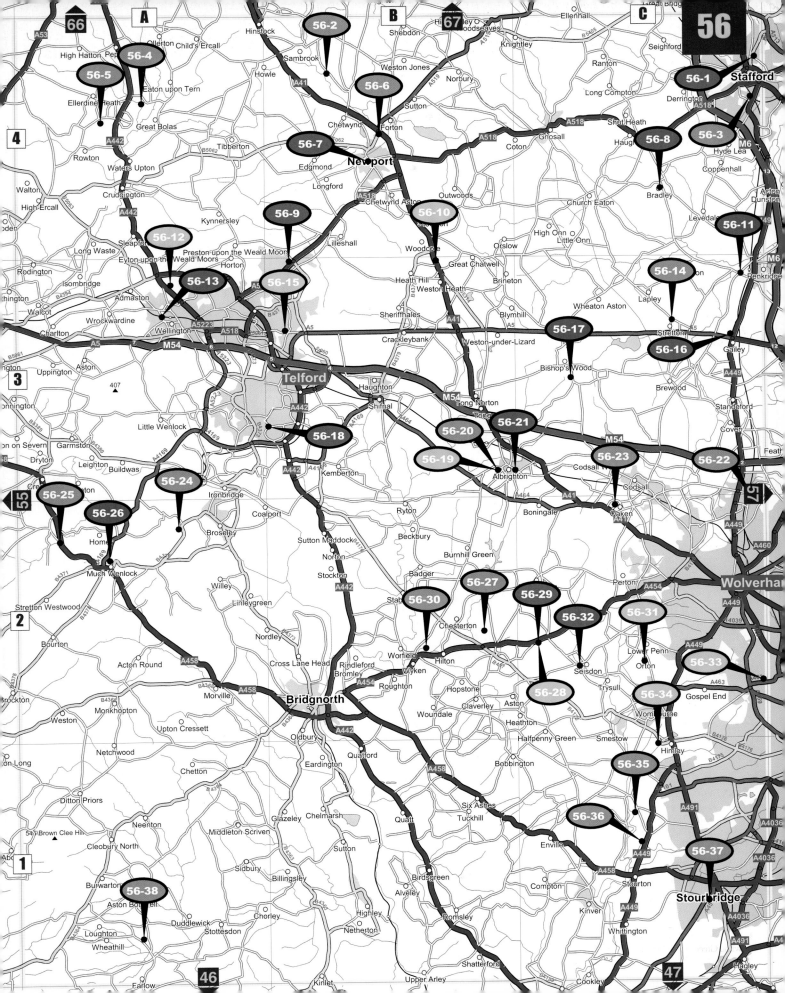

ROSEACRE NURSERY AND GARDEN CENTRE
Main Road, Stafford, Staffordshire
TEL: 01889 882 288

SHUGBOROUGH ESTATE, NT
Milford, Stafford, Staffordshire
TEL: 01889 881 388

BROMLEY HAYES GARDEN CENTRE
Shaw Lane, Lichfield, Staffordshire
TEL: 01543 472 230

COUNTRY LADY NURSERY
Lilac Cottage, Rugeley, Staffordshire
TEL: 01543 675 520

THE ORANGE TREE
Wheel Lane, Lichfield, Staffordshire
TEL: 01543 258 518

HATHERTON NURSERIES
Watling Street, Cannock, Staffordshire
TEL: 01543 503 627

WILLOW VALE GARDEN CENTRE
185 Hednesford Road, Walsall, West Midlands
TEL: 01543 275 082

NORTON LANE NURSERIES
105 Norton Lane, Walsall, West Midlands
TEL: 01922 418 291

FISHERS FARM GARDEN CENTRE
Upper Landywood Lane, Walsall, West Midlands
TEL: 01922 413 681

WESTWOOD NURSERIES
Muckley Corner, Lichfield, Staffordshire
TEL: 01543 373347

GRASMERE GARDEN CENTRE
Lichfield Road, Walsall, West Midlands
TEL: 01543 372 927

HOLLYBUSH GARDEN CENTRE & AQUARIA 57-12
Warstone Road, Wolverhampton, Staffordshire
TEL: 01922 418 050

FOSTER GARDEN CENTRE 57-13
Birmingham Road, Lichfield, Staffordshire
TEL: 01543 480 095

MOSELEY OLD HALL, NT 57-14
Moseley Old Hall Lane, Wolverhampton, Staffs.
TEL: 01902 782 808

RAILSWOOD NURSERIES 57-15
Railswood Drive, Walsall, West Midlands
TEL: 01922 691 563

WYEVALE GARDEN CENTRE 57-16
Chester Road, Walsall, West Midlands
TEL: 01922 451 401

WYNDLEY GARDEN CENTRE 57-17
Lichfield Road, Sutton Coldfield, West Midlands
TEL: 01213 084 646

THREE CROWNS GARDEN CENTRE 57-18
Sutton Road, Walsall, West Midlands
TEL: 01922 454 557

PACIFIC NURSERIES 57-19
Chester Road, Walsall, West Midlands
TEL: 0121 353 4017

VALLEY NURSERIES 57-20
297 Eedington Road, Walsall, West Midlands
TEL: 01922 456 060

ASHFURLONG NURSERIES 57-21
Tamworth Road, Sutton Coldfield, West Midlands
TEL: 0121 308 0530

SUTTON PARK 57-22
Blackroot Hill, Sutton Coldfield, West Midlands
TEL: 0121 354 1916

PETS & GARDENS 57-23
372-376 Birmingham Road, Sutton Coldfield, West Midlands
TEL: 0121 373 1491

SEDGLEY ROAD AQUARIUM 57-24
72-74 Sedgley Road, Dudley, West Midlands
TEL: 01902 670 098

GRAVELLY LANE GARDEN CENTRE 57-25
1-5 Gravelly Lane, Birmingham, West Midlands
TEL: 0121 384 2847

HIRONS GARDEN CENTRE 57-26
212 Wellington Road, Birmingham, West Midlands
TEL: 01213 565 185

THE LITTLE GARDEN CENTRE 57-27
97-101 Bromford Lane, West Bromwich, West Midlands
TEL: 0121 553 4048

 BIRMINGHAM BOTANICAL GARDENS & GLASSHOUSES 57-33
Westbourne Road, Edgbaston, Birmingham, West Midlands, B15 3TR
TEL: 0121 454 1860
EMAIL: admin@bham-bot-gdns.demon.co.uk
WEB: www.bham-bot-gdns.demon.co.uk

Only two miles from the city centre. Superb Tropical, Mediterranean and desert glasshouses. Fifteen acres of beautiful landscaped gardens with historic, rose, alpine, rock, rhododendron and theme gardens. National Bonsai Collection. Frequent specialist plant shows.
OPEN: Daily 9-dusk, Sun 10-dusk, closed Christmas day.
ENTRY COSTS: Adult £4.80, Children £2.60, Family £12.50, OAPs £2.60, Groups of 10 or more £2.30.
SPECIALITIES: Alpines, Bonsai, Exotic plants, Orangery, Scented garden for blind.

D. R. HARVEY & CO 57-2
7 North Street, Dudley, West Midlands
TEL: 01384 253 200

CASTLE BROMWICH HALL GARDENS 57-2
Chester Road, Birmingham, West Midlands
TEL: 0121 749 4100

HALL'S GARDEN SUPPLIES `57-30`
207-209 Chester Road, Birmingham, West Midlands
Tel: 01217 473 046

G-MART `57-31`
9 Newtown Lane, Cradley Heath, West Midlands
Tel: 01384 633 200

CYPRESS NURSERY `57-32`
28 Powke Lane, Rowley Regis, West Midlands
Tel: 0121 559 1495

WOODROFFE PETS & GARDENS `57-34`
26 Church Road, Birmingham, West Midlands
Tel: 0121 783 2735

HARTS GREEN NURSERY `57-35`
39 Harts Green Road, Birmingham, West Midlands
Tel: 0121 427 5200

CANNON HILL PARK `57-36`
Moseley, Birmingham, West Midlands
Tel: 0121 442 4226

SINGLETON FOR FLOWERS `57-37`
78A Harborne Lane, Birmingham, West Midlands
Tel: 0121 472 2575

WOODGATE VALLEY COUNTRY PARK `57-38`
Woodgate Visitors Centre, Birmingham, West
Midlands
Tel: 0121 421 7575

BARNES HILL NURSERIES & `57-39`
GARDEN CENTRE
Barnes Hill, Birmingham, West Midlands
Tel: 0121 427 7328

WYEVALE GARDEN CENTRE `57-40`
Maple Road, Birmingham, West Midlands
Tel: 0121 472 0303

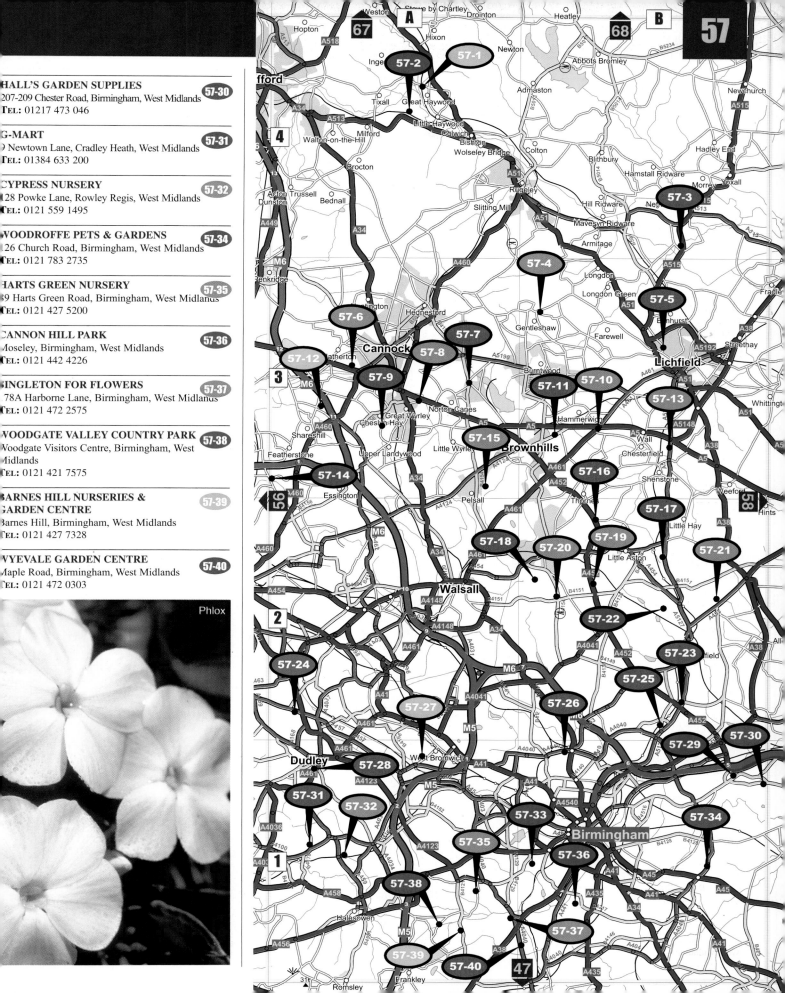

Phlox

MELBOURNE HALL GARDENS `58-1`
Melbourne, Derbyshire
TEL: 01332 862 502

F. M. HEATH & SON `58-2`
Woodhouse Farm Nurseries, Woodhouses,
Melbourne, Derbyshire, DE73 1DN
TEL: 01332 862 645
Small friendly family-run nursery. Fresh home grown vegetables. Vegetable plants, composts, bedding plants, hanging baskets, alpines, shrubs, stoneware.
OPEN: Open daily 9-5, closed from Christmas Day until Jan 2.
SPECIALITIES: Alpines, Bedding plants, Hardy plants, Seeds, Bulbs.

BRETBY NURSERIES AND NETLEY RIVERSIDE AQUATICS `58-3`
Bretby Lane, Burton upon Trent, Staffordshire
TEL: 01283 703 355

MARSHMENTS GARDEN CENTRE `58-4`
Forest Road, Burton upon Trent, Staffordshire
TEL: 01283 562 499

BYRKLEY PARK CENTRE `58-5`
Rangemoor, Burton upon Trent, Staffordshire
TEL: 01283 716 467

PRIORY NURSERIES `58-6`
Hall Farm, Derby, Derbyshire
TEL: 01332 862 406

WALLED GARDEN NURSERY `58-7`
The Sett, Burton upon Trent, Staffordshire
TEL: 01283 211 531

CALKE ABBEY, NATIONAL TRUST `58-8`
Ticknall, Derbyshire
TEL: 01332 863 822

STAUNTON HAROLD NURSERIES `58-9`
Ashby, Leicestershire
TEL: 01332 862 769

GARDEN KING GARDEN CENTRE `58-10`
Park Road, Swadlincote, Derbyshire
TEL: 01283 550 516

SAGE GARDEN PRODUCTS AND NURSERY `58-11`
41 Sandcliffe Road, Swadlincote, Derbyshire
TEL: 01283 217 377

STANTON NURSERIES `58-12`
44 Woodland Road, Burton upon Trent, Staffordshire
TEL: 01283 214 144

STANTON DALE NURSERIES `58-13`
Dale Cottage Farm, Ashbourne, Derbyshire
TEL: 01538 308 384

BLUEBELL ARBORETUM & NURSERY `58-14`
Annwell Lane, Ashby de la Zouch, Derbyshire
TEL: 01530 413 700

CHAPMAN'S NURSERIES `58-15`
Burton Road, Swadlincote, Derbyshire
TEL: 01283 564 353

NATIONAL FOREST PLANT CENTRE `58-16`
Bath Yard, Swadlincote, Derbyshire
TEL: 01283 558 140

GROTTO FARM NURSERY `58-17`
Main Street, Swadlincote, Derbyshire
TEL: 01283 760 277

GRANGEWOOD GARDEN CENTRE `58-18`
Lullington Road, Swadlincote, Derbyshire
TEL: 01283 762 026

HEATHER LANE NURSERIES `58-19`
Heather Lane, Coalville, Leicestershire
TEL: 01530 832 101

S. & S. PERENNIALS `58-20`
24 Main Street, Normanton le Heath, Leicestershire
TEL: 01530 262 250

ULVERSCROFT GRANGE NURSERY `58-21`
Priory Lane, Markfield, Leicestershire
TEL: 01530 243 635

T. PICKERING & SONS `58-22`
89 Bosworth Road, Swadlincote, Derbyshire
TEL: 01530 270 377

M. B. R. GREEN `58-23`
174 Leicester Road, Ibstock, Leicestershire
TEL: 01530 260 061

SUNNYSIDE GARDEN CENTRE HOUSE `58-24`
Sunnyside, Ibstock, Leicestershire
TEL: 01530 263 418

JACKSON'S NURSERIES `58-25`
Hillcrest, Tamworth, Staffordshire
TEL: 01827 373 307

TED BROWN UNUSUAL PLANTS `58-26`
1 Croftway, Leicester, Leicestershire
TEL: 01530 244 517

JOHN SMITH & SON `58-27`
Thornton Nurseries, Coalville, Leicestershire
TEL: 01530 230 331

WILLOW BROOK NURSERIES `58-28`
Shadows Lane, Nuneaton, Warwickshire
TEL: 01827 880 305

GARDENERS WORLD `58-29`
Plantation Lane, Tamworth, Staffordshire
TEL: 01827 506 61

BELGRAVE NURSERIES & FLOWERS `58-30`
Greta Nova, Tamworth, Staffordshire
TEL: 01827 289 516

PLANTERS KENTON ROAD `58-31`
Woodlands Farm, Tamworth, Staffordshire
TEL: 01827 251 511

DURNO'S NURSERY `58-32`
Old Holy Lane, Atherstone, Warwickshire
TEL: 01827 713 233

GREENACRES NURSERY `58-33`
Ashby Road, Leicester, Leicestershire
TEL: 01455 290 878

WOODLANDS NURSERIES `58-34`
Ashby Road, Leicester, Leicestershire
TEL: 01455 291 494

HILLVIEW NURSERY `58-35`
Croft Lane, Leicester, Leicestershire
TEL: 01455 888 393

CROSS LANES FARM GARDEN CENTRE `58-36`
Nuneaton Road, Atherstone, Warwickshire
TEL: 01827 715 511

NEWLAND NURSERIES `58-37`
Coppice Lane, Tamworth, Staffordshire
TEL: 0121 308 7197

OAKS NURSERIES `58-38`
326 Weddington Road, Nuneaton, Warwickshire
TEL: 024 7638 4550

PETER PLANTS `58-39`
Hinckley Road, Leicester, Leicestershire
TEL: 01455 274 049

WHITACRE GARDEN CENTRE `58-40`
Tamworth Road, Birmingham, West Midlands
TEL: 01675 481 306

WORLD OF WATER `58-41`
Whitacre Garden Centre, Tamworth Road,
Nether Whitacre, Coleshill, Warwickshire, B46 2DN
TEL: 01675 481 144
EMAIL: worldofwater@birmingham93.junglelink.co.uk
WEB: www.worldofwater.com
Everything for the pond and tropical fish enthusiast. Extensive showgardens. Expert advice.
OPEN: 9-5.30 Mon-Sat, Sun 10.30-4.30. Closed Easter Sun.
SPECIALITIES: Aquatic plants, Water features, Waterfalls.

ALPINE LANDSCAPES `58-42`
Garden Centre, Nuneaton, Warwickshire
TEL: 024 7635 0052

3 POTS NURSERY `58-43`
51 Newstead Avenue, Hinckley, Leicestershire
TEL: 01455 632 716

CORLEY NURSERY & CORLEY KOI AQUATICS `58-44`
Church Lane, Coventry, West Midlands
TEL: 01676 540 101

WITHYBROOK NURSERIES `58-45`
Overstone Road, Coventry, West Midlands
TEL: 01455 220 297

HILLTOP GARDEN CENTRE `58-46`
Shilton Lane, Coventry, West Midlands
TEL: 024 7661 4752

DALE'S `58-47`
315 Holbrook Lane, Coventry, West Midlands
TEL: 024 7666 5050

HYDROPONICS CENTRE `58-48`
994 Foleshill Road, Coventry, West Midlands
TEL: 024 7668 8586

WYEVALE GARDEN CENTRE `58-49`
Brownshill Green Road, Coventry, West Midlands
TEL: 024 7633 3998

TRIDENT WATER GARDEN PRODUCTS `58-50`
Carlton Road, Coventry, West Midlands
TEL: 024 7663 8802

BRACEYS NURSERIES `58-51`
Catherine de Barnes Lane, Solihull, West Midlands
TEL: 01675 442 587

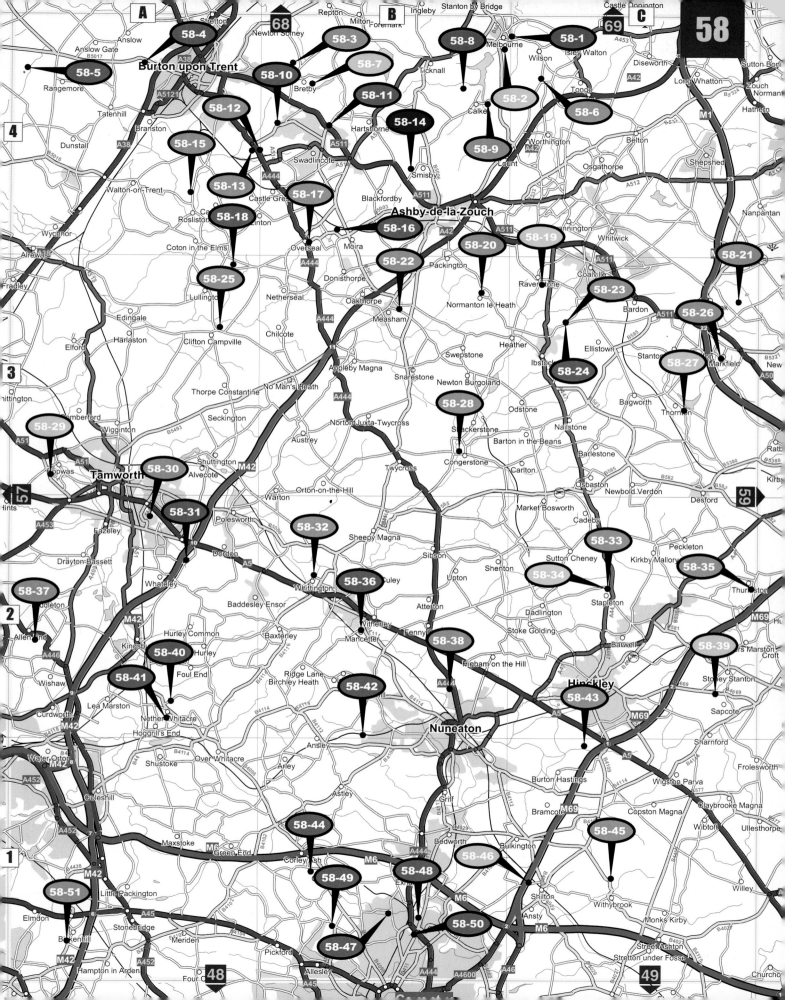

SIX ACRE NURSERIES `59-1`
Loughborough Road, Loughborough, Leicestershire
TEL: 01509 856 079

GRANGE GARDEN CENTRE `59-2`
Sysonby Grange House, Melton Mowbray,
Leicestershire
TEL: 01664 812 012

THE HERB NURSERY `59-3`
Thistleton, Oakham, Rutland
TEL: 01572 767 658

BEACON VIEW NURSERY `59-4`
126-128 Cotes Road, Loughborough, Leicestershire
TEL: 01509 412 787

SOAR VALLEY NURSERIES `59-5`
263 Loughbrorough Road, Loughborough,
Leicestershire
TEL: 01509 412681

GREETHAM GARDEN CENTRE `59-6`
Oakham Road, Oakham, Leicestershire
TEL: 01572 813 100

REARSBY ROSES `59-7`
Melton Road, Leicester, Leicestershire
TEL: 0116 260 1211

KAYES GARDEN NURSERY `59-8`
1700 Melton Road, Rearsby, Leicestershire
TEL: 01664 424 578

DERRY'S NURSERIES `59-9`
Main Street, Cossington, Leicestershire
TEL: 01509 812 815

ROWENA GARDEN CENTRE `59-10`
Loughborough Road, Leicester, Leicestershire
TEL: 0116 237 6500

GOSCOTE NURSERIES `59-11`
Syston Road, Cossington, Leicestershire
TEL: 01509 812 121

RECTORY FIELD NURSERY `59-12`
Wanlip, Leicester, Leicestershire
TEL: 0116 267 4613

BARSNDALE GARDENS `59-13`
Exton Avenue, Oakham, Rutland
TEL: 01572 813 200

GATES NURSERIES & GARDEN CENTRE `59-14`
Somerby Road, Oakham, Leicestershire
TEL: 01664 454 309

BARKBY VILLAGE NURSERY `59-15`
Queniborough Road, Leicester, Leicestershire
TEL: 0116 260 3600

BROOKSIDE NURSERIES `59-16`
129 Cropston Road, Leicester, Leicestershire
TEL: 0116 236 4564

BRADGATE NURSERIES `59-17`
Bradgate Garden Buildings, Leicester, Leicestershire
TEL: 01530 242 985

BIRSTALL AQUARIA & WATERGARDENS `59-18`
27 Sibson Road, Leicester, Leicestershire
TEL: 0116 267 6121

RUTLAND WATER GARDEN NURSERY `59-19`
Lyndon Road, Oakham, Leicestershire
TEL: 01572 737 711

COUNTY GARDENS `59-20`
Gorse Close, Billesdon, Leicestershire
TEL: 0116 259 6248

WINGWELL NURSERY `59-21`
Top Street, Oakham, Rutland
TEL: 01572 737 727

CRAIGHILL NURSERIES `59-22`
Craighill Road, Leicester, Leicestershire
TEL: 0116 270 7065

UNIVERSITY OF LEICESTER BOTANIC GARDEN `59-23`
Beaumont Hall, Oadby, Leicestershire
TEL: 0116 271 7725

HAWGRIP NURSERIES `59-24`
Hawgrip, Leicester, Leicestershire
TEL: 0116 284 8227

PALMERS GARDEN CENTRE `59-25`
St Johns, Leicester, Leicestershire
TEL: 01162 863 323

MOZART HOUSE NURSERY GARDEN `59-26`
84 Central Avenue, Wigston, Leicestershire
TEL: 0116 288 9548

ECOB'S GARDEN CENTRE `59-27`
Horsewell Lane, Wigston, Leicestershire
TEL: 0116 288 3627

CHAMNEY GARDEN CENTRE `59-28`
Lutterworth Road, Leicester, Leicestershire
TEL: 0116 277 7020

LYDDINGTON BEDE HOUSE `59-29`
Blue Coat Lane, Lyddington, Rutland
TEL: 01572 822 438

GLEBE GARDEN CENTRE `59-30`
Foston Road, Leicester, Leicestershire
TEL: 0116 277 1570

KIBWORTH GARDEN CENTRE `59-31`
Fleckney Road, Leicester, Leicestershire
TEL: 0116 2792754

DEENE PARK `59-32`
Deene, Corby, Northamptonshire
TEL: 01780 450 278

KIRBY HALL, ENGLISH HERITAGE `59-33`
Deene, Corby, Northamptonshire
TEL: 01536 203 230

GLEN STEWART NURSERY `59-34`
Melton Road, Market Harborough, Leicestershire
TEL: 01858 545 466

CHARLIE BROWN'S GARDEN CENTRE `59-35`
33 Dunton Road, Leicester, Leicestershire
TEL: 01455 282 310

LONGRIDGE NURSERIES `59-36`
Ashley Road, Market Harborough, Leicestershire
TEL: 01536 771 323

ASHBY PARVA NURSERIES `59-37`
Ashby Parva, Lutterworth, Leicestershire
TEL: 01455 209 225

ULLESTHORPE GARDEN & AQUATICS CENTRE `59-38`
Willowbrough House, Lutterworth, Leicestershire
TEL: 01455 202 144

TEALBY FARM NURSERY `59-39`
Mill Lane, Lutterworth, Leicestershire
TEL: 01455 558 771

GANDY'S ROSES `59-40`
North Kilworth, Lutterworth, Leicestershire
TEL: 01858 880 398

GEDDINGTON GARDENS HARDY PLANT NURSERY `59-41`
The Spinney, Geddington, Northamptonshire
TEL: 01536 461 020

CLIPSTON NURSERY `59-42`
Naseby Road, Market Harborough, Leicestershire
TEL: 01858 525 567

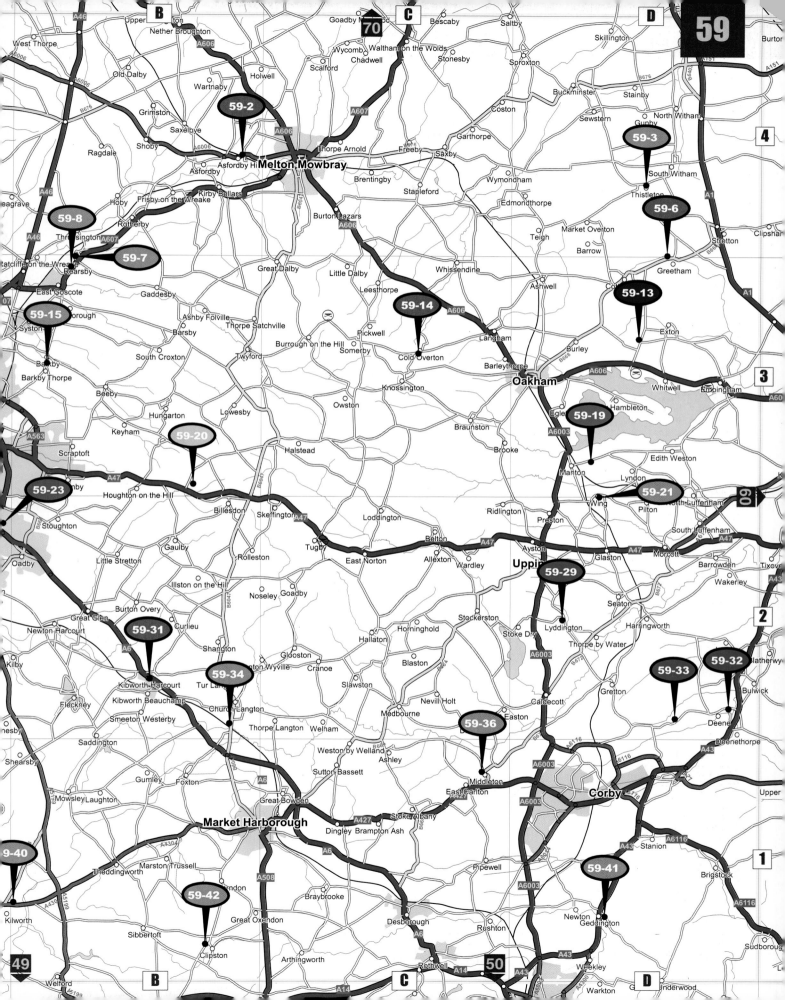

SPALDING TROPICAL FOREST `60-1`
Gleniside North, Spalding, Lincolnshire
TEL: 01775 710 882

BAYTREE NURSERIES & GARDEN CENTRE `60-2`
High Road, Spalding, Lincolnshire
TEL: 01406 370 242

SABAN GARDEN CENTRE `60-3`
Fleet Road, Spalding, Lincolnshire
TEL: 01406 422 942

TOM THUMB GARDEN CENTRE & PETSTORE `60-4`
210 Spalding Road, Spalding, Lincolnshire
TEL: 01775 722 726

SPRINGFIELDS SHOW GARDENS `60-5`
Camelgate, Spalding, Lincolnshire
TEL: 01775 724 843

SOUTHFIELD NURSERIES `60-6`
Bourne Road, Bourne, Lincolnshire
TEL: 01778 570 168

GRIMSTHORPE CASTLE PARK & GARDENS `60-7`
Grimsthorpe, Bourne, Lincolnshire
TEL: 01778 591 205

AYSCOUGHFEE HALL & GARDENS `60-8`
Churchgate, Spalding, Lincolnshire
TEL: 01775 725 468

NIMMERDOR NURSERIES `60-9`
Monks House Lane, Spalding, Lincolnshire
TEL: 01775 722 437

RASELLS NURSERIES `60-10`
Station Road, Grantham, Lincolnshire
TEL: 01780 410 345

WATERSIDE GARDEN CENTRE `60-11`
King Street, Peterborough, Cambridgeshire
TEL: 01778 560 000

KEVIN BARKER NURSERY `60-12`
153 Eastgate, Peterborough, Cambridgeshire
TEL: 01778 343 307

STAMFORD GARDEN & LEISURE CENTRE `60-13`
Casterton Hill, Stamford, Lincolnshire
TEL: 01780 765 656

BURGHLEY HOUSE `60-14`
Stamford, Lincolnshire
TEL: 01780 752 451

WOTHORPE NURSERIES `60-15`
Kettering Road, Stamford, Lincolnshire
TEL: 01780 763 268

BARN GARDEN & AQUATIC CENTRE `60-16`
Gunthorpe Road, Peterborough, Cambs
TEL: 01733 320 134

W. R. HORNE `60-17`
Stonebridge Bungalow, Peterborough, Cambridgeshire
TEL: 01733 271 066

THORPE HALL `60-18`
Longthorpe, Peterborough, Cambridgeshire
TEL: 01733 330 060

THOPRE HALL PLANT CENTRE `60-19`
Thorpe Hall, Peterborough, Cambridgeshire
TEL: 01733 334 443

FLETTON GARDEN & POND CENTRE `60-20`
102 High Street, Peterborough, Cambs
TEL: 01733 703 285

NOTCUTTS GARDEN CENTRE `60-21`
Oundle Road, Peterborough, Cambridgeshire
TEL: 01733 234 600

BLOOMS OF ELTON `60-22`
Elton Hall, Peterborough, Cambridgeshire
TEL: 01832 280 058

A1 CHERRIASH GARDEN CENTRE & PET SUPPLIES `60-23`
109 North Street, Peterborough, Cambridgeshire
TEL: 01733 241 653

THE GROWING GARDEN `60-24`
Barnwell Road, Peterborough, Cambridgeshire
TEL: 01832 273 478

TANDEE NURSERY `60-25`
Barnwell Road, Peterborough, Cambs
TEL: 01832 293 755

D. J.'S THE GARDENER'S DREAM `60-26`
134 London Road, Chatteris, Cambridgeshire
TEL: 01354 693 937

Flowering Cherry

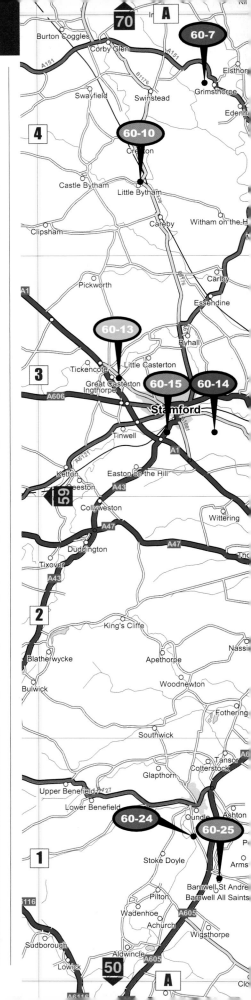

CONGHAM HALL HERB GARDEN `61-1`
Lynn Road, King's Lynn, Norfolk
TEL: 01485 600 250

ORNAMENTAL CONIFERS `61-2`
22 Chapel Road, King's Lynn, Norfolk
TEL: 01553 828 874

OAKDENE NURSERIES `61-3`
Gayton Road, King's Lynn, Norfolk
TEL: 01553 630 354

AFRICAN VIOLET CENTRE `61-4`
71 Station Road, Terrington St Clement,
Cambridgeshire
TEL: 01553 828 374

WEST ACRE GARDENS `61-5`
8 Pretoria Cottages, King's Lynn, Norfolk
TEL: 01760 755 562

LESLEY MARSHALL `61-6`
Islington Lodge Cottage, King's Lynn, Norfolk
TEL: 01553 765 103

JUNIPER NURSERIES `61-7`
Sutton Road, Wisbech, Cambridgeshire
TEL: 01945 420672

CASTLE ACRE PRIORY, ENGLISH HERITAGE `61-8`
Back Lane, King's Lynn, Norfolk
TEL: 01760 755 394

CHOICE LANDSCAPES `61-10`
Priory Farm Nursery, 101 Salts Road,
West Walton, Wisbech,
Cambridgeshire, PE14 7EF
TEL: 01945 585 051
*A small nursery with an interesting collection of
alpines, acers, pines, conifers and rhododen-
drons, azaleas, heathers and many unusual
plants.*
OPEN: 1 Mar-31 Oct, 10-5 Wed & Thurs. Other
times by appointment.
SPECIALITIES: Alpines, Bulbs, Conifers,
Japanese maples, Rhododendrons and azaleas.

GRASMERE PLANTS `61-9`
Grasmere, Wisbech, Cambridgeshire
TEL: 01945 880 514

M. A. SMITH ROSE BUDDING `61-11`
7 De Havilland Road, Wisbech, Cambridgeshire
TEL: 01945 474 413

NECTON GARDEN CENTRE `61-12`
Tuns Road, Swaffham, Norfolk
TEL: 01760 723 612

**PECKOVER HOUSE & GARDEN,
NATIONAL TRUST** `61-13`
North Brink, Wisbech, Cambridgeshire
TEL: 01945 583 463

ELGOOD'S BREWERY `61-14`
North Brink, Wisbech, Cambridgeshire
TEL: 01945 583 160

R. G. GOLDING & SON `61-15`
Hall Road, Wisbech, Cambridgeshire
TEL: 01945 772 802

WHISPERING TREES NURSERY `61-16`
West Way, King's Lynn, Norfolk
TEL: 01366 388 752

DOWNHAM GARDEN CENTRE `61-17`
14 Railway Road, Downham Market, Norfolk
TEL: 01366 382 384

**OXBURGH HALL & GARDEN,
NATIONAL TRUST** `61-18`
Oxburgh, Swaffham, Norfolk
TEL: 01366 328 258

HYTHE ALPINES `61-19`
Methwold Hythe, Thetford, Norfolk
TEL: 01366 728 543

MAGPIES `61-20`
Green Lane, Thetford, Norfolk
TEL: 01842 878 496

LYNFORD ARBORETUM `61-11`
Lynford Road, Thetford, Norfolk
TEL: 01842 810 271

Geranium

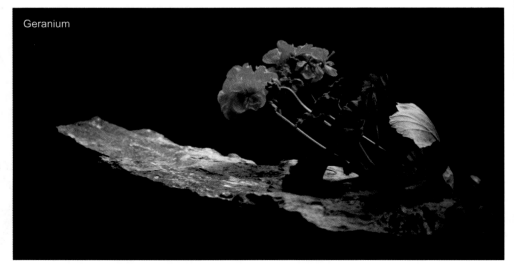

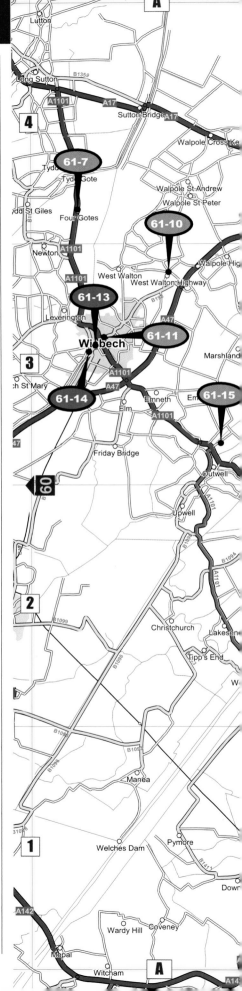

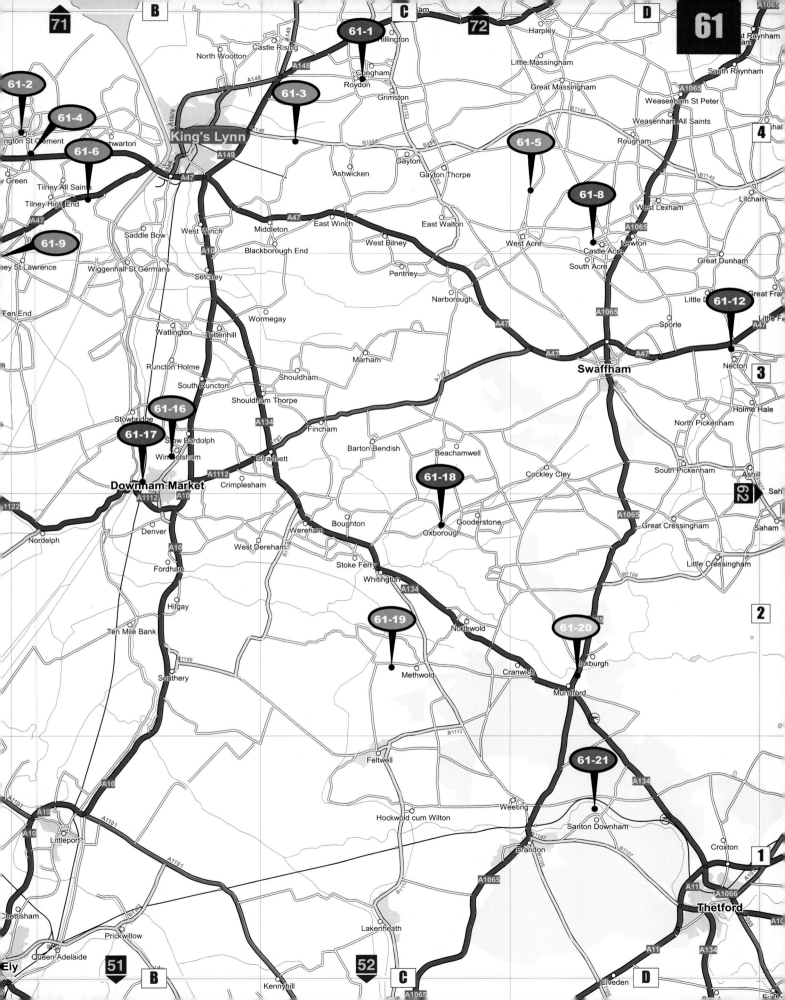

NORFOLK · SUFFOLK

- ○ GARDEN CENTRE
- ○ NURSERY
- ○ GARDEN
- ● NURSERY & GARDEN CENTRE
- ● GARDEN & NURSERY
- ● WATER GARDEN SPECIALIST

SIMPSONS NURSERY & LANDSCAPING `62-1`
62 High Street, Marsham, Norfolk
Tel: 01263 731 999

BAWDESWELL GARDEN CENTRE `62-2`
Norwich Road, East Dereham, Norfolk
Tel: 01362 688 387

THE ROMANTIC GARDEN NURSERY `62-3`
The Street, Swannington, Norfolk
Tel: 01603 261 488

BLACKROW NURSERIES `62-4`
Short Thorn Road, Norwich, Norfolk
Tel: 01603 754 878

TAVERHAM GARDEN & CRAFT CENTRE `62-5`
Fir Covert Road, Taverham, Norfolk
Tel: 01603 860 522

SWANTON ROAD NURSERIES `62-6`
Swanton Road, Dereham, Norfolk
Tel: 01362 697 156

RIVERSIDE GARDEN CENTRE `62-7`
Swaffham Road, Dereham, Norfolk
Tel: 01362 698 722

BOTANICUS `62-8`
The Nurseries, Norwich, Norfolk
Tel: 01603 742 063

OLD HALL NURSERIES `62-9`
Dumpling Green, Dereham, Norfolk
Tel: 01362 693 102

NIDUS GARDEN CENTRE `62-10`
153 Shipdham Road, Dereham, Norfolk
Tel: 01362 695 686

RIVERVIEW NURSERIES `62-11`
Longwater Lane, Norwich, Norfolk
Tel: 01603 742 772

BRECKLAND NURSERIES `62-12`
Yaxham, Dereham, Norfolk
Tel: 01362 696 750

CITY FARM STORES `62-13`
30 Magdalen Road, Norwich, Norfolk
Tel: 01603 665 982

ROYS ROSES `62-14`
Barham Broom Road, Norwich, Norfolk
Tel: 01603 880 210

SHIPDHAM GARDEN & LEISURE CENTRE `62-15`
The Old School House, Thetford, Norfolk
Tel: 01362 820 651

PARFITT NURSERIES `62-16`
Old Post Office Street, Thetford, Norfolk
Tel: 01362 820 907

NOTCUTTS GARDEN CENTRE `62-17`
Daniels Road, Norwich, Norfolk
Tel: 01603 453 155

THORNCROFT CLEMATIS NURSERY `62-18`
The Lings, Norwich, Norfolk
Tel: 01953 850 407

LODGE FARM NURSERIES `62-19`
Brick Kiln Lane, Swainsthorpe, Norfolk
Tel: 01508 471 104

WALNUT TREE GARDEN NURSERY `62-20`
Flymoor Lane, Attleborough, Norfolk
Tel: 01953 488 163

PETER BEALE'S ROSES `62-21`
London Road, Attleborough, Norfolk
Tel: 01953 454 707

TALL TREES NURSERY `62-22`
New Buckenham Road, Old Buckenham, Norfolk
Tel: 01953 860 412

SWALLOW AQUATIC `62-23`
Aqualife & Water Garden Centre, Norwich, Norfolk
Tel: 01953 718 184

PULHAM MARKET GARDEN CENTRE `62-24`
Ipswich Road, Diss, Norfolk
Tel: 01379 676 418

P. W. PLANTS `62-25`
Sunnyside, Norwich, Norfolk
Tel: 01953 888 212

BLACKSMITH'S COTTAGE NURSERY `62-26`
Langmere Green, Diss, Norfolk
Tel: 01379 740 982

THE PLANTSMAN'S PREFERENCE `62-27`
Lynwood, Diss, Norfolk
Tel: 01953 681 439

FOGGY BOTTOM `62-2`
Bressingham, Diss, Norfolk
Tel: 01379 688 402

DELL GARDEN `62-2`
Bressingham Steam Museum & Garden, Diss, Suffolk
Tel: 01379 687 386

BLOOMS OF BRESSINGHAM `62-30`
Bressingham, Diss, Norfolk, IP22 2AB
Tel: 01379 688 585
Web: www.bloomsofbressingham.co.uk

A mecca for gardeners and keen plantsmen, discover the Bressingham Steam Museum and two world famous gardens, Foggy Bottom and The Dell, all on site. A great day out.
Open: Mar-Oct, Mon-Sat 9-6. Nov-Feb, Mon-Sat 9-5. Sun 10.30-4.
Specialities: Aquatic plants, Ornamental grasses, Perennials, Shrubs, Terracotta pots.

GARBOLDISHAM GARDEN CENTRE `62-3`
Oakdene, Diss, Norfolk
Tel: 01953 681 326

Ranunculus

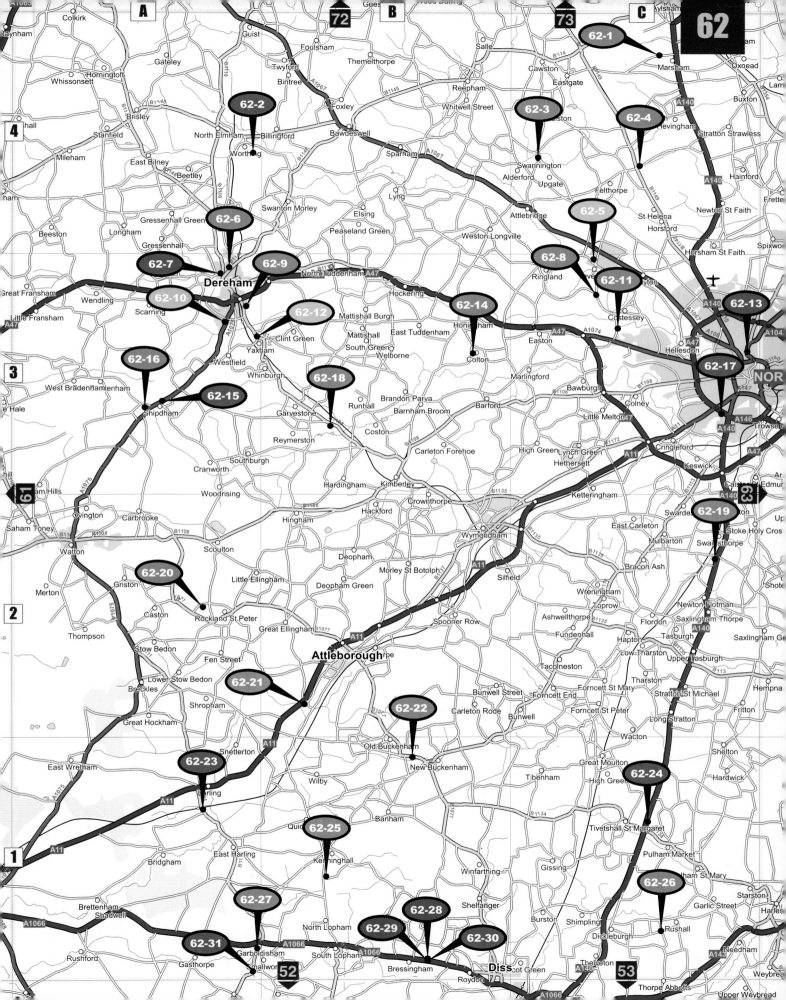

WAYFORD NURSERIES
Stalham, Norwich, Norfolk
TEL: 01692 580 226

HICKLING HEATH NURSERY
Nursery Cottage, Norwich, Norfolk
TEL: 01692 598 513

SCRATBY GARDEN CENTRE
Hall Farm, Great Yarmouth, Norfolk
TEL: 01493 730 950

FAIRHAVEN WOODLAND & WATER GARDEN
2 Wymers Lane, Norwich, Norfolk
TEL: 01603 270 449

BRIX NURSERIES
Main Road, Great Yarmouth, Norfolk
TEL: 01493 369 226

CROWFOOT NURSERIES
Hill Farm, Norwich, Norfolk
TEL: 01603 720 116

THRIGBY HALL WILDLIFE GARDENS 63-7
Filby, Great Yarmouth, Norfolk
TEL: 01493 369 477

M. GOULD 63-8
The Gardens, Norwich, Norfolk
TEL: 01493 750 549

WYEVALE GARDEN CENTRE 63-9
Blue Boar Lane, Norwich, Norfolk
TEL: 01603 412 239

MOULTON NURSERIES 63-10
Reedham Road, Norwich, Norfolk
TEL: 01493 750 458

BELTON NURSERIES 63-11
35 Station Road South, Great Yarmouth, Norfolk
TEL: 01493 780 494

POTS OF PLANTS 63-12
Alpington Hall, Norwich, Norfolk
TEL: 01508 494 480

ASHLEY NURSERIES & GARDEN CENTRE 63-13
Lowestoft Road, Great Yarmouth, Norfolk
TEL: 01502 731 327

THE WILD FLOWER CENTRE 63-14
Church Farm, Norwich, Norfolk
TEL: 01508 520 235

MIDWAY NURSERIES 63-15
Yarmouth Road, Lowestoft, Suffolk
TEL: 01502 730 419

B. BEEVOR 63-16
Hillfield, Norwich, Norfolk
TEL: 01508 548 306

HOLLY GARDENS NURSERIES 63-17
Flixton Road, Lowestoft, Suffolk
TEL: 01502 730 648

RAVENINGHAM HALL GARDENS 63-18
Norwich, Norfolk
TEL: 01508 548 222

READS NURSERY 63-19
Hales Hall, Loddon, Norfolk
TEL: 01508 548 395

HALES HALL 63-20
Loddon, Norfolk
TEL: 01508 548 395

OLD HALL PLANTS 63-21
1 The Old Hall, Beccles, Suffolk
TEL: 01502 717 475

THREE WILLOWS GARDEN CENTRE 63-22
Bardolph Road, Bungay, Suffolk
TEL: 01986 893 834

ASHLEY NURSERIES & GARDEN CENTRE 63-23
London Road, Lowestoft, Suffolk
TEL: 01502 740 264

Cassia

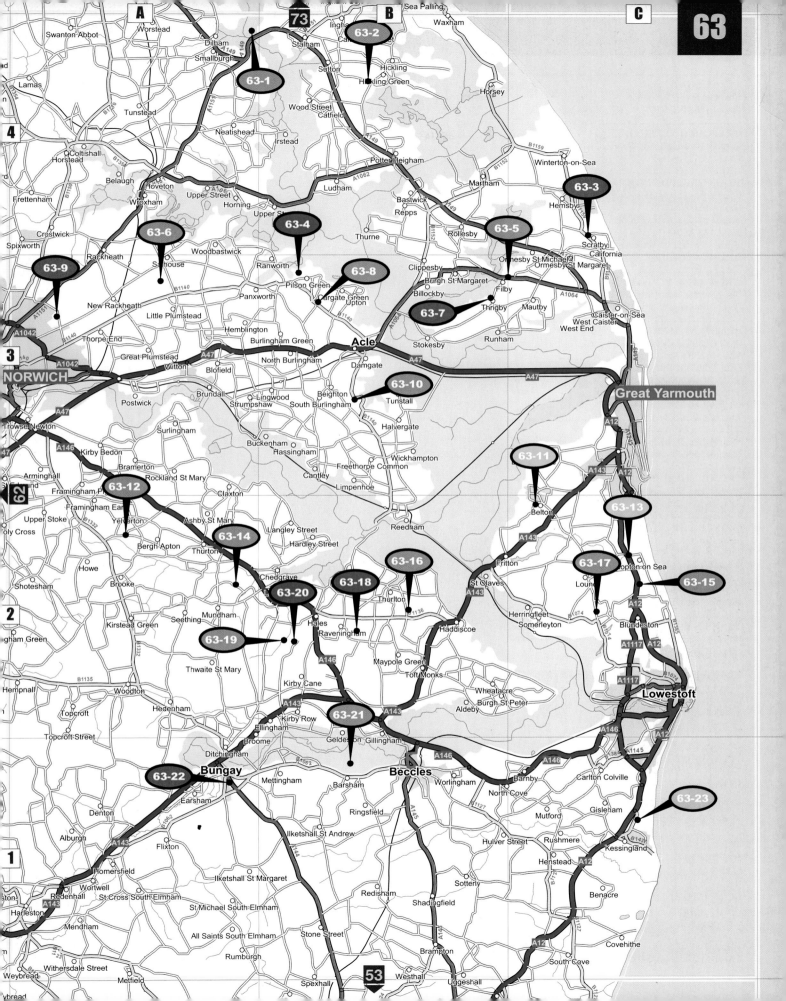

GWYNEDD

Sunflower

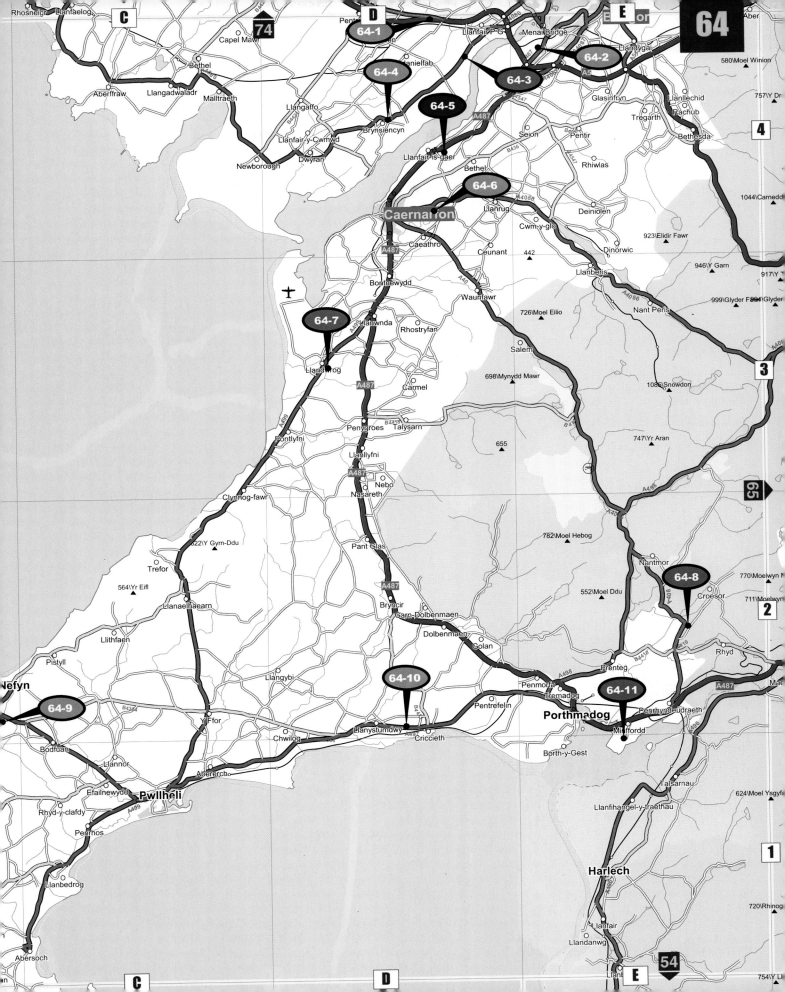

WALES

ABERWHEELER NURSERIES `65-1`
Mold Road, Denbigh, Denbighshire
TEL: 01745 710 673

GREEN FINGERS GARDEN CENTRE `65-2`
Rhyl Road, Denbigh, Denbighshire
TEL: 01745 815 279

FOUR SEASON THE GARDEN CENTRE `65-3`
Lon Parcwr Industrial Estate, Ruthin, Denbighshire
TEL: 01824 702 567

GWYDIR PLANTS `65-4`
Plas Muriau, Betws-y-coed, Conwy
TEL: 01690 750 379

GLYNDWR PLANTS `65-5`
Tafarn Bric, Corwen, Denbighshire
TEL: 01490 413 313

CELYN VALE EUCALYPTUS NURSERIES `65-6`
Allt Y Celyn, Corwen, Denbighshire
TEL: 01490 430 671

BRYNMELYN `65-7`
Cymerau, Ffestiniog, Gwynedd
TEL: 01766 762 684

Prickly Pear

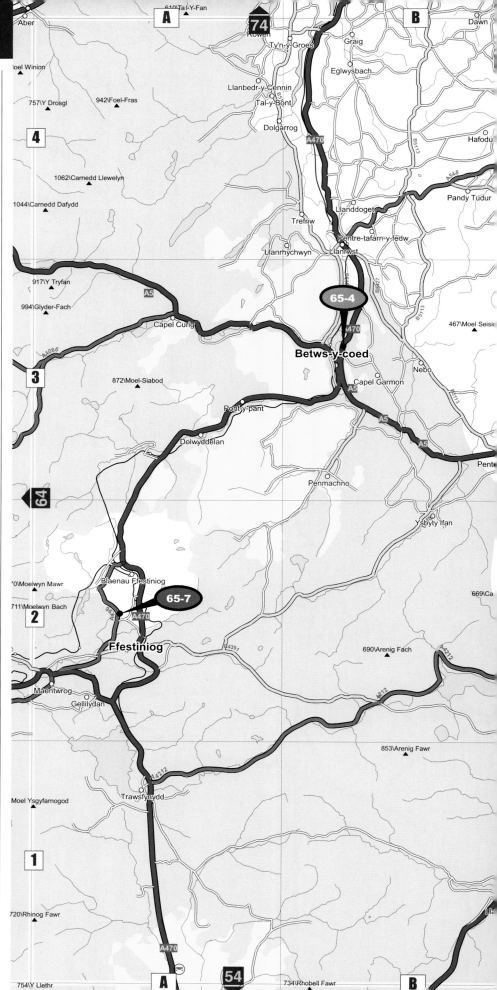

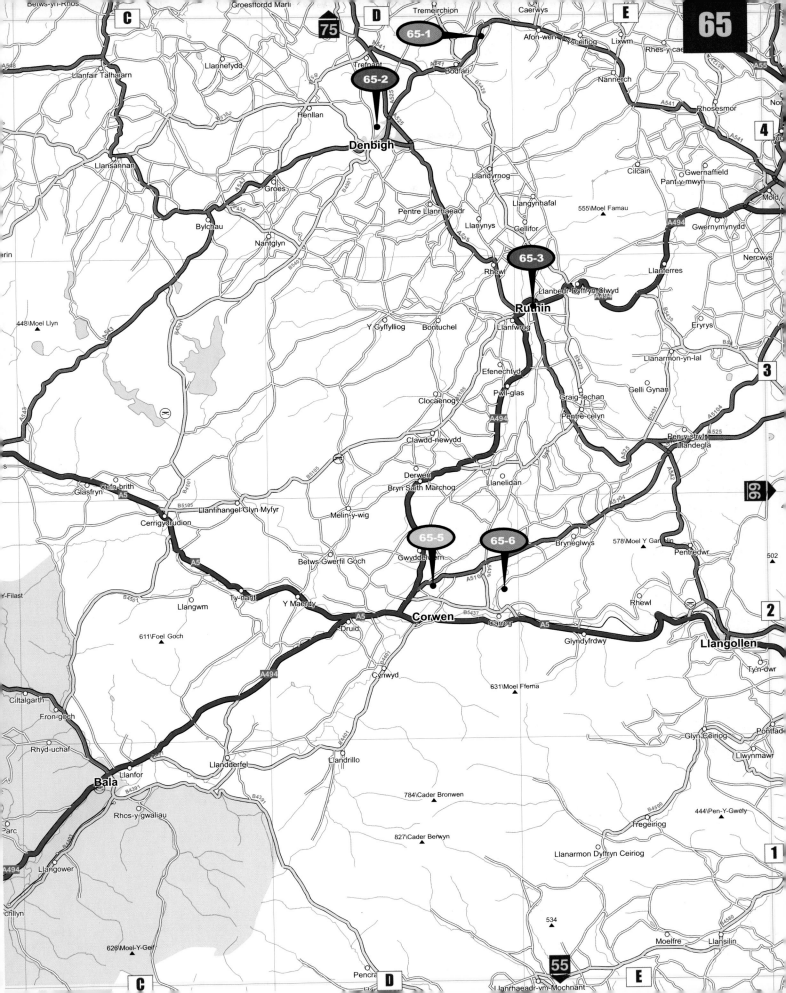

OLD VICARAGE GARDEN CENTRE `66-1`
Chester Road, Warrington, Cheshire
TEL: 01244 300 805

STONYFORD COTTAGE NURSERY `66-2`
Stonyford Lane, Northwich, Cheshire
TEL: 01606 888 128

GARDENLAND GARDEN CENTRE `66-3`
Lakemere Craft Centre, Northwich, Cheshire
TEL: 01606 888 312

OAK TREE FARM NURSERIES `66-4`
Fiddlers Lane, Chester, Cheshire
TEL: 01244 880 895

BARROW NURSERIES `66-5`
Wildmoor Lane, Chester, Cheshire
TEL: 01244 301 510

A. & P. PLANT CENTRE `66-6`
Chester Road Nursery, Tarporley, Cheshire
TEL: 01829 752 755

CHESHIRE HERBS `66-7`
Fourfields, Tarporley, Cheshire
TEL: 01829 760 578

C. & K. JONES `66-8`
Goldenfields Nursery, Tarvin, Cheshire
TEL: 01829 740 663

DALESIDE NURSERY `66-9`
Gladstone Way, Hawarden, Flintshire
TEL: 01244 532 041

VICARS CROSS GARDEN NURSERIES `66-10`
Tarvin Road, Chester, Cheshire
TEL: 01244 336 953

WYEVALE GARDEN CENTRE `66-11`
Forest Road, Tarporley, Cheshire
TEL: 01829 760 433

BEECHMOOR NURSERIES `66-12`
Whitchurch Road, Chester, Cheshire
TEL: 01244 336 922

OKELL'S NURSERIES `66-13`
Duddon Heath, Tarporley, Cheshire
TEL: 01829 741 512

GROSVENOR GARDEN CENTRE `66-14`
Wrexham Road, Chester, Cheshire
TEL: 01244 682 856

OAKFIELD NURSERIES `66-15`
Aldford Road, Chester, Cheshire
TEL: 01244 320 731

WETTENHALL NURSERY `66-16`
Winsford Road, Wettenhall, Cheshire
TEL: 01270 528 376

NANNY'S BRIDGE NURSERY `66-17`
Church Minshall, Nairn, Cheshire
TEL: 01270 522 239

WATERWAYS GARDEN CENTRE `66-18`
Chester Road, Wrexham, Flintshire
TEL: 01244 571 064

CARLTON GARDEN CENTRE `66-19`
Pinfold Lane, Wrexham, Flintshire
TEL: 01978 852 896

QUEEN'S PARK `66-20`
Victoria Avenue, Crewe, Cheshire
TEL: 01270 537 239

SPECTRUM HOME & GARDEN CENTRE `66-21`
Mold Road, Wrexham, Flintshire
TEL: 01978 760 634

CREWE ROAD NURSERIES `66-22`
209 Crewe Road, Nantwich, Cheshire
TEL: 01270 624 245

STAPELEY WATER GARDENS `66-23`
London Road, Nantwich, Cheshire
TEL: 01270 623 868

FERNDALE HOME & GARDEN CENTRE `66-24`
Berse Road, Wrexham, Flintshire
TEL: 01978 751 946

WATERWAYS GARDEN CENTRE `66-25`
Holt Road, Wrexham, Flintshire
TEL: 01978 660 289

BROMAC NURSERY `66-26`
Little Porters Hill Farm, Nantwich, Cheshire
TEL: 01270 780 319

ERDDIG, NATIONAL TRUST `66-27`
Wrexham, Flintshire
TEL: 01978 355 314

CHIRK CASTLE, NATIONAL TRUST `66-28`
Chirk, Wrexham, Flintshire
TEL: 01691 777 701

MORETON PARK GARDEN CENTRE `66-29`
Gledrid, Chirk, Wrexham,
Shropshire, LL14 5DG
TEL: 01691 777 722
FAX: 01691 777 766
WEB: www.moretonparkgardencentre.com

A purpose built garden centre for all your gardening and gift ideas.
OPEN: Daily, Mon-Sat 9-6, Sun 10.30-4.30.
SPECIALITIES: Climbers, Trees, Shrubs, Furniture, Aquatics & fish.

SPRINGWOOD NURSERIES `66-30`
3 Steel Road, Whitchurch, Shropshire
TEL: 01948 880 397

HEATHWOOD NURSERIES `66-31`
The Meadows, Whitchurch, Shropshire
TEL: 01948 840 120

BALMER GROVE PLANTS `66-32`
Bayston Hill Nurseries, Welshampton, Shropshire
TEL: 01948 710 403

HILLCREST CONIFERS `66-33`
Salisbury Road, Market Drayton, Shropshire
TEL: 01630 652 088

ELLESMERE ROAD ORGANIC NURSERY `66-34`
Shrewsbury Road, Ellesmere, Shropshire
TEL: 01939 270 270

HAWKSTONE HISTORIC PARK & FOLLIES `66-35`
Weston-under-Redcastle, Shrewsbury, Shropshire
TEL: 01939 200 611

HODNET HALL `66-36`
Hodnet, Market Drayton, Shropshire
TEL: 01630 685 202

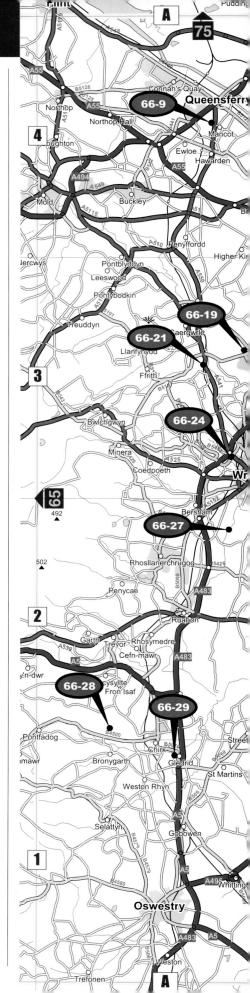

CHESHIRE · SHROPS · STAFFS

● GARDEN CENTRE
● NURSERY
● GARDEN
● NURSERY & GARDEN CENTRE
● GARDEN & NURSERY
● WATER GARDEN SPECIALIST

GRANADA ARBORETUM 67-1
Jodrell Bank, Macclesfield, Cheshire
Tel: 01477 571 339

MACCLESFIELD GARDEN CENTRE 67-2
Bullocks Lane, Macclesfield, Cheshire
Tel: 01625 618 933

HILL'S GARDEN CENTRE 67-3
London Road, Knutsford, Cheshire
Tel: 01565 722567

GAWSWORTH HALL 67-4
Macclesfield, Cheshire
Tel: 01260 223 456

WOODSIDE GARDEN CENTRE 67-5
Knutsford Road, Holyes Chapel, Cheshire
Tel: 01477 532 195

BOOSEY'S GARDEN CENTRE 67-6
Newton Bank, Middlewich, Cheshire
Tel: 01606 832 324

WALNUT TREE NURSERIES 67-7
Walnut Tree Farm, Sandbach, Cheshire
Tel: 01270 526 248

D. J. M. NURSERY 67-8
Newcastle Road, Congleton, Cheshire
Tel: 01260 275 032

ASTBURY MEADOW GARDEN CENTRE 67-9
Newcastle Road, Congleton, Cheshire
Tel: 01260 276 466

CONGLETON GARDEN CENTRE 67-10
Moss Road, Congleton, Cheshire
Tel: 01260 270 010

BIDDULPH GRANGE GARDEN, NATIONAL TRUST 67-11
Biddulph Grange, Stoke-on-Trent, Staffordshire
Tel: 01782 517 999

LITTLE MORETON HALL, HOLY ISLAND VILLAGE 67-12
Congleton, Cheshire
Tel: 01260 272 018

WINTERLEY NURSERY 67-13
42 Hassall Road, Sandbach, Cheshire
Tel: 01270 767 215

RODE HALL 67-14
Church Lane, Stoke on Trent, Staffordshire
Tel: 01270 882 961

JACKSONS GARDEN CENTRE 67-15
Tunstall Road, Stoke-on-Trent, Staffordshire
Tel: 01782 513 405

Q GARDEN 67-16
2 Church Street, Leek, Staffordshire
Tel: 01538 383 114

KNYPERSLEY HALL GARDEN CENTRE 67-17
Conway Road, Stoke-on-Trent, Staffordshire
Tel: 01782 512 766

BARNCROFT NURSERIES 67-18
Dunwood Lane, Stoke-on-Trent, Staffordshire
Tel: 01538 384 310

FLOWER POT GARDEN CENTRE 67-19
Crewe Road, Crewe, Cheshire
Tel: 01270 884 207

LITTLEWOOD FARM NURSERY 67-20
Cheddleton, Leek, Staffordshire
Tel: 01538 360 478

FORD GREEN HALL 67-21
Ford Green Road, Stoke-on-Trent, Staffordshire
Tel: 01782 233 195

KERRY HILL NURSERIES 67-22
Eaves Lane, Stoke-on-Trent, Staffordshire
Tel: 01782 302 498

NORTHWOOD GARDEN CENTRE 67-23
Clayton Road, Newcastle under Lyme, Staffordshire
Tel: 01782 635 081

BRIDGEMERE GARDEN WORLD 67-24
Bridgemere, Nantwich, Cheshire
Tel: 01270 521 100

WEST HOLME NURSERIES 67-25
London Road, Crewe, Cheshire
Tel: 01630 647 289

TRENTHAM PARK GARDENS 67-26
Stone Road, Stoke-on-Trent, Staffordshire
Tel: 01782 657 341

BARLASTON NURSERIES 67-28
Old Road, Stoke-on-Trent, Staffordshire
Tel: 01782 373 960

TRENT NURSERIES 67-29
Tittensor Road, Stoke-on-Trent, Staffordshire
Tel: 01782 372 395

HEATHER'S ROSES 67-30
Heather Nursery, Stone, Staffordshire
Tel: 01889 505 345

DOROTHY CLIVE GARDEN 67-27
Willoughbridge, Market Drayton,
Shropshire, TF9 4EU
Tel: 01630 647 237
Web: www.dorothyclivegarden.co.uk
This romantic garden is home to choice and unusual plants in informal settings. An alpine scree, water features and a spectacular woodland garden, once a gravel quarry, are just some of the delights.
Open: Daily 1 Apr-31 Oct, 10-5.30.
Entry costs: Adult £3.20. Child up to 11 free, 11-16 £1. OAPs £2.70. Groups 20+ £2.70.
Specialities: Rhododendrons and azaleas, Herbaceous plants, Perennials, Trees, Waterfalls.

HIGH FARM NURSERIES 67-3
High Farm, Stoke-on-Trent, Staffordshire
Tel: 01889 502 252

FLETCHER'S GARDEN & LEISURE CENTRE 67-3
Bridge Farm, Stafford, Staffordshire
Tel: 01785 851 057

JOHNSON HALL NURSERIES 67-3
Johnson Hall, Stafford, Staffordshire
Tel: 01785 850 400

AMERTON GARDEN CENTRE 67-3
Stow by Chartley, Stafford, Staffordshire
Tel: 01889 270 294

GREENHEART PLANTS 67-3
Hopton Hall Lane, Stafford, Staffordshire
Tel: 01785 257 975

Dutch Iris

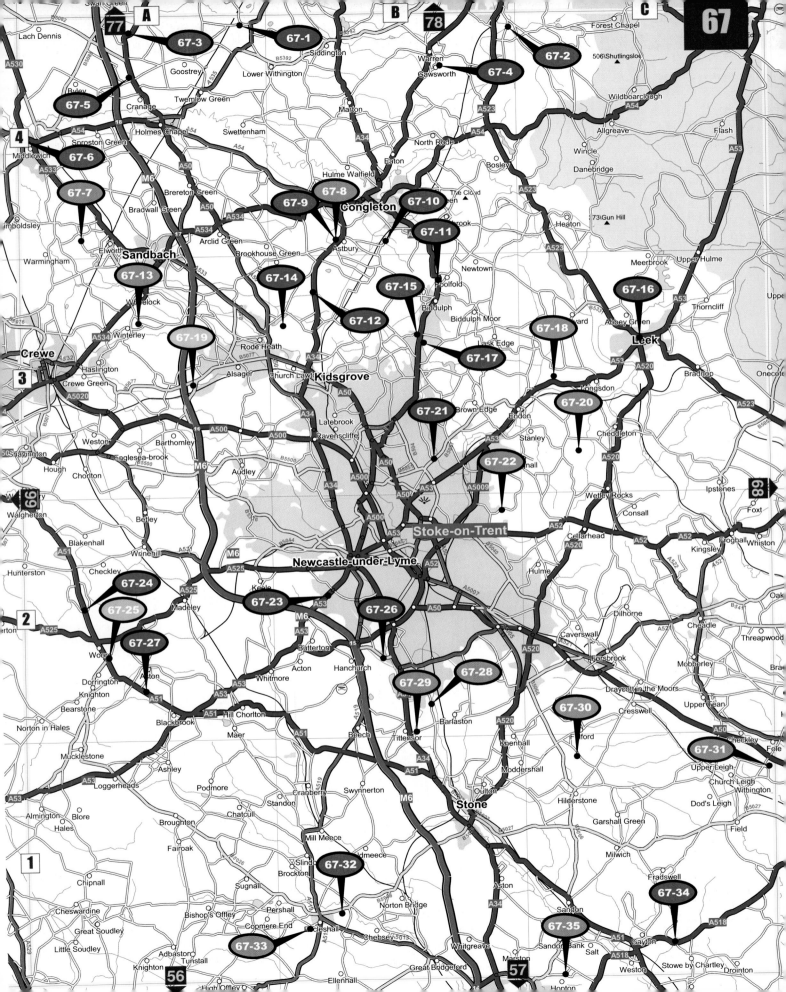

- ◖ GARDEN CENTRE
- ◖ NURSERY
- ◖ GARDEN
- ⬤ NURSERY & GARDEN CENTRE
- ⬤ GARDEN & NURSERY
- ⬤ WATER GARDEN SPECIALIST

GLENHYRST NURSERIES
Vincent Crescent, Chesterfield, Derbyshire
TEL: 01246 566 632

CHATSWORTH
Edensor, Bakewell, Derbyshire
TEL: 01246 582 204

CHATSWORTH GARDEN CENTRE
Calton Lees, Matlock, Derbyshire
TEL: 01629 734 004

HADDON HALL
Estate Office, Bakewell, Derbyshire
TEL: 01629 812 855

GREENLEAVES GARDEN CENTRE
Birkin Lane, Chesterfield, Derbyshire
TEL: 01246 204 214

FOREST NURSERIES
Oddford Lane, Matlock, Derbyshire
TEL: 01629 733 225

WHITELEA NURSERY
Whitelea Lane, Matlock, Derbyshire
TEL: 01629 550 10

KNABB HALL NURSERIES
Knabb Hall Lane, Matlock, Derbyshire
TEL: 01629 554 61

JAMES SMITH NURSERIES
Stretton Road, Matlock, Derbyshire
TEL: 01629 583 036

MATLOCK GARDEN WATER LIFE & PET CENTRE
Nottingham Road, Matlock, Derbyshire
TEL: 01629 580 500

LORNA CROSS NURSERY
3 Cliff Villas, Matlock, Derbyshire
TEL: 01629 583 207

CROMFORD GARDEN CENTRE
Derby Road, Matlock, Derbyshire
TEL: 01629 824 990

WESSINGTON GARDEN CENTRE
Matlock Road, Alfreton, Derbyshire
TEL: 01773 832 517

TISSINGTON NURSERY
Tissington, Ashbourne, Derbyshire
TEL: 01335 390 650

OLD HALL NURSERY
Old Hall Farm, Leek, Staffordshire
TEL: 01538 308 257

BROADHOLME LANE FARM NURSERY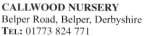
Broadholme Lane, Belper, Derbyshire
TEL: 01773 823 517

CALLWOOD NURSERY
Belper Road, Belper, Derbyshire
TEL: 01773 824 771

FAIRWAYS GARDEN CENTRE
Clifton, Ashbourne, Derbyshire
TEL: 01335 347 900

BIRCHWOOD FARM NURSERY
Portway, Coxbench, Derbyshire
TEL: 01332 880 685

ALTON TOWERS
Alton, Stoke-on-Trent, Staffordshire
TEL: 0990 204 060

DERBY GARDEN CENTRE
Alfreton Road, Derby, Derbyshire
TEL: 01332 831 666

KEDLESTON HALL, NATIONAL TRUST
Derby, Derbyshire
TEL: 01332 842 191

MEYNELL LANGLEY GARDENS 68-23
Langley Hall, Ashbourne, Derbyshire
TEL: 01332 824 358

MARKEATON GARDEN CENTRE & NURSERY
Markeaton Lane, Derby, Derbyshire
TEL: 01332 292 554

ALLARDS PLANT CENTRE 68-25
20-23 The Meadows, Derby, Derbyshire
TEL: 01332 205 135

DERBY ARBORETUM 68-26
Arboretum Square, Derby, Derbyshire
TEL: 01332 716 644

HELDON NURSERIES
Ashbourne Road, Uttoxeter, Staffordshire
TEL: 01889 563 377

DEVONSHIRE NURSERIES 68-28
13 Devonshire Drive, Mickelover, Derbyshire
TEL: 01332 513 211

GRANGECRAFT GARDEN CENTRE 68-29
Hospital Lane, Mickelover, Derbyshire
TEL: 01332 510 951

SUDBURY HALL, NATIONAL TRUST 68-30
Sudbury, Ashbourne, Derbyshire
TEL: 01283 585 305

WYEVALE GARDEN CENTRE 68-31
Burton Road, Derby, Derbyshire
TEL: 01332 514 268

FIRS FARM NURSERY 68-32
Firs Farm, Derby, Derbyshire
TEL: 01283 520 331

SAMUEL JACKSON GROWERS 68-33
The Glasshouse, Derby, Derbyshire
TEL: 01332 700 800

SLATER'S GARDENS 68-34
Dovecliffe Road, Burton upon Trent, Staffordshire
TEL: 01283 565 650

Wild Iris

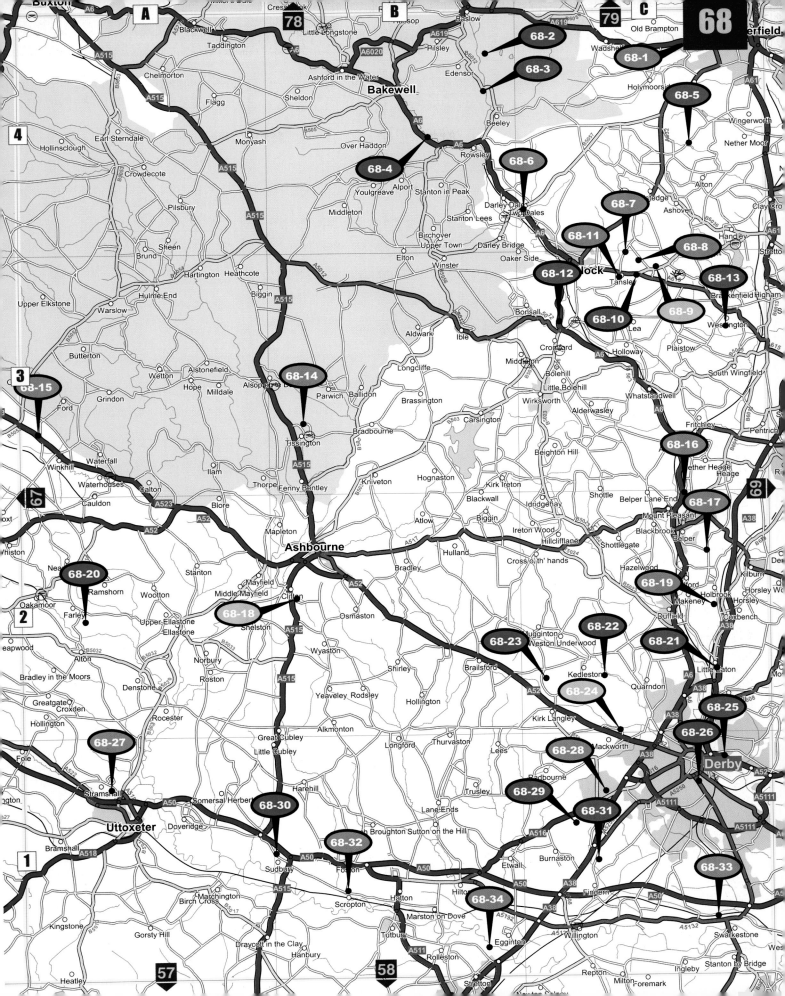

● GARDEN CENTRE
● NURSERY
● GARDEN

● NURSERY & GARDEN CENTRE
● GARDEN & NURSERY
● WATER GARDEN SPECIALIST

ROSE'S GARDEN CENTRE
Chesterfield Road, Chesterfield, Derbyshire
TEL: 01246 551 627

BOLSOVER CASTLE, ENGLISH HERITAGE
Bolsover, Derbyshire
TEL: 01246 823 349

THORESBY TREE & SHRUB NURSERY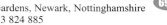
The Old Gardens, Newark, Nottinghamshire
TEL: 01623 824 885

FOURWAYS NURSERY
Rotherham Road, Chesterfield, Derbyshire
TEL: 01246 241 317

CHESTERFIELD AQUATICS
Mansfield Road, Chesterfield, Derbyshire
TEL: 01246 558 444

PLANTWORLD
Old Manor Nurseries, Chesterfield, Derbyshire
TEL: 01246 850 336

GLAPWELL NURSERIES
Bolsover Road, Chesterfield, Derbyshire
TEL: 01623 812 191

THE HERB GARDEN
Hall View Cottage, Chesterfield, Derbyshire
TEL: 01246 854 268

HARDWICK OLD HALL, ENGLISH HERITAGE
Doe Len, Chesterfield, Derbyshire
TEL: 01246 850 431

SPENCER'S
Fernlea, Chesterfield, Derbyshire
TEL: 01246 862 628

OILWELL NURSERY
Oilwell Nursery, Tibshelf, Derbyshire
TEL: 01773 874 321

SHERWOODS GARDEN CENTRE
7-9 Sherwood Hall Road, Mansfield,
Nottinghamshire
TEL: 01623 624 923

DALESTORTH GARDEN CENTRE
Dalestorth House, Sutton in Ashfield,
Nottinghamshire
TEL: 01623 557 817

WESTFIELD GARDEN CENTRE
Beck Lane, Sutton in Ashfield, Nottinghamshire
TEL: 01623 554 515

GREENHILLS GARDEN CENTRE
Greenhills Farm, Sutton in Ashfield, Nottinghamshire
TEL: 01623 554 418

CARNFIELD HALL GARDEN & CRAFT CENTRE
Carnfield Hill, Alfreton, Derbyshire
TEL: 01773 834 577

WILBOURN'S GARDEN CENTRE
Station Street, Nottingham, Nottinghamshire
TEL: 01623 753 100

THE GARDEN OUTLET
Building 2, South Normanton, Derbyshire
TEL: 01773 545 066

NEWSTEAD ABBEY PARK
Newstead Abbey, Ravenshead, Nottinghamshire
TEL: 01623 455 900

SHIRLEY NURSERIES
Mansfield Road, Papplewick, Nottinghamshire
TEL: 0115 963 2677

GREENWOOD BONSAI STUDIO & GARDENS
Ollerton Road, Nottingham, Nottinghamshire
TEL: 0115 920 5757

REUBEN SHAW & SON
Hollydean Nurseries, Nottingham, Nottinghamshire
TEL: 01773 714 326

GREENACRES NURSERY
322 Spring Lane, Nottingham, Nottinghamshire
TEL: 0115 926 2951

LAMBLEY AQUATICS
Floralands Garden Centre, Nottingham,
Nottinghamshire
TEL: 0115 926 2545

FLORALANDS GARDEN CENTRE
Catfoot Lane, Nottingham, Nottinghamshire
TEL: 0115 926 8137

SHIPLEY GARDEN CENTRE
Hassock Lane North, Heanor, Derbyshire
TEL: 01773 713 596

BROOKFIELDS GARDEN & LEISURE CENTRE
431 Mapperley Plains, Nottingham, Nottinghamshire
TEL: 0115 926 8200

NOEL CLAY GARDEN CENTRE
Gin Close Way, Awsworth, Nottinghamshire
TEL: 0115 938 4544

ANDERSEN'S NURSERY
Awsworth Lane, Nottingham, Nottinghamshire
TEL: 0115 930 1884

HILLTOP NURSERIES 69-3
166 Lambley Lane, Nottingham, Nottinghamshire
TEL: 0115 961 2054

WOODLANDS GARDEN CENTRE 69-3
Nottingham Road, Nottingham, Nottinghamshire
TEL: 0115 928 3200

DALE ABBEY PLANTS 69-3
Hagg Lane, Ilkeston, Derbyshire
TEL: 0115 932 2728

TROWELL GARDEN CENTRE 69-3
Stapleford Road, Trowell, Nottinghamshire
TEL: 0115 932 6920

WOLLATON PARK 69-3
Wollaton Road, Nottingham, Nottinghamshire
TEL: 0115 915 3900

HEWTHORN HERBS & WILD FLOWERS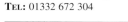
Simkins Farm, Nottingham, Nottinghamshire
TEL: 01602 812 861

LOCKO NURSERIES 69-3
144 Locko Road, Derby, Derbyshire
TEL: 01332 672 304

PIKES OAK FARM NURSERIES 69-3
Oak Farm, Keyworth, Nottinghamshire
TEL: 0115 937 5352

BARDILLS ROSES 69-3
Toton Lane, Nottingham, Nottinghamshire
TEL: 0115 949 0019

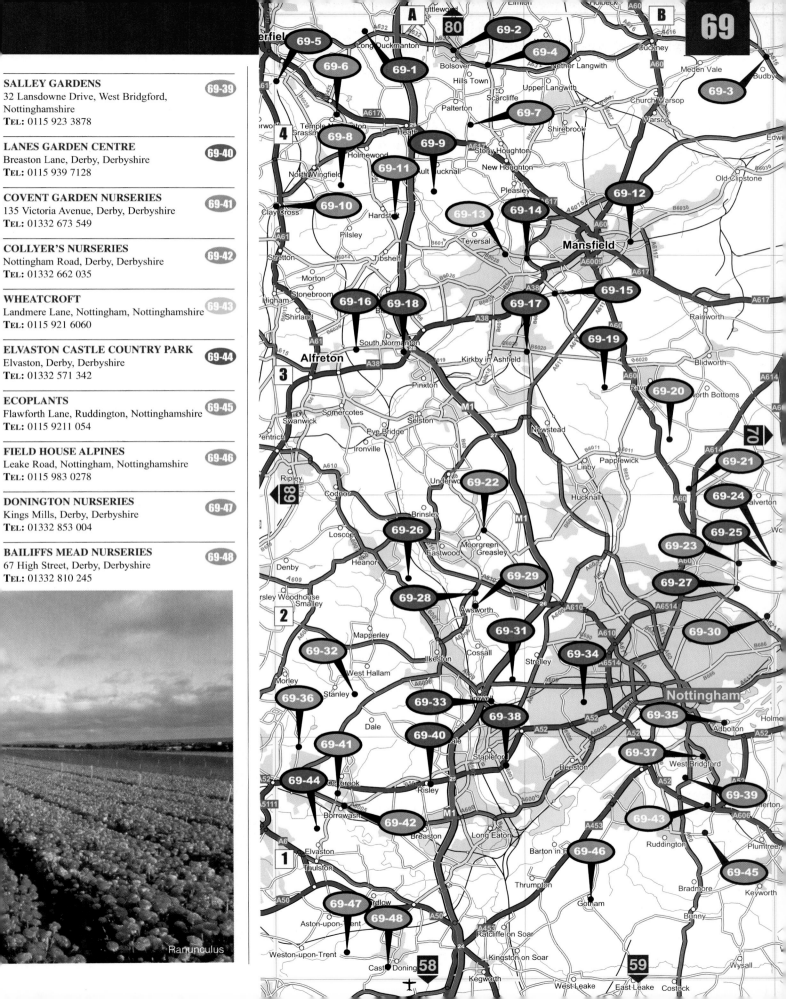

SALLEY GARDENS 69-39
32 Lansdowne Drive, West Bridgford,
Nottinghamshire
TEL: 0115 923 3878

LANES GARDEN CENTRE 69-40
Breaston Lane, Derby, Derbyshire
TEL: 0115 939 7128

COVENT GARDEN NURSERIES 69-41
135 Victoria Avenue, Derby, Derbyshire
TEL: 01332 673 549

COLLYER'S NURSERIES 69-42
Nottingham Road, Derby, Derbyshire
TEL: 01332 662 035

WHEATCROFT 69-43
Landmere Lane, Nottingham, Nottinghamshire
TEL: 0115 921 6060

ELVASTON CASTLE COUNTRY PARK 69-44
Elvaston, Derby, Derbyshire
TEL: 01332 571 342

ECOPLANTS 69-45
Flawforth Lane, Ruddington, Nottinghamshire
TEL: 0115 9211 054

FIELD HOUSE ALPINES 69-46
Leake Road, Nottingham, Nottinghamshire
TEL: 0115 983 0278

DONINGTON NURSERIES 69-47
Kings Mills, Derby, Derbyshire
TEL: 01332 853 004

BAILIFFS MEAD NURSERIES 69-48
67 High Street, Derby, Derbyshire
TEL: 01332 810 245

Ranunculus

PATIO PLANTING BY HAZEL `70-1`
Unit 6, Lincoln, Lincolnshire
TEL: 01522 536 573

EASTFIELD NURSERIES `70-2`
Eastfield Farm, Newark, Nottinghamshire
TEL: 01777 870 341

WALESBY GARDEN CENTRE `70-3`
Brake Road, Newark, Nottinghamshire
TEL: 01623 860 382

WHISBY WATER AND GARDEN CENTRE `70-4`
Whisby Road, Lincoln, Lincolnshire
TEL: 01522 685 395

RUFFORD ABBEY & COUNTRY PARK `70-5`
The Sawmill, Newark, Nottinghamshire
TEL: 01623 822 944

PENNELLS GARDEN CENTRE `70-6`
Newark Road, Lincoln, Lincolnshire
TEL: 01522 880 033

WADDINGTON NURSERIES `70-7`
123 Station Road, Lincoln, Lincolnshire
TEL: 01522 720 220

CEDAR LODGE NURSERY `70-8`
Whitemoor Lane, Newark, Nottinghamshire
TEL: 01636 893 360

NORWELL NURSERIES `70-9`
Woodhouse Road, Newark, Nottinghamshire
TEL: 01636 636 337

ERMINE COTTAGE NURSERIES `70-10`
Heath Road, Lincoln, Lincolnshire
TEL: 01522 810 396

DALESTORTH NURSERIES `70-11`
Cockett Lane, Newark, Nottinghamshire
TEL: 01623 883 187

WONDERLAND GARDEN CENTRE `70-12`
White Post, Newark, Nottinghamshire
TEL: 01623 883 395

REG TAYLOR GARDEN CENTRE `70-13`
Corkhill Lane, Southwell, Nottinghamshire
TEL: 01636 813 184

H. MERRYWEATHER & SON `70-14`
The Garden Centre, Southwell, Nottinghamshire
TEL: 01636 813 204

CRINK LANE NURSERIES `70-15`
Crink Lane, Southwell, Nottinghamshire
TEL: 01636 812 706

SOUTHWELL GARDEN CENTRE `70-16`
Fiskerton Road, Southwell, Nottinghamshire
TEL: 01636 812 886

DORRINGTONS GARDEN CENTRE `70-17`
Dorrington Fen, Lincoln, Lincolnshire
TEL: 01526 832 529

DANNY-LYP GARDEN CENTRE `70-18`
41 Sibcy Lane, Newark, Nottinghamshire
TEL: 01636 674 840

MILL HILL PLANTS `70-19`
Mill Hill House, Newark, Nottinghamshire
TEL: 01636 525 460

WORLD OF WATER `70-20`
Timmermans Garden Centre, Lowdham
Lane, Woodborough, Nottinghamshire, NG14 6DN
TEL: 0115 966 3333
WEB: www.worldofwater.com
Everything for the pond and tropical fish enthusiast. Extensive showgardens. Expert advice.
OPEN: 9-5.30 Mon-Sat, Sun 10.30-4.30. Closed Easter Sun.
SPECIALITIES: Aquatic plants, Water features, Waterfalls.

TIMMERMANS GARDEN CENTRE `70-21`
Lowdham Lane, Nottingham, Nottinghamshire
TEL: 0115 966 4033

LILY VALE NURSERIES `70-22`
Park Lane, Nottingham, Nottinghamshire
TEL: 0115 931 3506

AQUATIC CENTRE `70-23`
Main Road, Nottingham, Nottinghamshire
TEL: 0115 931 2986

TALL TREES GARDEN CENTRE `70-24`
Main Road, Nottingham, Nottinghamshire
TEL: 0115 931 2356

ORCHARD NURSERIES `70-25`
Tow Lane, Grantham, Lincolnshire
TEL: 01400 281 354

BRIDGFORD GARDEN WATER LIFE & PET CENTRE `70-26`
Fosse Road, East Bridgford, Nottinghamshire
TEL: 01949 200 55

BELTON HOUSE, NATIONAL TRUST `70-27`
Grantham, Lincolnshire
TEL: 01476 566 116

STRAGGLETHORPE NURSERIES `70-28`
Radcliffe on Trent, Nottinghamshire
TEL: 01602 332 158

CLAPTONS CONSERVATORY & GARDEN CENTRE `70-29`
Union Street, Grantham, Lincolnshire
TEL: 01476 564 728

IVOR THOMPSON NURSERIES `70-30`
82 Cotgrave Lane, Nottingham, Nottinghamshire
TEL: 0115 937 2360

NATURESCAPE WILDFLOWER FARM `70-31`
Coach Gap Lane, Langar, Nottinghamshire
TEL: 01949 851 045

BELVOIR CASTLE `70-32`
Belvoir, Grantham, Lincolnshire
TEL: 01476 870 262

MOORES NURSERIES `70-33`
156 Melton Road, Nottingham, Nottinghamshire
TEL: 0115 937 3717

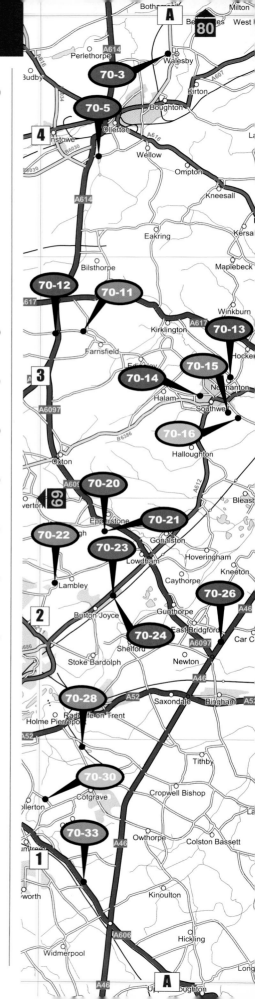

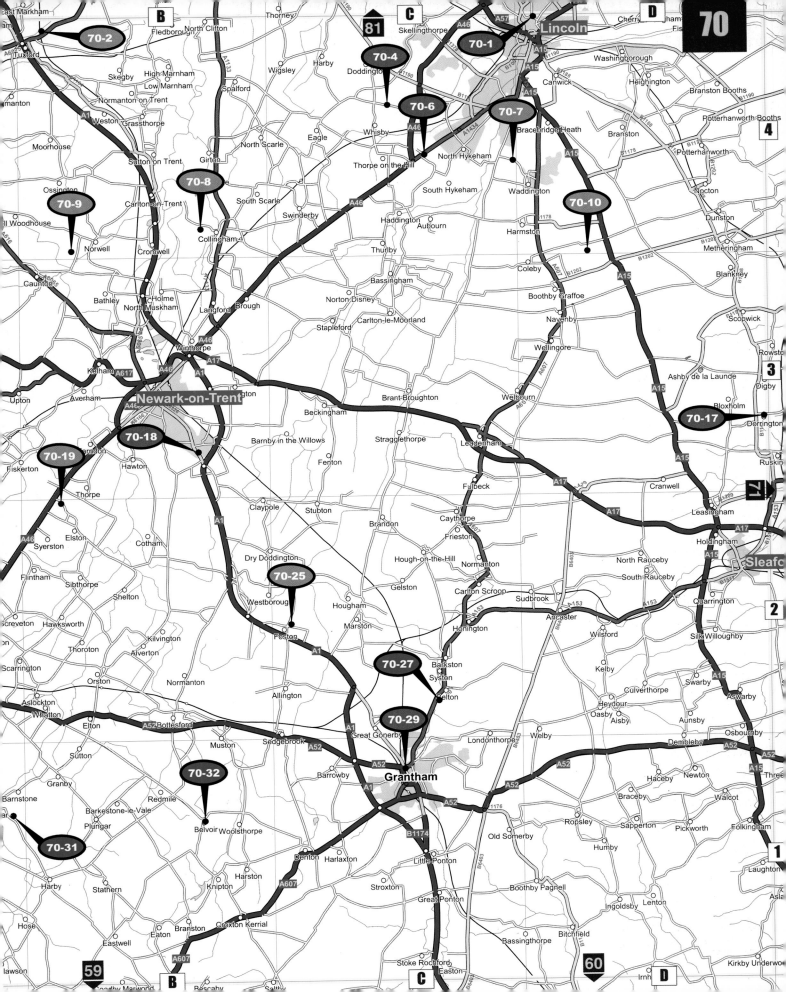

CAMBS · LINCS

CHAPEL GARDEN CENTRE   **71-1**
Skegness Road, Skegness, Lincolnshire
Tel: 01754 873 558

CROWDERS GARDEN CENTRE   **71-2**
Lincoln Road, Horncastle, Lincolnshire
Tel: 01507 525 252

THE CONTENTED GARDENER   **71-3**
The Garden House, Bardney, Lincolnshire
Tel: 01526 397307

PLANT LOVERS   **71-4**
Candlesby House, Spilsby, Cambridgeshire
Tel: 01754 890 256

EAST KEAL EARLS CROOME   **71-5**
Main Road, Spilsby, Cambridgeshire
Tel: 01790 752 396

BLANKNEY KOI & GARDEN CENTRE   **71-6**
Martin Road, Lincoln, Lincolnshire
Tel: 01526 378 880

SHENLEA NURSERIES   **71-7**
Main Road, Boston, Lincolnshire
Tel: 01205 750 424

RUSKINGTON GARDEN CENTRE   **71-8**
White House Farm, Sleaford, Lincolnshire
Tel: 01526 833 022

ANWICK GARDEN CENTRE   **71-9**
Old Manor Farm, Sleaford, Lincolnshire
Tel: 01526 832 277

WESTHOLME NURSERIES   **71-10**
The Gride, Boston, Lincolnshire
Tel: 01205 870 202

MAURICE ROWE   **71-11**
106 Horncastle Road, Boston, Lincolnshire
Tel: 01205 363 567

JOHNSONS GARDEN CENTRE   **71-12**
Wainfleet Road, Boston, Lincolnshire
Tel: 01205 363 408

GLENHIRST CACTUS NURSERY   **71-13**
Station Road, Boston, Lincolnshire
Tel: 01205 820 314

RAINBOW GARDEN & AQUATIC CENTRE   **71-14**
Grange Farm, Boston, Lincolnshire
Tel: 01205 723 555

BIRCHGROVE GARDEN CENTRE   **71-15**
Surfleet Road, Spalding, Lincolnshire
Tel: 01775 680 490

Barrel Cactus

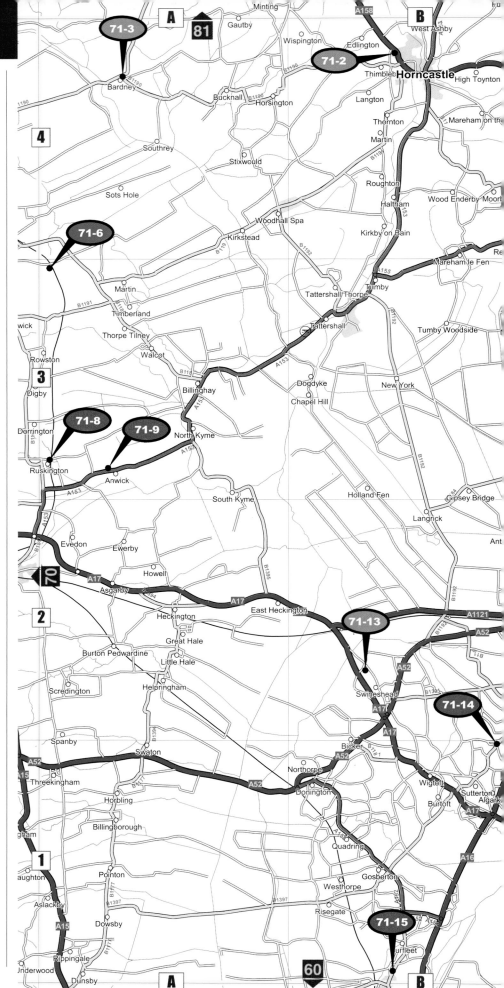

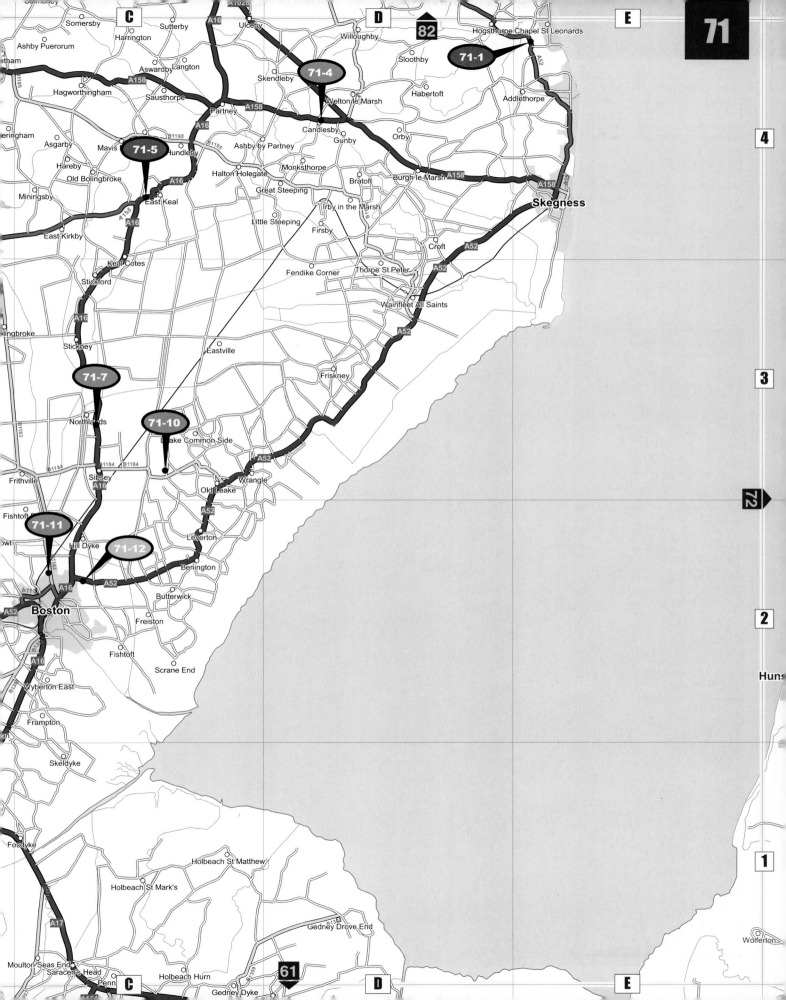

NORFOLK

- ● GARDEN CENTRE
- ● NURSERY
- ● GARDEN
- ● NURSERY & GARDEN CENTRE
- ● GARDEN & NURSERY
- ● WATER GARDEN SPECIALIST

CLEY NURSERIES
Rectory Hill Nursery, Holt, Norfolk
TEL: 01263 740 892

HOLKHAM NURSERY GARDENS
Holkham Park, Wells-next-the-sea, Norfolk
TEL: 01328 711 636

STUBBINGS - THE GARDEN SHOP
Market Place, Burnham Market, Norfolk
TEL: 01328 730 668

NORFOLK LAVENDER
Caley Mill, King's Lynn, Norfolk
TEL: 01485 570 384

CREAKE PLANT CENTRE 72-5
Nursery View, Fakenham, Norfolk
TEL: 01328 823 018

FAKENHAM GARDEN CENTRE 72-6
Mill Road, Fakenham, Norfolk
TEL: 01328 863 380

SANDRINGHAM HOUSE
Sandringham, King's Lynn, Norfolk
TEL: 01553 772 675

PENSTHORPE WATERFOWL PARK
Pensthorpe Waterfowl Trust, Fakenham, Norfolk
TEL: 01328 851 465

THE KNOT GARDEN 72-9
Heydon Lane, Wood Dalling, Norfolk
TEL: 01263 587 318

Lupine

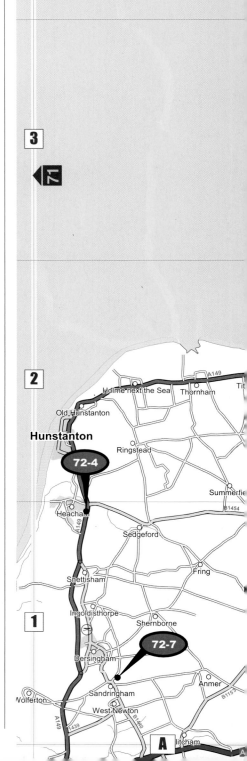

NORFOLK

GARDEN CENTRE
NURSERY
GARDEN

NURSERY & GARDEN CENTRE
GARDEN & NURSERY
WATER GARDEN SPECIALIST

SHERINGHAM PARK, NATIONAL TRUST `73-1`
Sheringham, Norfolk
TEL: 01263 823 778

OVERSTRAND COTTAGE GARDEN CENTRE `73-2`
6 Mundesley Road, Cromer, Norfolk
TEL: 01263 579485

FELBRIGG HALL & GARDEN, NATIONAL TRUST `73-3`
Felbrigg, Cromer, Norfolk
TEL: 01263 837 444

BILL LE GRICE NURSERIES `73-4`
Groveland, Norwich, Norfolk
TEL: 01263 833 111

ALBY CRAFTS GARDENS `73-5`
Cromer Road, Norwich, Norfolk
TEL: 01263 761 226

MANNINGTON GARDENS `73-6`
Saxthorpe, Norwich,
Norfolk, NR11 7BB
TEL: 01263 584 175
WEB: www.manningtongardens.co.uk
Beautiful gardens surround medieval moated manor. Heritage Rose Garden, wild flowers, trees and shrubs, lake. Extensive footpath network. Playground, tearooms. Events programme.
OPEN: Wed/Thu/Fri, Jun-Aug 11-5, Suns May-Sep 12-5.
ENTRY COSTS: Adult £3, Children Free, OAPs £2.50, Students £2.50.
SPECIALITIES: Arboretum, Roses, Trees, Walled garden, Wild flowers.

HOLLY HOCKS NURSERY `73-7`
Walcott Green, Norwich, Norfolk
TEL: 01692 650 732

NORTH WALSHAM GARDEN CENTRE & GARDEN MACHINERY CENTRE `73-8`
Norwich Road, North Walsham,
Norfolk, NR28 0DR
TEL: 01692 402 591 01692 500 666 for machinery

Garden design and landscaping service available, with a large range of garden machinery on site.
OPEN: Mon-Sat, 9-5.30, Sun 11-5.
SPECIALITIES: Garden machinery, Roses.

BLICKLING HALL & GARDEN, NATIONAL TRUST `73-9`
Blickling, Norfolk
TEL: 01263 733 084

Euryops

4

3

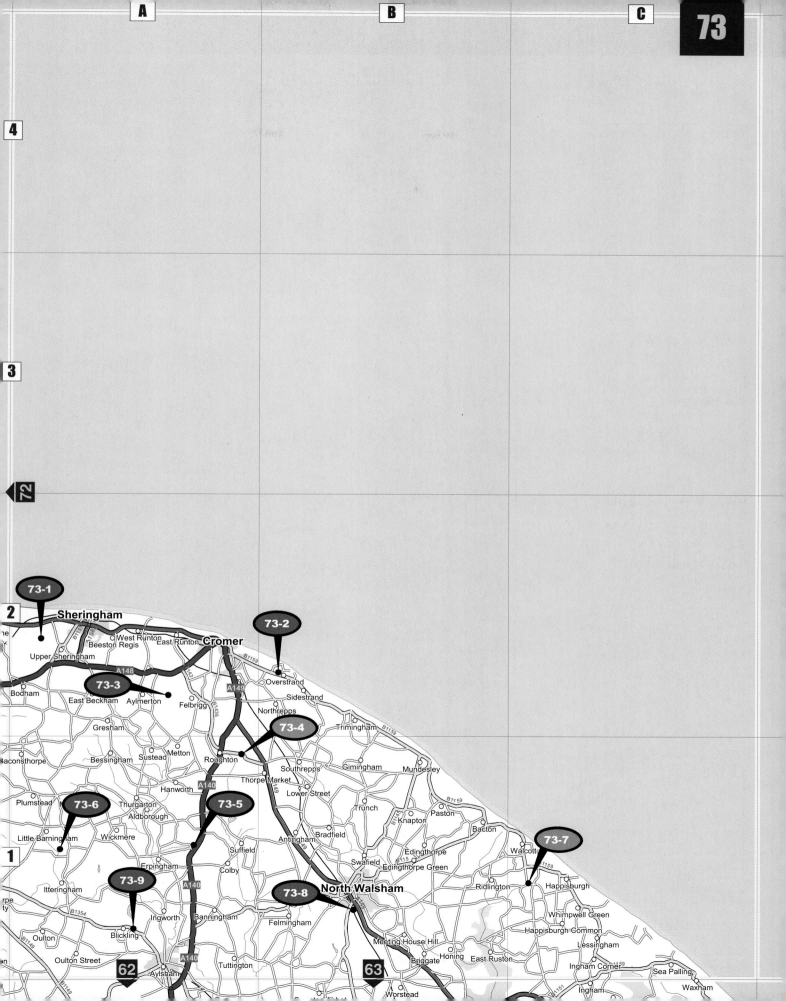

72

73-1

2 Sheringham

West Runton East Runton **Cromer**
Beeston Regis
Upper Sheringham **73-2**

Bodham Overstrand

73-3 Sidestrand
East Beckham Aylmerton Felbrigg Northrepps

Gresham Trimingham

73-4
Bessingham Sustead Metton
aconsthorpe Roughton Southrepps Gimingham Mundesley

Thorpe Market
Hanworth Lower Street

Plumstead Thurgarton Trunch Paston
73-6 Aldborough Knapton Bacton

Little Barningham Wickmere Bradfield
Antingham Edingthorpe **73-7**
73-5 Suffield Walcott
1 Swafield Edingthorpe Green
Erpingham
73-9 Colby Ridlington Happisburgh

Itteringham **73-8** **North Walsham**
Ingworth Banningham
Blickling Felmingham Whimpwell Green

Oulton Happisburgh Common
Meeting House Hill Lessingham
Oulton Street Honing East Ruston
62 Briggate Ingham Corner Sea Palling
Tuttington
63 Ingham Waxham
Worstead

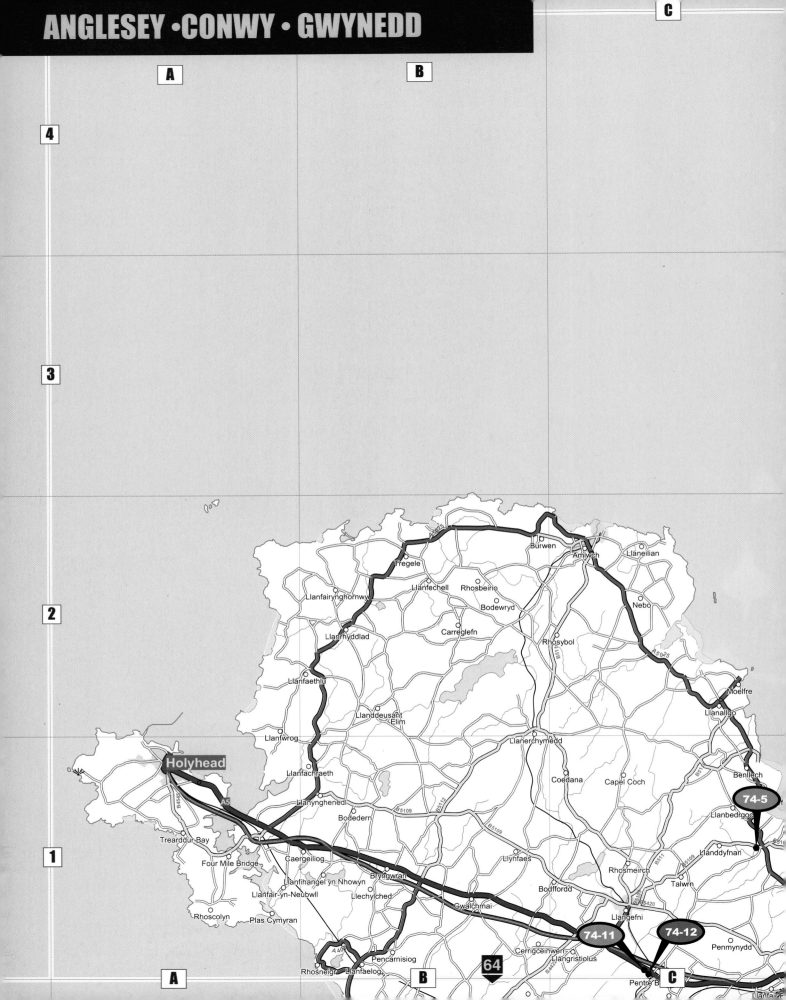

THE SECRET GARDEN CENTRE `74-1`
Old Station Yard, Llandudno, Gwynedd
TEL: 01492 872 767

BATTY'S NURSERIES `74-2`
Llandudno Road, Llandudno, Gwynedd
TEL: 01492 549 176

RHOS GARDEN CENTRE `74-3`
17 Rhos Road, Colwyn Bay, Conwy
TEL: 01492 544 567

BRYN EUR YN NURSERY `74-4`
Dinerth Road, Colwyn Bay, Conwy
TEL: 01492 546 757

PENTRAETH NURSERIES `74-5`
Chapel Bank, Pentraeth, Anglesey
TEL: 020 8294 2548

TY MAWR NURSERIES `74-6`
Henryd Road, Conwy, Conwy
TEL: 01492 593 829

SNOWDONIA NURSERIES `74-7`
Llanrwst Road, Glan Conwy, Colwyn Bay,
Conwy, LL28 5SR
TEL: 01492 580 703

Family run nursery/garden centre. Quality home-grown bedding plants, extensive plant range, new coffee shop and furniture showroom.
OPEN: Daily 9-5, Sun 10.30-4.30, closed Easter Sun & Christmas day to 1 Jan incl.
SPECIALITIES: Alpines, Bedding plants, Climbers, Garden & conservatory furniture, Fruit & fruit trees.

BRYN MYNAN NURSERY `74-8`
Bryn Mynan, Colwyn Bay, Conwy
TEL: 01492 596 095

ABERCONWY NURSERY `74-9`
Graig, Colwyn Bay, Conwy
TEL: 01492 580 875

CONWY VALLEY NURSERIES `74-10`
Tyn-y-Groes, Conwy, Conwy
TEL: 01492 650 228

HENLLYS LODGE PLANTS `74-11`
Henllys Lodge, Anglesey, Gwynedd
TEL: 01248 810 106

HOLLAND ARMS GARDEN CENTRE `74-12`
Gaerwen, Anglesey
TEL: 01248 421 655

PENRHYN CASTLE, NATIONAL TRUST `74-13`
Bangor, Gwynedd
TEL: 01248 353 084

BODNANT GARDENS NATIONAL TRUST `74-14`
Tal y Cafn, Colwyn Bay, Conwy
TEL: 01492 650 460

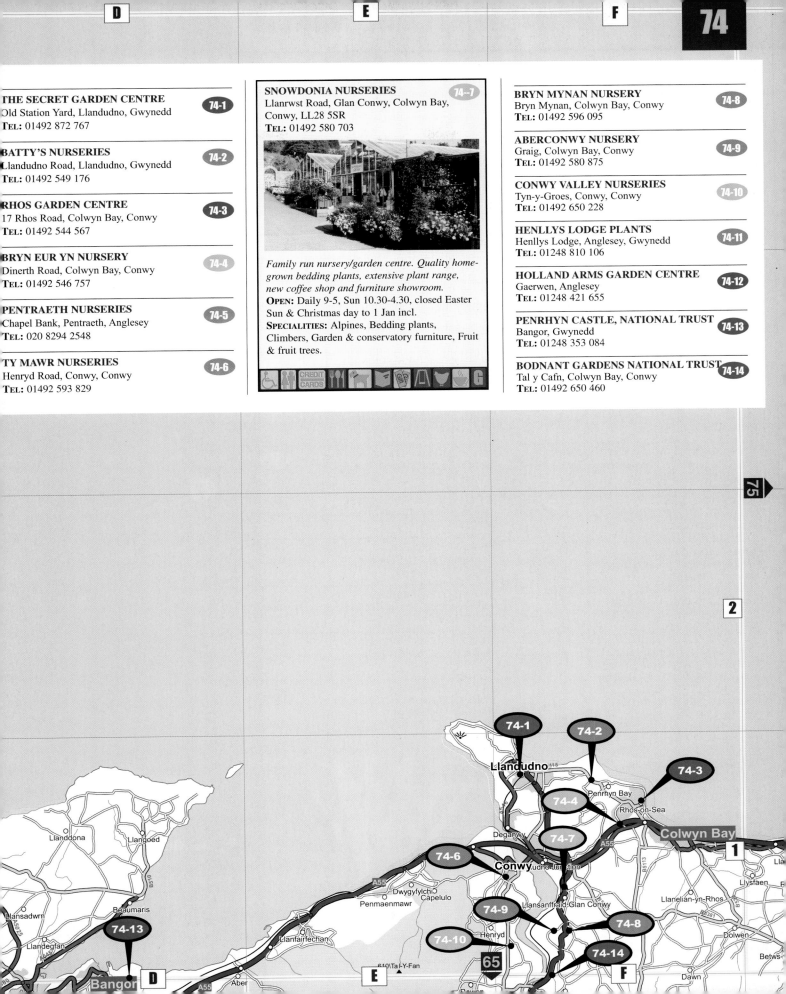

FOUR SEASONS
224a Liverpool Road, Southport, Merseyside
TEL: 01704 560 164

WHITE MOSS GARDEN CENTRE
New Cut Lane, Southport, Merseyside
TEL: 01704 550 095

FORMBY GARDEN CENTRE
1 Cable Street, Liverpool, Merseyside
TEL: 01704 879 198

ROSE NURSERIES
Altcar Road, Liverpool, Merseyside
TEL: 01704 878 488

LADY GREEN NURSERIES & GARDEN CENTRE
Lady Green Lane, Liverpool, Merseyside
TEL: 0151 929 3635

W. N. RUSHTON
Tanhouse Farm, Liverpool, Merseyside
TEL: 0151 924 2365

BROWNMOOR NURSERIES & WATER GARDENS
43 Brownmoor Lane, Liverpool, Merseyside
TEL: 0151 928 1292

TONY ALMOND DIY & GARDEN CENTRE
52-54 South Road, Liverpool, Merseyside
TEL: 0151 286 2460

K. CROSS & SON
Rostherne, Wirral, Cheshire
TEL: 0151 638 6240

MAGILL'S NURSERIES
Leasowe Road, Wirral, Cheshire
TEL: 0151 639 6784

WIRRAL WATER GARDENS
Birkenhead Road, Meols, Cheshire
TEL: 0151 632 2222

CARR FARM GARDEN CENTRE
Birkenhead Road, Hoylake, Merseyside
TEL: 0151 632 1457

SANDY LANE NURSERIES
1-2 Market Country Produce & Fish, Birkenhead, Merseyside
TEL: 0151 647 3137

FORIZO GARDEN SHOP
Walker Street, Birkenhead, Merseyside
TEL: 0151 652 2275

BERESFORD NURSERIES & GARDEN CENTRE
96 Storeton Road, Birkenhead, Merseyside
TEL: 0151 608 1950

PORT SUNLIGHT GARDEN CENTRE
The Causeway, Wirral, Cheshire
TEL: 01516 456 244

THINGWALL NURSERIES PLANT CENTRE
Lower Thingwall Lane, Wirral, Cheshire
TEL: 0151 648 0281

JACKSONS NURSERIES & GARDEN CENTRE
Marian, Rhyl, Conwy
TEL: 01745 570680

RABY NURSERIES
Benty Heath Lane, Neston, Cheshire
TEL: 0151 327 4221

PARKGATE NURSERIES
Boathouse Lane, Neston, Cheshire
TEL: 01513 364 178

FOLLY FIELD NURSERY
Folly Field, South Wirral, Cheshire
TEL: 0151 3274 999

BARRY'S OF PENSARN
17 Marine Road, Abergele, Conwy
TEL: 01745 825 056

TWO OAKS FARM NURSERY
Hanns Hall Road, Neston, Cheshire
TEL: 0151 336 1385

BURTON GARDEN NURSERIES
Chester High Road, Neston, Cheshire
TEL: 0151 336 2275

NORTH WALES WATER GARDENS
St Asaph Avenue, Rhyl, Conwy
TEL: 01745 338 222

NESS BOTANIC GARDENS
Ness, South Wirral, Cheshire
TEL: 0151 353 0123

GORDALE GARDEN CENTRE
Chester High Road, South Wirral, Cheshire
TEL: 0151 336 2116

SUNDAWN NURSERY & GARDEN CENTRE
St Asaph Road, Mold, Flintshire
TEL: 01352 720 840

WOODCOTE NURSERIES
Mudhouse Lane, Neston, Cheshire
TEL: 0151 336 1894

STATION HOUSE NURSERIES
Station House, Neston, Cheshire
TEL: 0151 353 0022

OLD HALL NURSERIES
Puddington Lane, Neston, Cheshire
TEL: 0151 336 2320

Gladiolus

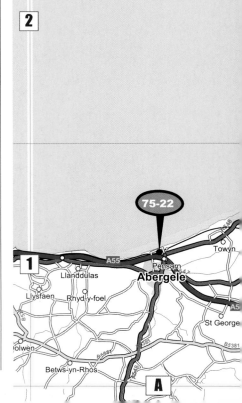

CROSTON CACTUS
43 Southport Road, Chorley, Lancashire
TEL: 01257 452 555

FIR TREE NURSERIES
Holmeswood Road, Ormskirk, Lancashire
TEL: 01704 823 334

RUFFORD OLD HALL, NATIONAL TRUST
Rufford, Ormskirk, Lancashire
TEL: 01704 821 254

BIRKACRE NURSERIES & GARDEN CENTRE
Birkacre Road, Chorley, Lancashire
TEL: 01257 270 473

WEST COAST BONSAI
Colin's Garden Centre, Southport, Merseyside
TEL: 01704 500 304

COLIN'S NURSERIES & GARDEN CENTRE
Southport Road, Southport, Merseyside
TEL: 01704 545 487

CAUSEWAY NURSERY
9 Causeway Cottage, Ormskirk, Lancashire
TEL: 01704 893 149

COPPULL MOOR LANE NURSERIES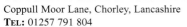
Coppull Moor Lane, Chorley, Lancashire
TEL: 01257 791 804

STONEY LEACH NURSERIES
40 Toogood Lane, Wigan, Lancashire
TEL: 01257 253 105

BRADLEY HALL NURSERIES
15a Bradley Hall Trading Estate, Wigan, Lancashire
TEL: 01257 427 085

KIWI NURSERIES
Arbour Lane, Wigan, Lancashire
TEL: 01257 472 511

ALAN ASHCROFT GARDEN CENTRE & ART STUDIO
Hall Lane, Ormskirk, Lancashire
TEL: 01704 892 315

WARBRECK GARDEN CENTRE
Lyelake Lane, Ormskirk, Lancashire
TEL: 01695 722 960

CICELY'S COTTAGE PLANTS
Cicely's Cottage, 43 Elmers Green,
Skelmersdale, Lancashire, WN8 6SG
TEL: 01695 720 790
EMAIL: maureen.duncan@ic24.net
A small nursery set in the garden of a 17th century cottage; specialising in cottage garden plants and other interesting perennials.
OPEN: All year - please ring to check times.
SPECIALITIES: Grasses, Hardy plants, Herbaceous plants, Lavender, Pelargoniums.

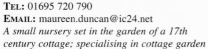

LLOYDS NURSERIES
1 Broad Lane, Ormskirk, Lancashire
TEL: 0151 526 0669

MILTON NURSERIES
Unit 1a, Wigan, Lancashire
TEL: 01942 825 445

LYDIATE BARN NURSERIES
Southport Road, Liverpool, Merseyside
TEL: 0151 520 1238

NORTHWAY NURSERIES
Moss Lane, Liverpool, Merseyside
TEL: 0151 526 4191

ROSE NURSERIES
Gathurst Road, Wigan, Lancashire
TEL: 01942 215 605

PIMBO NURSERIES & GARDEN CENTRE
30a Pimbo Lane, Skelmersdale, Lancashire
TEL: 01695 622 601

BILLINGE GARDEN CENTRE
New Home Farm, Wigan, Lancashire
TEL: 01695 632 317

SEFTON MEADOWS GARDEN & HOME CENTRE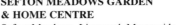
Sefton Meadows, Liverpool, Merseyside
TEL: 0151 531 6688

SANDY LANE NURSERIES
Sandy Lane, Liverpool, Merseyside
TEL: 0151 526 3232

STABLE YARD GARDEN CENTRE & BUILDERS SUPPLY
Stable Yard Estate, St Helens, Merseyside
TEL: 01744 617 307

BUCKELS NURSERY
Copplehouse Lane, Liverpool, Merseyside
TEL: 0151 5252712

SUREGROW GARDEN CENTRE
Merton Bank Road, St Helens, Merseyside
TEL: 01744 727 879

CROXTETH HALL COUNTRY PARK
Croxteth Hall Lane, Liverpool, Merseyside
TEL: 0151 228 5311

JAMES WHITAKER & SONS
Liverpool Road, Prescot, Merseyside
TEL: 0151 426 6455

C. & D. GARDEN & PET CENTRE
297 East Prescot Road, Liverpool, Merseyside
TEL: 0151 228 3143

WOODEND NURSERY
Warrington Road, Widnes, Cheshire
TEL: 0151 424 4932

WYEVALE GARDEN CENTRE
Mill Lane, Widnes, Cheshire
TEL: 0151 424 6264

RIVENDELL NURSERIES & GARDEN CENTRE
Mill Lane, Widnes, Cheshire
TEL: 0151 4232 638

WHITE MOSS NURSERY & GARDEN CENTRE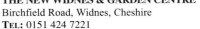
South Lane, Widnes, Cheshire
TEL: 01925 721 111

GATEACRE GARDEN CENTRE
Acrefield Road, Liverpool, Merseyside
TEL: 0151 428 6556

THE NEW WIDNES & GARDEN CENTRE
Birchfield Road, Widnes, Cheshire
TEL: 0151 424 7221

VICTORIA PARK
Birchfield Road, Widnes, Cheshire
TEL: 0151 4233 153

NORTON PRIORY MUSEUM AND GARDENS
Tudor Road, Runcorn, Cheshire
TEL: 01928 569 895

CALDERSTONE PARK
Liverpool, Merseyside
TEL: 0151 225 5921

REYNOLDS PARK WALLED GARDEN `76-39`
Church Road, Liverpool, Merseyside
TEL: 0151 724 2371

SPEKE HALL, NATIONAL TRUST `76-40`
The Walk, Liverpool, Merseyside
TEL: 0151 427 7231

BROOKFIELD GARDEN CENTRE `76-41`
2 Weston Road, Runcorn, Cheshire
TEL: 01928 576 754

FRODSHAM GARDEN CENTRE `76-42`
Mill Lane, Warrington, Cheshire
TEL: 01928 735 713

BURLEYDAM GARDEN CENTRE `76-43`
Chester Road, Ellesmere Port, Cheshire
TEL: 0151 339 3195

SYCAMORE PARK GARDEN CENTRE `76-44`
Chester Road, Great Sutton, Cheshire
TEL: 0151 339 1289

THE GARDEN OUTLET `76-45`
Unit 132-134, Ellesmere Port, Cheshire
TEL: 0151 357 3335

Gerber Daisy

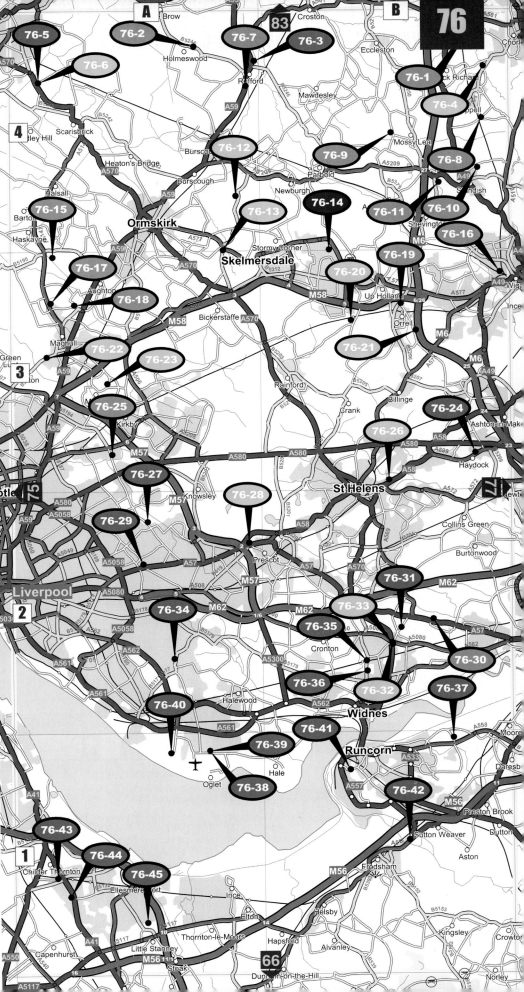

SUMMERSEAT GARDEN CENTRE
Railway Street, Bury, Lancashire
TEL: 01204 883 048

RIVINGTON TERRACED GARDENS
Great House Information Centre, Bolton, Lancashire
TEL: 01204 691 549

SMITHILLS COUNTRY PARK
Smithills Dean Road, Bolton, Lancashire
TEL: 01204 494 612

PARK VIEW GARDEN CENTRE
21a Park Road, Bolton, Lancashire
TEL: 01204 534 540

HAIGH HALL GARDENS
Haigh Country Park, Wigan, Lancashire
TEL: 01942 832 895

GOLDEN DAYS GARDEN CENTRE
Radcliffe Moor Road, Bolton, Lancashire
TEL: 01204 533 324

BARTON GRANGE GARDEN CENTRE
Wigan Road, Bolton, Lancashire
TEL: 01204 660 660

DARBY'S GARDEN CENTRE
Church Street, Bolton, Lancashire
TEL: 01942 818 430

GIANTS SEAT NURSERY
Ringley, Manchester, Greater Manchester
TEL: 0161 723 3462

BICKERSHAW HALL NURSERIES
Bickershaw Lane, Wigan, Lancashire
TEL: 01942 866 400

BROADOAK PARK GARDEN CENTRE
173 Worsley Road, Manchester, Greater Manchester
TEL: 01617 943 377

WORSLEY HALL GARDEN CENTRE
Leigh Road, Manchester, Greater Manchester
TEL: 0161 790 8792

E. ROGERS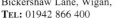
190A Church Street, Manchester, Greater Manchester
TEL: 01617 893 338

KENYON LANE NURSERIES
Kenyon Lane, Warrington, Cheshire
TEL: 01925 763324

BROOKEDGE NURSERIES
Woodhouse Road, Manchester, Greater Manchester
TEL: 0161 746 7300

TREBARON GARDEN CENTRE
Southworth Road, Newton le Willows, Merseyside
TEL: 01925 224 138

BENTS GARDEN CENTRE & NURSERIES
Warrington Road, Warrington, Cheshire
TEL: 01942 266 300

CULCHETH GARDEN CENTRE
Church Lane, Warrington, Cheshire
TEL: 01925 765 500

NEWCROFT NURSERIES 77-19
40 Newcroft Road, Manchester, Greater Manchester
TEL: 0161 7486 036

FLIXTON GARDEN CENTRE 77-20
Carrington Road, Manchester, Greater Manchester
TEL: 0161 748 5187

BRADLEY LANE NURSERIES 77-21
Bradley Lane, Manchester, Greater Manchester
TEL: 0161 976 5007

PRINCES PARK GARDEN CENTRE 77-22
Princes Park, Salford, Greater Manchester
TEL: 0161 775 0030

VICARAGE BOTANICAL GARDENS 77-23
Manchester Road, Manchester, Greater Manchester
TEL: 0161 775 2750

FAIRY LANE NURSERIES 77-24
Fairy Lane, Sale , Cheshire
TEL: 0161 905 1137

FERNDALE NURSERIES 77-25
273 Glazebrook Lane, Warrington, Cheshire
TEL: 0161 775 2977

WARD FUCHSIAS 77-26
5 Pollen Close, Sale , Cheshire
TEL: 0161 282 7434

WOOLSTON GARDEN CENTRE 77-27
1 New Cut Lane, Warrington, Cheshire
TEL: 01925 822 300

BATTMAN & SONS 77-28
29 Deans Gate Lane, Altrincham, Cheshire
TEL: 0161 928 0556

WORLD OF WATER 77-29
Thorley Lane, Timperley, Altrincham,
Cheshire WA15 7PJ
TEL: 0161 903 9944
EMAIL: wowmanchester@btclick.com
WEB: www.worldofwater.com
Everything for the pond and tropical fish enthusiast. Extensive showgardens. Expert advice.
OPEN: 9-5.30 Mon-Sat, Sun 10.30-4.30. Closed Easter Sun.
SPECIALITIES: Aquatic plants, Waterfalls, Water features.

WYEVALE GARDEN CENTRE 77-30
Green Lane, Altrincham, Cheshire
TEL: 0161 9806 036

DUNHAM MASSEY, NATIONAL TRUST 77-31
Altrincham, Cheshire
TEL: 0161 941 1025

WILLOW POOL GARDEN CENTRE 77-32
Burford Lane, Lymm, Cheshire
TEL: 01925 757 617

WALTON NURSERIES 77-33
54 Burford Lane, Lymm, Cheshire
TEL: 01925 759 026

CADDICK'S CLEMATIS NURSERY 77-34
Lymm Road, Warrington, Cheshire
TEL: 01925 757 196

CANTILEVER GARDEN CENTRE 77-35
Station Road, Warrington, Cheshire
TEL: 01925 635 799

LANE END NURSERY 77-36
Old Cherry Lane, Warrington, Cheshire
TEL: 01925 752 618

BELLHOUSE NURSERY 77-37
Bellhouse Lane, Warrington, Cheshire
TEL: 01925 740 874

WALTON HALL GARDENS 77-38
Walton Lea Road, Warrington, Cheshire
TEL: 01925 601 617

HIGH LEGH GARDEN CENTRE 77-39
High Legh, Knutsford, Cheshire
TEL: 01925 756 991

TATTON PARK, NATIONAL TRUST 77-40
Knutsford, Cheshire
TEL: 01625 534 400

ARLEY HALL NURSERY 77-41
Arley, Northwich, Cheshire
TEL: 01565 777 479

ARLEY HALL AND GARDENS 77-42
Arley, Northwich, Cheshire
TEL: 01565 777 353

Ranunculus

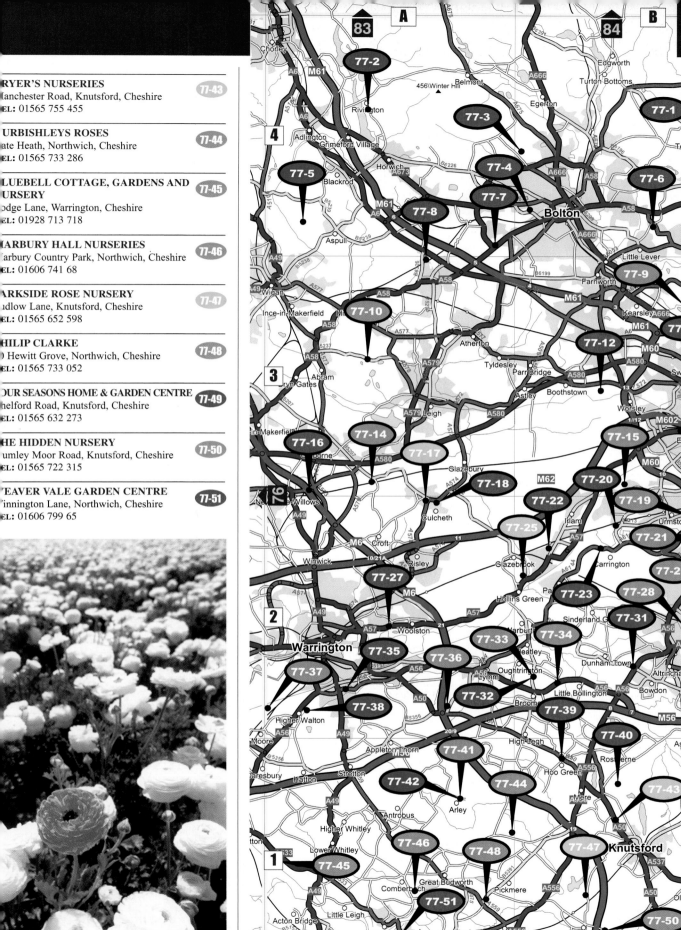

COLNE VALLEY GARDEN CENTRE
Scar Lane, Huddersfield, West Yorkshire
TEL: 01484 656 164

ALL-IN-ONE GARDEN CENTRE
Rochdale Road, Middleton, Manchester,
M24 2RB
TEL: 01706 711 711
EMAIL: info@allinone.co.uk
WEB: www.allinone.co.uk

*One of the country's leading garden centres,
complete with coffee shop, gift area, furniture,
garden ornaments, pet and aquatic centre, not
forgetting the massive array of plants and
shrubs.*
OPEN: Winter 9-5 Mon-Sat, 10-4 Sun. Summer
9-8 Mon-Fri, 9-5 Sat, 10-4 Sun.
SPECIALITIES: Aquatic plants, Shrubs,
Pet Centre.

HOPWOOD ARMS FARM SHOP & GARDEN CENTRE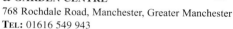
768 Rochdale Road, Manchester, Greater Manchester
TEL: 01616 549 943

STAKEHILL NURSERIES
Stakehill Lane, Manchester, Greater Manchester
TEL: 0161 643 3075

SHOLVERMOOR NURSERIES
Sholvermoor Farm, Oldham, Greater Manchester
TEL: 01616 245 553

BOOTH GARDEN CENTRE
Turf Lane, Oldham, Lancashire
TEL: 01706 845 337

NEWBANK GARDEN CENTRE
Irwell Bank Farm, Radcliffe, Greater Manchester
TEL: 0161 724 0585

BOWLEE NURSERY
Heywood Old Road, Manchester, Greater Manchester
TEL: 0161 653 9626

CLEVELAND GARDEN CENTRE
Bank Road, Manchester, Greater Manchester
TEL: 0161 795 2244

DAISY NOOK GARDEN CENTRE
Stannybrook Road, Manchester, Greater Manchester
TEL: 0161 681 4245

THE POND SHOP
Daisy Nook Garden Centre, Manchester, Greater
Manchester
TEL: 0161 681 5742

HEATON PARK
Prestwich, Manchester, M25 2SW
TEL: 0161 773 1085
EMAIL: heatonpark@ukonline.co.uk
WEB: www.manchester.gov.uk/leisure/parks

*Large horticultural centre set in formal gardens.
Extensive range of plants including roses,
herbaceous plants, bedding plants and hanging
baskets.*
OPEN: Daily, 9-3.30.
SPECIALITIES: Bedding plants, Rhododendrons
and azaleas, Roses, Shrubs, Trees.

PARKER'S GARDEN CENTRE
448 Chester Road, Manchester, Greater Manchester
TEL: 0161 877 4247

AQUA TONIC
24 Arundel Street, Glossop, Derbyshire
TEL: 01457 853 409

CHARLESWORTH NURSERY & GARDEN CENTRE
Glossop Road, Glossop, Derbyshire
TEL: 01457 863 998

LYMEFIELD GARDEN NURSERY
Lymefield Farm, Hyde, Greater Manchester
TEL: 01457 764 686

ROMILEY DIY & GARDEN CENTRE
23 Compstall Road, Stockport, Cheshire
TEL: 0161 430 3040

FLETCHER MOSS
Mill Gate Lane, Didsbury, Greater Manchester
TEL: 0161 445 4241

PHEDAR NURSERY
Bunkers Hill, Stockport, Cheshire
TEL: 0161 430 3772

WYTHENSHAWE PARK & HORTICULTURAL CENTRE
Wythenshawe Road, Manchester, Greater Manchester
TEL: 0161 998 2117

GOLDEN DAYS GARDEN CENTRE
Manchester Road, Cheadle, Cheshire
TEL: 0161 428 3098

WYEVALE GARDEN CENTRE
Otterspool, Stockport, Cheshire
TEL: 0161 427 7211

LOMAX NURSERIES
Adswood Road, Cheadle, Cheshire
TEL: 0161 485 1824

BRAMALL HALL
Bramall Park, Stockport, Cheshire
TEL: 0161 485 3708

PRIMROSE COTTAGE NURSERIES & GARDEN CENTRE
Ringway Road, Manchester, Greater Manchester
TEL: 0161 437 1557

BROOKSIDE GARDEN CENTRE
Macclesfield Road, Poynton, Cheshire
TEL: 01625 872 919

CROFTLAND NURSERY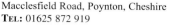
Altrincham Road, Wilmslow, Cheshire
TEL: 01625 539 616

BARTON GRANGE GARDEN CENTRE
Chester Road, Stockport, Cheshire
TEL: 0161 439 0745

MORLEY NURSERY
Altrincham Road, Wilmslow, Cheshire
TEL: 01625 528 953

WILMSLOW GARDEN CENTRE
Manchester Road, Wilmslow, Cheshire
TEL: 01625 525 700

LYME PARK, NATIONAL TRUST
Disley, Stockport, Cheshire
TEL: 01663 762 023

PURELY PERENNIAL PLANT CENTRE
9 Lees Lane, Macclesfield, Cheshire
TEL: 01625 523 871

CHESHIRE BASKETS
4 Lees Lane, Macclesfield, Cheshire
TEL: 01625 524 248

LONGDENDALE NURSERY
Blackbrook Lane, High Peak, Cheshire
TEL: 01298 813 940

ADLINGTON HALL
Mill Lane, Macclesfield, Cheshire
TEL: 01625 820 875

DUNGE VALLEY HIDDEN GARDENS
Windgather Rocks, High Peak, Cheshire
TEL: 01663 733 787

COLLINWOOD NURSERIES
Mottram St. Andrew, Macclesfield, Cheshire
TEL: 01625 582 272

HARE HILL, NATIONAL TRUST
Over Alderley, Macclesfield, Cheshire
TEL: 01625 828 981

ONE HOUSE NURSERY
Buxton New Road, Macclesfield, Cheshire
TEL: 01625 427 087

HENBURY GARDEN CENTRE
Chelford Road, Macclesfield, Cheshire
TEL: 01625 669007

FIRS HERBACEOUS PERENNIALS NURSERY
Chelford Road, Macclesfield, Cheshire
TEL: 01625 426 422

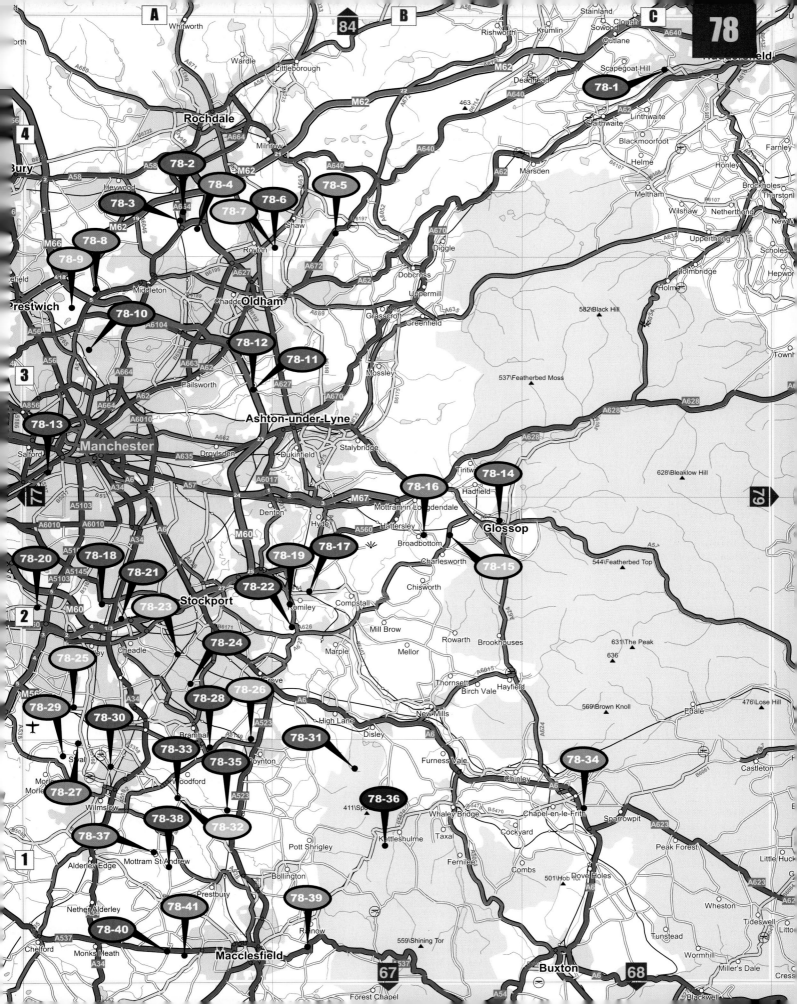

HAMPSONS PLANT WORLD GARDEN CENTRE `79-1`
Denby Dale Road, Wakefield, West Yorkshire
TEL: 01924 298 365

HAMPSONS PLANT WORLD GARDEN CENTRE `79-2`
Long Lane, Huddersfield, West Yorkshire
TEL: 01484 423 519

HALL GREEN NURSERIES `79-3`
Stoney Lane, Wakefield, West Yorkshire
TEL: 01924 259 589

YORKSHIRE SCULPTURE PARK `79-4`
Bretton Hall, Wakefield, West Yorkshire
TEL: 01924 830 302

OAK DENE NURSERIES `79-5`
10 Black Lane West, Barnsley, South Yorkshire
TEL: 01226 722 253

ARMITAGE'S PENNINE GARDEN CENTRE `79-6`
Huddersfield Road, Shelley, West Yorkshire
TEL: 01484 607 248

CANNON HALL GARDEN CENTRE `79-7`
Bark House Lane, Barnsley, South Yorkshire
TEL: 01226 790 785

CANNON HALL COUNTRY PARK `79-8`
Cawthorne, Barnsley, South Yorkshire
TEL: 01226 790 270

TOTTIES NURSERY `79-9`
Greenhill Bank Road, Huddersfield, West Yorkshire
TEL: 01484 683 363

CLAYCLIFFE GARDEN CENTRE `79-10`
Claycliffe Road, Barnsley, South Yorkshire
TEL: 01226 243 128

TOM HORSFIELD, ROSE GROWER & NURSERYMAN `79-11`
Pot House Mill Farm, Barnsley, South Yorkshire
TEL: 01226 790 441

CUTTING EDGE MARKET GARDEN `79-12`
Knowle Road, Barnsley, South Yorkshire
TEL: 01226 730 292

MILLHOUSE GREEN NURSERY `79-13`
350 Manchester Road, Barnsley, South Yorkshire
TEL: 01226 762 129

ROYD MARKET GARDEN & NURSERIES `79-14`
Hollin Busk Lane, Sheffield, South Yorkshire
TEL: 0114 283 0525

MOREHALL NURSERIES `79-15`
Morehall Farm, Sheffield, South Yorkshire
TEL: 0114 288 3239

BURNCROSS NURSERIES `79-16`
235 Burncross Road, Sheffield, South Yorkshire
TEL: 0114 257 0959

BARLOW NURSERIES `79-17`
94 Edge Lane, Sheffield, South Yorkshire
TEL: 0114 231 3758

HILLSBOROUGH WALLED GARDEN `79-18`
Middlewood Road, Sheffield, South Yorkshire
TEL: 0114 281 2167

RHINEGOLD NURSERIES `79-19`
West Lane, Sheffield, South Yorkshire
TEL: 0114 285 1487

HUTTONS NURSERIES `79-20`
Long Lane, Loxley, South Yorkshire
TEL: 01742 337 134

PEARSON GARDEN SUPPLIES `79-21`
Loxley Nurseries, Sheffield, South Yorkshire
TEL: 0114 233 7134

NORMANDALE NURSERIES `79-22`
66 Rodney Hill, Loxley, South Yorkshire
TEL: 0114 234 4703

HIGH RIGGS NURSERY `79-23`
Uppergate Road, Sheffield, South Yorkshire
TEL: 0114 285 4061

VALLEYSIDE GARDEN CENTRE `79-24`
Bell Hagg, Sheffield, South Yorkshire
TEL: 0114 230 1925

THE BOTANICAL GARDENS `79-25`
Clarkehouse Road, Sheffield, South Yorkshire
TEL: 0114 273 4599

W.O.R.K. `79-26`
Bents Green Workshops, Sheffield, South Yorkshire
TEL: 0114 262 0094

HOME AND GARDEN CENTRE `79-27`
237 Ringinglow Road, Sheffield, South Yorkshire
TEL: 01142 351 325

HIGH PEAK GARDEN CENTRE `79-28`
Hope Road, Hope Valley, Derbyshire
TEL: 01433 651 484

DORE MOOR NURSERY `79-29`
Brickhouse Lane, Sheffield, South Yorkshire
TEL: 0114 236 8144

ABBEYDALE GARDEN CO. `79-30`
Abbeydale Road South, Sheffield, South Yorkshire
TEL: 0114 236 9091

FERNDALE NURSERY & GARDEN CENTRE `79-31`
Dyche Lane, Dronfield, Derbyshire
TEL: 01246 412 763

WARD'S NURSERY & GARDEN CENTRE `79-33`
Eckington Road, Coal Aston, Derbyshire
TEL: 01246 412 622

CALVER SOUGH NURSERIES `79-34`
Calver Sough, Hope Valley, Derbyshire
TEL: 01433 630 692

GARDEN SUPPLIES `79-36`
The Mill Garden Centre, Chesterfield, Derbyshire
TEL: 01246 260 718

THE VICTORIAN GARDENS NURSERY `79-37`
Cressbrook, Buxton, Derbyshire
TEL: 01298 871 552

DIRECT CONIFER SUPPLIES `79-38`
Main Road, Chesterfield, Derbyshire
TEL: 01246 414 490

NEW LEAF PLANT CENTRE `79-32`
Dyche Lane, Coal Aston, Sheffield,
South Yorkshire, S18 6AA
TEL: 01246 413 311

Superb range of quality plants. Extensive range of mature stock for that instant impact. Expert advice. Large undercover areas and large car park.
OPEN: Open daily except Christmas.
SPECIALITIES: Climbers, Hardy plants, Roses, Seeds, Bulbs.

Tulips

DUNSTON HALL GARDEN CENTRE 79-35

Dunston Road, Newbold, Chesterfield,
Lancashire, S41 9RL
TEL: 01246 268 468
WEB: www.poplelandscapes.co.uk

*Situated in historic walled garden. Large
undercover shopping area stocking extensive
range of plants, sundries and gifts.
Inspirational display gardens. Expert advice.
Excellent catering facility.*
OPEN: Open daily except Christmas.
SPECIALITIES: Bedding plants, Garden &
conservatory furniture, Pot plants, Roses, Shrubs.

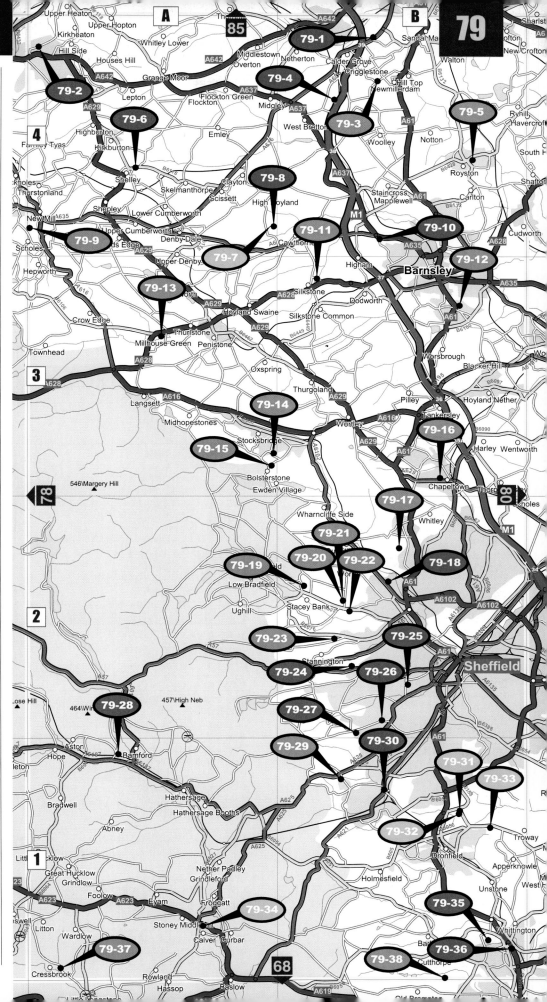

JAMES LAMPREY & SONS
The Nurseries, Pontefract, West Yorkshire
TEL: 01977 794 387

ACKWORTH GARDEN CENTRE
Barnsley Road, Pontefract, West Yorkshire
TEL: 01977 612 660

TAYLORS CLEMATIS NURSERY
Sutton Road, Doncaster, South Yorkshire
TEL: 01302 700 716

MAYFIELD GARDEN CENTRE
Kirton Lane, Doncaster, South Yorkshire
TEL: 01302 351 007

J. P. FOSS
Kirkby Common Farm, Barnsley, South Yorkshire
TEL: 01226 711 338

MARKHAM GRANGE NURSERY
Long Lands Lane, Doncaster, South Yorkshire
TEL: 01302 722 430

BRODSWORTH HALL, ENGLISH HERITAGE
Brodsworth, Doncaster, South Yorkshire
TEL: 01302 722 598

YEW TREE GARDEN CENTRE
Doncaster Road, Barnsley, South Yorkshire
TEL: 01226 750 500

OSCROFT NURSERIES
216 Sprotbrough Road, Doncaster, South Yorks
TEL: 01302 785 026

WOMBWELL AQUATICS & WATER GARDENS
52-56 Park Street, Barnsley, South Yorkshire
TEL: 01226 752 222

THE GARDEN OUTLET
Unit 45, Doncaster, South Yorkshire
TEL: 01302 366 772

BRANTON FARM NURSERIES
Doncaster Road, Doncaster, South Yorkshire
TEL: 01302 538 708

LLOYD WATH GARDEN CENTRE
Station Road, Rotherham, South Yorkshire
TEL: 01709 877 363

WALKERS NURSERIES
Mosham Road, Doncaster, South Yorkshire
TEL: 01302 770 325

PARROTTS CORNER NURSERY
325 Bawtry Road, Doncaster, South Yorkshire
TEL: 01302 863 339

WENTWORTH GARDEN CENTRE
Wentworth Park, Rotherham, South Yorkshire
TEL: 01226 744 842

OLD EDLINGTON NURSERIES
Edlington Lane, Doncaster, South Yorkshire
TEL: 01709 868 661

FOSTERS GARDEN CENTRE
Doncaster Road, Rotherham, South Yorkshire
TEL: 01709 850 337

MANOR GARDENS
Doncaster Road, Rotherham, South Yorkshire
TEL: 01709 852 433

STRINGERS NURSERIES
Hollyhead Farm, Crookhill Road,
Conisbrough, Doncaster,
South Yorkshire, DN12 2AE
TEL: 01709 863 228
WEB: www.stringers-nurseries.co.uk

The one worth finding. Huge selection of trees and shrubs; browse in our garden centre - relax in our conservatory cafe.
OPEN: Daily, summer 9-6, winter 9-5, closed Christmas, Boxing & New Year's Day.
SPECIALITIES: Alpines, Bedding plants, Fruit & fruit trees, Climbers, Hardy plants.

PLANTS OF SPECIAL INTEREST NURSERY
4 High Street, Rotherham, South Yorkshire
TEL: 01709 790 642

TICKHILL GARDEN CENTRE
Bawtry Road, Tickhill, Doncaster,
South Yorkshire, DN11 9EX
TEL: 01302 742 134
Plants of all shapes and sizes, our speciality top quality at reasonable prices, with an extensive range of pots and containers.
OPEN: Daily, summer 9-6, winter 9-5, closed Christmas Day & Boxing Day.
SPECIALITIES: Alpines, Climbers, Bedding plants, Fruit & fruit trees, Garden & conservatory furniture.

SEDGEWOOD NURSERY
2A Flanderwell Lane, Rotherham, South Yorkshire
TEL: 01709 532 669

BAWTRY GARDEN CENTRE
Great North Road, Doncaster, South Yorkshire
TEL: 01302 711 639

B. P. S. AQUATICS
Unit N, Rotherham, South Yorkshire
TEL: 01709 820 828

GODFREY'S GARDENS
Cedar Gables, Sheffield, South Yorkshire
TEL: 0114 287 2447

HODSOCK PRIORY GARDENS
Hodsock Priory, Worksop, Nottinghamshire
TEL: 01909 591 204

COOKS RIDGEWAY NURSERIES
High Lane, Sheffield, South Yorkshire
TEL: 0114 248 5944

CANAL TURN NURSERIES
Welham Road, Retford, Nottinghamshire
TEL: 01777 711 449

WAYSIDE WATER GARDENS
Doncaster Road, Oldcotes, Worksop,
Nottinghamshire, S81 8HT
TEL: 01909 731 367

Long established, family run watergardens, specialising in pondliners, fountains, aquatic plants, fish, pumps and filtration equipment. Highly recommended.
OPEN: Mar-Sep 10-1 & 2-6, Oct-Feb 10-1 & 2-4, closed Tue.
SPECIALITIES: Aquatic plants, Fish, Fountains, Waterfalls, Water features.

BIRLEY MOOR GARDEN CENTRE
27 Moor Valley, Sheffield, South Yorkshire
TEL: 0114 248 0666

THORPE SALVIN NURSERY
73 Common Road, Worksop, Nottinghamshire
TEL: 01909 515 393

CROFT NURSERIES
South Street, Sheffield, South Yorkshire
TEL: 0114 248 6541

MORTON HALL GARDENS
Morton Hall, Nottingham, Nottinghamshire
TEL: 01777 702 530

KENNILWORTH NURSERIES
London Road, Retford, Nottinghamshire
TEL: 01777 703 301

NORTHERN GARDEN SUPPLIES
Garden Centre & Nurseries, Worksop,
Nottinghamshire
TEL: 01909 731 600 / 731 024

HANDLEY ROSE NURSERIES
Lightwood Road, Sheffield, Derbyshire
TEL: 01246 432 921

SPRINGBANK NURSERIES
Westfield Lodge, Barlborough, South Yorkshire
TEL: 01246 810 393

VAN DYK GARDEN CENTRE
Southgate Nurseries, Chesterfield, Derbyshire
TEL: 01246 810 236

HIGHFIELDS NURSERIES
Highfields, Barlborough, South Yorkshire
TEL: 01246 810 636

DUKERIES GARDEN CENTRE
Welbeck, Worksop, Nottinghamshire
TEL: 01909 476 506

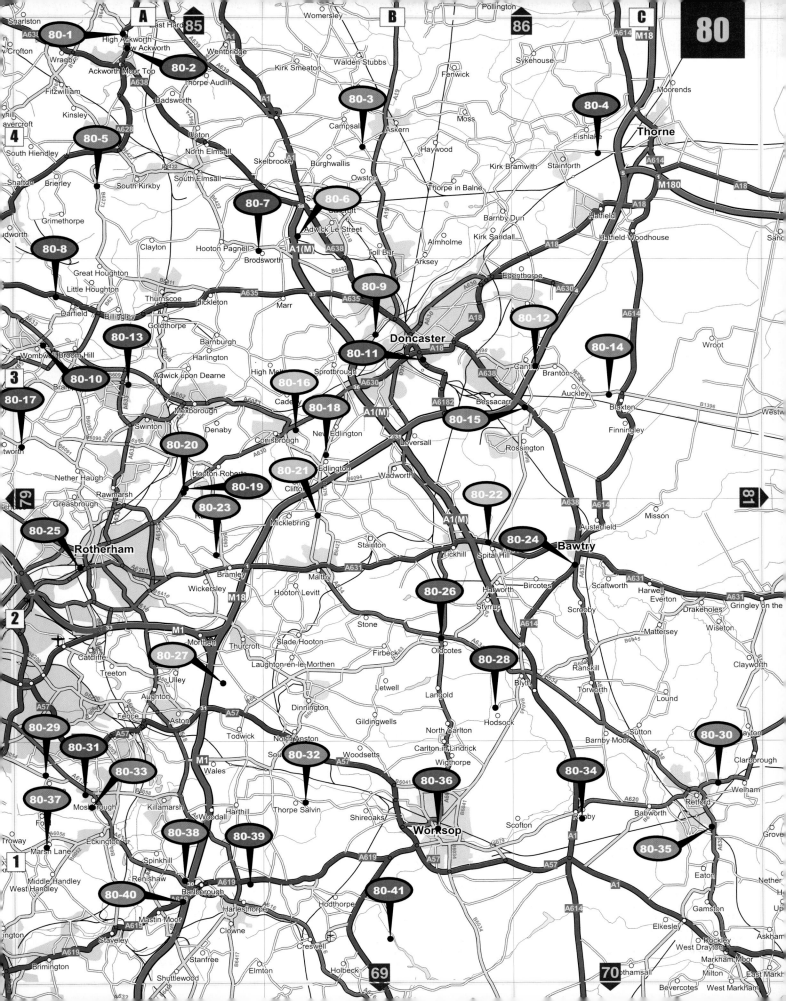

NORMANBY HALL VICTORIAN WALLED GARDEN `81-1`
Normanby, Scunthorpe, Lincolnshire
TEL: 01724 720 588

THE FERNERIES `81-2`
Killingholme Road, Ulceby, Lincolnshire
TEL: 01469 588 394

WILLOW NURSERIES `81-3`
31 Cravens Lane, Immingham, Lincolnshire
TEL: 01469 576 635

STEPHEN H SMITH GARDEN CENTRE `81-4`
Trent Valley Garden Centre, Scunthorpe, Lincolnshire
TEL: 01535 274 653

SILICA LODGE GARDEN CENTRE `81-5`
Scotter Road South, Scunthorpe, Lincolnshire
TEL: 01724 282 148

MENDLE NURSERY `81-6`
Holme, Scunthorpe, Lincolnshire
TEL: 01724 850 864

FROSTS GARDEN CENTRE `81-7`
Bigby High Road, Brigg, Lincolnshire, DN20 9HE
TEL: 01652 650 484
A rapidly growing centre which now has an undercover plant area, a huge choice of plants, terracotta pots, ornaments and patio furniture. Newly opened restaurant.
OPEN: Mon-Sat 9-5. Sun 10.30-4.30.
SPECIALITIES: Bedding plants, Furniture, Herbaceous plants, Paving, gates, railings & fencing, Terracotta pots.

GRANGE PARK AQUATICS `81-8`
Sands Farm, Scunthorpe, Lincolnshire
TEL: 01724 762 115

ROSEHOLME NURSERY `81-9`
Roseholme Farm, Lincoln, Lincolnshire
TEL: 01652 678 661

SCOTTER NURSERIES `81-10`
26 High Street, Gainsborough, Lincolnshire
TEL: 01724 762 562

POTTERTON & MARTIN `81-11`
Moortown Road, Market Rasen, Lincolnshire
TEL: 01472 851 792

FAIR GARDENS PLANT CENTRE `81-12`
Station Road, Kirton in Lindsey, Lincolnshire
TEL: 01652 648 631

BLAND TAVERN NURSERIES `81-13`
Station Road, Doncaster, South Yorkshire
TEL: 01427 752 267

SUNNYSIDE `81-14`
Sunnyside Farm, Gainsborough, Lincolnshire
TEL: 01427 628 240

KATHLEEN MUNCASTER FUCHSIAS `81-15`
18 Field Lane, Gainsborough, Lincolnshire
TEL: 01427 612 329

WICKENTREE NURSERIES `81-16`
Wicken Tree Farm, Market Rasen, Lincolnshire
TEL: 01673 842 918

MARTIN NEST NURSERIES `81-17`
Grange Cottage, Gainsborough, Lincolnshire
TEL: 01427 668 369

HALL FARM AND NURSERY `81-18`
Harpswell, Gainsborough, Lincolnshire
TEL: 01427 668 412

MILLFIELD NURSERIES `81-19`
Mill Lane, Retford, Nottinghamshire
TEL: 01427 880 422

GROVE GARDEN CENTRE `81-20`
Grove, Retford, Nottinghamshire
TEL: 01777 703 182

SCOTHERN NURSERIES `81-21`
Dunholme Road, Lincoln, Lincolnshire
TEL: 01673 862 297

JAPANESE GARDEN `81-22`
Pureland Meditation Centre, Newark, Nottinghamshire
TEL: 01777 228 567

Larkspur and Delphinium

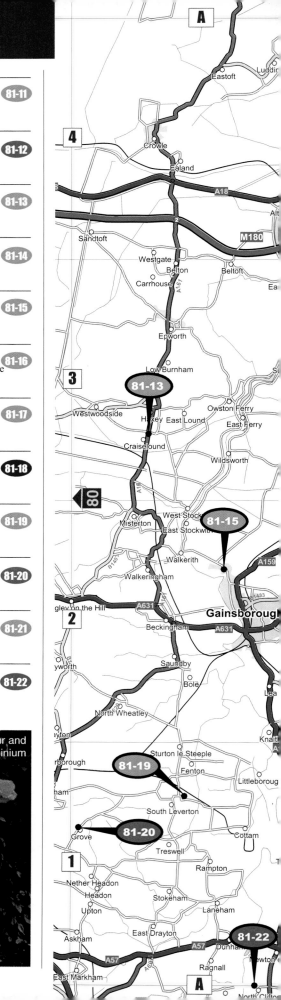

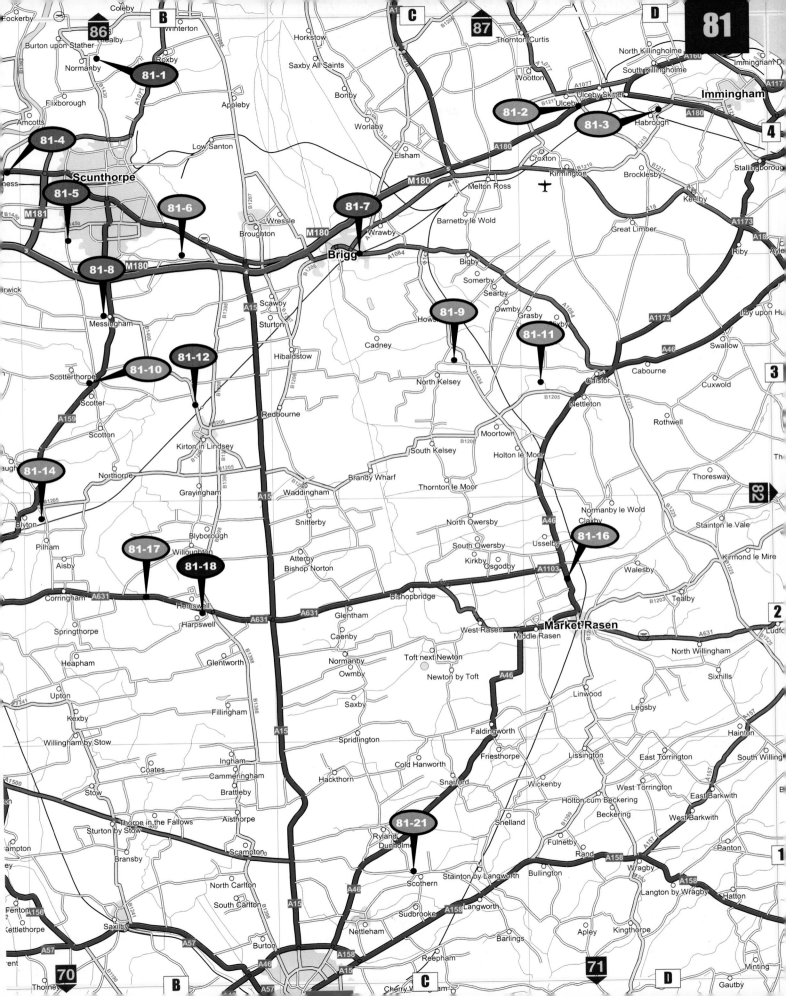

LINCOLNSHIRE

GARDEN CENTRE — NURSERY & GARDEN CENTRE
NURSERY — GARDEN & NURSERY
GARDEN — WATER GARDEN SPECIALIST

PENNELLS GARDEN CENTRE
Humberston Road, Grimsby, Lincolnshire
TEL: 01472 313 600

ALFORD'S GARDEN CENTRE
Grimsby Road, Grimsby, Lincolnshire
TEL: 01472 871 280

MAKHAMS NURSERIES
Boudary Farm, Grimsby, Lincolnshire
TEL: 01472 823 305

MILLSTONE GARDEN CENTRE
Wold View, Grimsby, Lincolnshire
TEL: 01472 828 150

NORBURNS PLANT CENTRE
Blenheim House, Grimsby, Lincolnshire
TEL: 01472 815 515

LINCOLNFIELD NURSERIES
Ludborough Road, North Thoresby, Lincs
TEL: 01472 840 461

THE FERN NURSERY
Grimsby Road, Binbrook, Lincolnshire
TEL: 01472 398 092

WOODTHORPE HALL GARDEN CENTRE 82-11
Woodthorpe, Withern, Alford,
Lincolnshire, LN13 0DD
TEL: 01507 450 509
One of Lincolnshire's largest undercover plant areas with a huge choice of plants, terracotta pots, gravels, fencing, ornaments and patio furniture including copper kettle restaurant.
OPEN: Mon-Sat 9-6. Sun 10.30-4.30.
SPECIALITIES: Bedding plants, Furniture, Herbaceous plants, Paving, gates, railings & fencing, Terracotta pots.

GREENWAYS GARDEN ORNAMENTS 82-9
Gayton-le-Marsh, Louth Road, Alford,
Lincolnshire, LN13 0NH
TEL: 01507 450 336
EMAIL: greenways@ntlworld.com

The garden centre with a difference. Manufacturers of high quality garden statuary beautifully displayed with a wealth of unusual garden ornamental products.
OPEN: Daily, Mon-Sat, 9-5. Sun, 10.30-4.30, closed Easter Sun.
SPECIALITIES: Stone ornaments, Water features.

LOUTH GARDEN CENTRE 82-8
Legbourne Road, Louth, Lincolnshire
TEL: 01507 605 381

TRUSTHORPE GARDEN CENTRE 82-10
Sutton Road, Mablethorpe, Lincolnshire
TEL: 01507 478 191

ASTERBY NURSERIES 82-12
Dairy Farm, Louth, Lincolnshire
TEL: 01507 343 549

COTTAGE NURSERIES 82-13
Thoresthorpe, Alford, Lincolnshire
TEL: 01507 466 968

Gerber Daisy

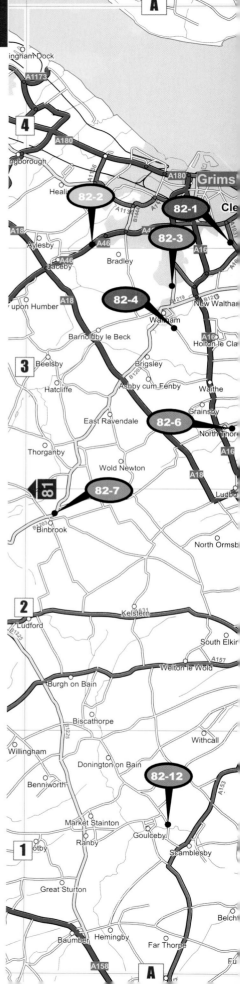

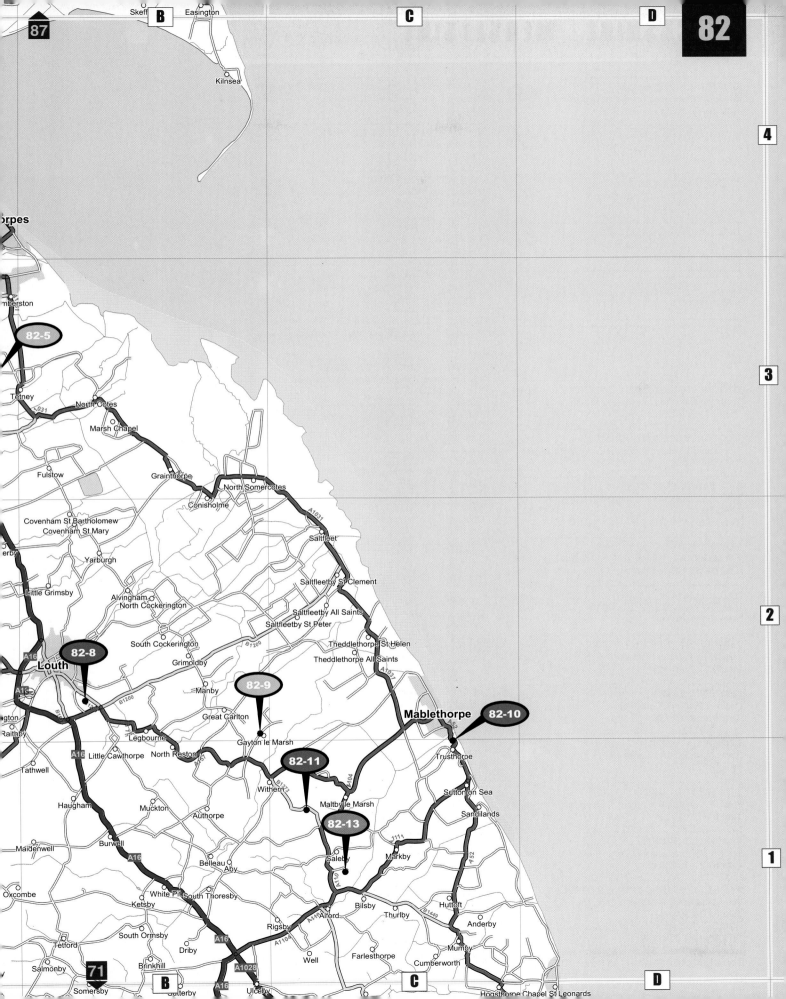

GREENFINGERS GARDEN SHOP `83-1`
3a Great John Street, Lancaster, Lancashire
TEL: 01524 382115

PINEWOOD GARDEN CENTRE `83-2`
Wallace Lane, Preston, Lancashire
TEL: 01524 792 453

W ROBINSON & SONS `83-3`
Sunny Bank, Preston, Lancashire
TEL: 01524 791 210

BEECHGROVE NURSERIES `83-4`
Station Lane, Preston, Lancashire
TEL: 01524 791 286

CLEGGS NURSERIES `83-5`
Hammersfield, Poulton le Fylde, Lancashire
TEL: 01253 700 250

DAISY BANK GARDEN CENTRE `83-6`
172 Victoria Road West, Thornton-Cleveleys,
Lancashire
TEL: 01253 856 802

HAMBLETON GARDEN CENTRE `83-7`
Bank View, Poulton le Fylde, Lancashire
TEL: 01253 702 212

BURNSIDE GARDEN CENTRE `83-8`
New Lane, Blackpool, Lancashire
TEL: 01253 821 383

THE PLANT PLACE `83-9`
Within Alt Nurseries, Thornton-Cleveleys,
Lancashire
TEL: 01253 856 414

BURTONWOOD NURSERIES `83-10`
109 Mains Lane, Poulton le Fylde, Lancashire
TEL: 01253 892 404

BARTON GRANGE GARDEN CENTRE `83-11`
Garstang Road, Preston, Lancashire
TEL: 01772 864242

JANE LANE NURSERIES `83-12`
Jane Lane, Preston, Lancashire
TEL: 01772 690 350

OAK NURSERIES `83-13`
Pudding Pie Nook Lane, Preston, Lancashire
TEL: 01772 862 828

CATFORTH GARDENS `83-14`
Roots Lane, Preston, Lancashire
TEL: 01772 690 561

WYEVALE GARDEN CENTRE `83-15`
Preston New Road, Kirkham, Lancashire
TEL: 01772 684 129

BLAYLOCK SHRUBS `83-16`
Lea Nurseries, Blackpool, Lancashire
TEL: 01253 761 009

BAGULEY'S THE GARDEN PEOPLE `83-17`
Midgeland Road, Blackpool, Lancashire
TEL: 01253 762 981

THE PLANT EMPORIUM `83-18`
Preston New Road, Blackpool, Lancashire
TEL: 01253 761 034

CROPPER MANOR GARDEN CENTRE `83-19`
Cropper Road, Blackpool, Lancashire
TEL: 01253 699 987

TREBARON GARDEN CENTRE `83-20`
350 Common Edge Road, Blackpool, Lancashire
TEL: 01253 691368

NEWTON NURSERIES `83-21`
Preston New Road, Preston, Lancashire
TEL: 01772 684 097

THE POND SHOP `83-22`
Clifton Garden Centre, Preston, Lancashire
TEL: 01772 673 244

ASHTON MEMORIAL `83-23`
Williamson Park , Preston, Lancashire
TEL: 01772 884 444

BEARDWOOD GARDEN CENTRE `83-24`
Preston New Road, Blackburn, Lancashire
TEL: 01254 693 121

ASHTON'S NURSERY GARDENS `83-25`
Mythop Road, Lytham St Annes, Lancashire
TEL: 01253 736 627

HAWTHORNES NURSERY `83-26`
Marsh Road, Preston, Lancashire
TEL: 01772 812 379

CLAREMONT AQUATIC NURSERIES `83-27`
Cocker Bar Road, Preston, Lancashire
TEL: 01772 421 860

CHARNOCK FARM GARDEN CENTRE `83-28`
Charnocks Farm, Preston, Lancashire
TEL: 01772 623 350

BRIARLEEGARDEN CENTRE `83-29`
35 Chapel Lane, Southport, Merseyside
TEL: 01704 226 647

TARLETON SPECIMEN PLANTS `83-30`
Gorse Lane, Preston, Lancashire
TEL: 01772 816 879

BLUNDELLS NURSERIES `83-31`
68 Southport New Road, Preston, Lancashire
TEL: 01772 815 442

DUNSCAR NURSERIES & `83-32`
GARDEN CENTRE
118 Southport New Road, Tarleton, Preston,
Lancashire, PR4 6HY
TEL: 01772 812 684
EMAIL: dunscar@uk2.net
WEB: www.dunscar.com
*Family run centre with superb quality plant
stock, much produced on site. Professional florist
on site. Finalist for Retail Nursery of the Year
2000.*
OPEN: Open 7 days a week 9-5. Sun 10.30-4.30.
SPECIALITIES: Hardy plants, Sundries, Shrubs,
Trees.

LYNDENE NURSERIES `83-33`
143 Southport New Road, Preston, Lancashire
TEL: 01772 813 611

AULDENE GARDEN CENTRE `83-34`
Southport Road, Preston, Lancashire
TEL: 01772 600 271

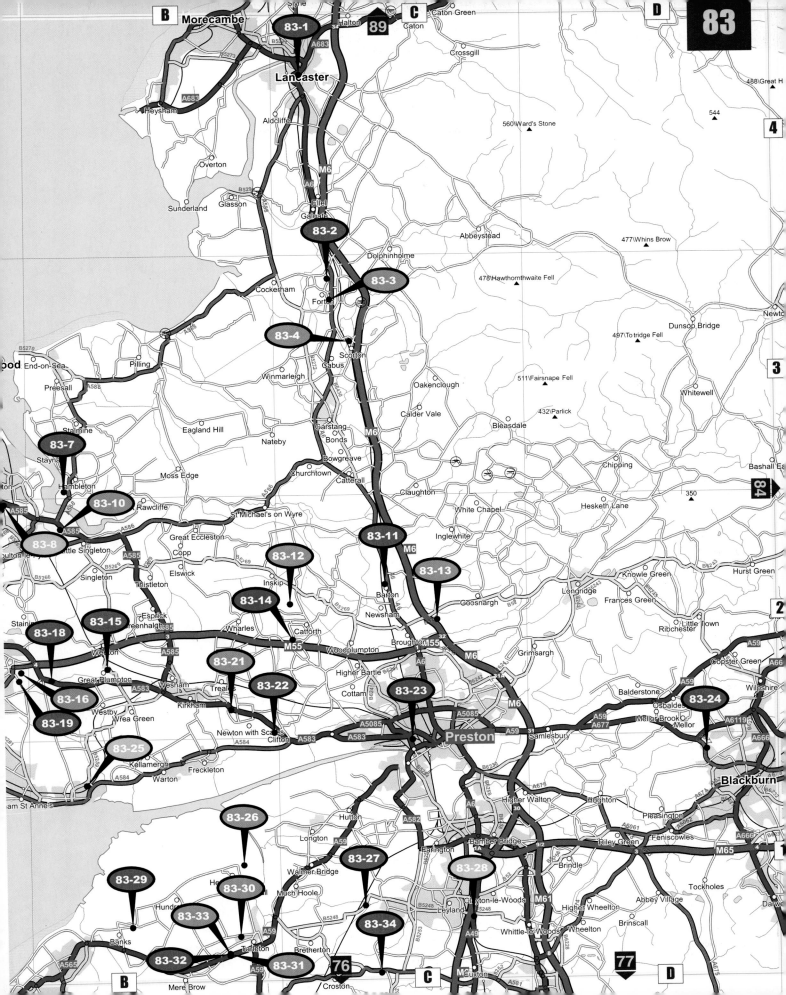

PERCEVALL HALL GARDENS `84-1`
Skyreholme, Skipton, North Yorkshire
TEL: 01756 720 311

BAILEY GARDEN CENTRE `84-2`
The Bailey, Skipton, North Yorkshire
TEL: 01756 791 619

HOLDEN CLOUGH NURSERY `84-3`
Holden, Clitheroe, Lancashire
TEL: 01200 447 615

GARDENIA GARDEN & SHOP `84-4`
Slisden Caravan and Lesiure, Silsen, West Yorkshire
TEL: 01535 656 351

ILKLEY MOOR GARDEN CENTRE `84-5`
Robin Hole, Ilkley, West Yorkshire
TEL: 01943 864303

GARDENERS CHOICE `84-6`
7a Aire Street, Keighley, West Yorkshire
TEL: 01535 631 630

SALTERFORTH NURSERIES & LANDSCAPES `84-7`
Moor Lane, Barnoldswick, Lancashire
TEL: 01282 850 649

EAST RIDDLESDEN HALL, NATIONAL TRUST `84-8`
Bradford Road, Keighley, West Yorkshire
TEL: 01535 607 075

LAKESIDE GARDEN CENTRE `84-9`
Skipton Road, Colne, Lancashire
TEL: 01282 865 650

HEDGEROW NURSERY `84-10`
24 Braithwaite Edge Road, Keighley, West Yorkshire
TEL: 01535 606 531

BARKERS GARDEN CENTRE `84-11`
Whalley Road, Clitheroe, Lancashire
TEL: 01200 423 521

CRAVEN'S BRONTE VIEW NURSERY `84-12`
1 Foulds Terrace, Bingley, West Yorkshire
TEL: 01274 561 412

PENDLE HERITAGE CENTRE `84-13`
Park Hill, Nelson, Lancashire
TEL: 01282 611 718

WOODWARD NURSERIES `84-14`
Barnsley Beck Grove, Shipley, West Yorkshire
TEL: 01274 414 789

TOM HANSEN & SONS (BARROW NURSERIES) `84-15`
Whalley Road, Clitheroe, Lancashire
TEL: 01254 822 145

IVY LEA NURSERY `84-16`
3 Fry Street, Nelson, Lancashire
TEL: 01282 613 604

HIRSTWOOD NURSERIES `84-17`
Hirst Lane, Shipley, West Yorkshire
TEL: 01274 591 251

SANDY BANKS WATER LIFE `84-18`
Sandy Banks Garden Centre, Bingley, West Yorkshire
TEL: 01535 275 032

REEDLEY NURSERY `84-19`
Reedley Cottage, Nelson, Lancashire
TEL: 01282 693 376

CARLTON NURSERIES & LANDSCAPE GARDENERS `84-20`
Cottingley Moor Road, Bingley, West Yorkshire
TEL: 01274 496 270

HUNTROYDE NURSERIES `84-21`
Whins Lane, Burnley, Lancashire
TEL: 01282 770 753

READ GARDEN CENTRE `84-22`
Old Coal Staithe, Burnley, Lancashire
TEL: 01254 884215

GAWTHORPE HALL `84-23`
Padiham, Burnley, Lancashire
TEL: 01282 771 004

SPRINGWOOD NURSERIES `84-24`
Springwood Road, Burnley, Lancashire
TEL: 01282 425 316

MOS FARM CONIFERS `84-25`
Moss Farm, Halifax, West Yorkshire
TEL: 01422 245 196

TOWNELEY GARDEN CENTRE `84-26`
Deerpark Nurseries, Burnley, Lancashire
TEL: 01282 424 162

SLACK TOP ALPINES `84-27`
1 Waterloo House, Hebden Bridge, West Yorkshire
TEL: 01422 845 348

WYEVALE GARDEN CENTRE `84-28`
Denholmegate Road, Halifax, West Yorkshire
TEL: 01422 206 418

DOVE COTTAGE PLANTS `84-29`
23 Shibden Hall Road, Halifax, West Yorkshire
TEL: 01422 203 553

BROOKSIDE NURSERIES `84-30`
Roundhill Road, Accrington, Lancashire
TEL: 01706 216 491

KERSHAW'S GARDEN CENTRE `84-31`
Halifax Road, Brighouse, West Yorkshire
TEL: 01484 713435

LEABROOK NURSERIES `84-32`
Burnley Road, Rossendale, Lancashire
TEL: 01706 230 856

FOUR SEASONS GARDEN CENTRE `84-33`
Ashton Road, Darwen, Lancashire
TEL: 01254 706890

THAT GARDENING PLACE! `84-34`
Spring Vale Road, Darwen, Lancashire
TEL: 01254 702 915

WHITWORTH GARDEN CENTRE `84-35`
Grange Road, Rochdale, Greater Manchester
TEL: 01706 853 623

ARMITAGE'S MOWER WORLD & GARDEN CENTRE `84-36`
Birchencliffe Hill Road, Huddersfield, West Yorkshire
TEL: 01484 536 010

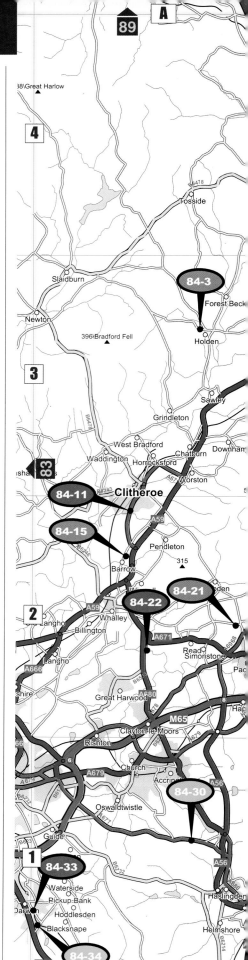

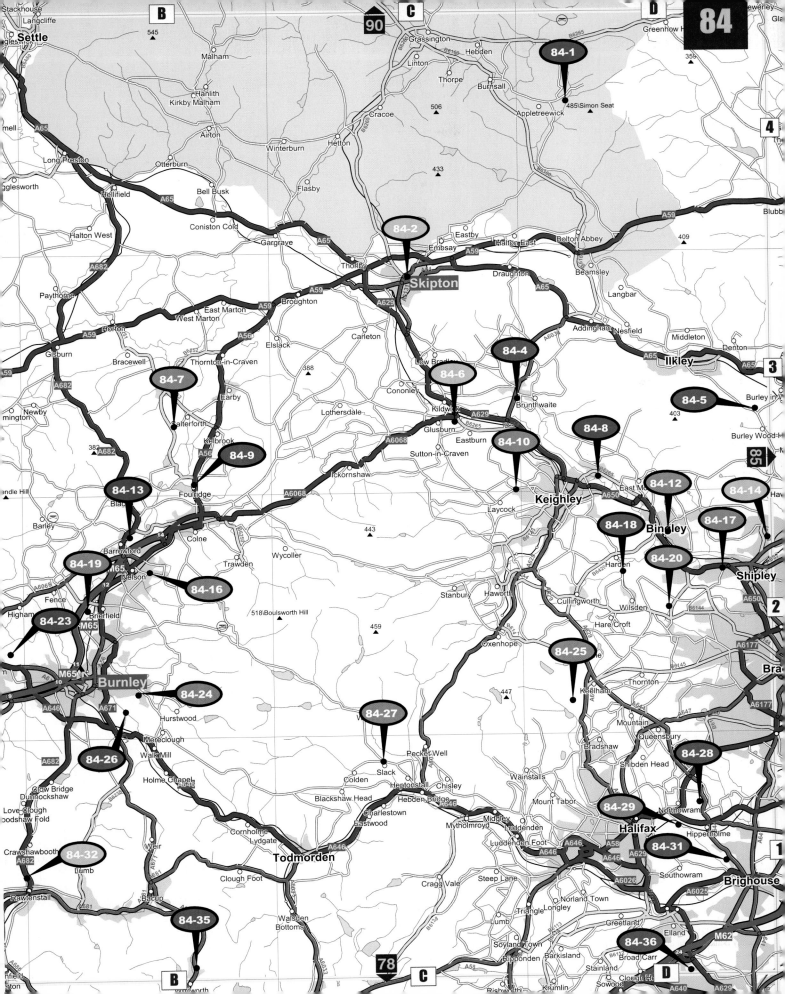

- GARDEN CENTRE
- NURSERY
- GARDEN
- NURSERY & GARDEN CENTRE
- GARDEN & NURSERY
- WATER GARDEN SPECIALIST

ORCHARD HOUSE NURSERY `85-1`
Wormald Green, Harrogate, North Yorkshire
TEL: 01765 677 541

WOODLANDS COTTAGE NURSERY `85-2`
Summerbridge, Harrogate, North Yorkshire
TEL: 01423 780 765

WAYSIDE NURSERIES `85-3`
Minskip Road, Knaresborough, North Yorkshire
TEL: 01423 340 293

RIPLEY CASTLE `85-4`
Ripley, Harrogate, North Yorkshire
TEL: 01423 770 152

PARK NURSERIES `85-5`
Bar Lane, Knaresborough, North Yorkshire
TEL: 01423 865 182

WILLIAM STRIKE `85-6`
York Road, Knaresborough, North Yorkshire
TEL: 01423 865 351

THE VALLEY GARDENS `85-7`
Harrogate, North Yorkshire
TEL: 01423 500 600

**MOORLAND NURSERIES
& GARDEN CENTRE** `85-8`
Forest Moor Road, Knaresborough, North Yorkshire
TEL: 01423 866 054

RICHARD GRIFFITHS HOUSE PLANTS `85-9`
Moorland Nurseries, Knaresborough, North Yorkshire
TEL: 01423 860 672   859

THE POTTING SHED `85-10`
Thistle Hill Nurseries, Knaresborough, North Yorkshire
TEL: 01423 869 949

HARLOW CARR BOTANICAL GARDENS `85-11`
Crag Lane, Harrogate, North Yorkshire
TEL: 01423 565 418

BLUECOAT WOOD NURSERIES `85-12`
Otley Road, Harrogate, North Yorkshire
TEL: 01423 522 876

CRIMPLE VALLEY GARDEN CENTRE `85-13`
Leeds Road, Harrogate, North Yorkshire
TEL: 01423 872 463

RIVERSIDE NURSERIES `85-14`
Linton Common, Wetherby, West Yorkshire
TEL: 01937 582 598

GREENERY GARDEN CENTRE `85-15`
The Shopping Centre, Wetherby, West Yorkshire
TEL: 01937 844 778

OLD MILL GARDEN CENTRE `85-16`
Leeds Road, Wetherby, West Yorkshire
TEL: 01937 572 870

**STEPHEN H. SMITH'S GARDEN
& LEISURE, WHARFE VALLEY** `85-17`
Pool Road, Otley, West Yorkshire
TEL: 01943 462 195

HAREWOOD HOUSE `85-18`
Harewood, Leeds, West Yorkshire
TEL: 0113 288 6331

SWINCAR NURSERIES `85-19`
Chevin End Road, Guiseley, West Yorkshire
TEL: 01943 874 614

HIGHTREES GARDEN CENTRE `85-20`
Otley Old Road, Leeds, West Yorkshire
TEL: 0113 258 7788

BRAMHAM PARK `85-21`
Wetherby, West Yorkshire
TEL: 01937 844 265

GRIMSTON PARK NURSERIES `85-22`
Grimston Park, Tadcaster, North Yorkshire
TEL: 01937 832 188

**GREENSCAPES NURSERY & GARDEN
DESIGN CENTRE** `85-23`
Brandon Crescent, Leeds, West Yorkshire
TEL: 0113 289 2922

WOLINSKI NURSERY `85-24`
Bay Horse Lane, Leeds, West Yorkshire
TEL: 0113 289 2873

WILLIAM STRIKE `85-25`
Red Hall Lane, Leeds, West Yorkshire
TEL: 0113 265 7839

ROUNDHAY PARK `85-26`
Tropical World Canal Gardens, Leeds, West Yorkshire
TEL: 0113 266 1850

HAYES GARDEN WORLD `85-27`
York Road, Leeds, West Yorkshire
TEL: 01132 731 949

HOLLIES PARK `85-28`
Westwood Lane, Leeds, West Yorkshire
TEL: 0113 247 8361

PALMER NURSERIES `85-29`
Calverley Lane, Pudsey, West Yorkshire
TEL: 0113 256 3331

A. C. W. GARDEN CENTRE `85-30`
Canal Road, Bradford, West Yorkshire
TEL: 01274 392 344

GOLDEN ACRE PARK `85-31`
Otley Road, Leeds, West Yorkshire
TEL: 0113 261 0374

TEMPLE NEWSAM PARK `85-32`
Leeds, West Yorkshire
TEL: 0113 247 7960

PUDSEY PARK `85-33`
Church Lane, Pudsey, West Yorkshire
TEL: 0113 255 1334

WILLIAM STRIKE `85-34`
Selby Road, Leeds, West Yorkshire
TEL: 0113 286 2981

LUMBY GARDEN CENTRE `85-3`
Leys House, Leeds, West Yorkshire
TEL: 01977 682 815

TONG GARDEN CENTRE `85-3`
Tong Lane, Bradford, West Yorkshire
TEL: 0113 285 3506

A. J. KEELING & SON `85-3`
North View Road, Bradford, West Yorkshire
TEL: 01274 682 120

BEECHES NURSERIES `85-3`
31 Back Lane, Bradford, West Yorkshire
TEL: 0113 287 9077

SPEN NURSERIES `85-3`
Spen Lane, Cleckheaton, West Yorkshire
TEL: 01274 869 282

M. G. W. PLANTS `85-4`
45 Potovens Lane, Wakefield, West Yorkshire
TEL: 01924 820 096

PARK HOUSE NURSERIES `85-4`
Eddercliffe Crescent, Liversedge, West Yorkshire
TEL: 01274 861 500

D. C. GRAHAM & SON `85-4`
Stranglands Lane, Knottingley, West Yorkshire
TEL: 01977 552 362

THE GARDEN OUTLET `85-4`
Unit j2/j3, Castleford, West Yorkshire
TEL: 01977 519 238

CARR GATE NURSERIES `85-4`
Old Bradford Road, Wakefield, West Yorkshire
TEL: 01924 823 002

NEWTON HILL ALPINES `85-4`
335 Leeds Road, Wakefield, West Yorkshire
TEL: 01924 377 056

LINDHILL NURSERY `85-4`
Batley Road, Wakefield, West Yorkshire
TEL: 01924 372 433

WHITELEYS GARDEN CENTRE `85-4`
Leeds Road, Mirfield, West Yorkshire
TEL: 01924 495 944

WESTFIELD NURSERIES `85-4`
Shillbank Lane, Mirfield, West Yorkshire
TEL: 01924 498 259

SPRING GREEN NURSERIES `85-4`
Pontefract Road, Wakefield, West Yorkshire
TEL: 01924 863 859

Marigold

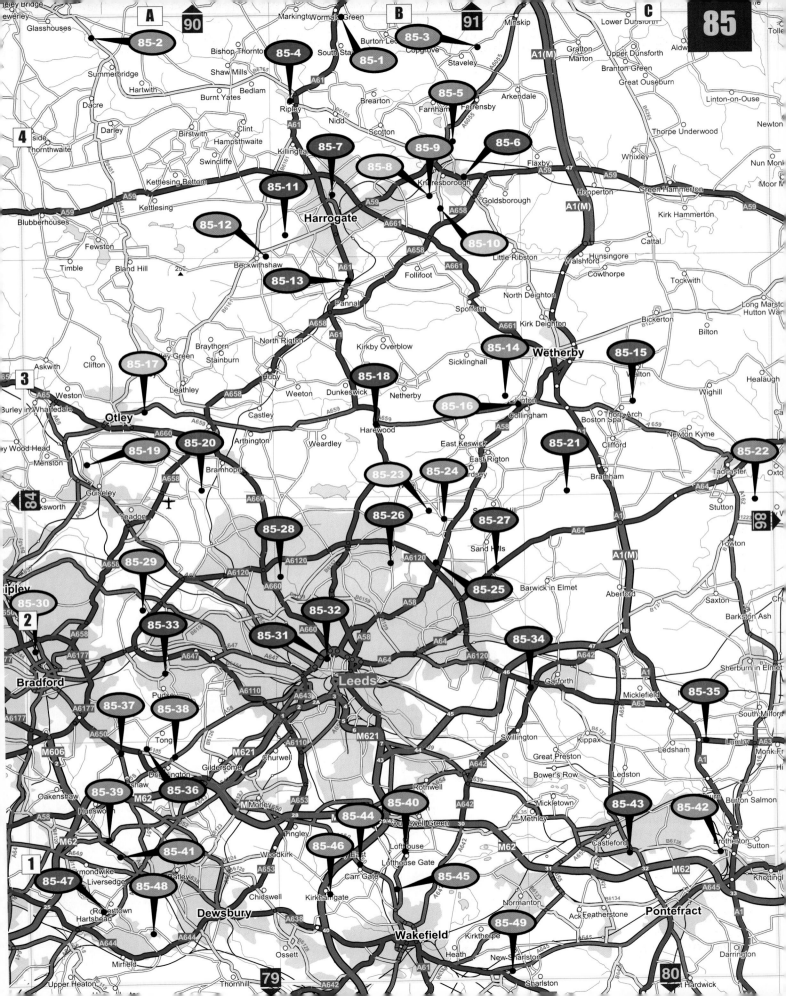

FLAXTON HOUSE NURSERY

Flaxton, York,
Yorkshire, YO60 7RJ
TEL: 01904 468 753
Wide variety of home grown stock, speciality herbaceous but interesting shrubs and climbers too. Display garden.
OPEN: 1 Mar-30 Sep, 10-5. Closed Mon except Bank hols.
SPECIALITIES: Alpines, Climbers, Hardy plants, Roses, Shrubs.

BENINGBROUGH HALL & GARDENS, NATIONAL TRUST

Beningbrough, York, North Yorkshire
TEL: 01904 470 666

MOOR MONKTON NURSERIES

York Road, York, North Yorkshire
TEL: 01904 738 319

WIGGINTON ROAD NURSERIES

Wigginton Road, York, North Yorkshire
TEL: 01904 762 250

ORCHARD NURSERIES

48 Hopgrove Lane South, York, North Yorkshire
TEL: 01904 421 153

WYEVALE GARDEN CENTRE

Northfield Lane, York, North Yorkshire
TEL: 01904 795 920

TREASURER'S HOUSE, NATIONAL TRUST

Minster Yard, York, North Yorkshire
TEL: 01904 624 247

BORETREE NURSERIES

Grimston Court, York, North Yorkshire
TEL: 01904 488 437

MERCHANT ADVENTURERS' HALL & GARDEN

Fossgate, York, North Yorkshire
TEL: 01904 654 818

DAVID W. SMITH GARDEN CENTRE

Sunray, York, North Yorkshire
TEL: 01759 388 863

BRUNSWICK ORGANIC NURSERY

Appleton Road, York, North Yorkshire
TEL: 01904 701 869

BURNBY HALL GARDENS

The Balk, Pocklington, East Riding of Yorkshire
TEL: 01759 302 068

SPRINGWELL GARDEN CENTRE

Main Street, York, North Yorkshire
TEL: 01904 448 733

STILLINGFLEET LODGE NURSERIES

Stillingfleet, North Yorkshire
TEL: 01904 728 506

SELBY GARDEN CENTRE

Hull Road, Selby, North Yorkshire
TEL: 01757 708658

LANGLANDS NURSERIES & GARDEN CENTRE

York Road, Shiptonthorpe, York, North Yorkshire, YO43 3PN
TEL: 01430 873 426
Large nurseries open to the public. Specialist growers of fuchsias, geraniums, bedding and patio plants. Well worth a visit any time of year.
OPEN: Daily, Mon-Sat 9-5.30, Sun 10.30-4.30.
SPECIALITIES: Alpines, Bedding plants, Climbers, Greenhouses & sheds, Hardy plants.

ASHFIELD HELLEBORES, RARER PLANTS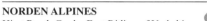

Ashfield House, Leeds, West Yorkshire
TEL: 01977 682 263

YORKSHIRE GARDEN CENTRE

Scalby Lane, Brough, East Riding of Yorkshire
TEL: 01430 440 169

OAK TREE NURSERY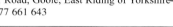

Mill Lane, Selby, North Yorkshire
TEL: 01757 618 409

CALIFORNIA GARDENS

Boothberry Road, Howden, East Riding of Yorkshire
TEL: 01430 430 824

NORDEN ALPINES 86-21

Hirst Road, Goole, East Riding of Yorkshire
TEL: 01405 861 348

TWO HOOTS NURSERIES & GARDEN CENTRE 86-22

Hirst Road, Goole, East Riding of Yorkshire
TEL: 01405 862 854

CROWN GARDEN CENTRE 86-23

Doncaster Road, Goole, East Riding of Yorkshire
TEL: 01977 661 643

WESTSHORES NURSERIES 86-24

82 West Street, Winterton, Lincolnshire
TEL: 01724 733 940

Pansy

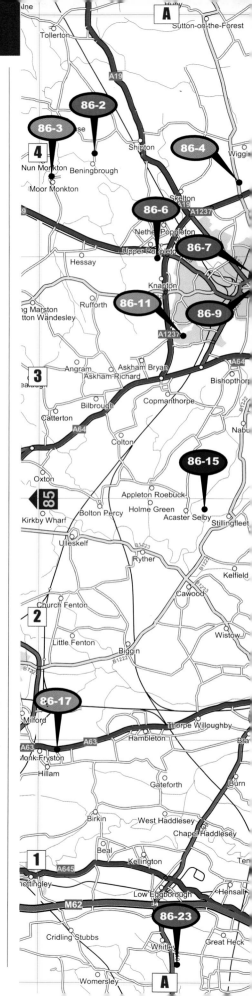

BURTON AGNES HALL GARDENS 87-1
Estate Office, Burton Agnes, Driffield,
East Riding of Yorkshire, YO25 4NB
TEL: 01262 490 324
EMAIL: burton-agnes@farmline.com
WEB: www.burton-agnes.com

*Lawns and topiary surround the Elizabethan
house while the walled garden contains a riot of
flowers including a maze and potager.*
OPEN: Daily, Apr 1-Oct 31, 11-5.
ENTRY COSTS: Adult £2.40, Children £1.00,
OAPs £2.15.
SPECIALITIES: Hardy plants, Seeds, Vegetables.

J. & D. MARSTON 87-2
Culag, Driffield, East Riding of Yorkshire
TEL: 01377 254 487

BELL MILLS GARDEN CENTRE 87-3
Bell Mills, Driffield, East Riding of Yorkshire
TEL: 01377 254 043

LONDESBORO NURSERIES & GARDEN CENTRE 87-4
Hutton Cranswick, East Yorkshire
TEL: 01377 270 272

MIDDLE FARM NURSERIES 87-5
Main Road, Hornsea, East Riding of Yorkshire
TEL: 01964 532 542

SPRING GARDEN CENTRE 87-6
Main Street, Hull, East Riding of Yorkshire
TEL: 01964 543 040

WHITE COTTAGE ALPINES 87-7
Sunnyside Nurseries, Sigglesthorne,
East Riding of Yorkshire
TEL: 01964 542 692

DEVINE NURSERIES & GARDEN CENTRE 87-8
Main Road, Withernsea, East Riding of Yorkshire
TEL: 01964 613840

TUPLINS NURSERIES 87-9
The Nurseries, Barrow upon Humber, Lincolnshire
TEL: 01469 532 662

THE PALM FARM 87-10
Thornton Hall Gardens, Station Road,
Thornton Curtis, Ulceby,
Lincolnshire, DN39 6XF
TEL: 01469 531 232
EMAIL: bill@palmfarm.fsbusiness.co.uk
WEB: www.palmfarm.com

*Specialists in
palms and exotics
for the garden
and conservatory.
Unusual trees,
shrubs, climbers.
Palm garden and
other demonstra-
tion plantings.*
OPEN:
Daily, 2-5.
SPECIALITIES:
Palms.

Rose

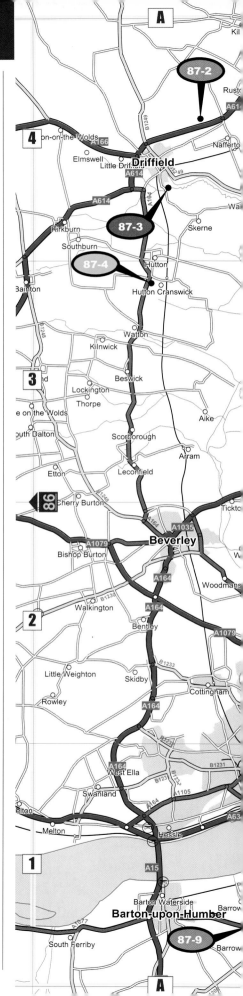

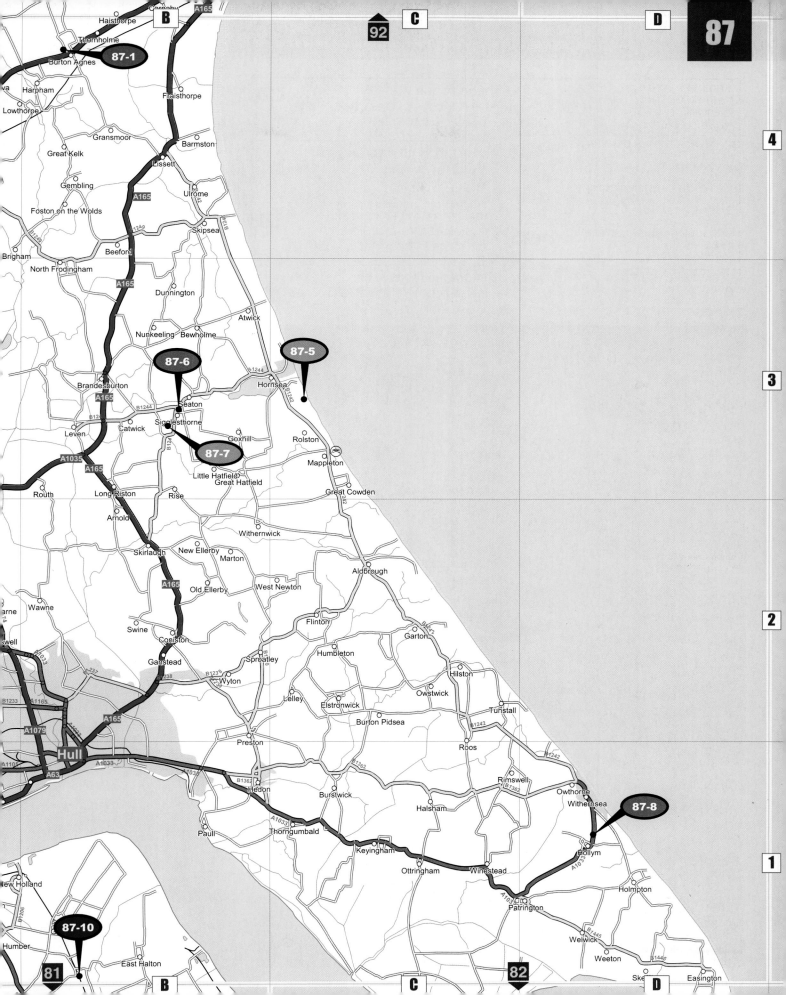

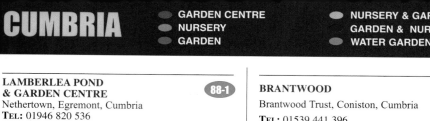

CUMBRIA

- ● GARDEN CENTRE
- ● NURSERY
- ● GARDEN
- ● NURSERY & GARDEN CENTRE
- ● GARDEN & NURSERY
- ● WATER GARDEN SPECIALIST

LAMBERLEA POND & GARDEN CENTRE **88-1**
Nethertown, Egremont, Cumbria
TEL: 01946 820 536

GRASMERE GARDEN CENTRE **88-2**
Church Stile, Grasmere, Cumbria
TEL: 01539 435 255

BOONWOOD GARDEN CENTRE **88-3**
Gasforth, Seascale, Cumbria
TEL: 01946 725 330

WALK MILL GARDEN CENTRE **88-4**
Wellington, Seascale, Cumbria
TEL: 01946 723 293

MUNCASTER CASTLE, GARDENS & OWL CENTRE **88-5**
Ravenglass, Cumbria
TEL: 01229 717 614

BRANTWOOD **88-6**
Brantwood Trust, Coniston, Cumbria
TEL: 01539 441 396

BUSH GREEN COTTAGE NURSERY **88-7**
Foxfield Road, Boughton in Furness , Cumbria
TEL: 01229 716 724

HILLFOOT GARDEN CENTRE **88-8**
County Road, Ulverston, Cumbria
TEL: 01229 587 282

CROOKLANDS NURSERIES **88-9**
Crouplands Brow, Dalton in Furness, Cumbria
TEL: 01229 464 225

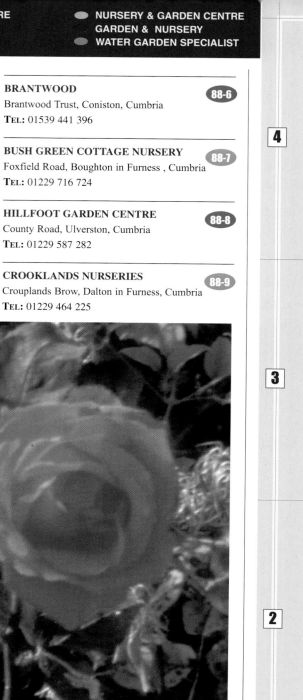

Rose

St Bees

88-1

A

1

2

3

4

A

RYDAL MOUNT & GARDENS
Ambleside, Cumbria
TEL: 01539 433 002

HAYES GARDEN WORLD
Lake District Nurseries, Ambleside, Cumbria
TEL: 01539 433 434

BROCKHOLE
Lake District Visitor Centre, Windermere, Cumbria
TEL: 01539 446 601

WEBBS GARDEN & AQUATICS CENTRE
Burneside Road, Kendal, Cumbria
TEL: 01539 720 068

J. H. PARK
Underhill, Kendal, Cumbria
TEL: 01539 568 301

GRAYTHWAITE HALL
Ulverston, Graythwaite, Cumbria
TEL: 01539 531 248

HOLMES OF NATLAND
Abbey Gardens, Kendal, Cumbria
TEL: 01539 560 224

SIZERGH CASTLE & GARDEN, NATIONAL TRUST
Sizergh, Kendal, Cumbria
TEL: 01539 560 070

HALECAT GARDEN NURSERY 89-11
Halecat House, Witherslack,
Grange-over-Sands, Cumbria, LA11 6RU
TEL: 01539 552 536
EMAIL: halecat@fsmail.net

Excellent value nursery in quiet peaceful backwater, with majority of plants self propagated. Lovely house, garden open free to the public.
OPEN: Daily, Mon-Fri, 9-4.30, April-Sep. Sat & Sun, 1-4, closed Christmas week.
SPECIALITIES: Bedding plants, Hardy plants, Roses, Shrubs.

FELL FOOT PARK, NATIONAL TRUST
Newby Bridge, Ulverston, Cumbria
TEL: 01539 531 273

LEVENS HALL 89-10
Kendal, Cumbria
TEL: 01539 560 321

T. H. BARKER & SONS
Baines Padock, Ulverston, Cumbria
TEL: 01539 558 236

HOLEHIRD GARDENS
Patterdale Road, Windermere, Cumbria
TEL: 01539 446 008

BROWNTHWAITE HARDY PLANTS
Fell Yeat, Carnforth, Lancashire
TEL: 01524 271 340

CARR BANK GARDEN CENTRE
Carr Bank Road, Milnthorpe, Cumbria
TEL: 01524 762 313

GRANGE PLANT CENTRE
Main Street, Grange-over-Sands, Cumbria
TEL: 01539 533 510

HOLKER HALL
Cark-in-Cartmel, Grange-over-Sands, Cumbria
TEL: 01539 558 328

WAITHMAN NURSERIES
36 Lindeth Road, Carnforth, Lancashire
TEL: 01524 701 252

TOLL BAR NURSERIES
Gate House, Lancaster, Lancashire
TEL: 01524 261 301

BAY VIEW NURSERY & GARDEN CENTRE
Mill Lane, Carnforth, Lancashire
TEL: 01524 733 780

W. C. F. COUNTRY CENTRE 89-21
Hornby Road, Claughton, Lancashire
TEL: 01524 771 444

Orchid

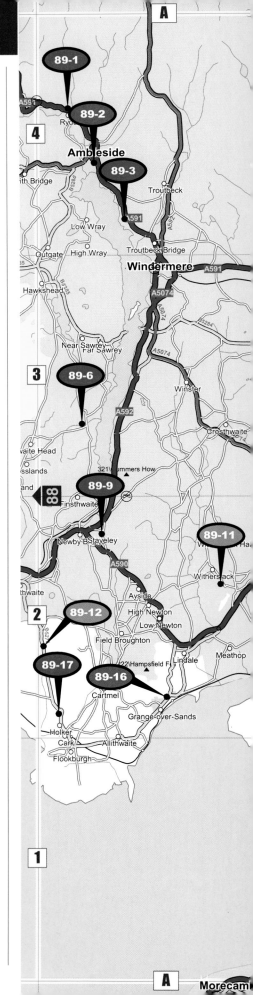

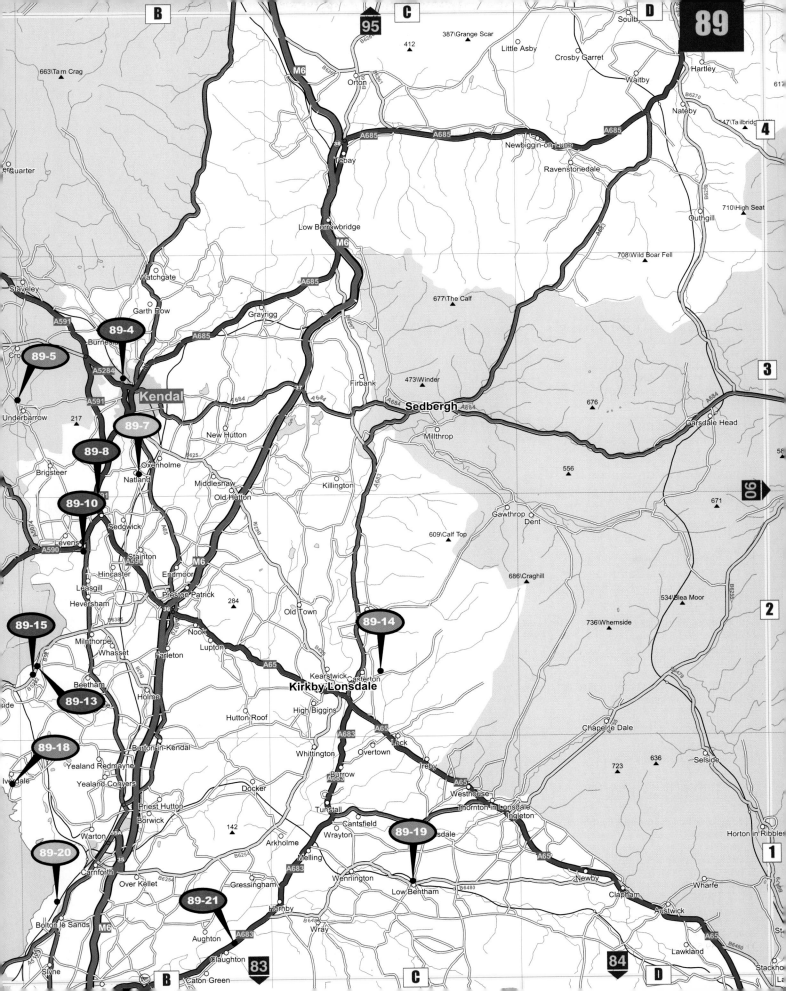

RAVENSWORTH NURSERIES 90-1
Ravensworth, Richmond, North Yorkshire
TEL: 01325 718 370

PADDOCK FARM NURSERIES 90-2
West Lane, Darlington, Durham
TEL: 01325 378 286

MILLGATE HOUSE 90-3
Richmond, North Yorkshire
TEL: 01748 823 571

PARWOODS NURSERY 90-4
Darlington Road, Northallerton, North Yorkshire
TEL: 01609 760 970

WILLIAM STRIKE 90-5
Boroughbridge Road, Northallerton, North Yorkshire
TEL: 01609 773 694

BURTON CONSTABLE HALL GARDENS 90-6
Leyburn, North Yorkshire
TEL: 01677 450 428

KERSHAWS NURSERIES 90-7
Woodhall Lodge, Leyburn, North Yorkshire
TEL: 01969 663 652

FAIRVIEW NURSERY 90-8
Fairview Gardens, Bedale, North Yorkshire
TEL: 01677 422 256

THORP PERROW ARBORETUM 90-9
Bedale, North Yorkshire
TEL: 01677 425 323

F. A. JOBLING 90-10
Main Street, Ripon, North Yorkshire
TEL: 01677 470 481

STUDLEY ROYAL GARDEN CENTRE 90-11
Studley Roger, Ripon, North Yorkshire
TEL: 01765 604 385

DEANSWOOD PLANTS 90-12
Potteries Lane, Ripon, North Yorkshire
TEL: 01765 603 441

**FOUNTAINS ABBEY & STUDLEY ROYAL
WATER GARDEN, NATIONAL TRUST** 90-13
Fountains, Ripon, North Yorkshire
TEL: 01765 608 888

**OLANDS GARDEN
AND PLANT CENTRE** 90-14
Sawley Nursery, Risplith, Ripon,
North Yorkshire, HG4 3EW
TEL: 01765 620 622
EMAIL: olandplants@barclays.net
WEB: www.olands.com
*Small intimate nursery within a two-acre garden.
Choice and interesting plants surrounded by
beautiful countryside close to Fountains Abbey.*
OPEN: Daily, Feb-Oct, 9.30-5. Garden entry free.
SPECIALITIES: Alpines, Climbers, Hardy plants,
Rhododendrons and azaleas, Roses.

NEWBY HALL AND GARDENS 90-15
Ripon, North Yorkshire
TEL: 01423 322 583

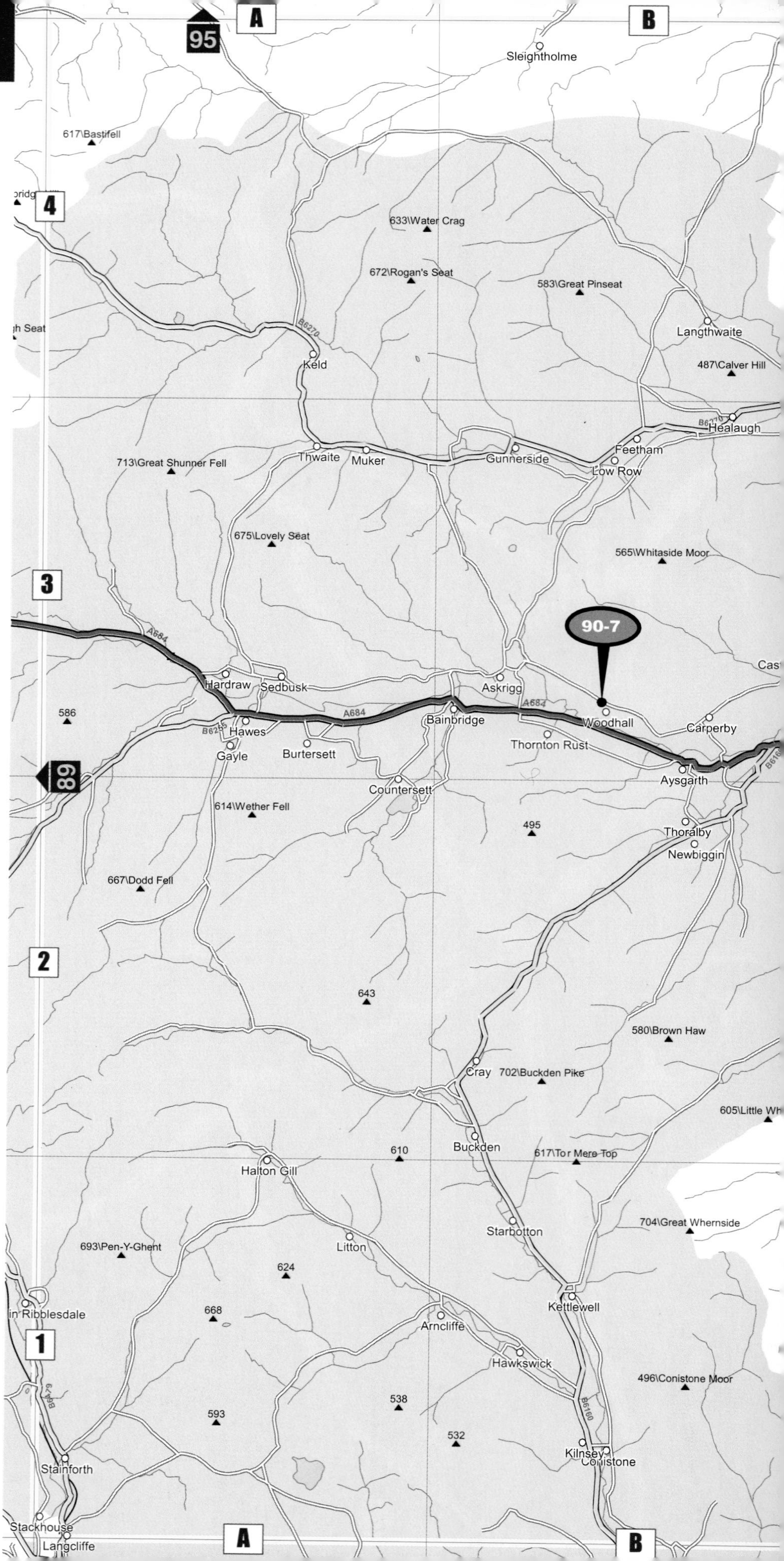

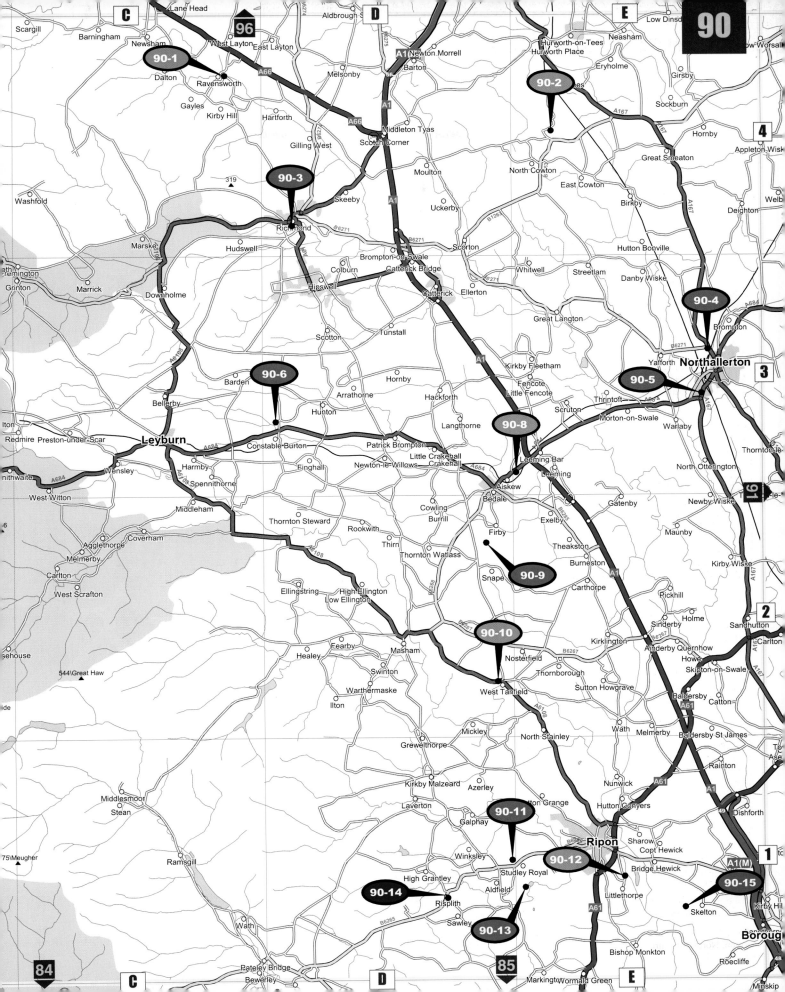

WILLIAM STRIKE
The Roundabout, Stokesley, North Yorkshire
TEL: 01642 710 419

BATTERSBY ROSES
Peartree Cottage, Great Ayton, North Yorkshire
TEL: 01642 723 402

POETS COTTAGE SHRUB NURSERY
Lealholm, Whitby, North Yorkshire
TEL: 01947 897 424

KINROSS NURSERIES
Skutterskelfe, Yarm, North Yorkshire
TEL: 01642 710 831

FIR TREES PELARGONIUM NURSERY
Fir Tree Cottage, Middlesborough, North Yorkshire
TEL: 01642 713 066

MOUNT GRACE PRIORY, ENGLISH HERITAGE
Saddlebridge, Northallerton, North Yorkshire
TEL: 01609 883 494

R. V. ROGER
The Nurseries, Pickering, South Yorkshire
TEL: 01751 472 226

SIMPSON'S GARDEN CENTRE
Wold View House, Pickering, South Yorkshire
TEL: 01751 473 382

DUNCOMBE PARK
Helmsley, North Yorkshire
TEL: 01439 770 213

WHITESTONE GARDENS
The Cactus House, Thirsk, North Yorkshire
TEL: 01845 597 467

NUNNINGTON HALL, NATIONAL TRUST
Nunnington, York, North Yorkshire
TEL: 01439 748 283

SHANDY HALL
Coxwold, York, North Yorkshire
TEL: 01347 868 465

GILLING CASTLE
Gilling East, North Yorkshire
TEL: 01439 788 238

CASTLE HOWARD
York, North Yorkshire
TEL: 01653 648 444

YORKSHIRE LAVENDER
The Yorkshire Lavender Farm, York, North Yorkshire
TEL: 01653 648 430

Jonquils

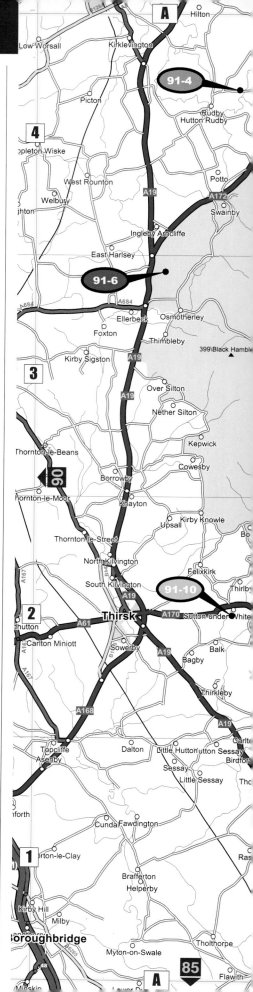

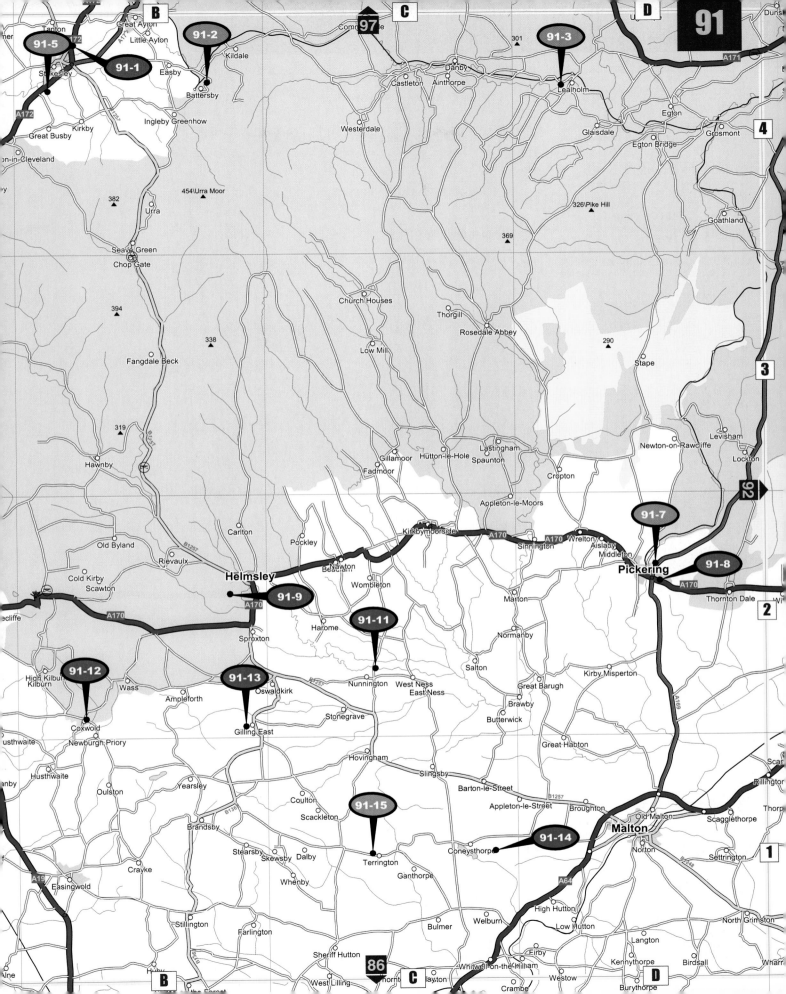

YORKSHIRE

- GARDEN CENTRE
- NURSERY
- GARDEN
- NURSERY & GARDEN CENTRE
- GARDEN & NURSERY
- WATER GARDEN SPECIALIST

PERRY'S PLANTS — 92-1
The River Garden , Whitby, North Yorkshire
TEL: 01947 810 329

BURNISTON NURSERIES — 92-2
Coastal Road, Scarborough, North Yorkshire
TEL: 01723 871 078

WOMACK'S GARDEN CENTRE — 92-3
170 Filey Road, Scarborough, North Yorkshire
TEL: 01723 367 672

IRTON GARDEN CENTRE — 92-4
Irton Moor Lane, Scarborough, North Yorkshire
TEL: 01723 862 978

FLIXTON GARDEN CENTRE — 92-5
Three Acres, Scarborough, North Yorkshire
TEL: 01723 890 470

REIGHTON NURSERY — 92-6
Gable Cottage, Filey, North Yorkshire
TEL: 01723 890 359

HIGHFIELD NURSERIES — 92-7
6 Main Street, Bridlington, East Riding of Yorkshire
TEL: 01262 850 404

ARGHAM VILLAGE NURSERY — 92-8
Argham Grange, Bridlington, East Riding of Yorkshire
TEL: 01723 892 141

EASTFIELD GARDEN CENTRE — 92-9
Easton Road, Bridlington, East Riding of Yorkshire
TEL: 01262 676 285

Park flowers

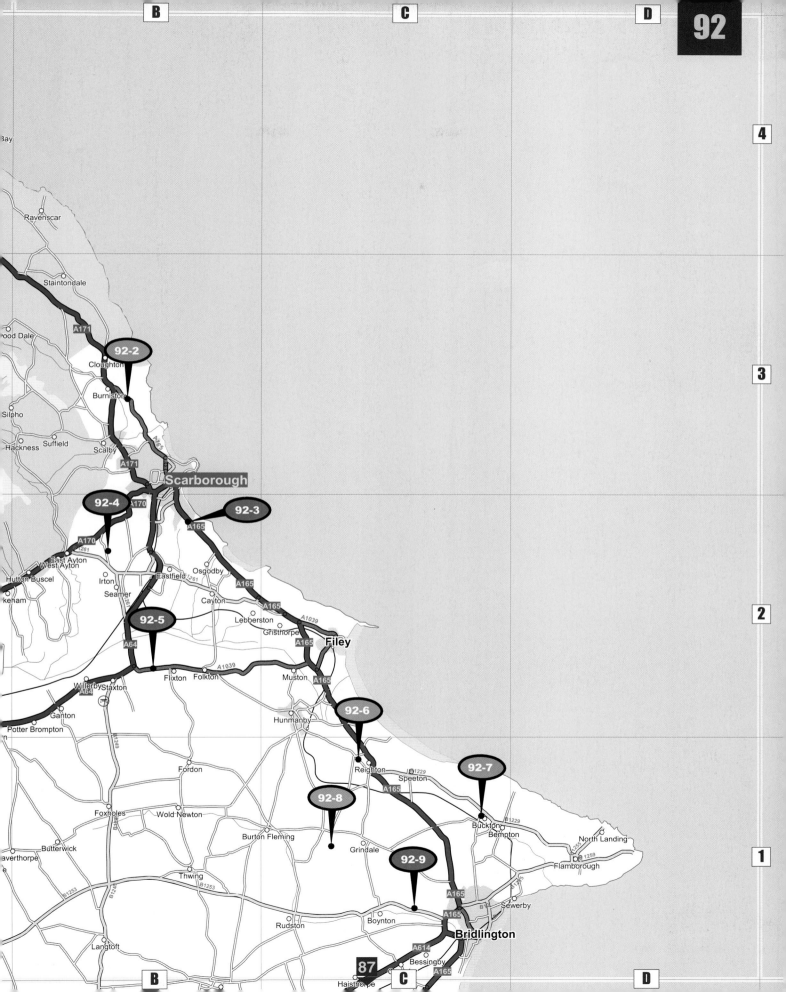

Bay

Ravenscar

Staintondale

A171

92-2

Cloughton

Burniston

ood Dale

Silpho

Hackness Suffield

Scalby

A171

A165

Scarborough

92-4

A170

92-3

A165

East Ayton
West Ayton

Hutton Buscel

Irton

Eastfield

Osgodby

A261

keham

Seamer

Cayton

A165

92-5

Lebberston

A165

A1039

A64

Gristhorpe

A165

Filey

WillerbyStaxton

Flixton Folkton

A1039

Muston

A165

A64

Ganton

Hunmanby

92-6

Potter Brompton

B1249

Fordon

Reighton

B1229

Speeton

92-7

A165

92-8

Foxholes

Wold Newton

Bucktón

B1229

Bempton

North Landing

Butterwick

Burton Fleming

Grindale

D61259

averthorpe

92-9

Flamborough

A165

Thwing

Boynton

A165

Sewerby

Langtoft

B1253

B1253

Rudston

A614

Bridlington

B1244

87

Bessingby

A165

Haisthorpe

DUMFRIES & GALLOWAY

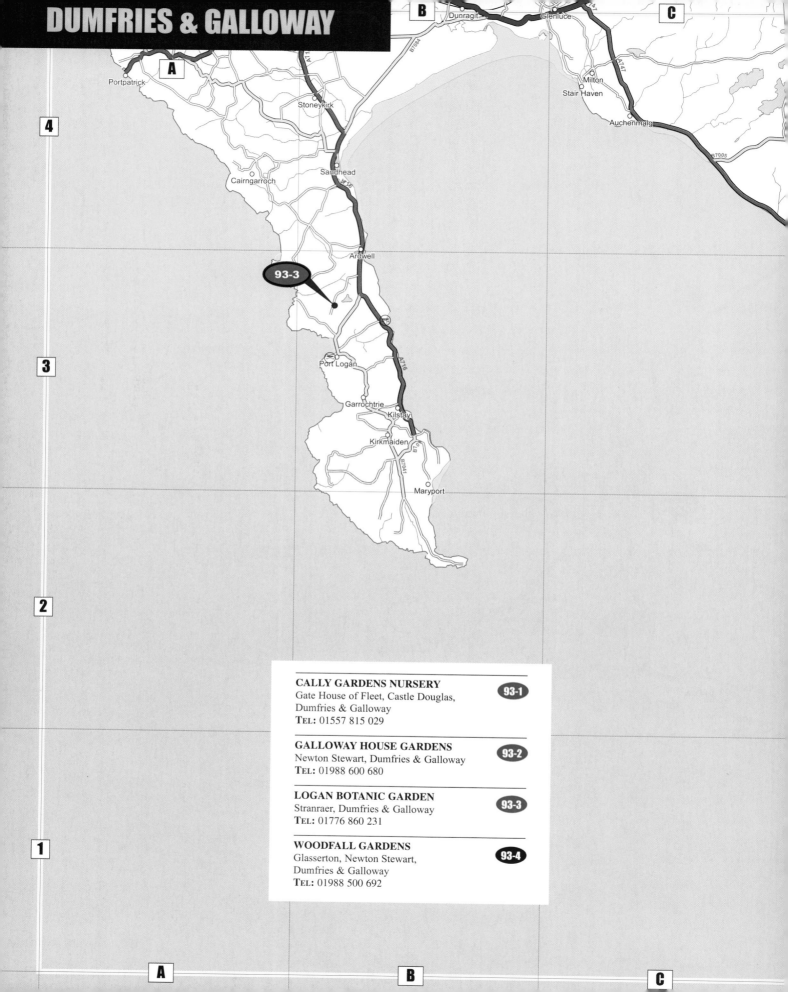

93-3

CALLY GARDENS NURSERY **93-1**
Gate House of Fleet, Castle Douglas,
Dumfries & Galloway
TEL: 01557 815 029

GALLOWAY HOUSE GARDENS **93-2**
Newton Stewart, Dumfries & Galloway
TEL: 01988 600 680

LOGAN BOTANIC GARDEN **93-3**
Stranraer, Dumfries & Galloway
TEL: 01776 860 231

WOODFALL GARDENS **93-4**
Glasserton, Newton Stewart,
Dumfries & Galloway
TEL: 01988 500 692

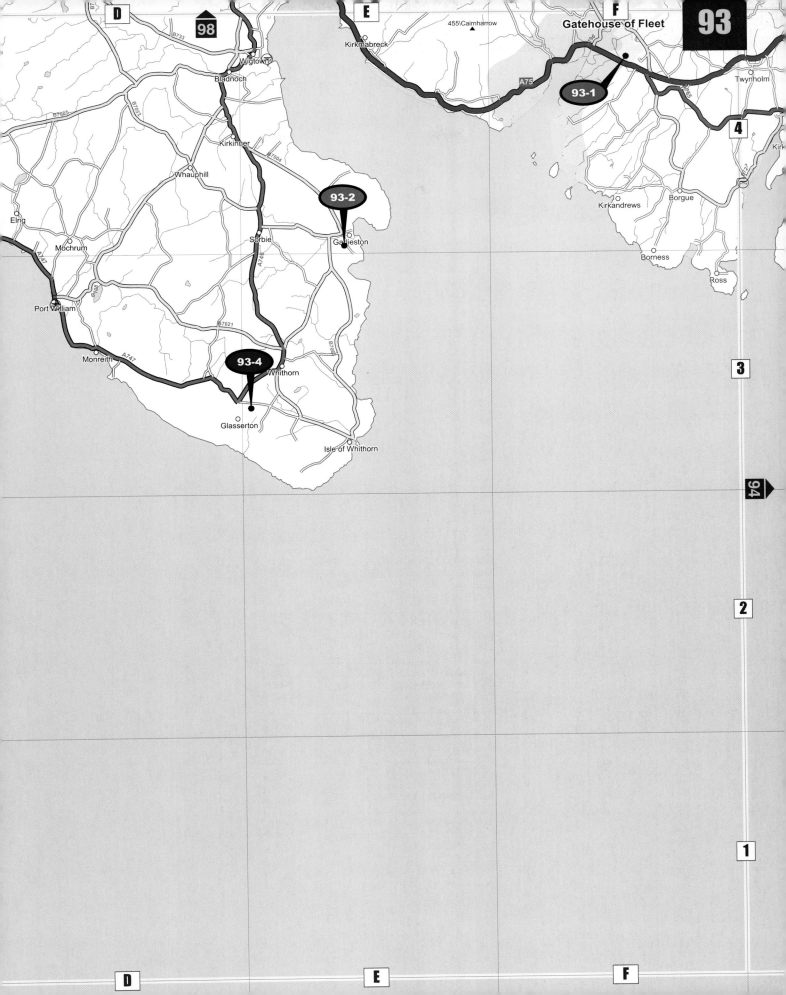

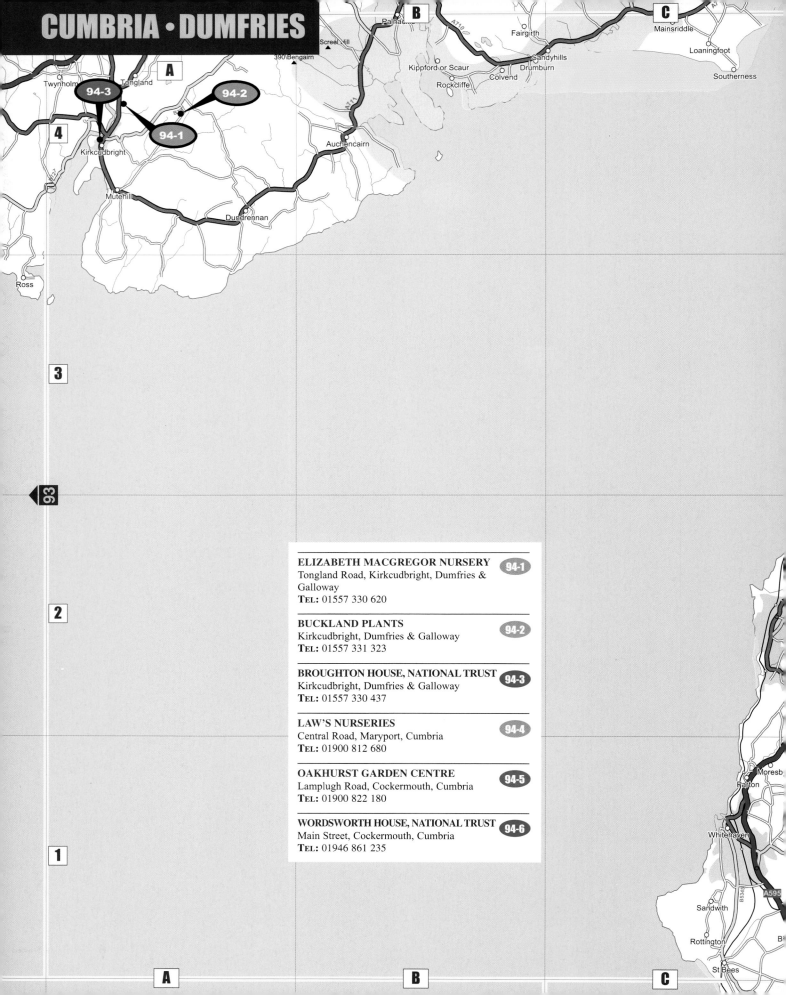

94-3

94-2

94-1

Twynholm

Tongland

A

4

Kirkcudbright

Mutehill

Dundrennan

Ross

390\Bengairn

Screel Hill

Palnac...

B

A711

A710

Auchencairn

Fairgirth

Sandyhills
Drumburn

Kippford or Scaur
Colvend

Rockcliffe

Mainsriddle

Loaningfoot

Southerness

C

93

3

2

1

ELIZABETH MACGREGOR NURSERY **94-1**
Tongland Road, Kirkcudbright, Dumfries &
Galloway
TEL: 01557 330 620

BUCKLAND PLANTS **94-2**
Kirkcudbright, Dumfries & Galloway
TEL: 01557 331 323

BROUGHTON HOUSE, NATIONAL TRUST **94-3**
Kirkcudbright, Dumfries & Galloway
TEL: 01557 330 437

LAW'S NURSERIES **94-4**
Central Road, Maryport, Cumbria
TEL: 01900 812 680

OAKHURST GARDEN CENTRE **94-5**
Lamplugh Road, Cockermouth, Cumbria
TEL: 01900 822 180

WORDSWORTH HOUSE, NATIONAL TRUST **94-6**
Main Street, Cockermouth, Cumbria
TEL: 01946 861 235

Moresb
Parton

Whitehaven

Sandwith

Rottington

St Bees

B5345

A595

A

B

C

CUMBRIA

R. LESLIE & SONS
Durdar Road, Carlisle, Cumbria
TEL: 01228 521 476

D. W. HICKSON & SONS
Garden House Nurseries, Carlisle, Cumbria
TEL: 01228 710 499

PROUDPLANTS
Shadyvale Nurseries, Carlisle, Cumbria
TEL: 01768 896 604

HARTSIDE NURSERY GARDEN
Alston, Cumbria
TEL: 01434 381 372

THIEFSIDE GARDEN CENTRE
Homelands, Penrith, Cumbria
TEL: 01768 885 073

HUTTON-IN-THE-FOREST
Penrith, Cumbria
TEL: 01768 484 449

R. & D. COWIN
Hazzeldene, Penrith, Cumbria
TEL: 01768 882 52

ACORN BANK GARDEN
The National Trust, Penrith, Cumbria
TEL: 01768 361 893

DALEMAIN HISTORIC HOUSE & GARDENS
Estate Office, Penrith, Cumbria
TEL: 01768 486 450

LARCH COTTAGE NURSERIES
Melkinthorpe, Penrith, Cumbria
TEL: 01931 712 404

BEECHCROFT NURSERIES
Bongate, Appleby, Cumbria
TEL: 01768 351 201

Forest Eucalypt

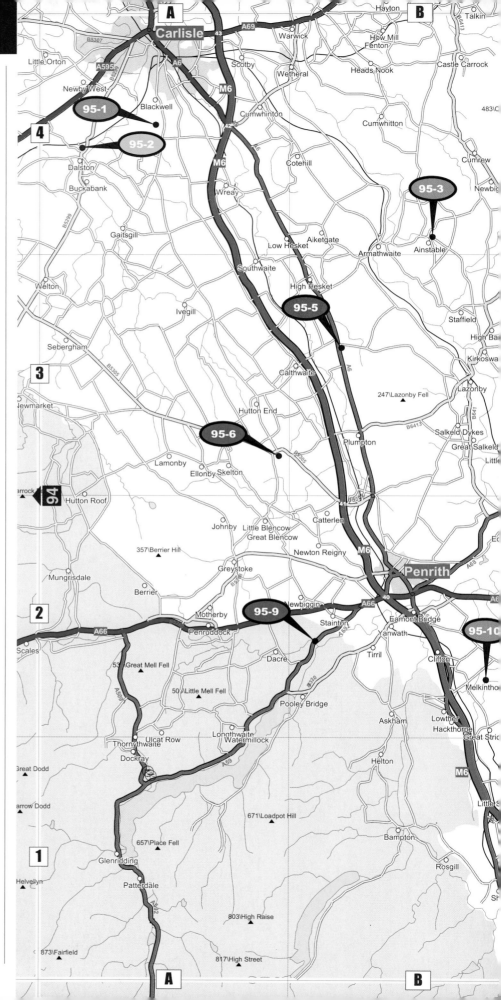

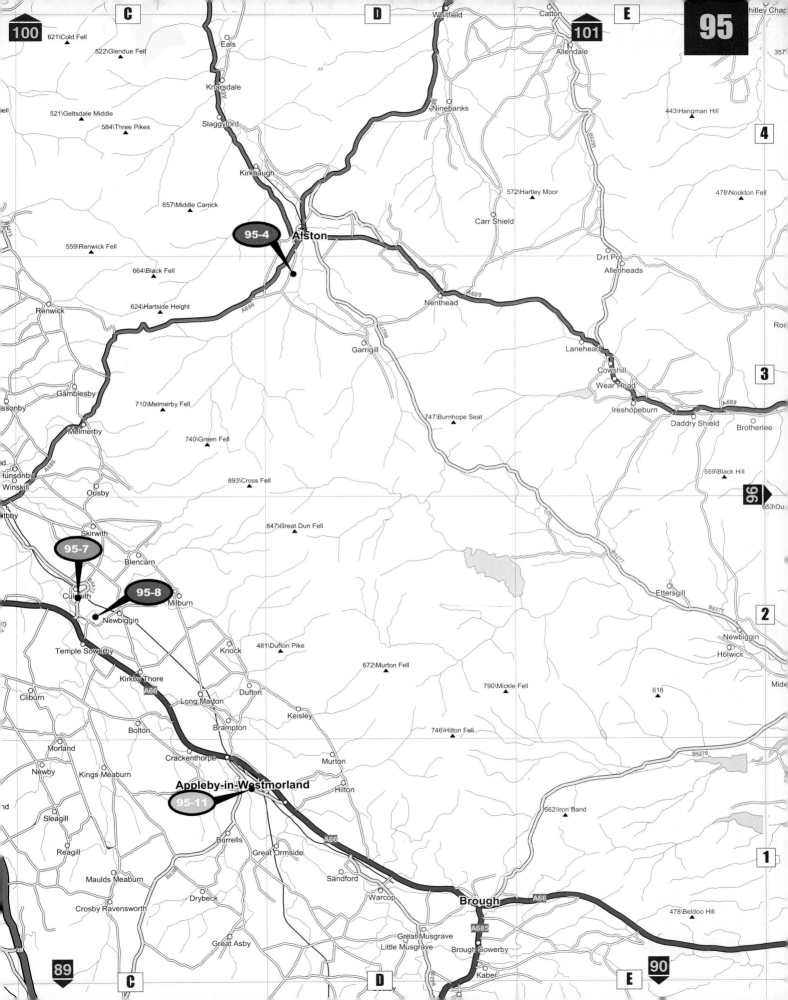

BIRKHEAD'S COTTAGE GARDEN NURSERY
Causey Arch, Newcastle Upon Tyne, Tyne & Wear
Tel: 01207 232 262

DOBBIES GARDEN CENTRE
Durham Road, Birtley, Tyne & Wear
Tel: 0191 410 2556

CLAYS GARDEN CENTRE
Silksworth Lane, Sunderland, Tyne & Wear
Tel: 0191 522 0911

THE NURSERIES
Ebchester, Consett, Durham
Tel: 01207 560 228

BEAMISH CLEMETIS NURSERY
Burntwood Cottage, Beamish, Durham
Tel: 0191 370 0202

STRIKES GARDEN CENTRE
Burnmoor, Chester le Street, Durham
Tel: 0191 385 5154

FOXWOOD GARDEN CENTRE
Holm Hill Lane, Chester le Street, Durham
Tel: 0191 389 0044

ACORN NURSERY
Bargate Bank, Durham, Durham
Tel: 01207 521 133

LEAMSIDE NURSERIES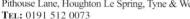
Pithouse Lane, Houghton Le Spring, Tyne & Wear
Tel: 0191 512 0073

A.N. SANDERSON & CO.
Chestnut Cottage, Durham, Durham
Tel: 01913 842 086

UNIVERSITY OF DURHAM BOTANIC GARDEN
Green Lane, Durham, Durham
Tel: 0191 374 7971

POPLAR TREE GARDEN CENTRE
Hall Lane, Durham, Durham
Tel: 01913 847 553

C. & C. GARDEN SUPPLIES
Station Road, Durham, Durham
Tel: 0191 378 2573

THINFORD FARM NURSERIES
Thinford Farm, Durham, Durham
Tel: 01740 655 704

AUCKLAND PARK
Auckland Castle, Bishop Auckland, Durham
Tel: 01388 601 627

BLOSSOMS NURSERIES
The Gardens, Ferry Hill, Durham
Tel: 01388 720 216

EGGLESTON HALL GARDENS
Eggleston, Barnard Castle, Durham
Tel: 01833 650 403

WOODLEA NURSERIES
Woodlea, Darlington, Durham
Tel: 01388 710 735

RABY CASTLE PARK & GARDENS
Staindrop, Darlington, Durham
Tel: 01833 660 207

NINE ACRES NURSERIES
Whinney Hill, Stockton on Tees, Durham
Tel: 01642 582 718

BOWES MUSEUM
Barnard Castle, Durham
Tel: 01833 690 606

PAULS KOI & POND SUPPLIES
Darlington Forge, Darlington, Durham
Tel: 01325 340 084

Frangipani

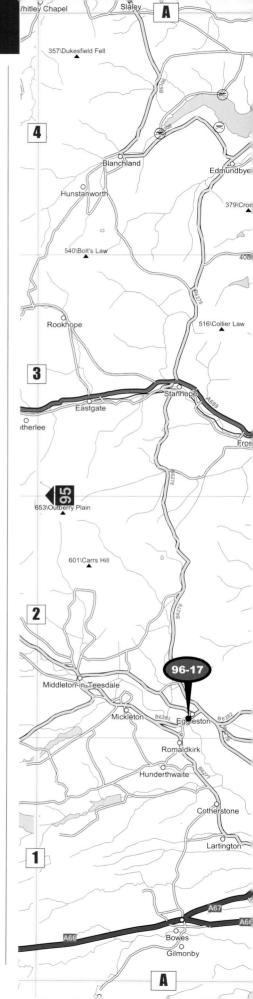

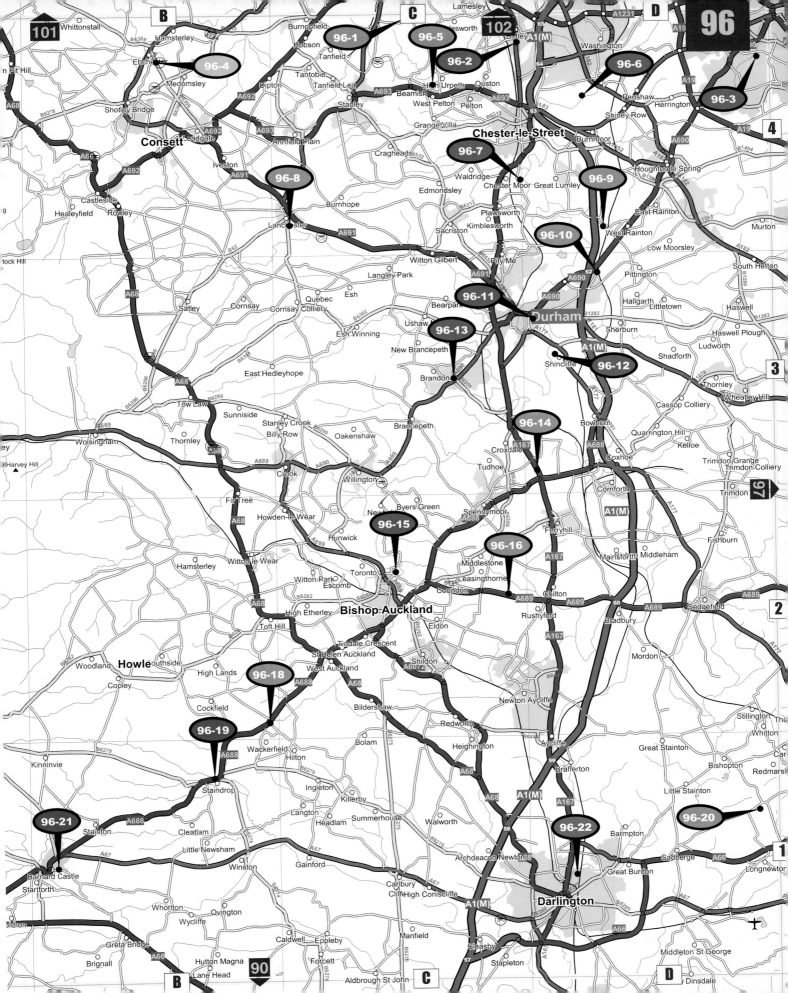

SEATON BUILDINGS & GARDEN CENTRE 97-1
Seaton Lane, Seaham, Durham
TEL: 040 252 1132

HORNS GARDEN CENTRE 97-2
Dixon Estate, Peterlee, Durham
TEL: 0191 526 2987

BLACKFORD NURSERIES 97-3
Stockton Road, Hartlepool, Durham
TEL: 01429 268 509

GOLDEN GATES NURSERIES 97-4
Sandy Lane West, Billingham, Durham
TEL: 01740 644 627

GOLDEN ACRE NURSERY 97-5
Longbeck Road, Redcar, North Yorkshire
TEL: 01642 492 332

HARPERS GARDEN CENTRE 97-6
Junction Road, Stockton on Tees, Durham
TEL: 01642 674 636

ORMESBY HALL, NATIONAL TRUST 97-7
Ormesby, Middlesbrough, North Yorkshire
TEL: 01642 324 188

PETER BARRATT'S GARDEN CENTRE 97-8
Yarn Road, Stockton on Tees, Durham
TEL: 01642 613434

LYNDHURST NURSERIES 97-9
Ormesby Bank, Ormesby, North Yorkshire
TEL: 01642 314 547

ROWE'S NURSERIES 97-10
Priory Gardens, Guisborough, Northamptonshire
TEL: 01287 632 563

WINDLEBRIDGE GARDEN NURSERY 97-11
Middlesborough Road, Guisborough,
Northamptonshire
TEL: 01287 635 642

PLANTARAMA GARDEN CENTRE 97-12
Sandy Flatts Lane, Middlesbrough, North Yorkshire
TEL: 01642 320 514

CHERRY HILL NURSERIES 97-13
Stokesley Road, Middlesborough, North Yorkshire
TEL: 01642 590 650

ARCADIA NURSERIES 97-14
Brasscastle Lane, Middlesborough, North Yorkshire
TEL: 01642 310 782

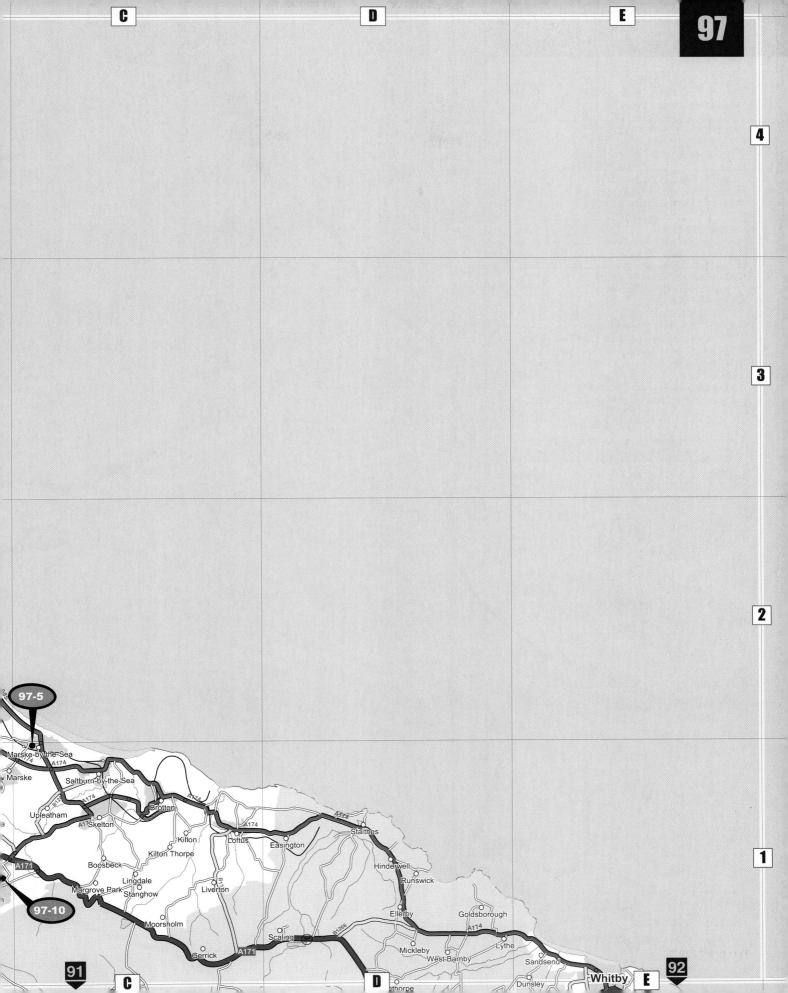

4

3

2

97-5

Marske-by-the-Sea
A174
w Marske
Saltburn-by-the-Sea
B17
Upleatham
A174
A1 Skelton
Brotton
A174
A174
Kilton
Loftus
Easington
Staithes
Kilton Thorpe
Boosbeck
Hinderwell
A171
Runswick
Lingdale
Margrove Park Liverton
Stanghow
B1

97-10

Moorsholm
Ellerby
Goldsborough
Scaling
B1266
A174
Mickleby
Lythe
Gerrick A171
West-Barnby
Sandsend
Dunsley
Whitby

1

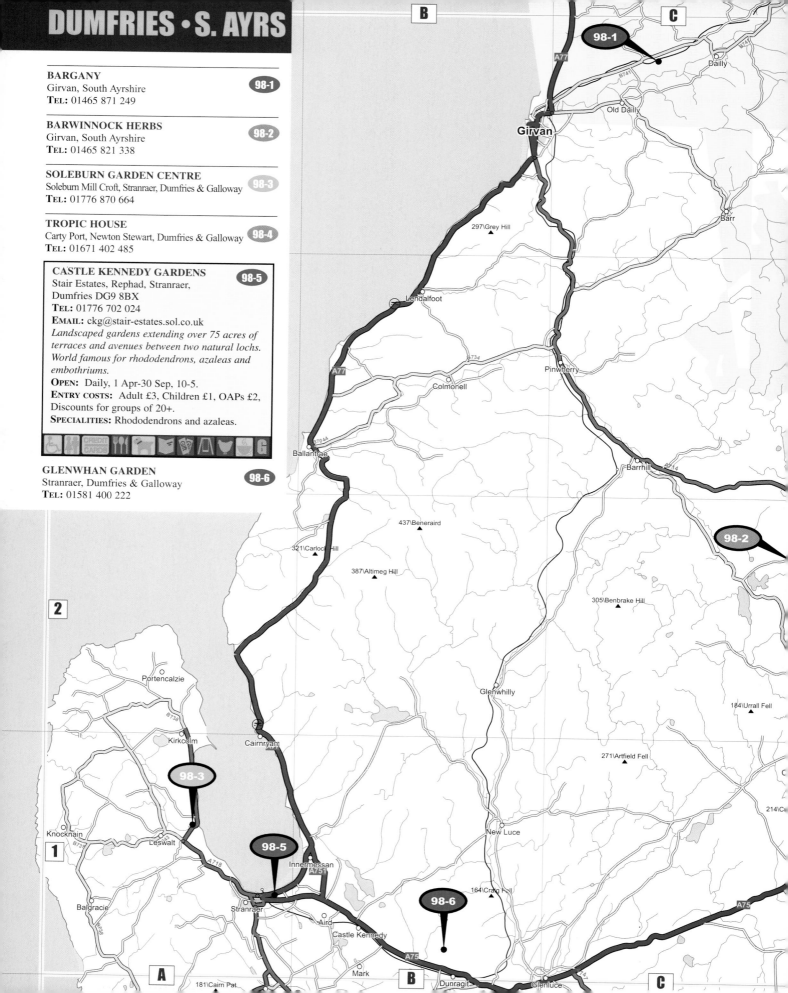

BARGANY `98-1`
Girvan, South Ayrshire
TEL: 01465 871 249

BARWINNOCK HERBS `98-2`
Girvan, South Ayrshire
TEL: 01465 821 338

SOLEBURN GARDEN CENTRE `98-3`
Soleburn Mill Croft, Stranraer, Dumfries & Galloway
TEL: 01776 870 664

TROPIC HOUSE `98-4`
Carty Port, Newton Stewart, Dumfries & Galloway
TEL: 01671 402 485

CASTLE KENNEDY GARDENS `98-5`
Stair Estates, Rephad, Stranraer,
Dumfries DG9 8BX
TEL: 01776 702 024
EMAIL: ckg@stair-estates.sol.co.uk
*Landscaped gardens extending over 75 acres of
terraces and avenues between two natural lochs.
World famous for rhododendrons, azaleas and
embothriums.*
OPEN: Daily, 1 Apr-30 Sep, 10-5.
ENTRY COSTS: Adult £3, Children £1, OAPs £2,
Discounts for groups of 20+.
SPECIALITIES: Rhododendrons and azaleas.

GLENWHAN GARDEN `98-6`
Stranraer, Dumfries & Galloway
TEL: 01581 400 222

CHARTER HOUSE NURSERY
99-1
Dumfries, Dumfries & Galloway
Tel: 01387 720 363

TWEEEDIE FRUIT TREES
99-2
Maryfield, Dumfries, Dumfries & Galloway
Tel: 01387 720 880

HEATHHALL GARDEN CENTRE
99-3
Edinburgh Road, Dumfries, Dumfries & Galloway
Tel: 01387 263 101

GARDEN WISE PLANT & GARDEN CENTRE
99-4
Dumfries, Dumfries & Galloway
Tel: 01387 262 654

SHEILA NORTHWAY AURICULAS
99-5
Balmaclellan, Castle Douglas, Dumfries & Galloway
Tel: 01644 420 661

CRICHTON GARDEN CENTRE
99-6
Glencaple Road, Dumfries, Dumfries & Galloway
Tel: 01387 266 540

DEZ PLANTS
99-7
Ecclefechan, Lockerbie, Dumfries & Galloway
Tel: 01576 300 688

CASTLE DOUGLAS GARDEN CENTRE
99-8
Castle Douglas, Kirkcudbright, Dumfries & Galloway
Tel: 01556 503 266

THREAVE GARDEN, NATIONAL TRUST
99-9
Castle Douglas, Dumfries & Galloway
Tel: 01556 502 575

CLIFTON PLACE GARDEN CENTRE
99-10
318 High Street, Dalbeattie, Dumfries & Galloway
Tel: 01556 610 777

HOLME LEA NURSERY
99-11
Holme Lea, Carlisle, Cumbria
Tel: 01697 351 688

Dianella

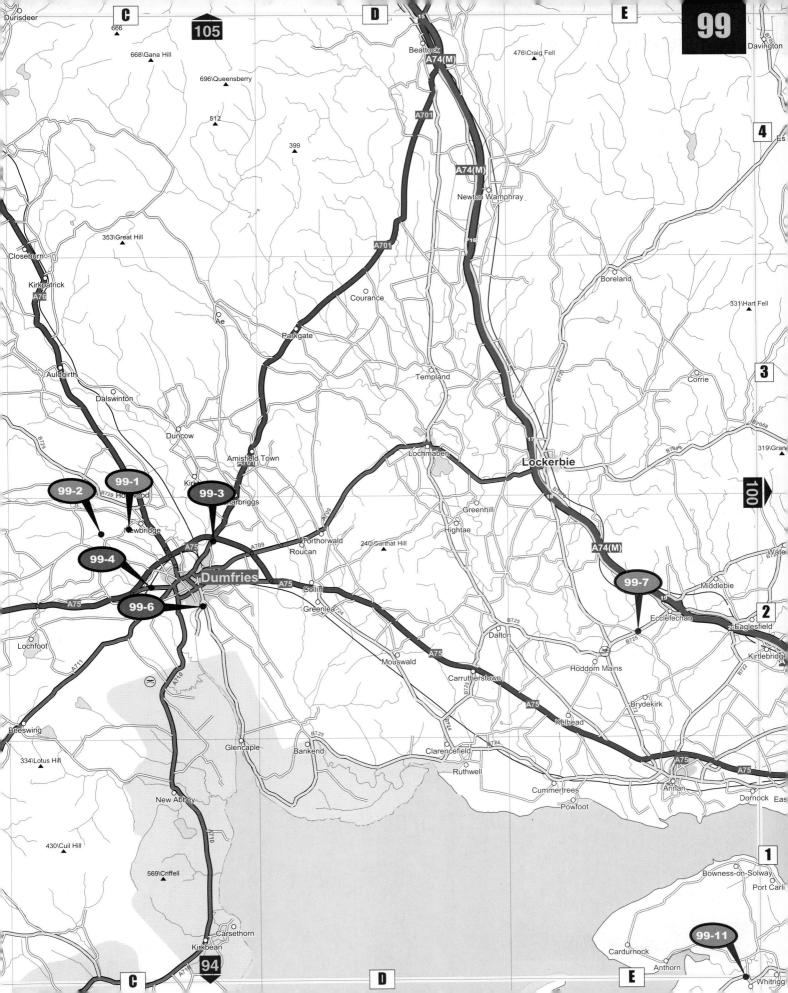

CUMBRIA · DUMFRIES

BRIDGE END NURSERIES `100-1`
Gretna Green, Dumfries & Galloway
TEL: 01461 800 612

OAKABANK GARDENS `100-2`
Brampton, Carlisle, Cumbria
TEL: 01697 739 08

AERO NURSERIES & GARDEN CENTRE `100-3`
Harker Road Ends, Carlisle, Cumbria
TEL: 01228 674 612

TARN ROAD NURSERIES `100-4`
Tarn Road, Brampton, Cumbria
TEL: 01697 737 81

Petunia

Map

- Davington
- 476\Stock Hill
- 594\Wisp Hill
- 598\Tudhope Hill
- Eskdalemuir
- 492\Broad Head
- 521\Arkleton Hill
- 568
- Bentpath
- Kirkstile
- Burnfoot
- 31\Hart Fell
- 450\Cauldkinerig
- 404\Tinnis Hill
- Langholm
- 319\Grange Fell
- 252\Collin Hags
- Claygate
- Waterbeck
- Rowanburn
- Pentonbridge
- Evertown
- Canonbie
- Milltown
- Eaglesfield
- Chapelknowe
- `100-1`
- Kirtlebridge
- A74(M)
- Kirkpatrick-Fleming
- Longtown
- Springfield
- Gretna Green
- Gretna
- Kirklinton
- Rigg
- Dornock
- Eastriggs
- Smithfield
- Westlinton
- Scalebyhill
- Scaleb
- `100-3`
- Port Carlisle
- Todhills
- Rockcliffe
- Glasson
- A689
- High
- Low Cross
- Drumburgh
- Beaumont
- Cargo
- Easton
- Burgh by Sands
- Monkhill
- Grinsdale
- M6
- Linstock
- 94
- Whitrigglees
- Kirkbride

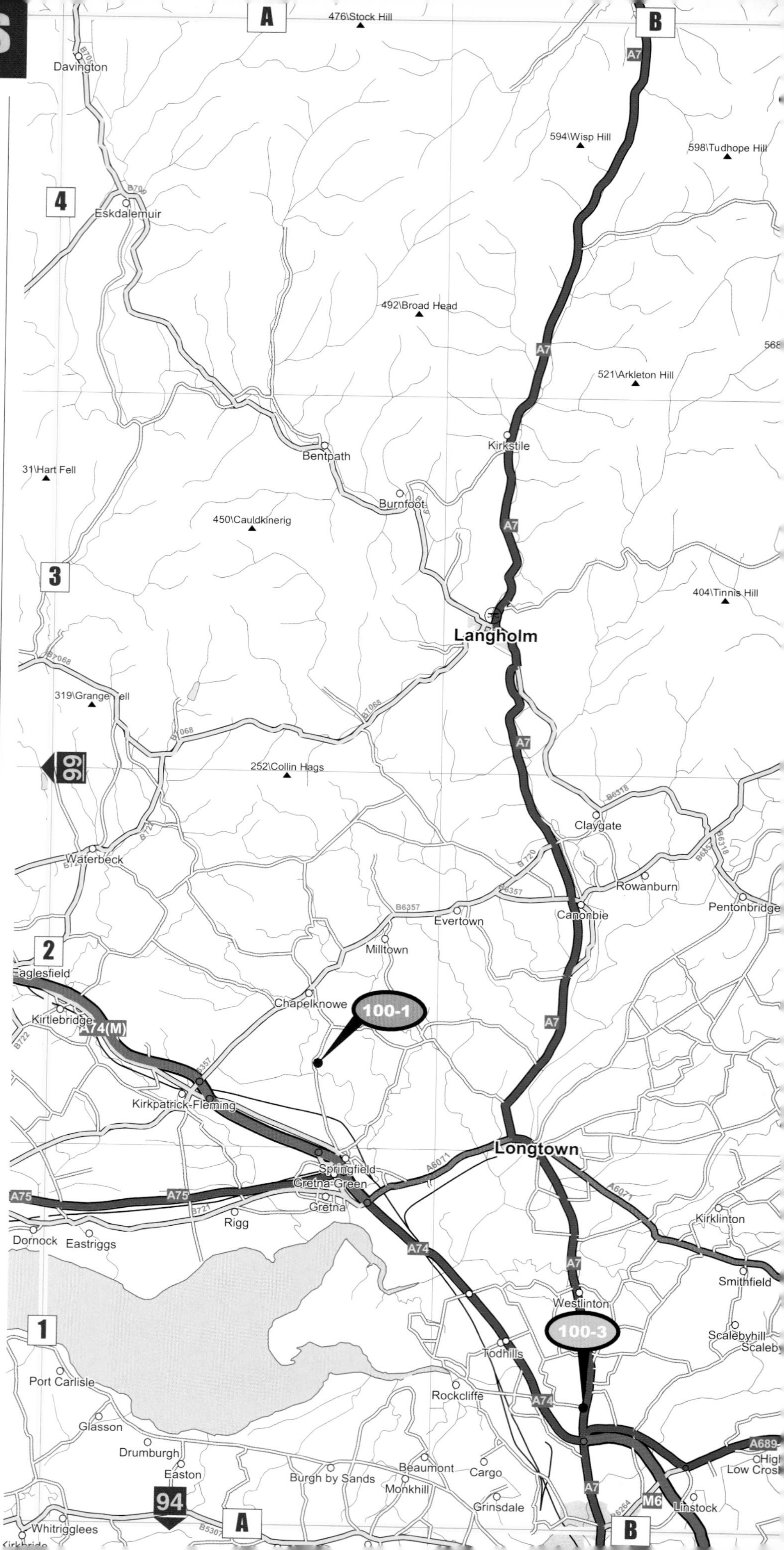

NORTHUMB · TYNE & WEAR

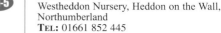

- GARDEN CENTRE
- NURSERY
- GARDEN
- NURSERY & GARDEN CENTRE
- GARDEN & NURSERY
- WATER GARDEN SPECIALIST

CRAGSIDE HOUSE & GARDEN, NATIONAL TRUST `101-1`
Rothbury, Morpeth, Northumberland
TEL: 01669 620 333

THE LONGFRAMLINGTON CENTRE FOR PLANTS `101-2`
Swarland Road, Morpeth, Northumberland
TEL: 01665 570 382

HERTERTON HOUSE GARDEN & NURSERY `101-3`
Hartington, Cambo, Northumberland
TEL: 01670 774 278

WALLINGTON HALL, NATIONAL TRUST `101-4`
Cambo, Morpeth, Northumberland
TEL: 01670 774 283

BELSAY HALL, ENGLISH HERITAGE `101-5`
Belsay, Newcastle Upon Tyne, Tyne & Wear
TEL: 01661 881 636

CHIPCHASE CASTLE NURSERY `101-6`
Chipchase Castle, Hexham, Northumberland
TEL: 01434 230 083

RYAL NURSERY `101-7`
East Farm Cottage, Ryal, Northumberland
TEL: 01661 886 562

HEXHAM HERBS `101-8`
Chesters Walled Garden, Hexham, Northumberland
TEL: 0403 220 930

HALLS OF HEDDON
Westheddon Nursery, Heddon on the Wall, Northumberland
TEL: 01661 852 445

WYLAM NURSERIES `101-10`
End of Stephenson Terrace, Wylam, Northumberland
TEL: 01661 852 025

BRADLEY NURSERY & GARDENS `101-11`
Sled Lane, Wylam, Northumberland
TEL: 01661 852 176

HALLS OF HEDDON `101-12`
The Nursery, Ovington, Northumberland
TEL: 01661 832 467

SHIELD GREEN NURSERIES `101-13`
Dipton Mill, Hexham, Northumberland
TEL: 01912 612 826

Impatience

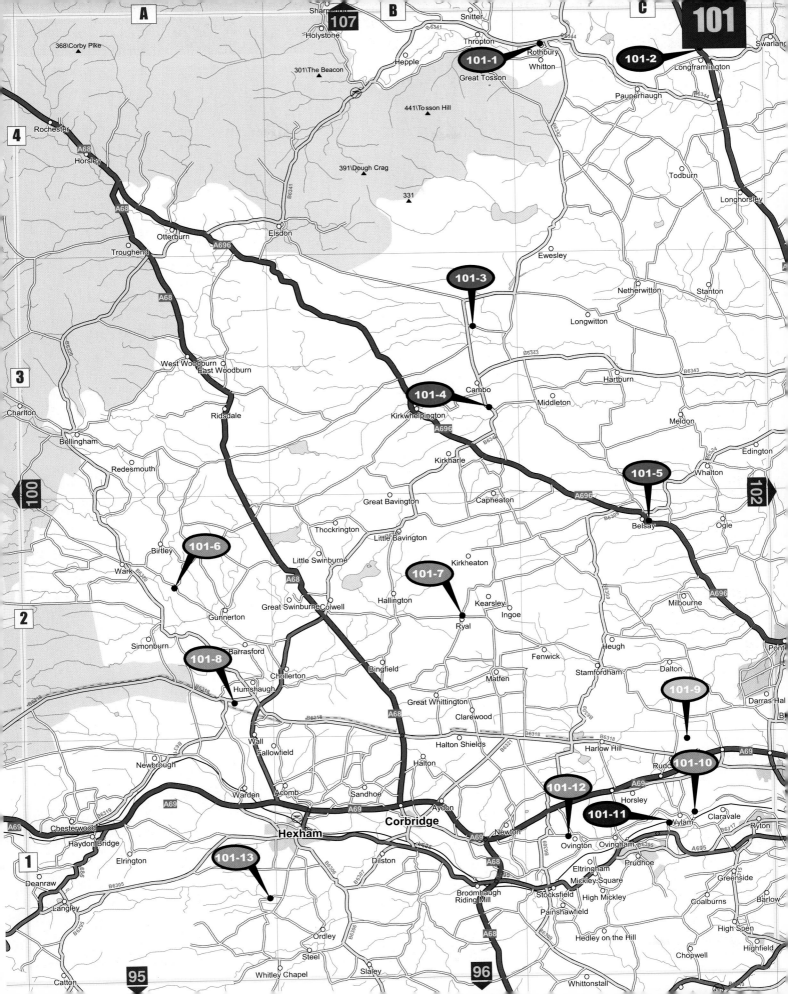

NORTHUMB · TYNE & WEAR

● GARDEN CENTRE
● NURSERY
● GARDEN

● NURSERY & GARDEN CENTRE
● GARDEN & NURSERY
● WATER GARDEN SPECIALIST

**HEIGHLEY GATE NURSERY
& GARDEN CENTRE**
Morpeth, Northumberland
TEL: 01670 513 416

NEW HORIZONS GARDEN CENTRE
Saint George's Hospital, Morpeth, Northumberland
TEL: 01670 503 217

STATION ROAD NURSERIES
58 Station Road, Morpeth, Northumberland
TEL: 01670 789 377

PERENNIAL FAVOURITES
Ridley Park Nurseries, Blyth, Northumberland
TEL: 01670 540 653

SHAW GARDEN CENTRE
Station Road, Cramlington, Northumberland
TEL: 01670 733 762

KIRKLEY HALL COLLEGE GARDENS
Ponteland, Northumberland
TEL: 01661 860 808

DOBBIES GARDEN CENTRE
Streethouse Farm, Ponteland, Northumberland
TEL: 01661 820 202

CHANDLERS GARDEN CENTRE
High Gosforth Park, Newcastle Upon Tyne,
Tyne & Wear
TEL: 0191 236 5775

COWELLS GARDEN CENTRE
Main Road, Newcastle Upon Tyne, Tyne & Wear
TEL: 0191 286 3403

MANOR ROAD NURSERIES
Manor Road, North Shields, Tyne & Wear
TEL: 0191 2577 264

**BEDE'S WORLD MUSEUM
& HERB GARDEN**
Church Bank, Jarrow, Tyne & Wear
TEL: 0191 489 2106

BARNES GARDEN CENTRE
Rackley Way, Whitburn, Tyne & Wear
TEL: 0191 5294 423

RED FOX NURSERIES
Newcastle Road, Gateshead, Tyne & Wear
TEL: 0191 438 0821

E. TONES
Thornley Nurseries, Rowland's Gill, Tyne & Wear
TEL: 01207 542 454

GRANGE GARDEN CENTRE
Thompson Road, Sunderland, Tyne & Wear
TEL: 0191 548 7132

COTTAGE GARDEN NURSERY
Hunters Lodge, Gateshead, Tyne & Wear
TEL: 0191 482 0059

SILVERHILLS NURSERIES
Haggs Lane, Gateshead, Tyne & Wear
TEL: 0191 4877 557

WYEVALE GARDEN CENTRE
The Peel Centre, Washington, Tyne & Wear
TEL: 0191 417 7777

Water Lily

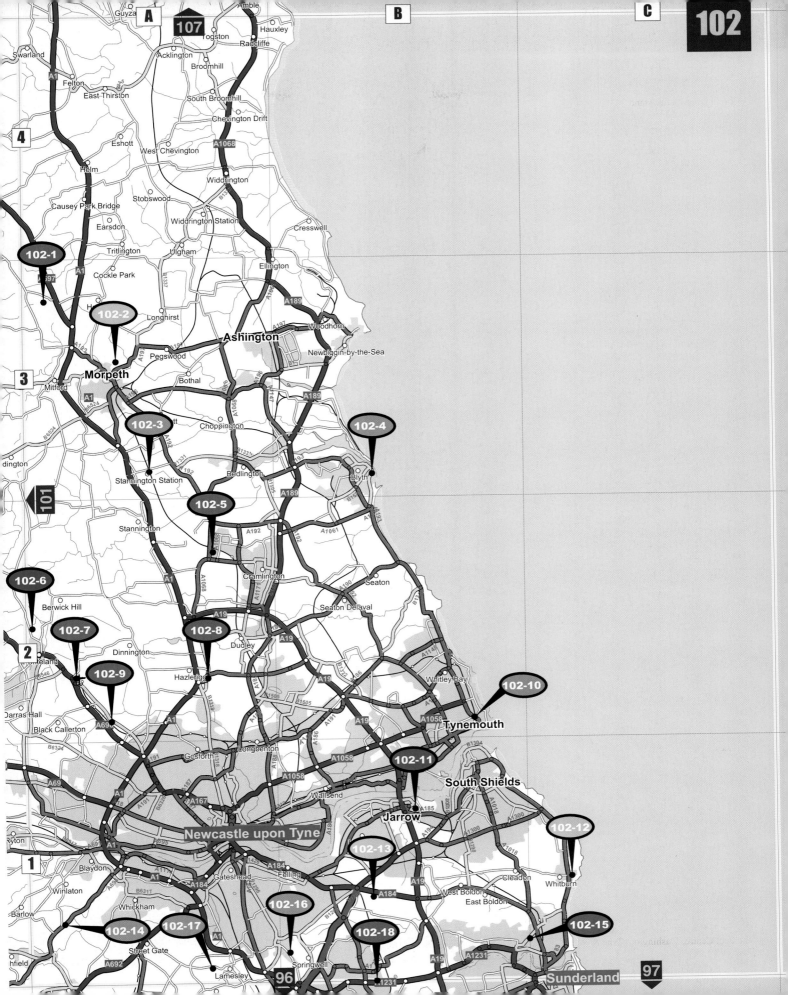

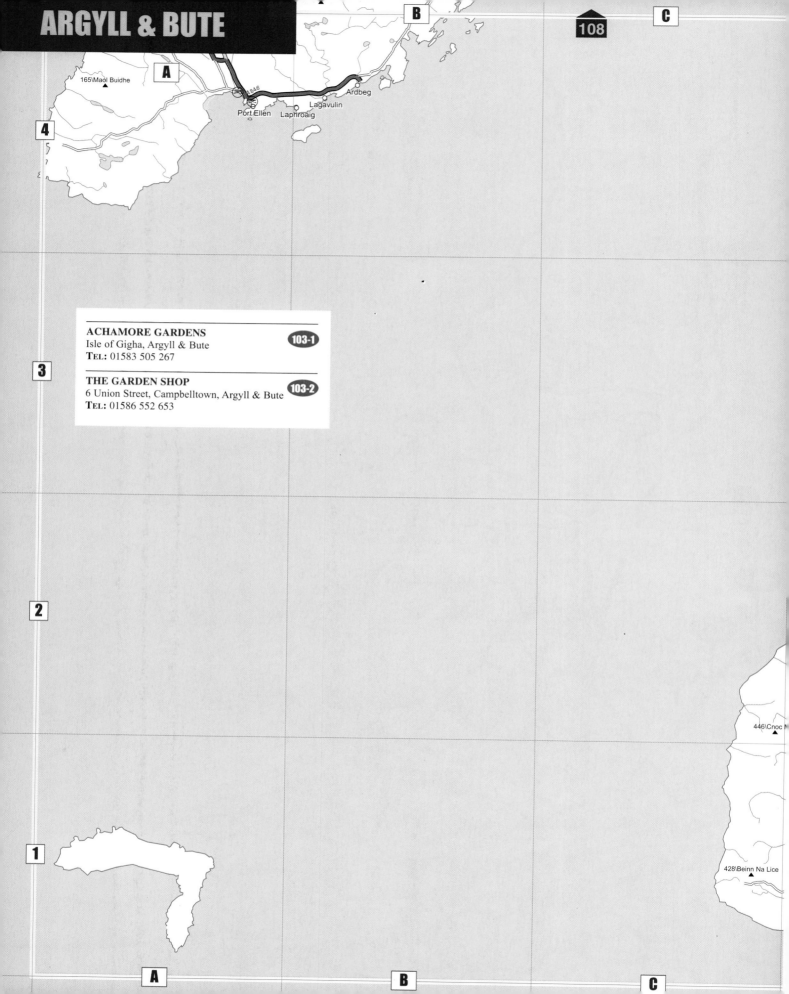

165\Maol Buidhe

A

B846
Ardbeg
Lagavulin
Port Ellen
Laphroaig

4

108

C

ACHAMORE GARDENS
Isle of Gigha, Argyll & Bute
TEL: 01583 505 267
103-1

THE GARDEN SHOP
6 Union Street, Campbelltown, Argyll & Bute
TEL: 01586 552 653
103-2

3

2

446\Cnoc

1

428\Beinn Na Lice

A

B

C

AYRSHIRE

THE PLANT MAN 104-1
Seamill, West Kilbride, South Ayrshire
TEL: 01294 822 995

STANLEY NURSERIES 104-2
Ardrossan, North Ayrshire
TEL: 01294 461 771

WESTFIELD NURSERY 104-3
Glasgow Road, Kilmarnock, South Ayrshire
TEL: 01563 524 544

BRODICK CASTLE, NATIONAL TRUST 104-4
Isle of Arran, North Ayrshire
TEL: 01770 302 202

FRASERS GARDEN CENTRE 104-5
6 Ploughland, Kilmarnock, South Ayrshire
TEL: 01563 850 215

M. G. M. GARDEN & LEISURE 104-6
Ayr Road, Kilmarnock, South Ayrshire
TEL: 01563 528 911

AIRPORT GARDEN CENTRE 104-7
Shawfarm Road, Prestwick, South Ayrshire
TEL: 01292 476 221

STRATHAYRE NURSERY 104-8
Ayr, South Ayrshire
TEL: 01292 266 053

NURSERIES DIRECT 104-9
Stair, Mauchline, East Ayrshire
TEL: 01292 591 900

DOONBANK GARDEN CENTRE 104-10
Doonfoot, Ayr, South Ayrshire
TEL: 01292 442 334

CASSILLIS NURSERY 104-11
Cassillis, Maybole, South Ayrshire
TEL: 01292 442 201

CULZEAN CASTLE & COUNTRY PARK, NATIONAL TRUST 104-12
Maybole, South Ayrshire
TEL: 01655 884 455

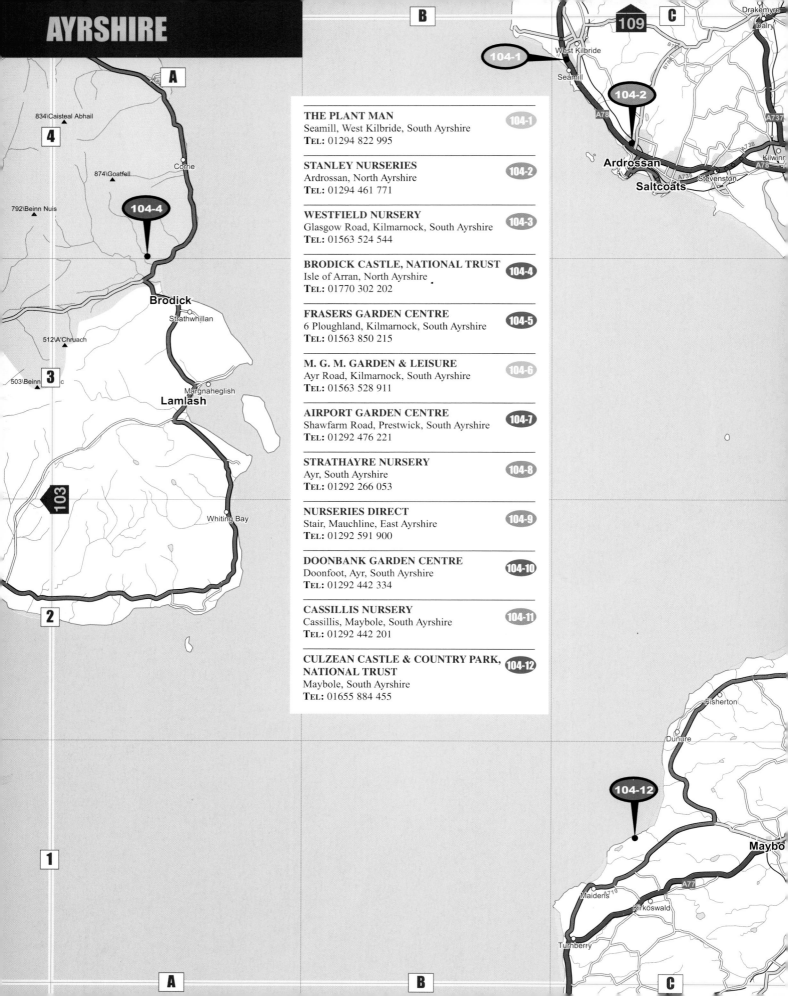

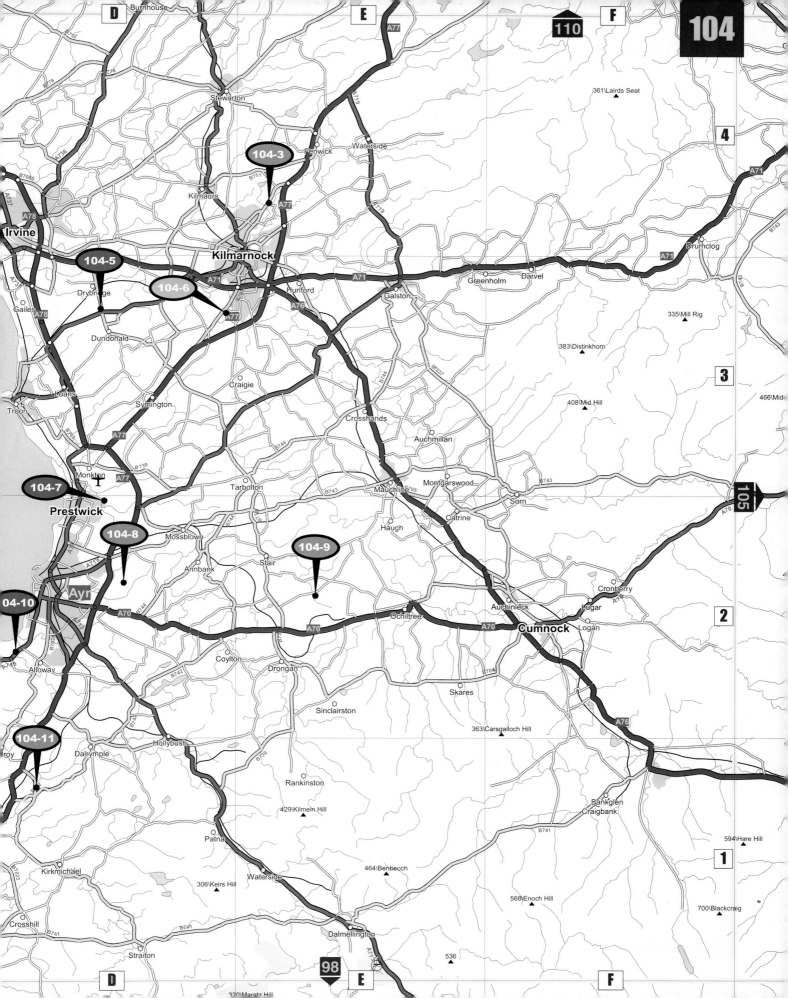

SCOTLAND

HEADS POINT NURSERY
Braidwood, Carluke, South Lanarkshire
Tel: 01555 772 303

ROBERT JOHNSTONE PATHHEAD NURSERY
Lesmahagow, South Lanarkshire
Tel: 01698 792 264

BROUGHTON PLACE
Biggar, South Lanarkshire
Tel: 01899 830 234

DAWYCK BOTANIC GARDEN
Peebles, Borders
Tel: 01721 760 254

MOFFAT GARDEN CENTRE 105-5
High Street, Moffat, Dumfries & Galloway
Tel: 01683 220 442

CRAIGIEBURN CLASSIC PLANTS 105-6
Moffat, Dumfries & Galloway
Tel: 01683 221 250

Boronia

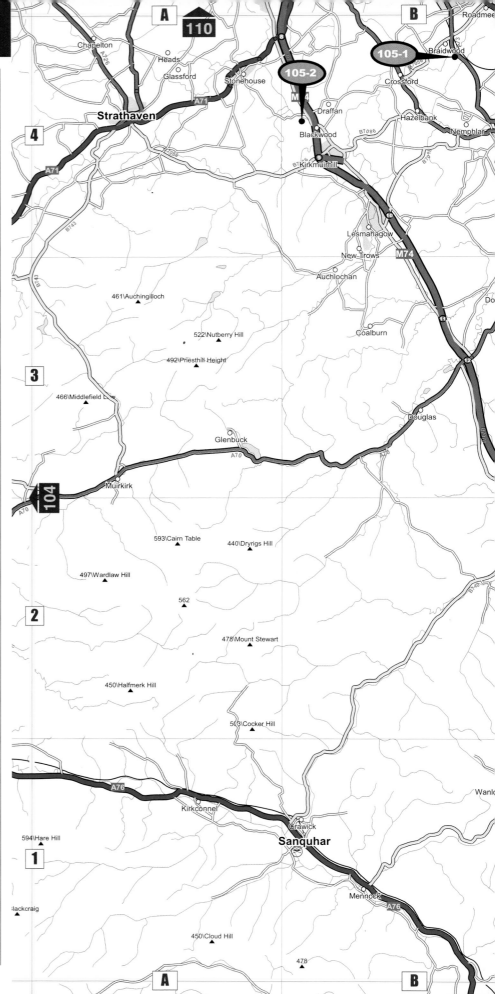

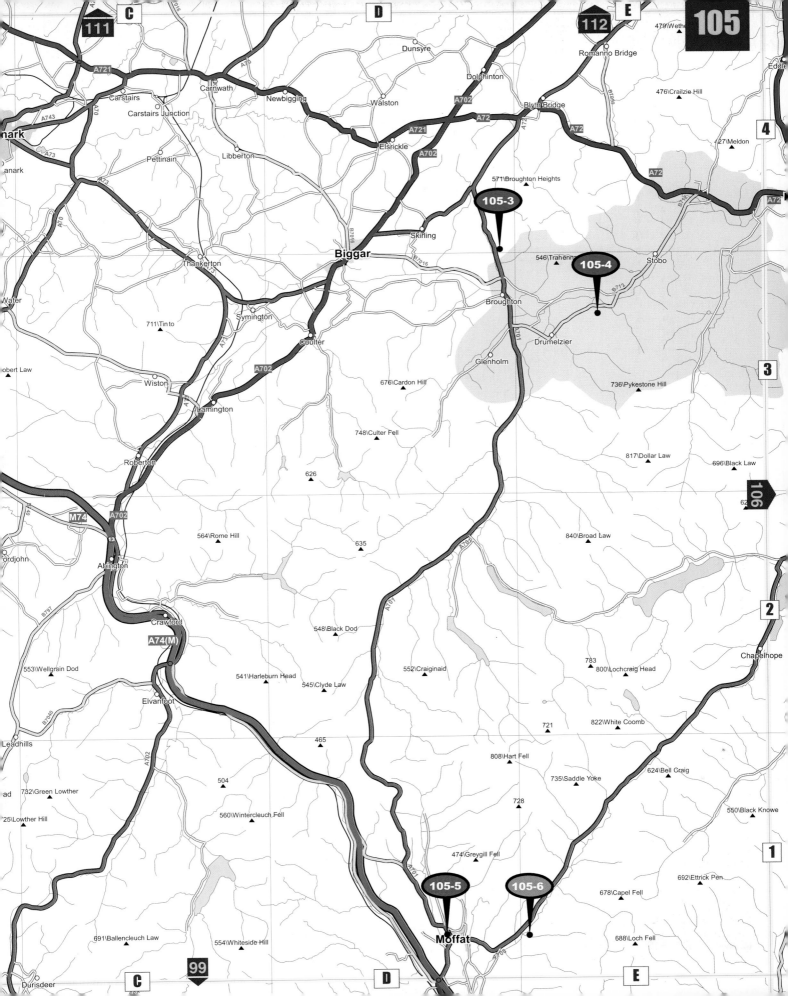

BORDERS

GARDEN CENTRE
NURSERY
GARDEN

NURSERY & GARDEN CENTRE
GARDEN & NURSERY
WATER GARDEN SPECIALIST

MELLERSTAIN HOUSE
Gordon, Borders
TEL: 01573 410 225

KAILZIE GARDENS
Peebles, Borders
TEL: 01721 720 007

EILDON PLANTS
Melrose, Borders
TEL: 01896 755 530

HARMONY GARDEN, NATIONAL TRUST
Melrose, Borders
TEL: 01896 823 464

WAVERLEY NURSERIES
Darnick, Melrose, Borders
TEL: 01896 822 257

ABBOTSFORD
Melrose, Borders
TEL: 01896 752 043

PRIORWOOD GARDEN, NATIONAL TRUST
Melrose, Borders
TEL: 01896 822 493

ORMISTON & RENWICK
High Street, Melrose, Borders
TEL: 01896 822 163

LILLIESLEAF NURSERY
Linthill, Lillisleaf, Borders
TEL: 01835 870 415

MONTEVIOT HOUSE GARDENS
Jedburgh, Borders
TEL: 01835 830 380

JEDBURGH ABBEY, HISTORIC SCOTLAND
Jedburgh, Borders, TD8 6JQ
TEL: 01835 863 925
WEB: www.historic-scotland.gov.uk
Cloister garden recreated as the monks would have had it.
OPEN: Apr-Sep 9.30-6.30 7 days. Oct-Mar 9.30-4.30 Mon-Sat, 2.00-4.30 Sun.
OPEN: Adult £3.30, Children £1.20, Conc. £2.50.
SPECIALITIES: Shrubs, Roses, Herbs.

HAWICK GARDEN CENTRE
Earl Street, Hawick, Borders
TEL: 01450 374 727

Tea Tree Flower

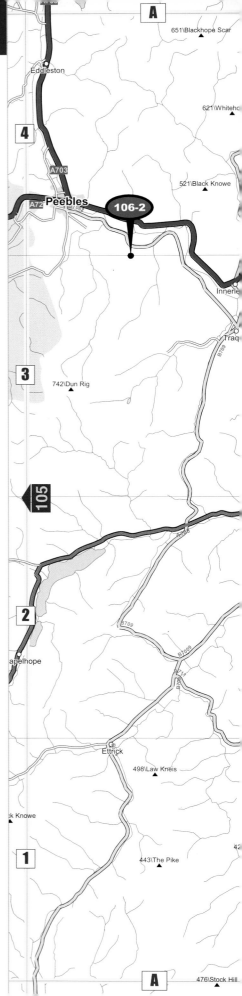

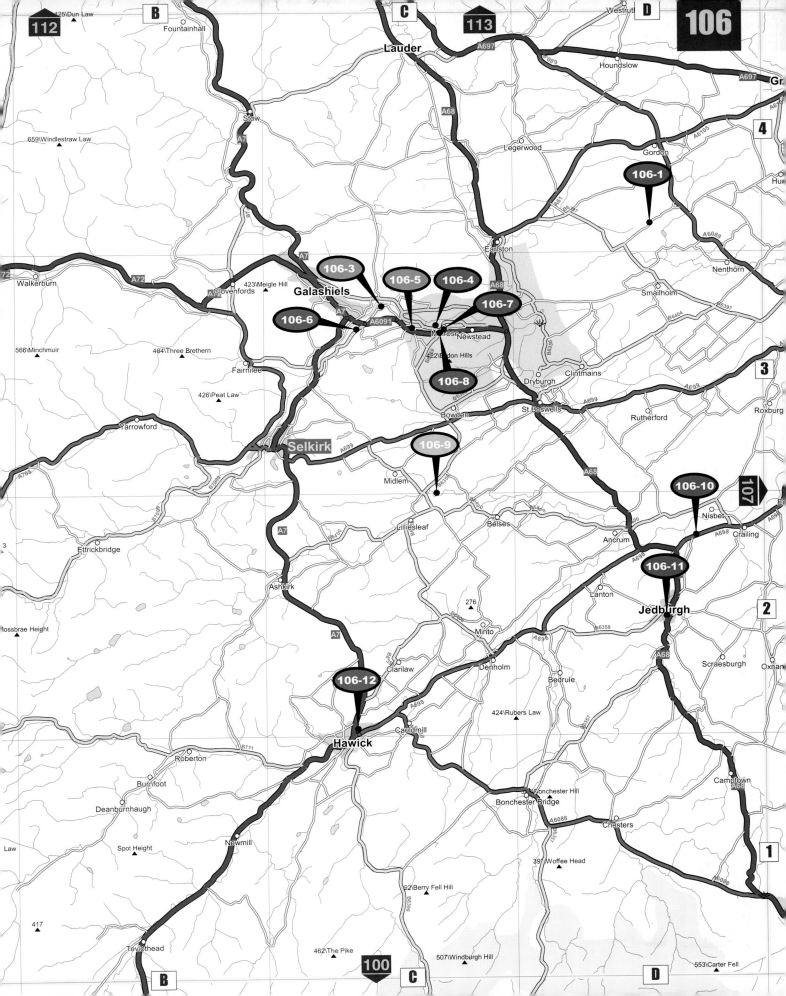

LINDISFARNE CASTLE, NATIONAL TRUST `107-1`
Holy Island, Berwick upon Tweed, Northumberland
TEL: 01289 389 244

THE HIRSEL `107-2`
Coldstream, Borders
TEL: 01890 882 834

STICHILL FOREST NURSERY `107-3`
Kelso, Borders
TEL: 01573 470 261

FORD NURSERY `107-4`
Ford, Berwick upon Tweed, Northumberland
TEL: 01890 820 379

FLOORS CASTLE `107-5`
Kelso, Borders
TEL: 01573 223 333

KLONDYKE GARDEN CENTRE `107-6`
Kelso, Borders
TEL: 01573 224 124

TEVIOT WATER GARDEN `107-7`
Eckford, Kelso, Borders
TEL: 01835 850 734

CHILLINGHAM CASTLE `107-8`
Chillingham, Northumberland
TEL: 01668 215 359

CRASTER TOWERS STABLE YARD
FARM SHOP & NURSERY `107-9`
Craster Tower, Alnwick, Northumberland
TEL: 01665 576 898

HOWICK HALL `107-10`
Howick, Alnwick, Northumberland
TEL: 01665 577 285

ALNWICK NURSERY & GARDEN CENTRE `107-11`
Denwick Lane, Alnwick, Northumberland
TEL: 01665 510 193

Heath

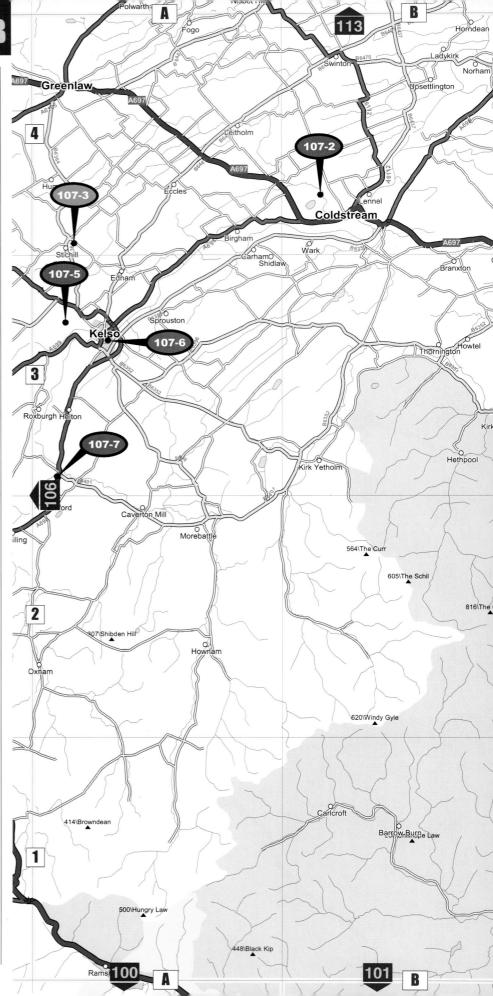

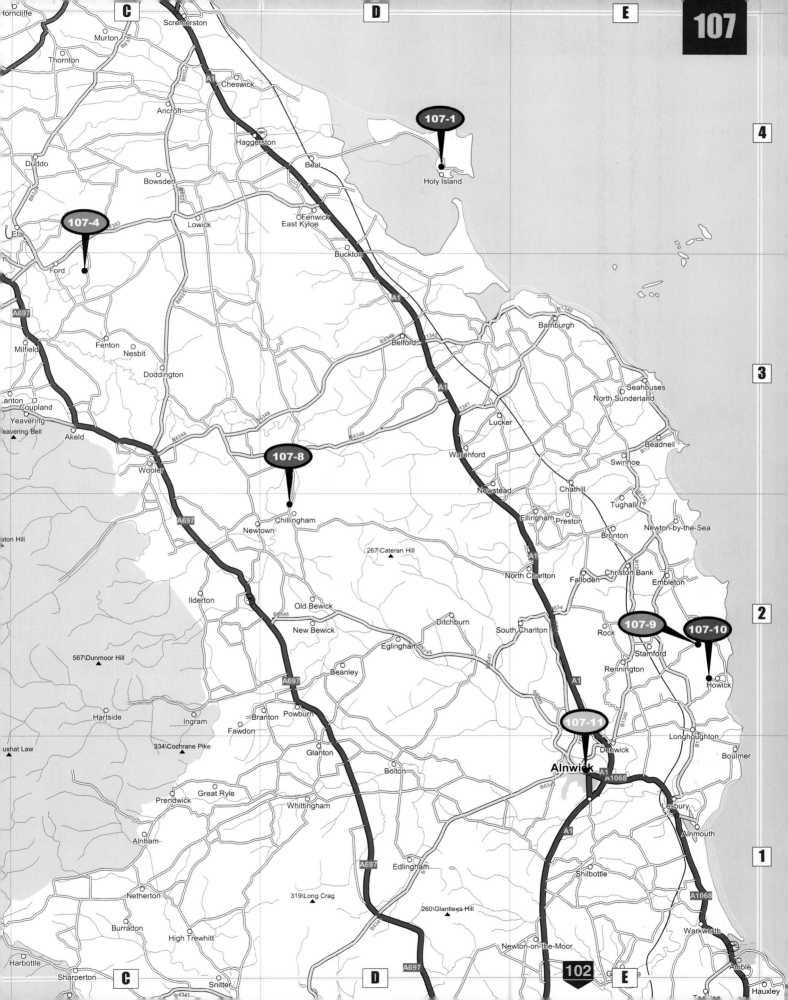

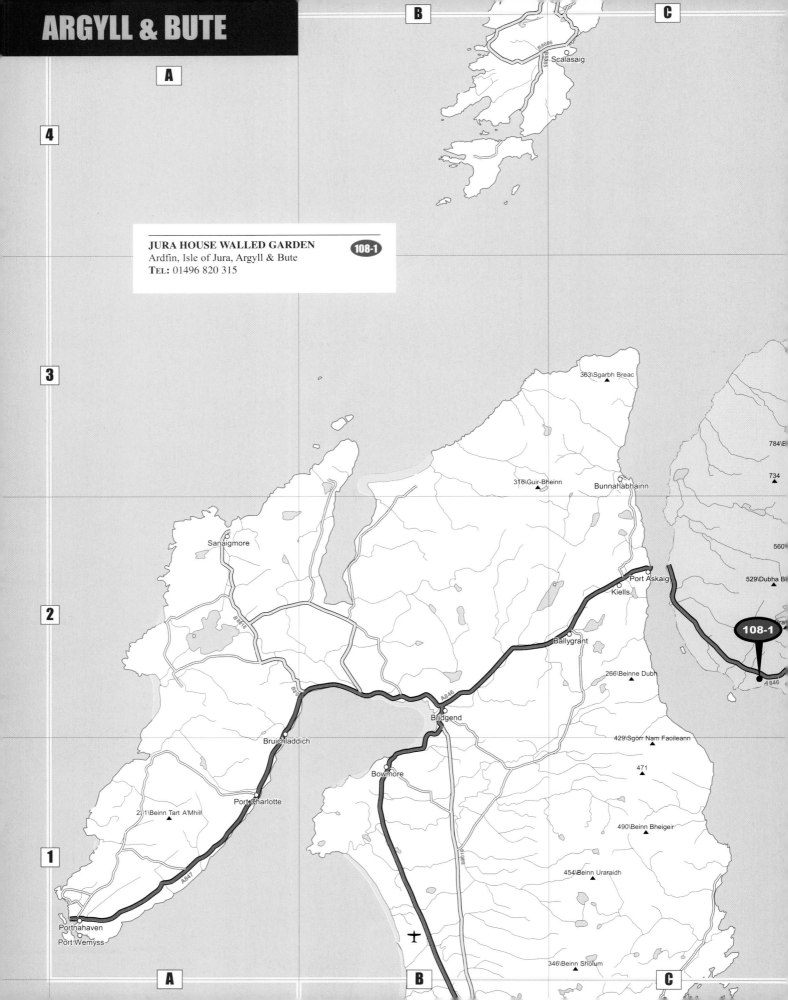

ARGYLL & BUTE

JURA HOUSE WALLED GARDEN 108-1
Ardfin, Isle of Jura, Argyll & Bute
TEL: 01496 820 315

A

B

C

4

3

2

1

Scalasaig

363\Sgarbh Breac

784\B

734

316\Guir-Bheinn

Bunnahabhainn

560

529\Dubha Bl

Sanaigmore

Port Askaig
Kiells

108-1

Ballygrant

266\Beinne Dubh

Bridgend

429\Sgòrr Nam Faoileann

Bruichladdich

471

Bowmore

490\Beinn Bheigeir

Port Charlotte

2\1\Beinn Tart A'Mhill

454\Beinn Uraraidh

Portnahaven
Port Wemyss

346\Beinn Sholum

364\Ben Garrisdale

466\Beinn Bhreac

453\Rainberg Mor

Crinan

4   A816

Lochgilp

Ta.vallich

Achnamara

Ardrishaig

331\Beinn Bheag

466\Cruach Lusach

398\Beinn Tarsuinn

A846

Brenfield

3

A83

Ellary

561\Sliabh Gaoil

B8024

480\Dubh Chreag

109

Tarbert

Craighouse

2

343\Cruac

A83

Kilberry 3\Cruach Airde

422\Cnoc A' Bhaile

Kennacraig

Whitehouse

B8001

B 024

Portachoillan

A83

Claor

Clachan

1

Tarbert

Ballochroy

247\Cruach Mhic Gougain

Crossaig

264\ h T-Samhlaidh

SCOTLAND

YOUNGER BOTANIC GARDEN, BENMORE
Dunoon, Argyll, Argyll & Bute
TEL: 01369 706 261

BALLAGAN GARDEN CENTRE
Alexandria, North Lanarkshire
TEL: 01389 752 947

GLENARN
Helensburgh, Argyll & Bute
TEL: 01436 820 493

HILL HOUSE, NATIONAL TRUST
Helensburgh, Argyll & Bute
TEL: 01436 673 900

DOBBIES GARDEN WORLD
Helensburgh, Argyll & Bute
TEL: 01436 671 202

LINN BOTANIC GARDENS & NURSERY
Cove, Helensburgh, Argyll & Bute
TEL: 01436 842 242

GEILSTON PARK, NATIONAL TRUST
Dumbarton, Glasgow
TEL: 01389 841 867

WALKER HOME & GARDEN CENTRE
Dunoon, Argyll & Bute
TEL: 01369 704 003

CARDWELL NURSERY GARDEN CENTRE
Gourock, Inverclyde, Renfrewshire
TEL: 01475 521 536

FINLAYSTONE 109-10
Langbank, Renfrewshire
TEL: 01475 540 285

MOUNT STUART GARDENS 109-11
Isle of Bute, Argyll & Bute
TEL: 01700 503 877

Bird of Paradise

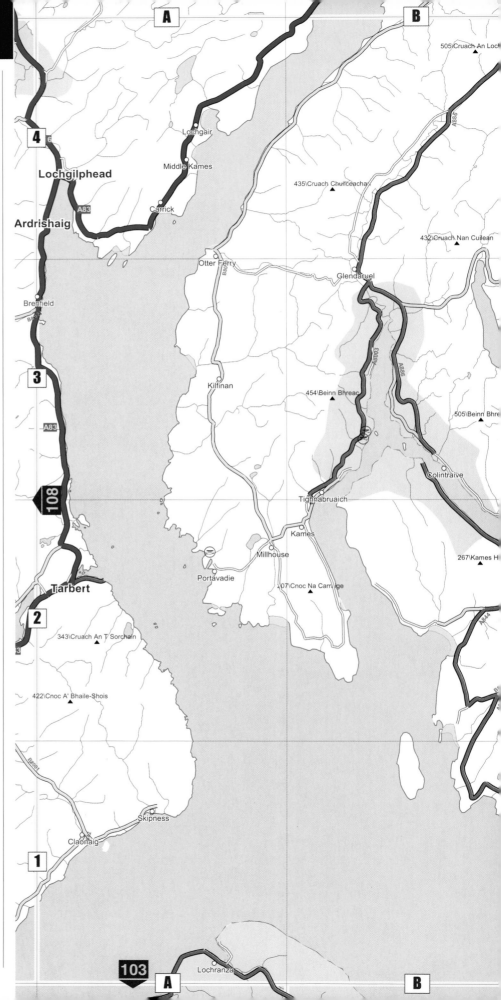

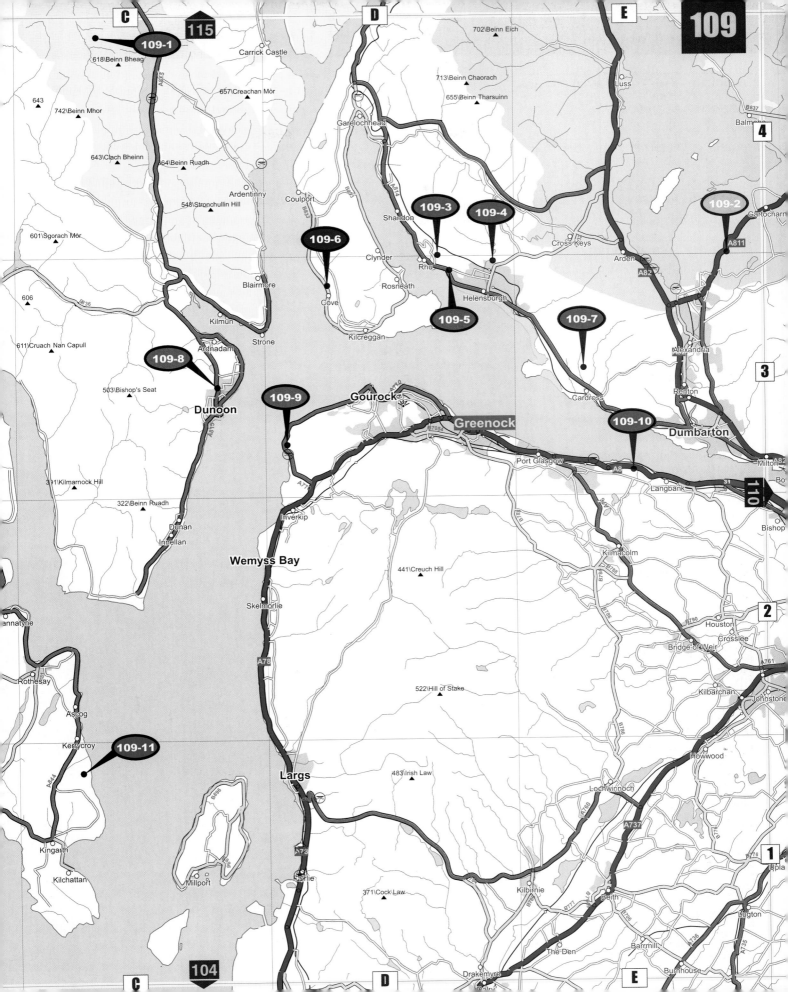

HEDGEROW HERBS NURSERY & PLANT CENTRE
Gargunnock, Stirling, Stirling
TEL: 01786 860 552

DOBBIES GARDEN CENTRE
Westerwood, Cumbernauld, Glasgow
TEL: 01236 736 100

BARRASTON NURSERY
Torrance, Glasgow, Glasgow
TEL: 01360 620 354

KLONDYKE GARDEN CENTRE
Kirkintilloch, Glasgow, Glasgow
TEL: 0141 776 2001

WEST CARLSTON GARDEN CENTRE
Campsie Road, Glasgow, Glasgow
TEL: 01360 620 248

BALMORE NURSERIES
Torrance, Glasgow, Glasgow
TEL: 01360 620 508

ERSKINE HOSPITAL GARDEN CENTRE
Erskine Hospital, Bishopton, Renfrewshire
TEL: 0141 812 0657

HUNTERSHILL GARDEN & GIFT CENTRE
Bishopbriggs, Glasgow
TEL: 01417 625 100

ANNIESLAND GARDEN & GIFT CENTRE
950A Crow Road North, Glasgow, Glasgow
TEL: 01414 023 551

GREENHEAD NURSERY
Inchinnan, Renfrew, Renfrewshire
TEL: 0141 812 0121

LOCHEND NURSERY
Gartcosh, Glasgow, Glasgow
TEL: 01236 875 800

GLASGOW BOTANIC GARDENS
Glasgow, Glasgow
TEL: 0141 334 2422

ROUKEN GLEN GARDEN CENTRE
Giffnock, Glasgow
TEL: 0141 620 0566

IRVINES OF POLLOKSHIELDS
128 Nithsdale Road, Glasgow, Glasgow
TEL: 01414 240 357

DOBBIES GARDEN WORLD
Barrhead Road, Paisley, Renfrewshire
TEL: 0141 887 5422

QUEENS PARK
Glasgow, Glasgow
TEL: 0141 649 0331

GLENROYAL NURSERY
95 Cathcart Road, Rutherglen, South Lanarkshire
TEL: 0141 647 6921

BELLSHILL GARDEN CENTRE
Reema Road, Bellshill, North Lanarkshire
TEL: 01698 840 000

HOLMWOOD HOUSE, NATIONAL TRUST
Cathcart, Glasgow
TEL: 0141 637 2129

FERENEZE GARDEN CENTRE 110-20
Barrhead, Glasgow, Glasgow
TEL: 0141 881 1564

ROBERTSON OF BROOMHOUSE
Whistleberry Road, Hamilton, South Lanarkshire
TEL: 01698 286 332

GREENBANK GARDEN, NATIONAL TRUST
Clarkson, Renfrewshire
TEL: 0141 616 2266

PHILIPSHILL GARDEN CENTRE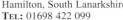
Philipshill Road, Glasgow, Glasgow
TEL: 0141 644 3638

AVONHILL NURSERY SOILS & BARK SUPPLIES 110-24
Hamilton, South Lanarkshire
TEL: 01698 422 099

BRAIDBAR NURSERIES 110-25
Hazelden Mearns Road, Glasgow, Glasgow
TEL: 0141 616 0007

CHATELHERAULT GARDEN CENTRE 110-26
Ferniegaur, Hamilton, South Lanarkshire
TEL: 01698 457 700

BROOKSIDE HOMES & GARDENS 110-27
Larkhall, North Lanarkshire
TEL: 01698 886 464

THE COTTAGE NURSERY 110-28
Larkhall, North Lanarkshire
TEL: 01698 884 511

Dahlia Rose

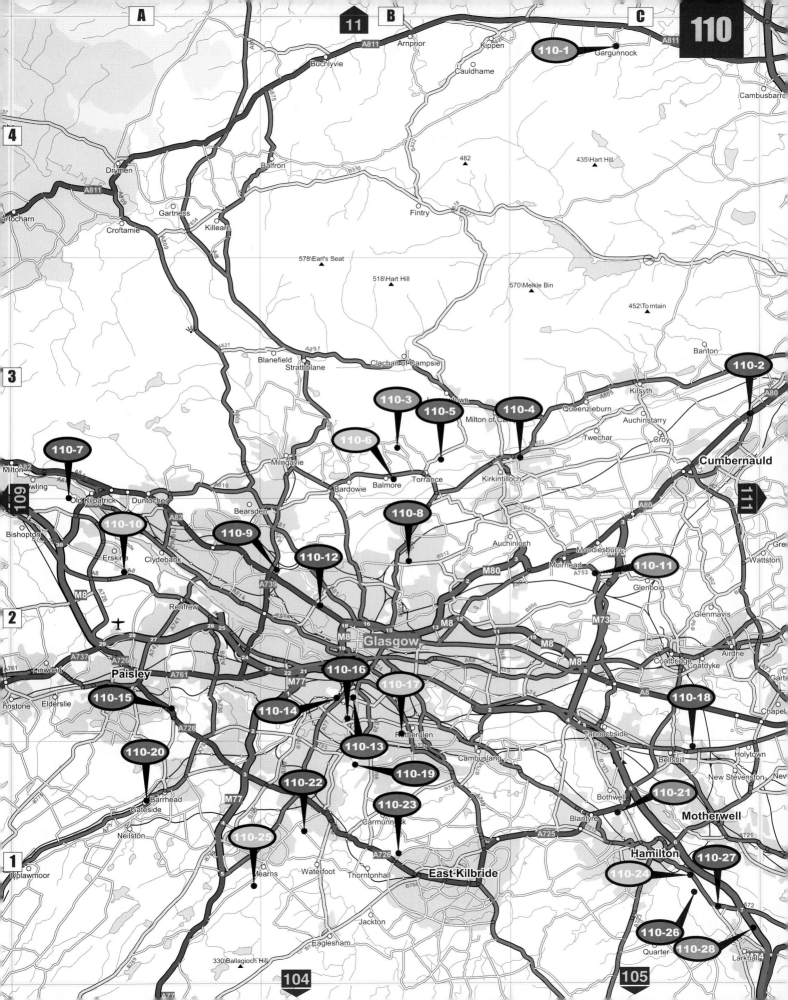

STIRLING CASTLE, HISTORIC SCOTLAND
Stirling, FK8 1EJ
TEL: 01786 450 000
WEB: www.historic-scotland.gov.uk
Perhaps the grandest of Scotland's castles, with outstanding architecture: the gatehouse and recently restored Great Hall of James IV, the Renaissance Palace of James V and Chapel Royal of James VI. Mary Queen of Scots was crowned here.
OPEN: Apr-Sep, Mon-Sun, 9.30-6.30 (last entry 5.15). Oct-Mar 9.30-5 (last entry 4.15)
ENTRY COSTS: Adult £6.50, Children £2.
SPECIALITIES: Knot, Walled garden.

GREENYARDS GARDEN CENTRE
Bannockburn, Stirling, Stirling
TEL: 01786 817 369

KLONDYKE GARDEN CENTRE
Whins of Milton, Stirling, Stirling
TEL: 01786 816 167

LUSCAR NURSERY
Gowkhall, Dunfermline, Fife
TEL: 01383 850 536

HENDRY'S GARDEN CENTRE & BISTRO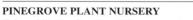
Leadside, Dunfermline, Fife
TEL: 01383 733 367

PINEGROVE PLANT NURSERY
Cairneyhill, Dunfermline, Fife
TEL: 01383 881 493

FAIRLEY'S GARDEN CENTRE
Cairneyhill, Dunfermline, Fife
TEL: 01383 880 223

CULROSS PALACE, NATIONAL TRUST
Dunfermline, Fife
TEL: 01383 880 359

TORWOOD GARDEN CENTRE
Torwood, Larbert, Stirling
TEL: 01324 553 152

GREENYARDS GARDEN CENTRE
Carron Grove Road, Falkirk, Falkirk
TEL: 01324 555 410

BONNYVIEW NURSERY
Larbert, Stirling
TEL: 01324 562 207

KLONDYKE GARDEN CENTRE
Polmont, Falkirk, Stirling
TEL: 01324 717 035

J. B. MCINTOSH
Dennyloanhead, Bonnybridge, Falkirk
TEL: 01324 840 941

HOPETOUN HOUSE
South Queensferry, Edinburgh
TEL: 0131 331 2451

HOUSE OF THE BINNS, NATIONAL TRUST
Linlithgow, West Lothian
TEL: 01506 834 255

DOUGAL PHILIP
Newton Village, Broxburn, West Lothian
TEL: 01506 834 433

BINNY PLANTS
Ecclesmachan, Uphall, West Lothian
TEL: 01506 858 931

SOUTH LOGIE NURSERY
Westfield, Bath, West Lothian
TEL: 01506 631 769

MILL GARDEN CENTRE
Barbauchlaw Mill, Bath, West Lothian
TEL: 01501 732 347

AMMANDALE GARDEN CENTRE
Raw Farm Nurseries, Livingston, West Lothian
TEL: 01506 880 018

BROOMPARK PLANT CENTRE
Mid Calder, Livingston, West Lothian
TEL: 01506 881 513

KLONDYKE GARDEN CENTRE
Livingston, West Lothian
TEL: 01506 410 053

FIVE SISTERS GARDEN CENTRE
Gavieside, West Calder, West Lothian
TEL: 01506 873 727

POND SERVICES
Polbeth, West Calder, West Lothian
TEL: 01506 873 653

RIDGEVIEW NURSERY
Crossroads, Bath, West Lothian
TEL: 01501 771 144

ANDERSONS
Lanark Road, Larkhall, North Lanarkshire
TEL: 01698 883 492

CLYDE VALLEY GARDEN CENTRE
Garrion Bridge, Larkhall, North Lanarkshire
TEL: 01698 888 880

GLENROSE GARDEN CENTRE
Ashgillhead Road, Larkhall, North Lanarkshire
TEL: 01698 888 244

GOULDING GROWERS
Dalpatrick Farm, Carluke, South Lanarkshire
TEL: 01555 860 259

Ranunculus

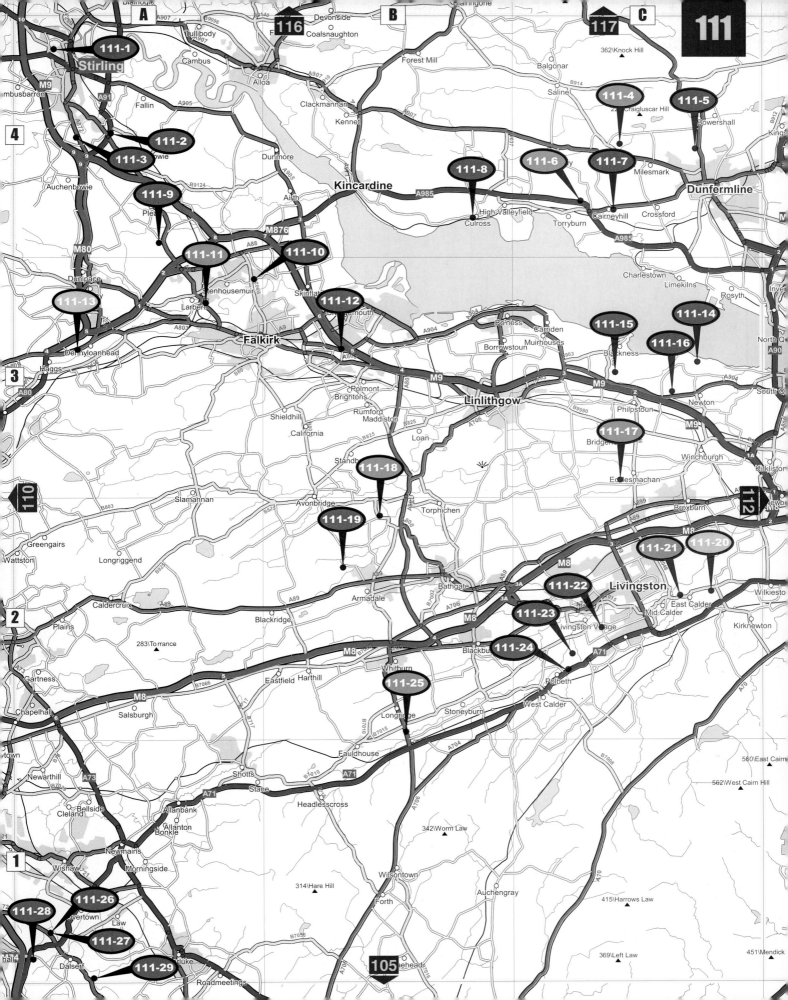

KIRKCALDY GARDEN CENTRE
Thornton Road, Kirkcaldy, Fife
TEL: 01592 652 861

LADY HELEN NURSERIES
Cardenden, Lochgelly, Fife
TEL: 01592 720 740

ABERDOUR CASTLE, HISTORIC SCOTLAND
Aberdour, Fife, KY3 0SL
TEL: 01383 860 519
WEB: www.historic-scotland.gov.uk

A 13th century castle built by the Douglas family. The gallery on the first floor gives an idea of how it was furnished at the time. The castle has a delightful walled garden and dovecote.
OPEN: Apr-Sep Daily, 9.30-6.30. Oct-Mar 9.30-4.30 Mon-Sat, 2-4.30 Sun. Closed Thur pm, Fri & Sun am.
ENTRY COSTS: Adult £2, Children 75p, Concession £1.50.
SPECIALITIES: Walled garden.

THE NURSERIES
Middlebank Small Holdings, Dunfermline, Fife
TEL: 01383 413 787

DOBBIES GARDEN CENTRE 112-5
Dalgety Bay, Fife
TEL: 01383 823 841

ROYAL BOTANIC GARDEN, EDINBURGH 112-6
Edinburgh, Edinburgh
TEL: 0131 552 7171

ROUKEN GLEN GARDEN CENTRE 112-7
Linlithgow, West Lothian
TEL: 01506 834 346

PRINCES STREET GARDENS EAST AND WEST 112-8
Edinburgh, EH1 3JD
TEL: 0131 529 7915
Historic landscaped park and garden.
OPEN: Throughout the year, dawn till dusk.
ENTRY COSTS: Free.
SPECIALITIES: Bedding plants, Hardy plants, Rhododendrons and azaleas, Roses, Shrubs.

CONIFOX NURSERIES 112-9
Kirkliston, West Lothian
TEL: 0131 333 3334

MEADOWMILL GARDEN CENTRE & NURSERY 112-10
Tranent, East Lothian
TEL: 01875 610 664

INVERESK LODGE, NATIONAL TRUST
Musselburgh, East Lothian
TEL: 0131 665 1855

NEWHAILES NURSERY
Musselburgh, East Lothian
TEL: 0131 665 8291

NEWHAILES ESTATE, NATIONAL TRUST
Musselburgh, East Lothian
TEL: 0131 665 0253

MACPLANTS
5 Boggs Holdings, Pencaitland, East Lothian
TEL: 01875 341 179

KLONDYKE GARDEN CENTRE
Mortonhall, Edinburgh, Edinburgh
TEL: 0131 664 8698

DOBBIES GARDEN WORLD
Lasswade, Midlothian
TEL: 0131 663 1941

MALLENY GARDEN, NATIONAL TRUST
Edinburgh, Edinburgh
TEL: 0131 449 2283

Japanese Iris

DIRLETON CASTLE, HISTORIC SCOTLAND

113-1

Dirleton, East Lothian, EH39 5ER
Tel: 01620 850 330
Web: www.historic-scotland.gov.uk

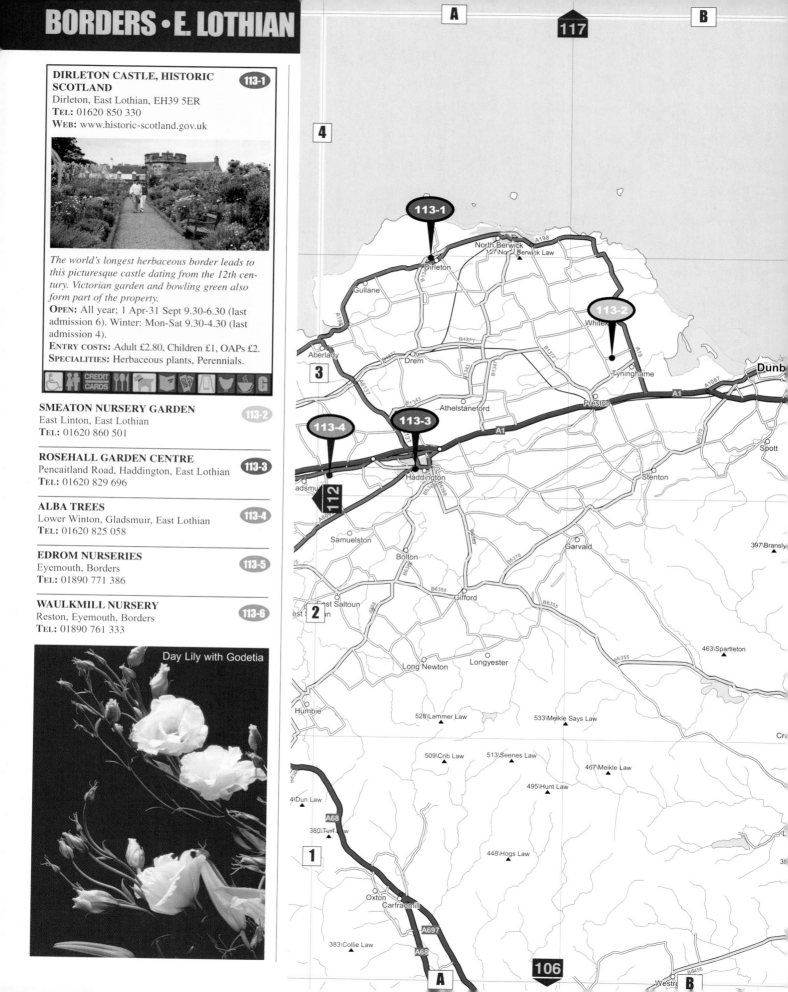

The world's longest herbaceous border leads to this picturesque castle dating from the 12th century. Victorian garden and bowling green also form part of the property.

Open: All year; 1 Apr-31 Sept 9.30-6.30 (last admission 6). Winter: Mon-Sat 9.30-4.30 (last admission 4).
Entry costs: Adult £2.80, Children £1, OAPs £2.
Specialities: Herbaceous plants, Perennials.

SMEATON NURSERY GARDEN

113-2

East Linton, East Lothian
Tel: 01620 860 501

ROSEHALL GARDEN CENTRE

113-3

Pencaitland Road, Haddington, East Lothian
Tel: 01620 829 696

ALBA TREES

113-4

Lower Winton, Gladsmuir, East Lothian
Tel: 01620 825 058

EDROM NURSERIES

113-5

Eyemouth, Borders
Tel: 01890 771 386

WAULKMILL NURSERY

113-6

Reston, Eyemouth, Borders
Tel: 01890 761 333

Day Lily with Godetia

4

3

xburn

Innerwick

319\Cocklaw Hill

Cove

Cockburnspath

Oldhamstocks

A1107

A1

A1

391\Heart Law

196\Brown Rig

113-5

St Abbs

2

Grantshouse

Coldingham

113-6

Eyemouth

A6438

262\Horseley Hill

A1

haws

Heugh Head

Reston

Abbey St Bathans

Ayton

Burnmouth

Ellemford

25\Cockburn Law

Auchencrow

B6438

B6355

B6438

gformacus

Lintlaw

B6355

Primrosehill

Preston

irrington Great Law

Chirnside

1

Edrom

Chirnsidebridge

Foulden

A6105

Allanton

Hutton

Duns

A6112

B6460

Paxton

B6461

A6105

Berwick-upon-Tweed

Gavinton

A6112

B6460

A6437

A1

A698

A1

Nisbet Hill

Sinclair's Hill

Pol

Whitsome

Horncliffe

ARGYLL & BUTE

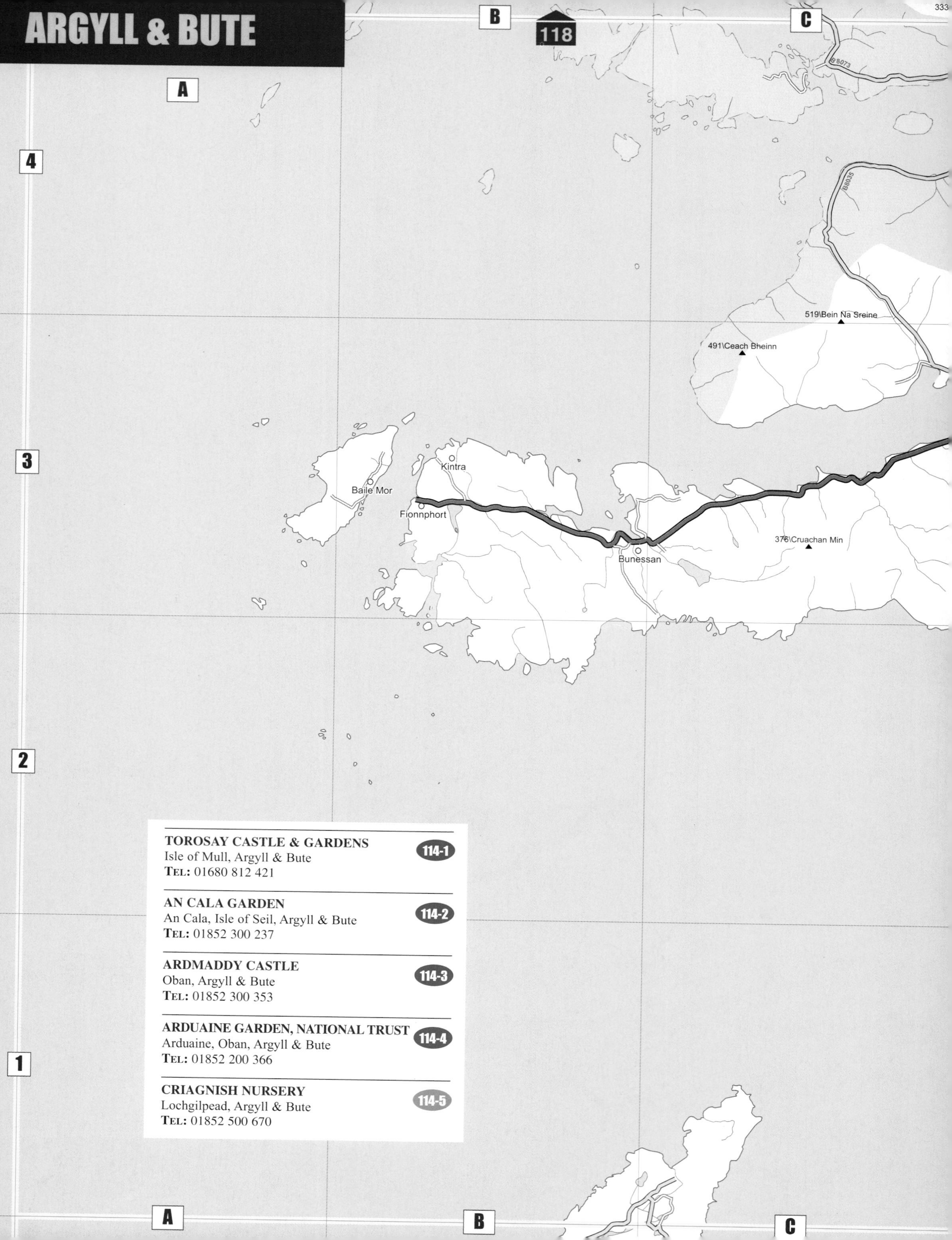

A

B

C

4

3

519\Bein Na Sreine

491\Ceach Bheinn

Kintra

Baile Mor

Fionnphort

Bunessan

376\Cruachan Min

2

TOROSAY CASTLE & GARDENS	114-1
Isle of Mull, Argyll & Bute	
TEL: 01680 812 421	

AN CALA GARDEN	114-2
An Cala, Isle of Seil, Argyll & Bute	
TEL: 01852 300 237	

ARDMADDY CASTLE	114-3
Oban, Argyll & Bute	
TEL: 01852 300 353	

ARDUAINE GARDEN, NATIONAL TRUST	114-4
Arduaine, Oban, Argyll & Bute	
TEL: 01852 200 366	

CRIAGNISH NURSERY	114-5
Lochgilpead, Argyll & Bute	
TEL: 01852 500 670	

1

A

B

C

ARGYLL & BUTE

ARDCHATTEN PRIORY GARDEN `115-1`
Oban, Argyll & Bute
TEL: 01631 750 238

ACHNACLOICH `115-2`
Connel, Oban, Argyll & Bute
TEL: 01631 710 221

BARGUILLEAN ANGUS GARDEN `115-3`
Taynuilt, Argyll & Bute
TEL: 01866 822 381

ANGUS GARDEN `115-4`
Taynuilt, Oban, Argyll & Bute
TEL: 01866 822 254

ARDANAISEIG HOTEL GARDEN `115-5`
Kilchrenan, Argyll & Bute
TEL: 01866 833 333

TREE SHOP `115-6`
Cairndow, Argyll & Bute, PA26 8BH
TEL: 01499 600 263
EMAIL: tree.shop@virgin.net
Plant centre and quality gift shop, specialising in trees, rhododendrons and woodwork.
OPEN: Daily 9.30-5.
SPECIALITIES: Alpines, Hardy plants, House plants, Rhododendrons and azaleas, Trees.

ARDKINGLAS WOODLAND GARDEN `115-7`
Cairndow, Argyll & Bute
TEL: 01499 600 261

HIGHLAND HEATHERS `115-8`
Lochgilpead, Argyll & Bute
TEL: 01546 810 253

CRARAE GARDENS `115-9`
Minard, Inveraray, Argyll & Bute
TEL: 01546 886 614

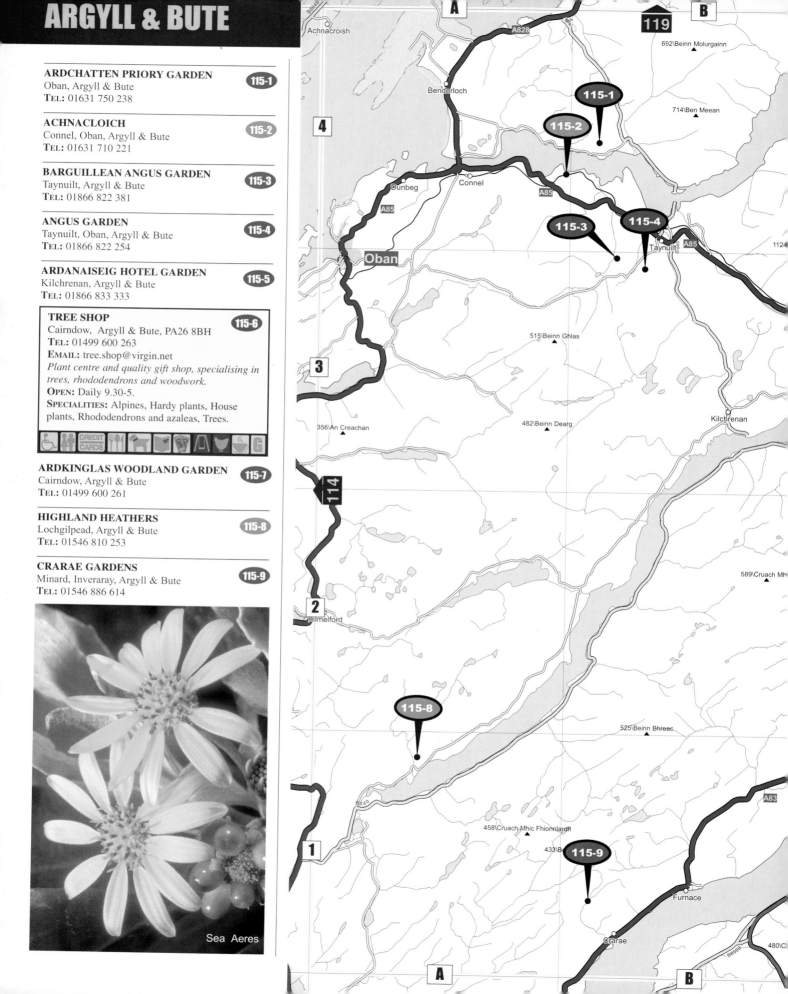

Sea Aeres

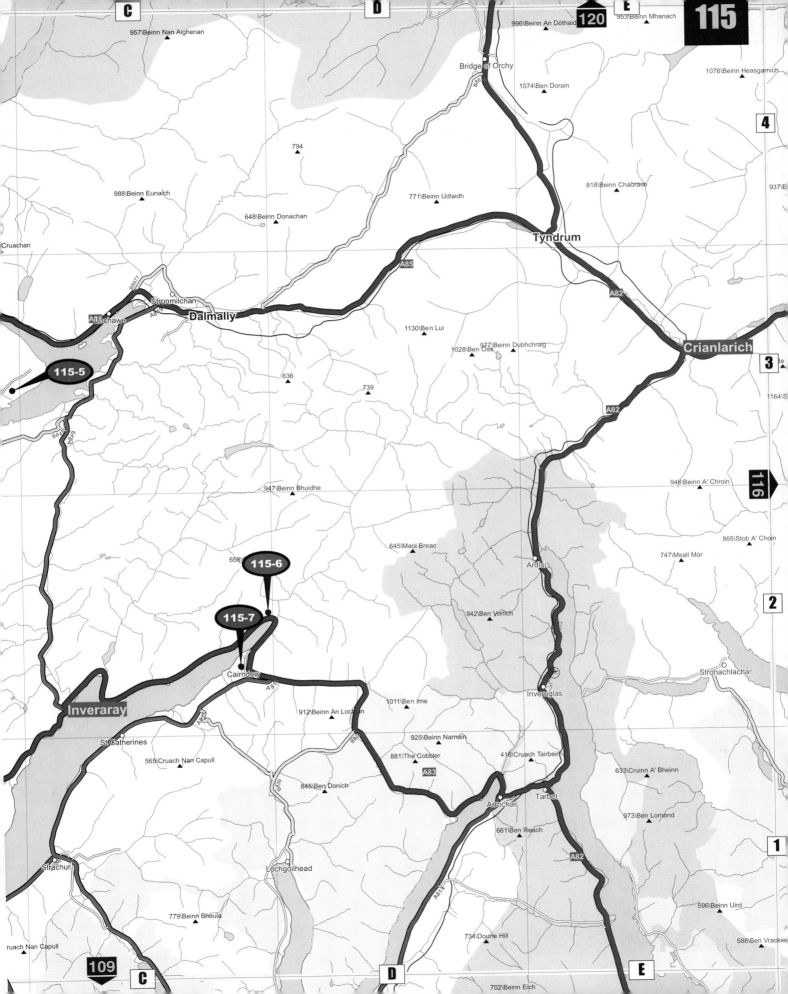

SCOTLAND

WOODLANDS NURSERY
Comrie, Crieff, Perthshire & Kinross
TEL: 01764 670 038

CRIEFF PLANT CENTRE
Muthill Road, Crieff, Perthshire & Kinross
TEL: 01764 652 722

DRUMMOND CASTLE GARDENS
Crieff, Perthshire & Kinross
TEL: 01764 681 550

BLAIRHOYLE NURSERY
Blairhoyle, Stirling, Stirling
TEL: 01877 385 669

STOCKBRIDGE NURSERY
Dunblane, Perthshire & Kinross
TEL: 01786 821 515

CASTLE CAMPBELL, HISTORIC SCOTLAND
Dollar, Stirling, FK14 7PP
TEL: 01259 742 408
WEB: www.historic-scotland.gov.uk
Set at the head of Dollar Glen, this spectacularly sited 15th century fortress was the lowland stronghold of the Campbells. Stunning views from the parapet walk.
OPEN: Apr-Sep Daily, 9.30-6.30. Oct-Mar 9.30-4.30 Mon-Sat, 2-4.30 Sun, closed Thur pm and Fri.
ENTRY COSTS: Adult £2.80, Children £1, Concession £2.
SPECIALITIES: Woodland plants, Waterfalls.

WILSON NURSERY 116-7
Tillicoultry, Falkirk
TEL: 01259 752 867

Cherry blossom

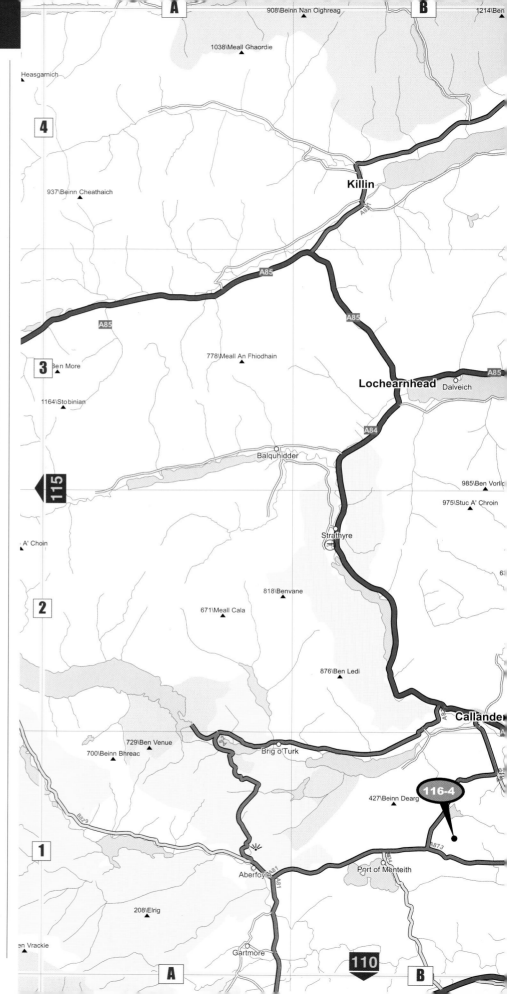

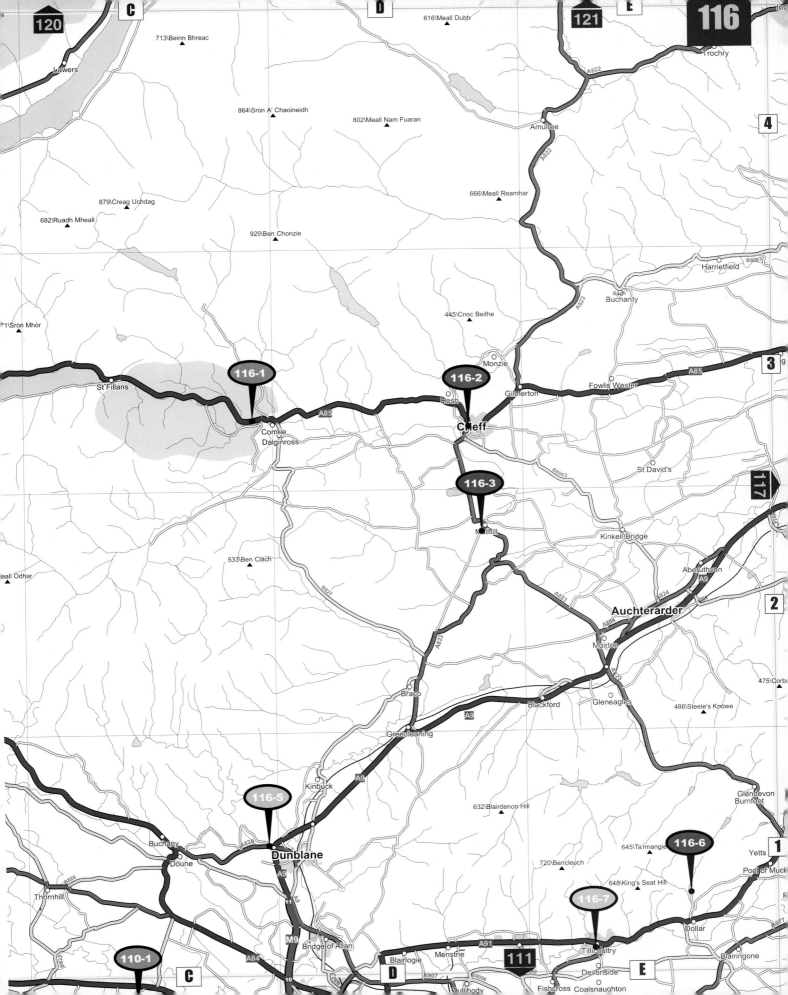

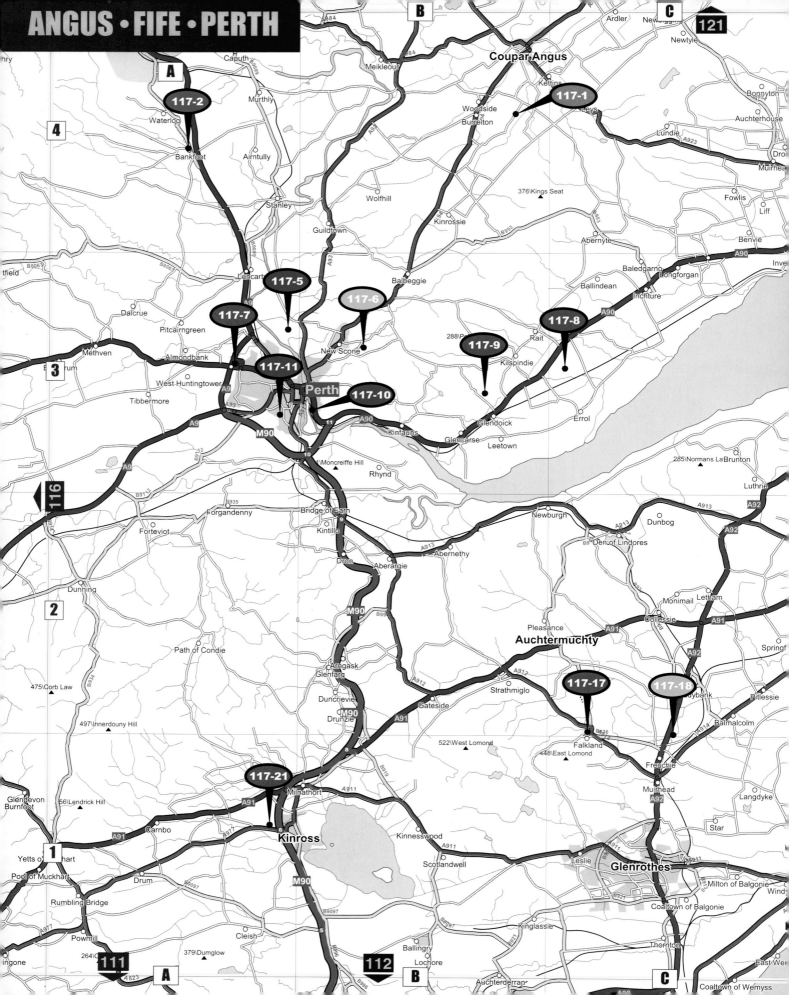

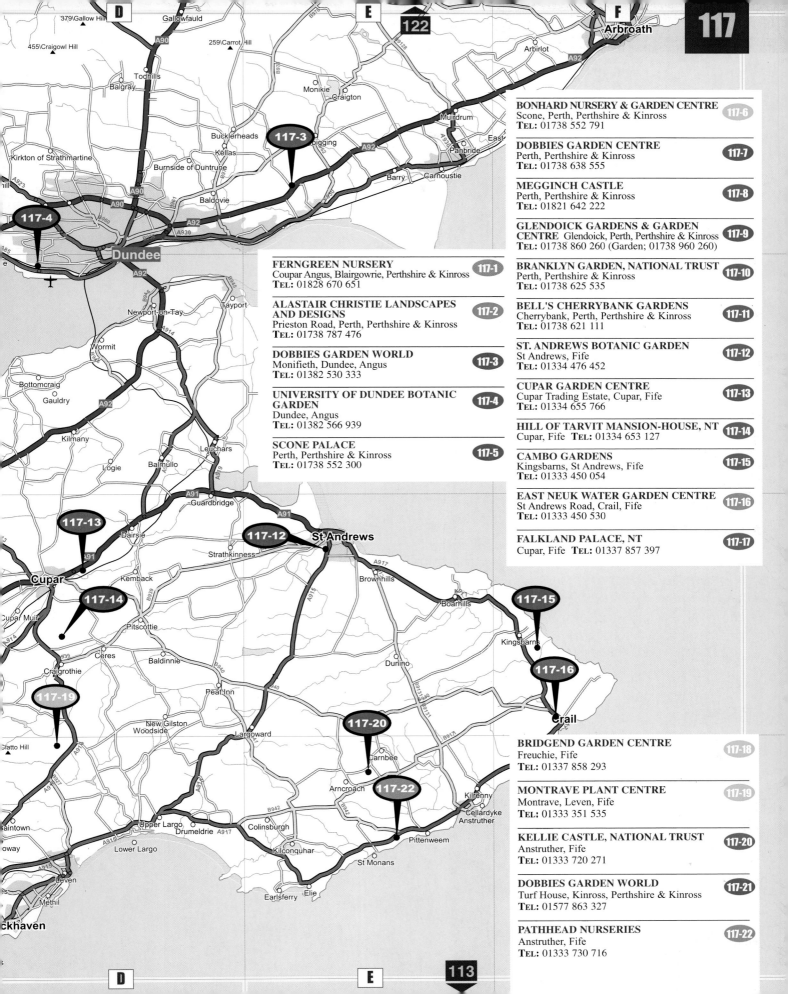

BONHARD NURSERY & GARDEN CENTRE `117-6`
Scone, Perth, Perthshire & Kinross
TEL: 01738 552 791

DOBBIES GARDEN CENTRE `117-7`
Perth, Perthshire & Kinross
TEL: 01738 638 555

MEGGINCH CASTLE `117-8`
Perth, Perthshire & Kinross
TEL: 01821 642 222

GLENDOICK GARDENS & GARDEN CENTRE `117-9`
Glendoick, Perth, Perthshire & Kinross
TEL: 01738 860 260 (Garden; 01738 960 260)

BRANKLYN GARDEN, NATIONAL TRUST `117-10`
Perth, Perthshire & Kinross
TEL: 01738 625 535

BELL'S CHERRYBANK GARDENS `117-11`
Cherrybank, Perth, Perthshire & Kinross
TEL: 01738 621 111

ST. ANDREWS BOTANIC GARDEN `117-12`
St Andrews, Fife
TEL: 01334 476 452

CUPAR GARDEN CENTRE `117-13`
Cupar Trading Estate, Cupar, Fife
TEL: 01334 655 766

HILL OF TARVIT MANSION-HOUSE, NT `117-14`
Cupar, Fife TEL: 01334 653 127

CAMBO GARDENS `117-15`
Kingsbarns, St Andrews, Fife
TEL: 01333 450 054

EAST NEUK WATER GARDEN CENTRE `117-16`
St Andrews Road, Crail, Fife
TEL: 01333 450 530

FALKLAND PALACE, NT `117-17`
Cupar, Fife TEL: 01337 857 397

FERNGREEN NURSERY `117-1`
Coupar Angus, Blairgowrie, Perthshire & Kinross
TEL: 01828 670 651

ALASTAIR CHRISTIE LANDSCAPES AND DESIGNS `117-2`
Prieston Road, Perth, Perthshire & Kinross
TEL: 01738 787 476

DOBBIES GARDEN WORLD `117-3`
Monifieth, Dundee, Angus
TEL: 01382 530 333

UNIVERSITY OF DUNDEE BOTANIC GARDEN `117-4`
Dundee, Angus
TEL: 01382 566 939

SCONE PALACE `117-5`
Perth, Perthshire & Kinross
TEL: 01738 552 300

BRIDGEND GARDEN CENTRE `117-18`
Freuchie, Fife
TEL: 01337 858 293

MONTRAVE PLANT CENTRE `117-19`
Montrave, Leven, Fife
TEL: 01333 351 535

KELLIE CASTLE, NATIONAL TRUST `117-20`
Anstruther, Fife
TEL: 01333 720 271

DOBBIES GARDEN WORLD `117-21`
Turf House, Kinross, Perthshire & Kinross
TEL: 01577 863 327

PATHHEAD NURSERIES `117-22`
Anstruther, Fife
TEL: 01333 730 716

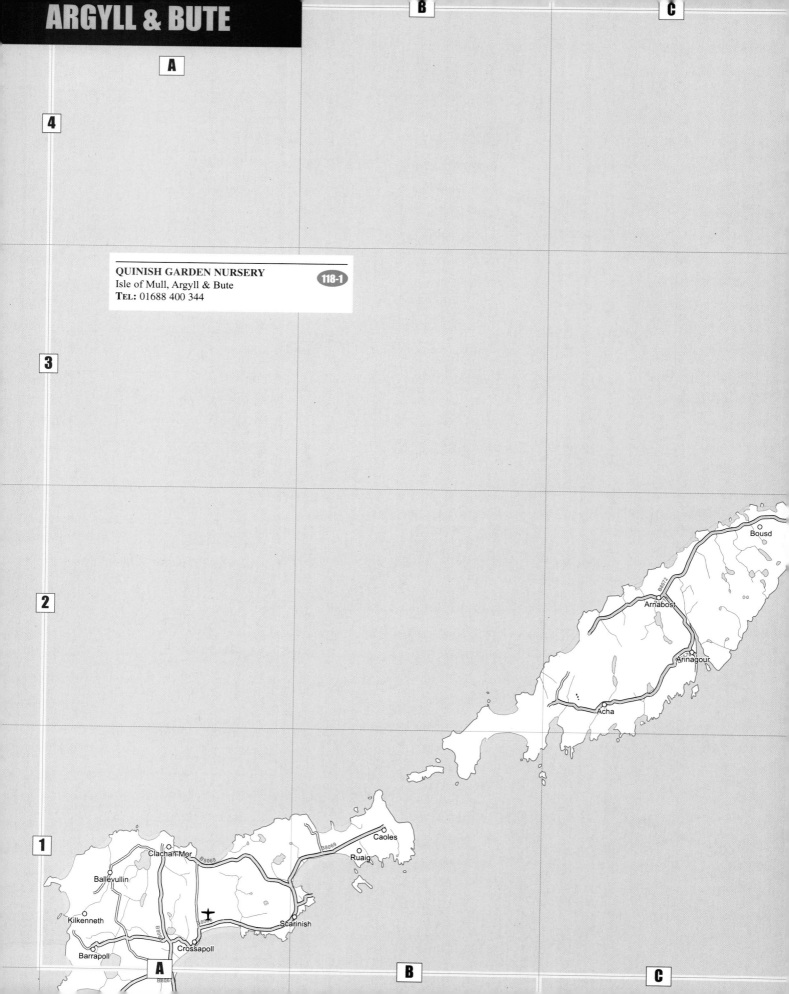

4

A

B

C

QUINISH GARDEN NURSERY
Isle of Mull, Argyll & Bute
TEL: 01688 400 344

118-1

3

2

Bousd

B8072

Arnabost

Arinagour

Acha

1

Caoles

B8069

Clachan-Mor

Ruaig

B8068

Ballevullin

Kilkenneth

B8065

Scarinish

Barrapoll

Crossapoll

B8066

239\An Cruachan

103\Cruach D

4

393\An Sgurr

3

Ockle

356\Beinn Bhreac

Branault

436\Meall Nan Con

437

Achosnich

342\Beinn Na Seilg

527\Ben Hiant

119

Kilchoan

Glenbor dale

2

118-1

Tobermory

292\'S Airde Beinn

Drimnin

437\Beinn Bhuidhe

550\Sithea

B8073

Dervaig

Calgary

444\Speinne Mòr

342\Càrn Mòr

1

390\Cnoc An Dà Chinn

Aros

Salen

333\Beinn Nan Càrn

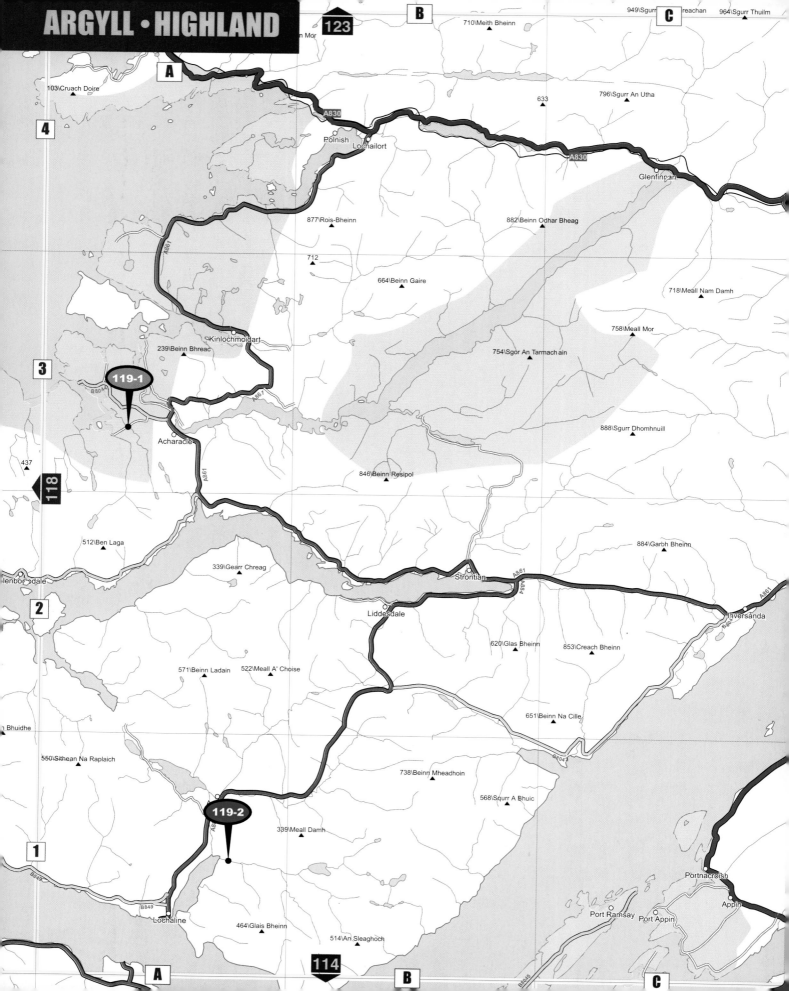

ARGYLL · HIGHLAND

103\Cruach Doire

710\Meith Bheinn

949\Sgurr ...reachan   964\Sgurr Thuilm

796\Sgurr An Utha

633

A830

Polnish   Lochailort

Glenfinnan

877\Rois-Bheinn

882\Beinn Odhar Bheag

712

718\Meall Nam Damh

664\Beinn Gaire

758\Meall Mor

Kinlochmoidart

754\Sgor An Tarmachain

239\Beinn Bhreac

119-1

888\Sgurr Dhomhnuill

Acharacle

437

846\Beinn Resipol

512\Ben Laga

884\Garbh Bheinn

339\Gearr Chreag

Strontian   A861

...lenbo...dale

Liddesdale

Inversanda

620\Glas Bheinn   853\Creach Bheinn

571\Beinn Ladain   522\Meall A' Choise

651\Beinn Na Cille

n Bhuidhe

550\Sithean Na Raplaich

738\Beinn Mheadhoin

568\Sgurr A Bhuic

119-2

339\Meall Damh

Portnacroish

Lochaline   464\Glais Bheinn

Port Ramsay   Port Appin   Appin

514\An Sleaghoch

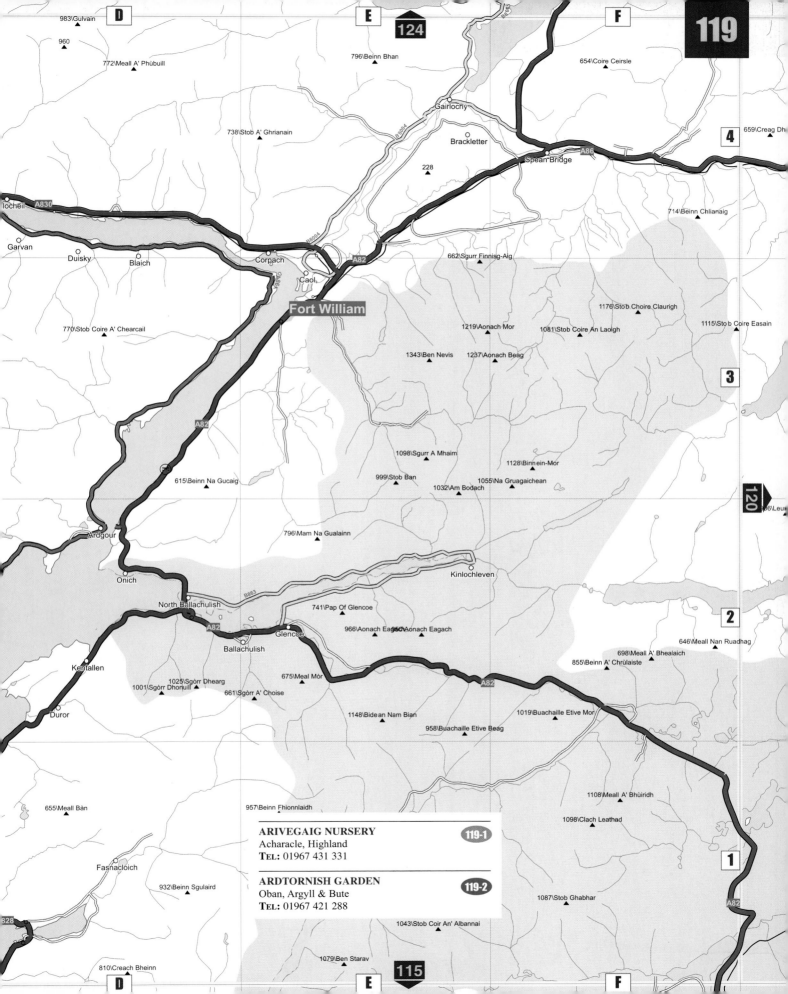

983\Gulvain ▲

960 ▲

772\Meall A' Phùbuill ▲

796\Beinn Bhan ▲

654\Coire Ceirsle ▲

Gairlochy

Brackletter

738\Stob A' Ghrianain ▲

4

659\Creag Dh

228 ▲

Spean Bridge   A86

714\Beinn Chlianaig ▲

Iocheil   A830

Garvan

Duisky   Blaich

Corpach   A82

662\Sgurr Finnisg-Aig ▲

1176\Stob Choire Claurigh ▲

Caol

1115\Stob Coire Easain ▲

Fort William

1219\Aonach Mor ▲   1081\Stob Coire An Laoigh ▲

770\Stob Coire A' Chearcail ▲

1343\Ben Nevis ▲   1237\Aonach Beag ▲

3

1098\Sgurr A Mhaim ▲

1128\Binnein-Mor ▲

615\Beinn Na Gucaig ▲

999\Stob Ban ▲   1055\Na Gruagaichean ▲

1032\Am Bodach ▲

Ardgour

796\Mam Na Gualainn ▲

120 ▲

6\Leu

Onich

Kinlochleven

North Ballachulish   B863

741\Pap Of Glencoe ▲

2

Ballachulish   Glencoe

966\Aonach Eagach ▲ 953\Aonach Eagach ▲

646\Meall Nan Ruadhag ▲

698\Meall A' Bhealaich ▲

Kentallen

1025\Sgòrr Dhearg ▲

675\Meal Mòr ▲

855\Beinn A' Chrùlaiste ▲

1001\Sgòrr Dhonuill ▲   661\Sgòrr A' Choise ▲

Duror

1148\Bidean Nam Bian ▲   1019\Buachaille Etive Mor ▲

958\Buachaille Etive Beag ▲

655\Meall Bàn ▲

957\Beinn Fhionnlaidh ▲

1108\Meall A' Bhùiridh ▲

1098\Clach Leathad ▲

Fasnacloich

932\Beinn Sgulaird ▲

1

810\Creach Bheinn ▲

1087\Stob Ghabhar ▲

828

1043\Stob Coir An' Albannai ▲

1079\Ben Starav ▲

A82

ARIVEGAIG NURSERY	119-1
Acharacle, Highland	
TEL: 01967 431 331	

ARDTORNISH GARDEN	119-2
Oban, Argyll & Bute	
TEL: 01967 421 288	

PERTHSHIRE

CLUNY HOUSE GARDENS 120-1
Aberfeldy, Perthshire & Kinross
TEL: 01887 820 795

BOLFRACKS 120-2
Aberfeldy, Perthshire & Kinross
TEL: 01887 820 207

Clivea

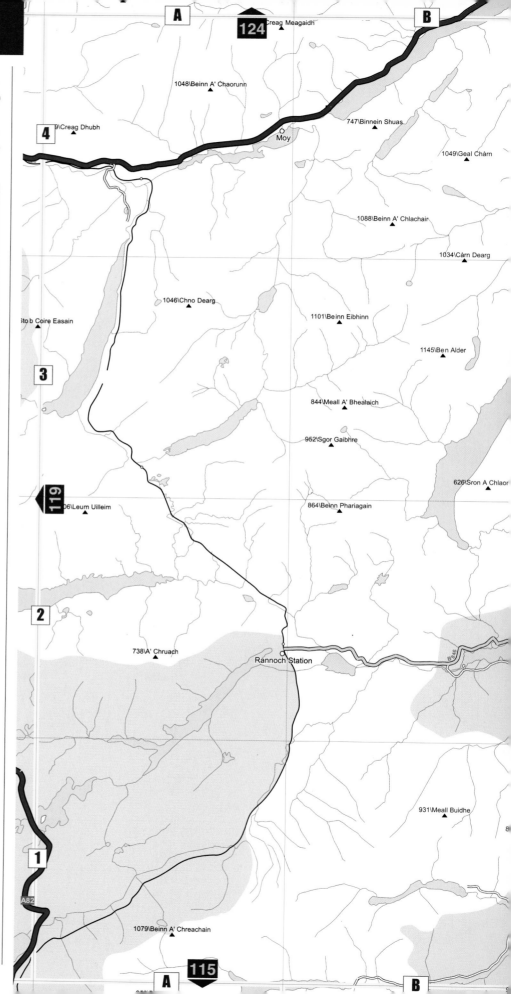

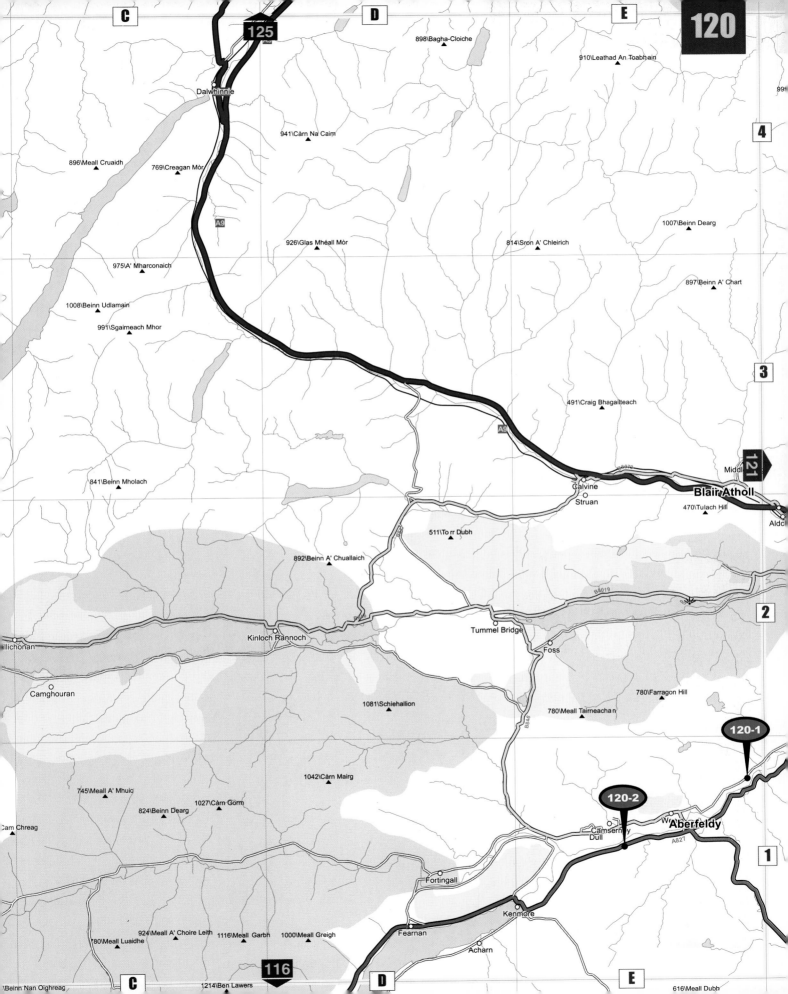

C
D
E

4

3

2

1

125

898\Bagha-Cloiche
910\Leathad An Toabhain

Dalwhinnie

941\Càrn Na Caim

896\Meall Cruaidh
769\Creagan Mòr

1007\Beinn Dearg

926\Glas Mhéall Mòr
814\Sron A' Chleirich

897\Beinn A' Chart

975\A' Mharconaich

A9

1008\Beinn Udlamain

991\Sgairneach Mhor

491\Craig Bhagailteach

A9

121

Middl

841\Beinn Mholach

Calvine
Blair Atholl

Struan
470\Tulach Hill

Aldc

511\To rr Dubh

892\Beinn A' Chuallaich

B8019

Illichonan

Kinloch Rannoch
Tummel Bridge

Foss

Camghouran

780\Farragon Hill

1081\Schiehallion
780\Meall Tairneacha n

B846

120-1

1042\Càrn Mairg

120-2

745\Meall A' Mhuic

Aberfeldy

824\Beinn Dearg
1027\Càrn Gorm

Camsern y
Dull
W

A827

Cam Chreag

Fortingall

Kenmore

Fearnan

924\Meall A' Choire Leith
1116\Meall Garbh
1000\Meall Greigh

780\Meall Luaidhe

Acharn

\Beinn Nan Oighreag

116

C
D
E

1214\Ben Lawers

616\Meall Dubh

ANGUS · PERTHSHIRE

PATHHEAD NURSERIES `121-1`
Kirriemuir, Angus
TEL: 01307 819 007

CHRISTIE'S NURSERY `121-2`
Downfield, Kirriemuir, Angus
TEL: 01575 572 977

ALEX BUTTER & SON `121-3`
Ballinluig, Pitlochry, Perthshire & Kinross
TEL: 01796 482 614

FERNGREEN GARDEN CENTRE `121-4`
Angus, Angus
TEL: 01307 460 012

BELWOOD TREES `121-5`
Meigle, Perthshire & Kinross
TEL: 01828 640 219

GLAMIS CASTLE `121-6`
Glamis, Forfar, Angus
TEL: 01307 840 393

SCOTTS GARDEN & PET CENTRE `121-7`
29 Reform Street, Blairgowrie, Perthshire & Kinross
TEL: 01250 874 230

MOYNESS NURSERIES `121-8`
Coupar Angus Road, Blairgowrie, Perthshire & Kinross
TEL: 01250 873 135

Cymbydium

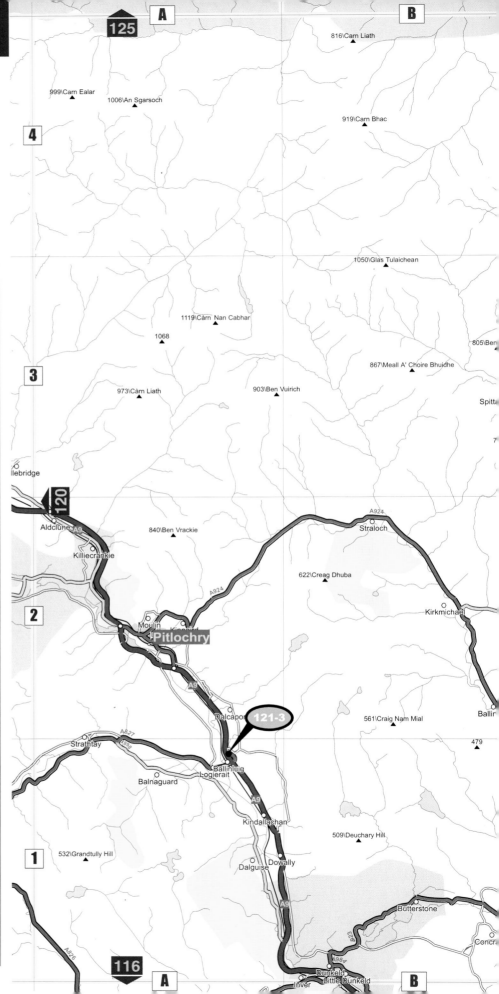

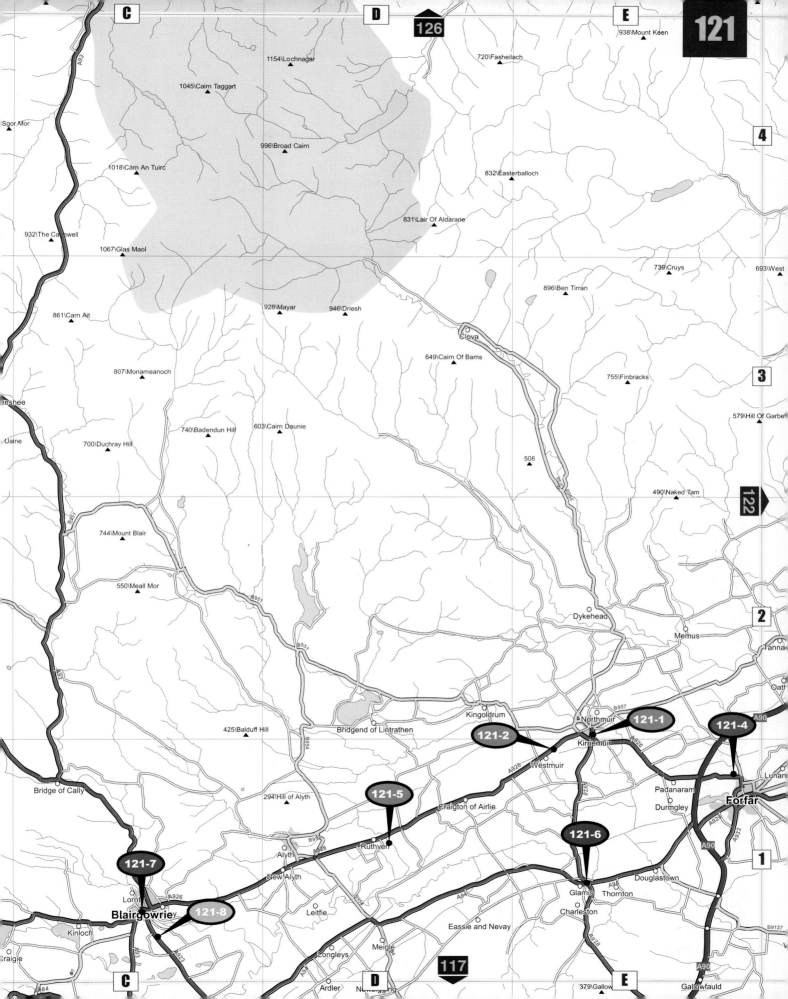

Sgor Mor ▲

1154\Lochnagar ▲

1045\Cairn Taggart ▲

938\Mount Keen ▲

720\Fasheilach ▲

1018\Carn An Tuirc ▲

996\Broad Cairn ▲

832\Easterballoch ▲

932\The Cairnwell ▲

1067\Glas Maol ▲

831\Lair Of Aldararie ▲

739\Cruys ▲

693\West ▲

861\Carn Ait ▲

928\Mayar ▲   946\Driesh ▲

896\Ben Tirran ▲

enshee

807\Monameanoch ▲

Clova

649\Cairn Of Bams ▲

755\Finbracks ▲

579\Hill Of Garbe ▲

Uaine

740\Badendun Hill ▲

603\Cairn Daunie ▲

508 ▲

490\Naked Tam ▲

700\Duchray Hill ▲

744\Mount Blair ▲

550\Meall Mor ▲

Dykehead

Memus

Tanna

425\Balduff Hill ▲

Bridgend of Lintrathen

Kingoldrum

Northmuir

B 957

121-1

121-4

121-2

Kirriemuir

Oath

Bridge of Cally

294\Hill of Alyth ▲

Westmuir

Craigton of Airlie

121-5

Padanaram

Lunan

Forfar

Durmgley

121-6

Ruthven

Alyth

New Alyth

Glamis Thornton

Douglastown

121-7

Lorn

121-8

Leitfie

Charleston

Blairgowrie

Kinloch

Eassie and Nevay

Longleys

Meigle

Craigie

Ardler   Ne

379\Gallow

Gallowfauld

B9127

2

3

DUNNOTTAR NURSERIES `122-1`
Stonehaven, Aberdeenshire
TEL: 01569 763 422

EDZELL CASTLE, `122-2`
HISTORIC SCOTLAND
Brechin, Angus
TEL: 01356 648 631

HOUSE OF DUN, NATIONAL TRUST `122-3`
Montrose, Angus
TEL: 01674 810 264

PATHHEAD NURSERIES `122-4`
Burnside, Forfar, Angus
TEL: 01575 572 173

HOUSE OF PITMUIES `122-5`
Guthrie, Angus, Angus
TEL: 01241 828 245

SILVERWELLS PLANT NURSERY `122-6`
& GARDEN CENTRE
Arbroath, Angus
TEL: 01241 875 634

Marigold

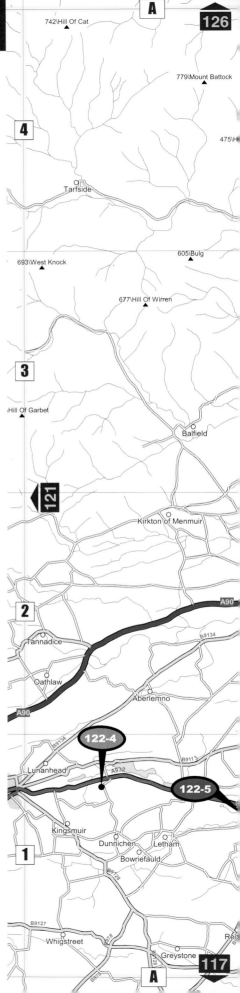

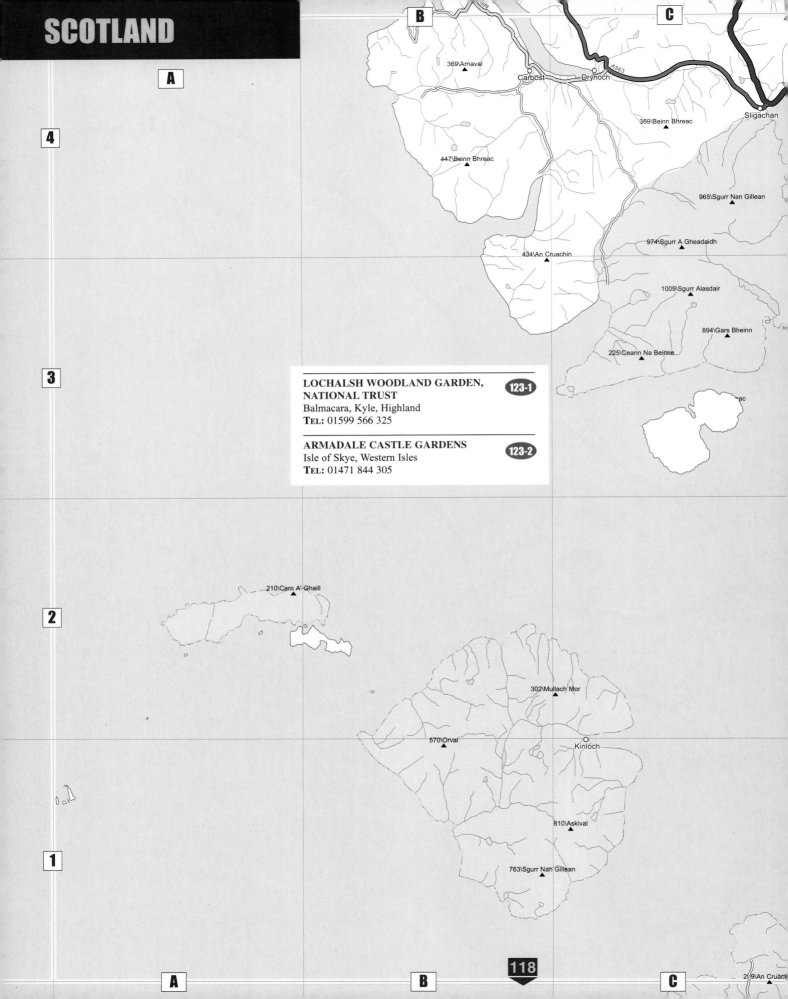

A

B

C

4

3

2

1

369\Arnaval ▲

Carbost ○ — Drynoch ○

Sligachan ○

369\Beinn Bhreac ▲

447\Beinn Bhreac ▲

965\Sgurr Nan Gillean ▲

974\Sgurr A Gheadaidh ▲

434\An Cruachin ▲

1009\Sgurr Alasdair ▲

894\Gars Bheinn ▲

225\Ceann Na Beinne ▲

LOCHALSH WOODLAND GARDEN,
NATIONAL TRUST   **123-1**
Balmacara, Kyle, Highland
TEL: 01599 566 325

ARMADALE CASTLE GARDENS   **123-2**
Isle of Skye, Western Isles
TEL: 01471 844 305

210\Carn A' Ghaill ▲

302\Mullach Mor ▲

570\Orval ▲

Kinloch ○

810\Askival ▲

763\Sgurr Nan Gillean ▲

A

B

C

2\9\An Cruach

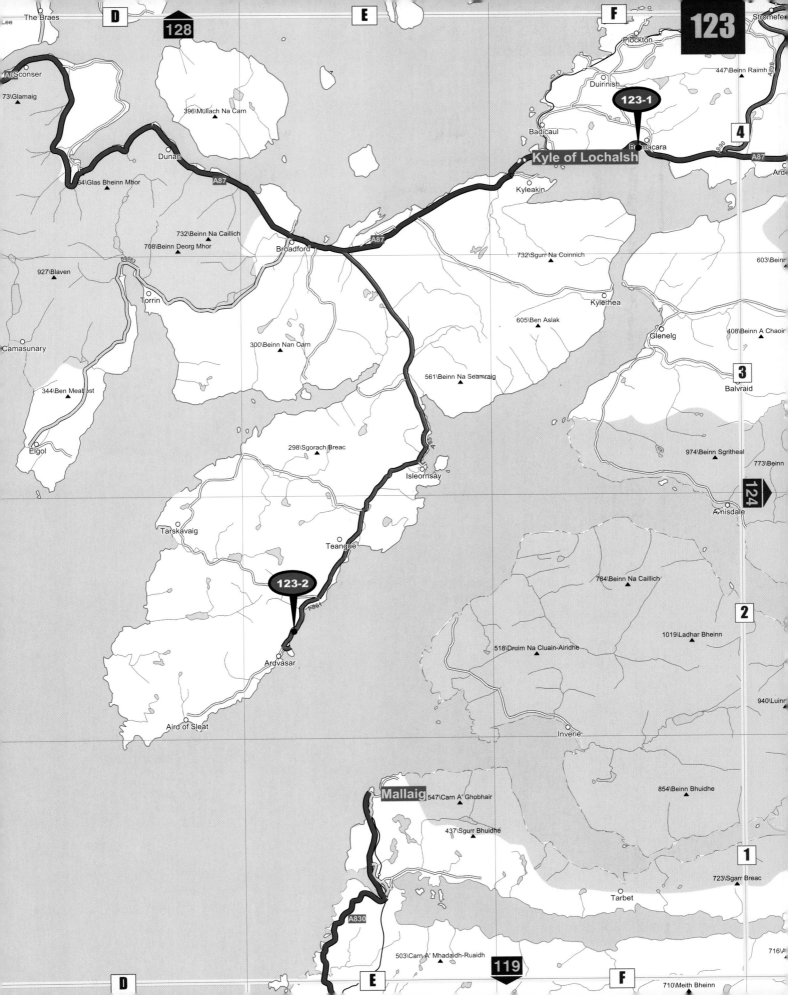

HIGHLAND

Pink Orchid

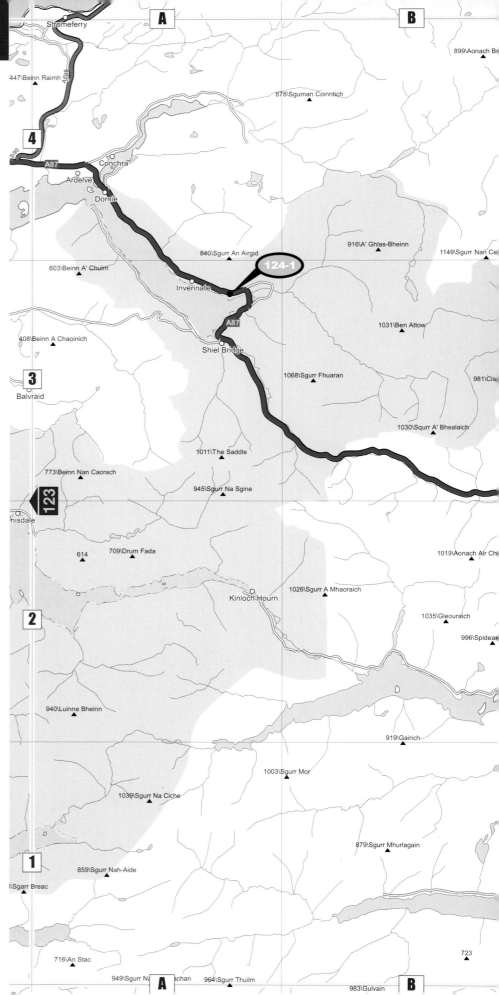

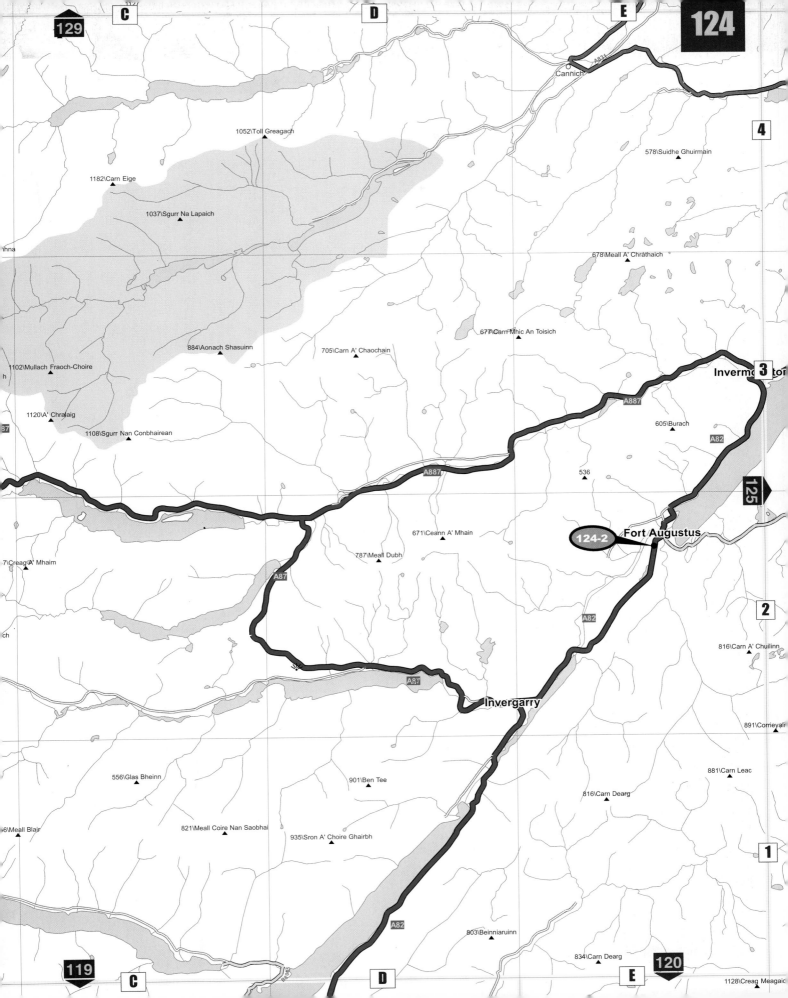

Cannich

578\Suidhe Ghuirmain

1052\Toll Greagach

1182\Carn Eige

678\Meall A' Chràthaich

1037\Sgurr Na Lapaich

884\Aonach Shasuinn

677\Carn Mhic An Toisich

705\Carn A' Chaochain

1102\Mullach Fraoch-Choire

Invermoriston

A887

3

605\Burach

1120\A' Chralaig

1108\Sgurr Nan Conbhairean

A82

A887

536

671\Ceann A' Mhain

124-2

Fort Augustus

125

787\Meall Dubh

7\Creag A' Mhaim

A87

816\Carn A' Chuilinn

2

A82

891\Corrieyair

A87

A87

Invergarry

881\Carn Leac

556\Glas Bheinn

901\Ben Tee

816\Carn Dearg

821\Meall Coire Nan Saobhai

6\Meall Blair

935\Sron A' Choire Ghairbh

1

A82

803\Beinniaruinn

834\Carn Dearg

HIGHLAND

SPEYSIDE HEATHER CENTRE 125-1
Skye of Curr, Grantown-on-Spey, Highland
TEL: 01479 851 359

JACK DRAKE'S ALPINE NURSERY 125-2
Aviemore, Highland
TEL: 01540 651 287

Lilly

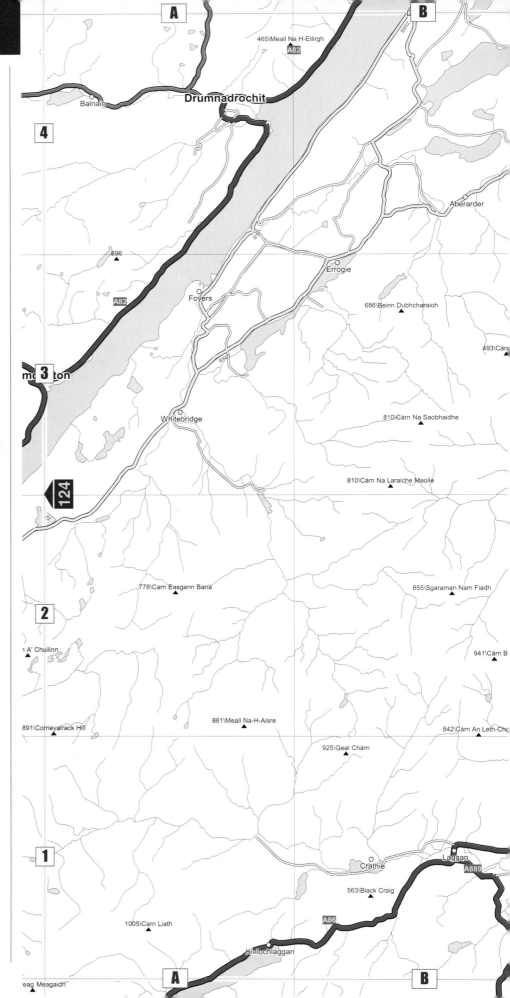

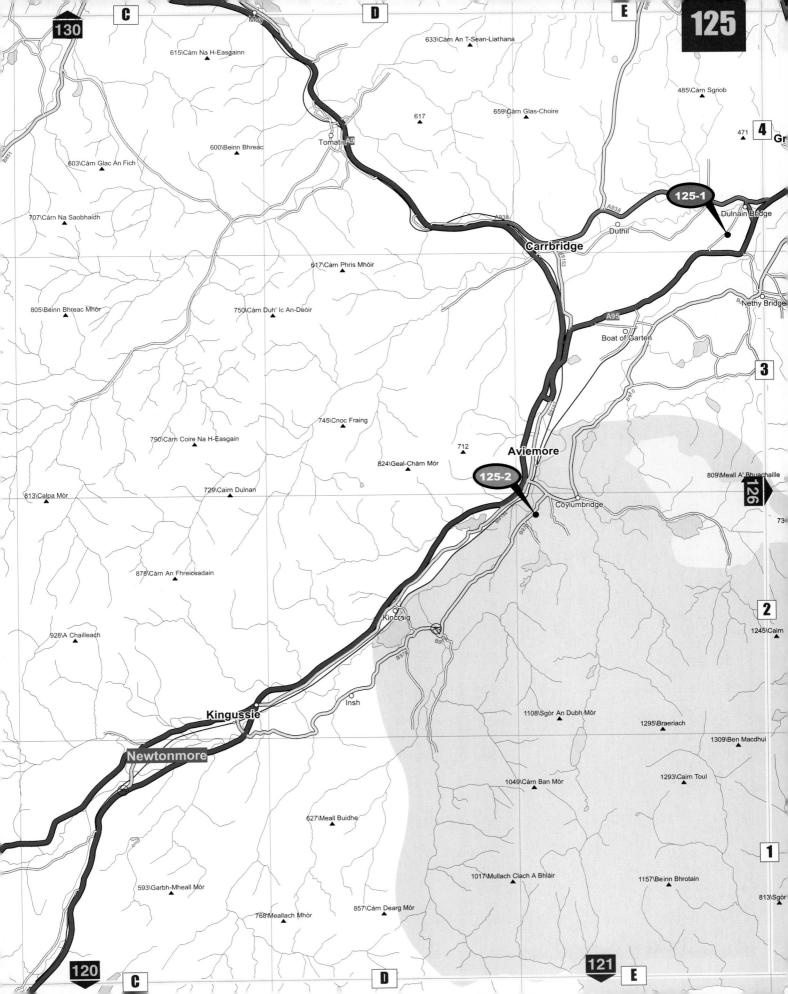

ABERDEENSHIRE

LEITH HALL, NATIONAL TRUST
Huntly, Aberdeenshire
TEL: 01464 831 216

KILDRUMMY CASTLE GARDENS
Alford, Aberdeenshire
TEL: 01975 571 203

CANDACRAIG GARDENS
Strathdon, Aberdeenshire
TEL: 01975 651 226

Iris

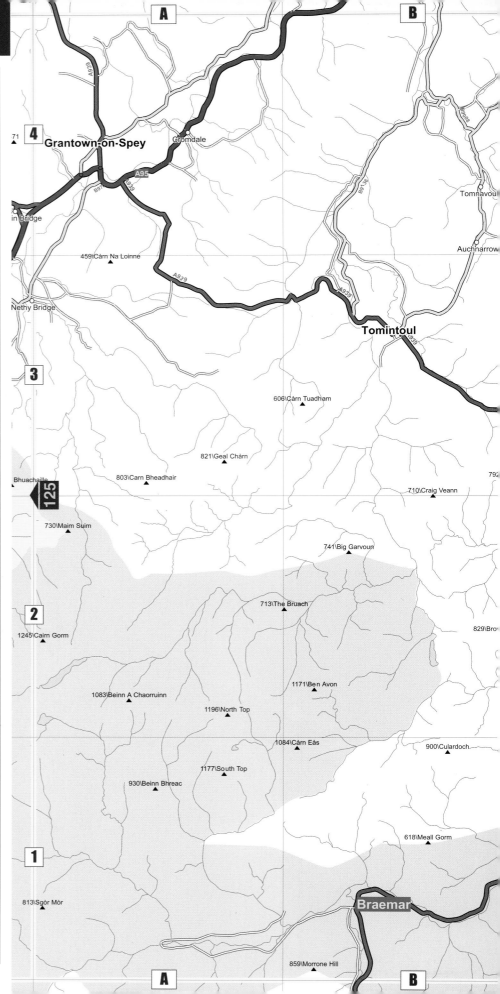

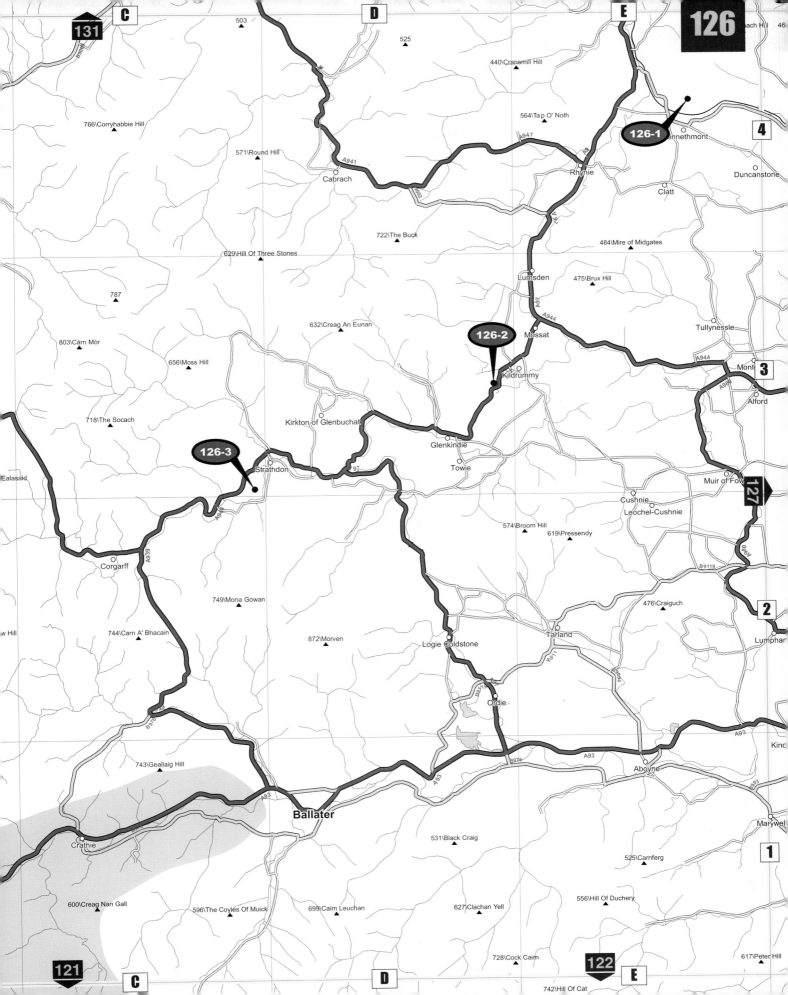

LOCH-HILLS PLANT CENTRE `127-1`
Ellon, Aberdeenshire
TEL: 01358 720 694

PITMEDDEN GARDEN, NT `127-2`
Ellon, Aberdeenshire
TEL: 01651 842 352

BENNACHIE GARDENS & GIFTS `127-3`
Oyne, Aberdeenshire
TEL: 01464 851 489

INVERURIE GARDEN & MACHINERY CENTRE `127-4`
Old Meldrum Road, Inverurie, Aberdeenshire
TEL: 01467 621 402

ORNAMENTAL GRASSES `127-5`
Kemnay, Inverurie, Aberdeenshire
TEL: 01467 643 544

MONYMUSK WALLED GARDEN `127-6`
Monymusk, Inverurie, Aberdeenshire
TEL: 01467 651 543

CASTLE FRASER, NT `127-7`
Inverurie, Aberdeenshire
TEL: 01330 833 463

SPRINGHILL NURSERIES `127-8`
Dunecht, Westhill, Aberdeenshire
TEL: 01330 860 246

COCKERS GARDEN CENTRE `127-9`
Whitemyres, Aberdeen, Aberdeenshire
TEL: 01224 313 261

DOBBIES GARDEN WORLD `127-10`
Hazledene, Aberdeen, Aberdeenshire
TEL: 01224 318 658

DUTHIE PARK WINTER GARDENS `127-11`
Aberdeen, Aberdeenshire
TEL: 01224 522 984

PINEWOOD PARK NURSERIES `127-12`
Aberdeen, Aberdeenshire
TEL: 01224 318 744

FOXLANE GARDEN CENTRE `127-13`
Aberdeen, Aberdeenshire
TEL: 01224 861 222

DRUM CASTLE, NT `127-14`
Banchory, Aberdeenshire
TEL: 01330 811 204

PLANTS 'N' THINGS `127-15`
Aboyne, Aberdeenshire
TEL: 01339 884 308

HEATHER CENTRE `127-16`
Banchory, Aberdeenshire
TEL: 01330 811 234

CRATHES CASTLE GARDEN, NT `127-17`
Banchory, Aberdeenshire
TEL: 01330 844 525

DEESIDE HOUSE & GARDEN CENTRE `127-18`
North Deeside Road, Banchory, Aberdeenshire
TEL: 01330 820 118

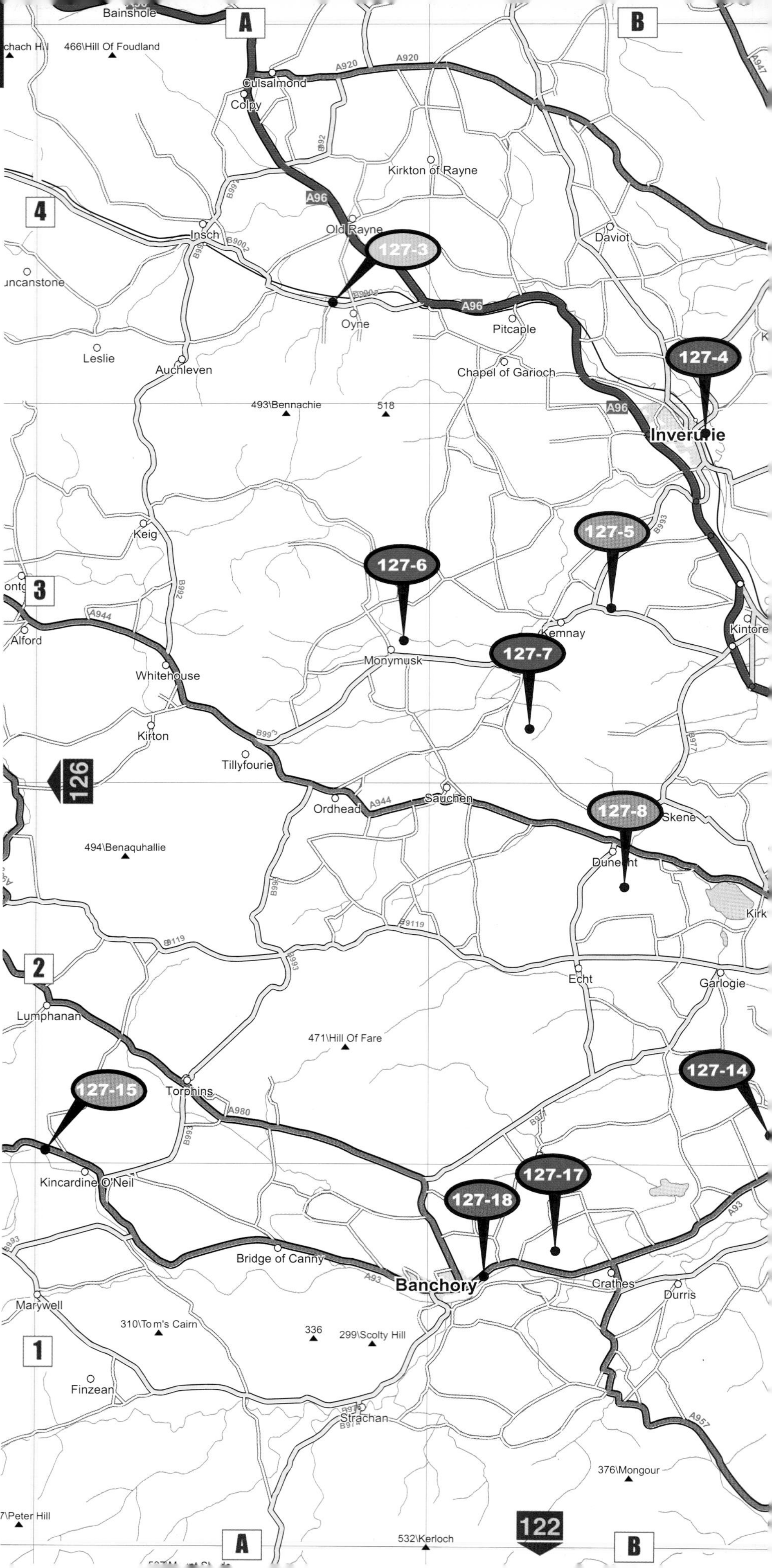

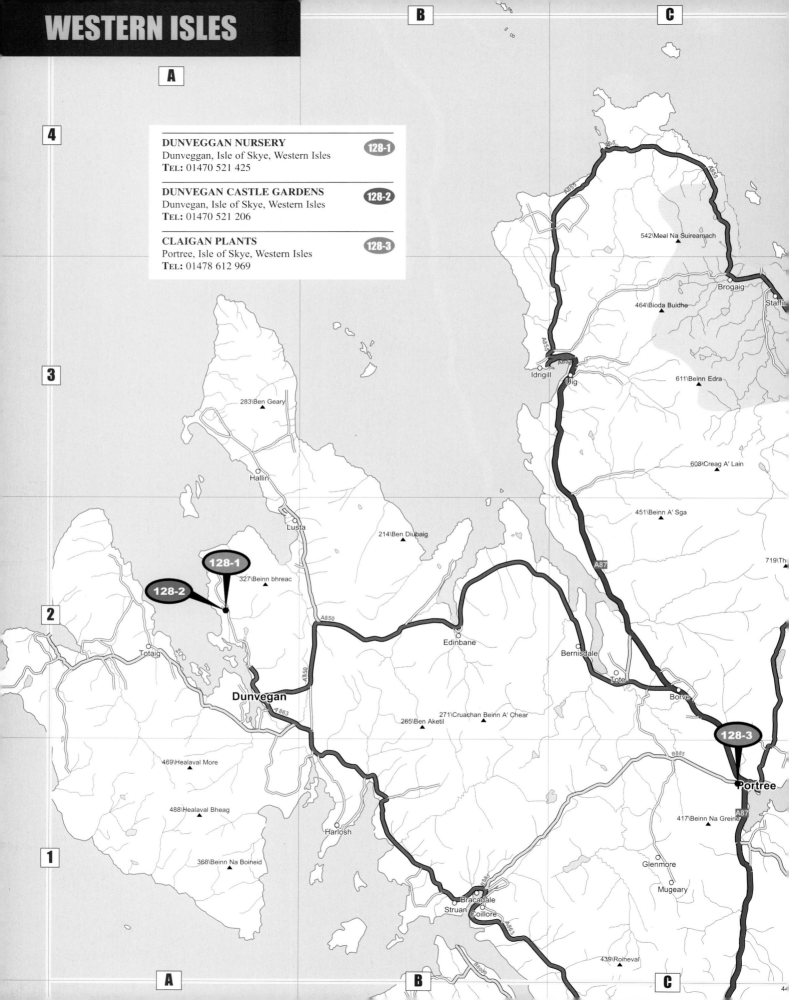

WESTERN ISLES

DUNVEGGAN NURSERY 128-1
Dunveggan, Isle of Skye, Western Isles
Tel: 01470 521 425

DUNVEGAN CASTLE GARDENS 128-2
Dunvegan, Isle of Skye, Western Isles
Tel: 01470 521 206

CLAIGAN PLANTS 128-3
Portree, Isle of Skye, Western Isles
Tel: 01478 612 969

HIGHLAND

ATTADALE
Wester Ross, Highland
TEL: 01520 722 217

Clerodendrum

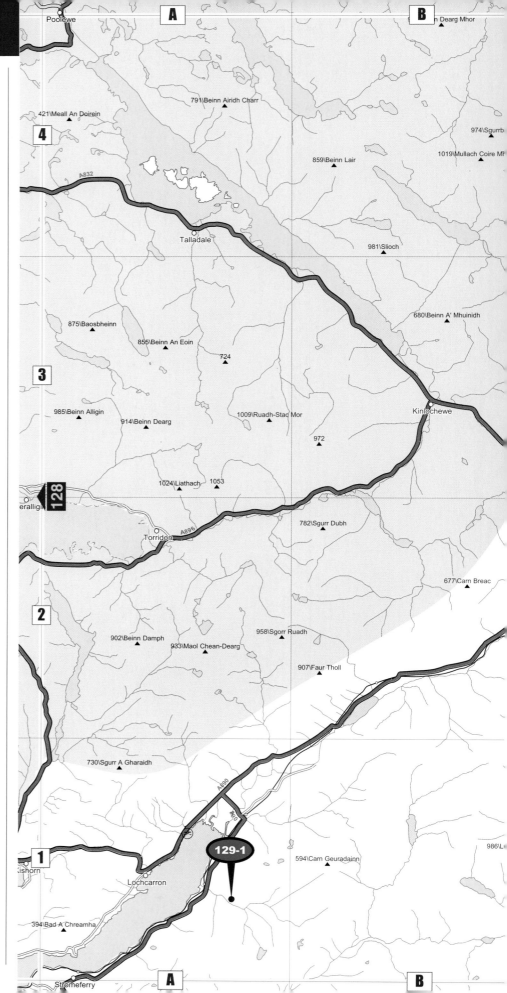

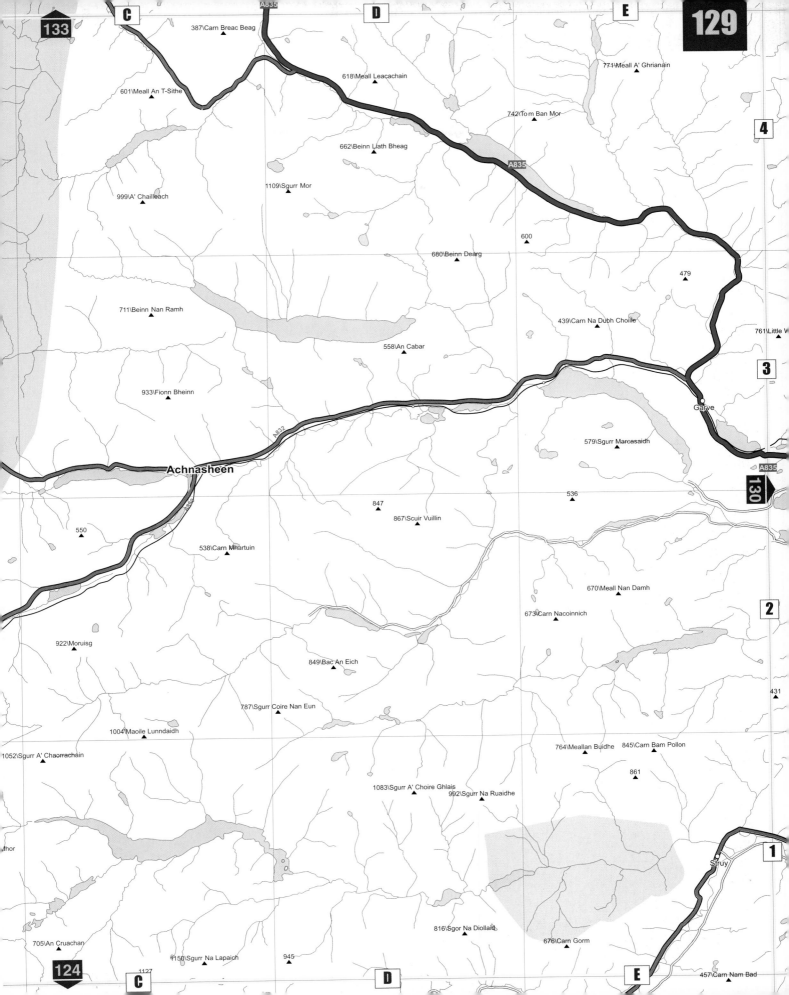

133

4

387\Carn Breac Beag

771\Meall A' Ghrianain

618\Meall Leacachain

742\Tom Ban Mor

601\Meall An T-Sithe

662\Beinn Liath Bheag

A835

999\A' Chailleach

1109\Sgurr Mor

600

680\Beinn Dearg

479

711\Beinn Nan Ramh

439\Carn Na Dubh Choille

761\Little W

558\An Cabar

3

933\Fionn Bheinn

Garve

A832

579\Sgurr Marcasaidh

Achnasheen

536

847

130

867\Scuir Vuillin

550

538\Carn Mhartuin

670\Meall Nan Damh

673\Carn Nacoinnich

2

922\Moruisg

849\Bac An Eich

431

787\Sgurr Coire Nan Eun

1004\Maoile Lunndaidh

764\Meallan Buidhe

845\Carn Bam Pollon

1052\Sgurr A' Chaorrachain

861

1083\Sgurr A' Choire Ghlais

992\Sgurr Na Ruaidhe

1

Struy

Mhor

816\Sgor Na Diollaid

705\An Cruachan

676\Carn Gorm

124

1150\Sgurr Na Lapaich

945

1127

457\Carn Nam Bad

CAMERON'S GARDEN CENTRE `130-1`
Invergordon, Highland
TEL: 01349 854 303

POYNTZFIELD HERB NURSERY `130-2`
Dingwall, Highland
TEL: 01381 610 352

DYKE NURSERIES `130-3`
Dyke, Forres, Moray
TEL: 01309 641 362

BRODIE CASTLE, NATIONAL TRUST `130-4`
Forres, Moray
TEL: 01309 641 371

CANONBURY NURSERY & GARDEN CENTRE `130-5`
Fortrose, Highland
TEL: 01381 620 043

RIVERBANK NURSERY GARDEN CENTRE `130-6`
Conon Bridge, Dingwall, Highland
TEL: 01349 861 720

BROADLEY GARDEN CENTRE `130-7`
Nairn, Highland
TEL: 01667 452 955

CAWDOR CASTLE & GARDENS `130-8`
Nairn, Highland, IV12 5RD
TEL: 01667 404 615
EMAIL: info@cawdorcastle.com
WEB: www.cawdorcastle.com
Walled garden, paradise garden and flower garden, with herbaceous borders, paeony border, rose tunnel and a mass of lavender. There are also majestic trees and nature trails.
OPEN: Daily, 1 May-mid Oct, 10-5.
ENTRY COSTS: Adult £3, Children £3, Blind people free.
SPECIALITIES: Herbaceous plants, Knot, Maze, Walled garden, Yews.

GREENS NURSERIES `130-9`
Nairn, Highland
TEL: 01667 452 760

HOWDENS GARDEN CENTRE `130-10`
51 Telford Street, Inverness, Highland
TEL: 01463 711 134

ARDFEARN NURSERY `130-11`
Bunchrew, Inverness, Highland
TEL: 01463 243 250

DOCHFOUR GARDENS `130-12`
Inverness, Highland
TEL: 01463 861 218

HIGHLAND LILIUMS `130-13`
10 Loaneckheim, Beauly, Highland
TEL: 01463 741 365

ABRIACHAN GARDENS & NURSERY `130-14`
Loch Ness Side, Inverness, Highland
TEL: 01463 861 232

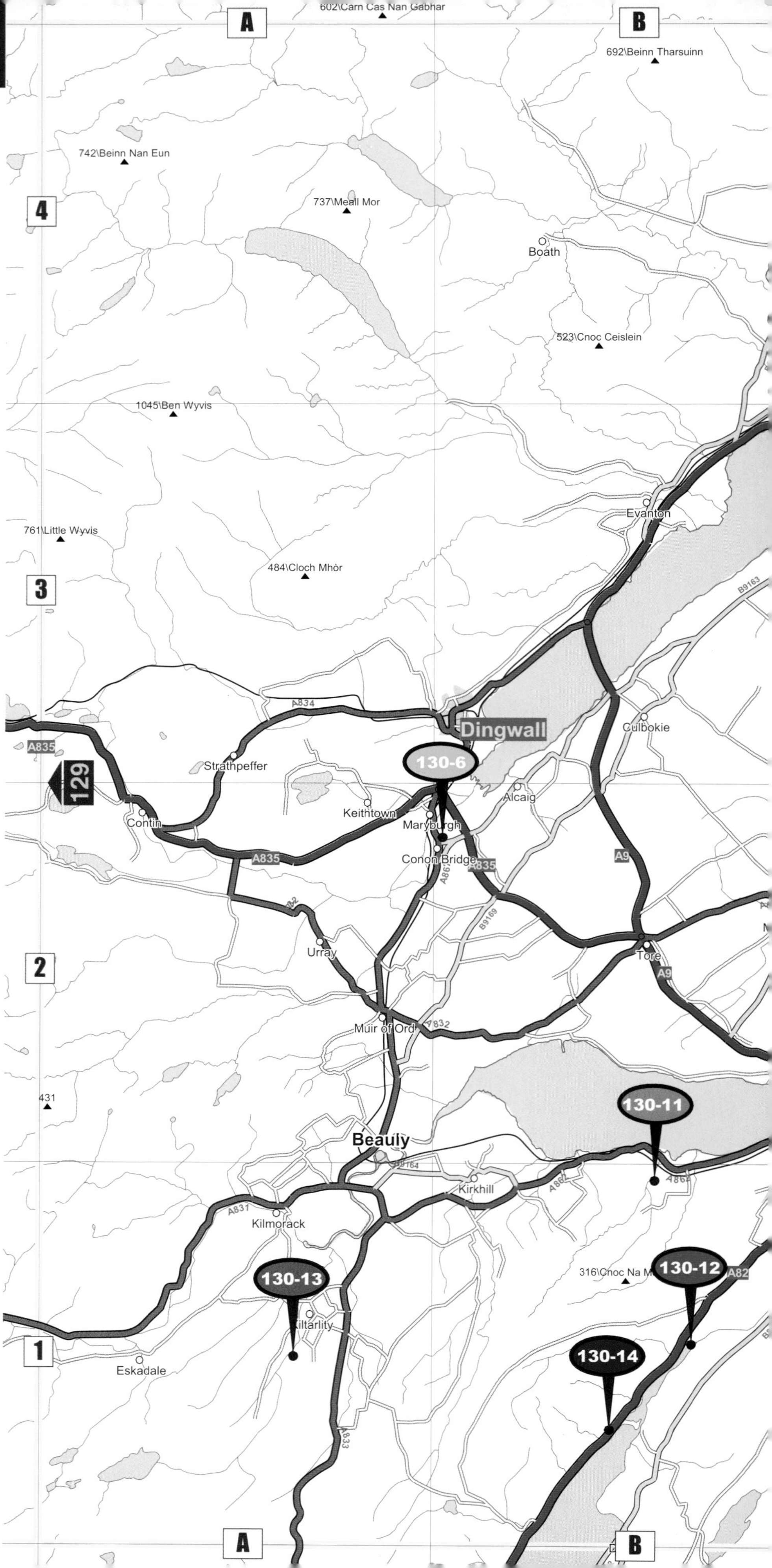

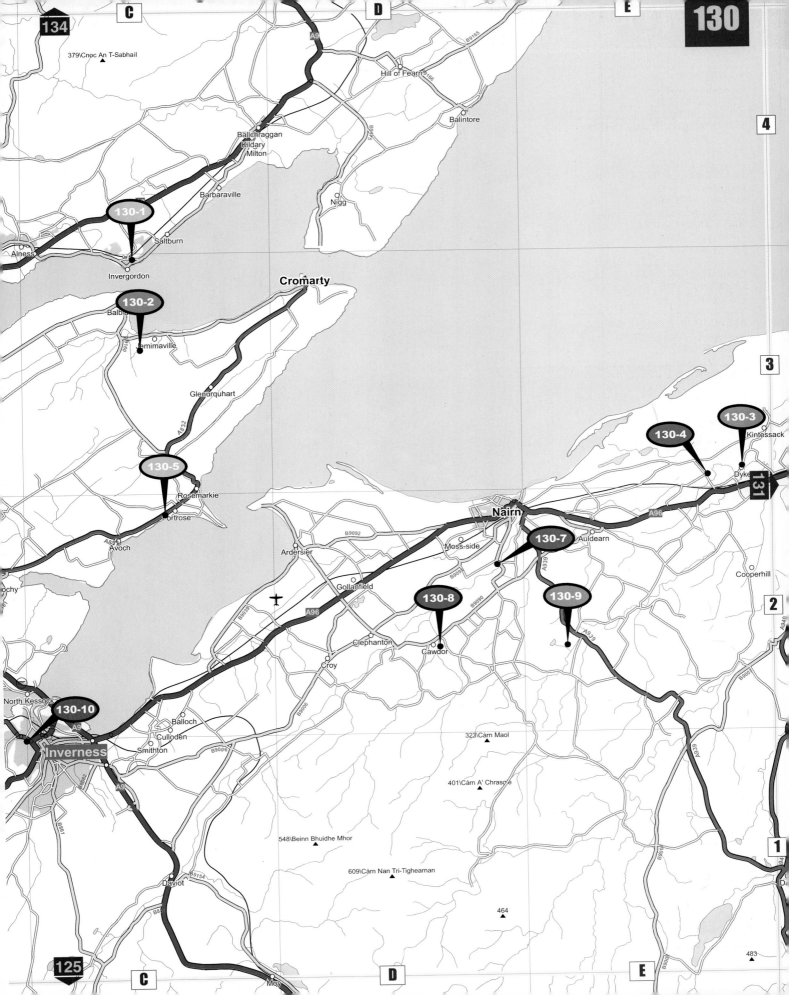

SCOTLAND

TOM THUMB'S `131-1`
Lossiemouth, Moray
TEL: 01343 814 333

CHRISTIES ELITE NURSERIES `131-2`
Forres, Moray
TEL: 01309 672 633

CHRISTIES GARDEN CENTRE `131-3`
Fochabers, Moray
TEL: 01343 820 362

GLEN GRANT GARDEN `131-4`
Rothes, Aberlour, Moray
TEL: 01542 783 318

KING GEORGE V GARDEN CENTRE `131-5`
Steven Road, Huntly, Aberdeenshire
TEL: 01466 793 908

BALLINDALLOCH CASTLE `131-6`
Grantown-on-Spey, Highland
TEL: 01807 500 205

Correa

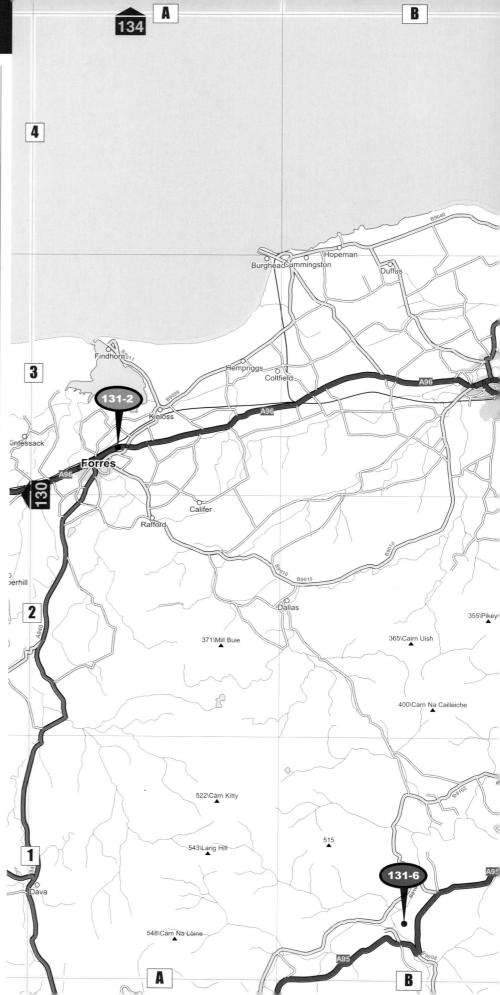

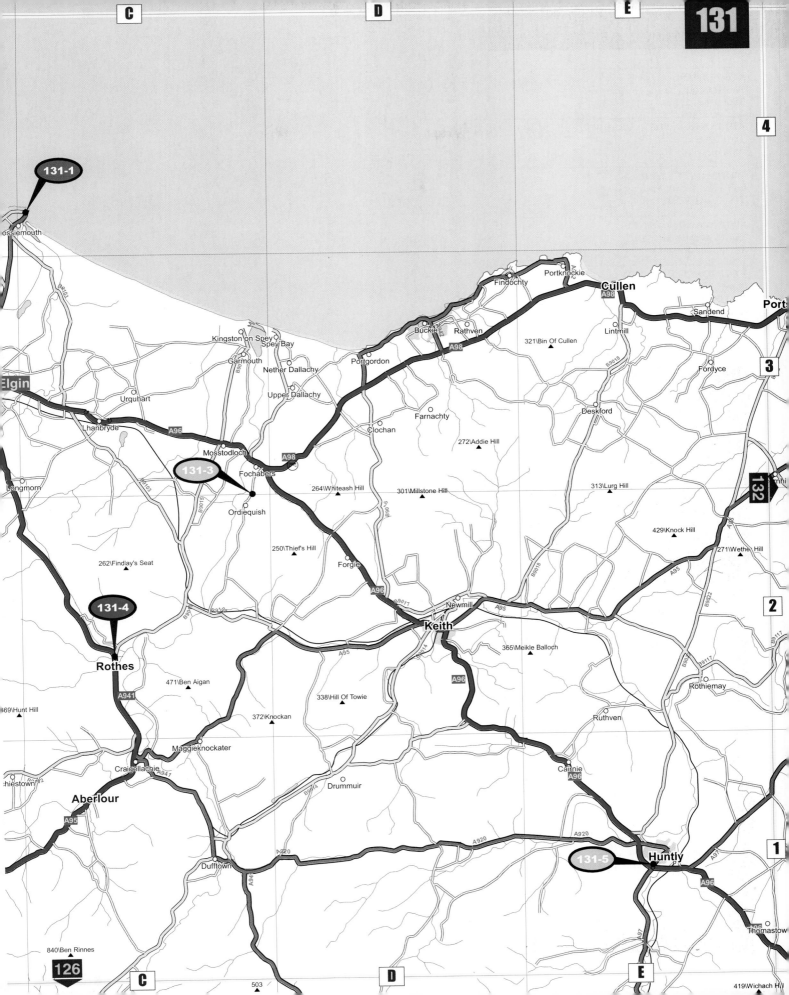

ABERDEENSHIRE

C. & E. LAING
The Nurseries, Turriff, Aberdeenshire
Tel: 01888 563 236
`132-1`

AULTAN NURSERY
Turriff, Aberdeenshire
Tel: 01888 544 702
`132-2`

WHITE LODGE NURSERY
Carnousie, Turriff, Aberdeenshire
Tel: 01888 562 924
`132-3`

SIMPSON & FLORENCE
Turriff, Aberdeenshire
Tel: 01888 563 511
`132-4`

FYVIE CASTLE, NATIONAL TRUST
Turriff, Aberdeenshire
Tel: 01651 891 266
`132-5`

HADDO HOUSE, NATIONAL TRUST
Ellon, Aberdeenshire
Tel: 01651 851 440
`132-6`

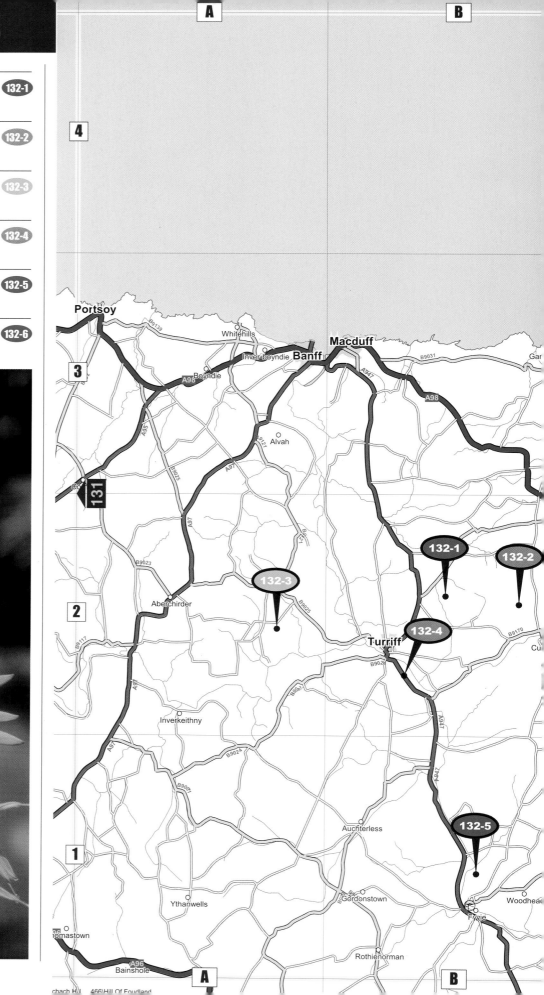

4

Crovie
town
Pennan

Rosehearty
Pittulie
Sandhaven
Peathill
A98
Fraserburgh
A387
A90
Inverallochy
B9033

3

New Aberdour
Memsie
St Combs

221\Bracklamore Hill
Rathen

A98
234\Waughton Hill
A952
Crimond

A105
New Pitsligo
B9030
Strichen
B9093
New Leeds

armond
estown

2

A981
Fetterangus
Rora
St Fergus
A90

A98
A950
A982

B9170
Maud
B9029
Mintlaw
A950
Longside
Peterhead

New Deer
Old Deer
Burnhaven

B9170
B9030
Stuartfield
Blackhill
Boddam

Millbrex
Clola
A90
A975

Auchnagatt

1

Methlick
132-6
Hatton
Cruden Bay
A90
B9005
A948
Bogbrae
A975
A915

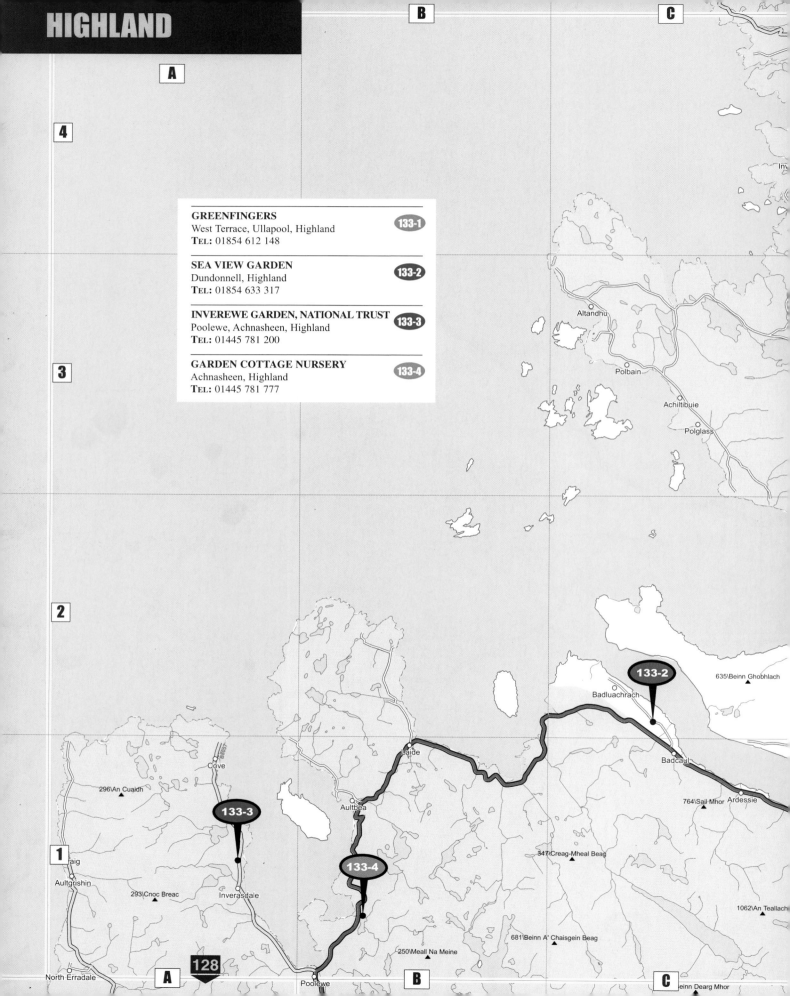

GREENFINGERS `133-1`
West Terrace, Ullapool, Highland
Tel: 01854 612 148

SEA VIEW GARDEN `133-2`
Dundonnell, Highland
Tel: 01854 633 317

INVEREWE GARDEN, NATIONAL TRUST `133-3`
Poolewe, Achnasheen, Highland
Tel: 01445 781 200

GARDEN COTTAGE NURSERY `133-4`
Achnasheen, Highland
Tel: 01445 781 777

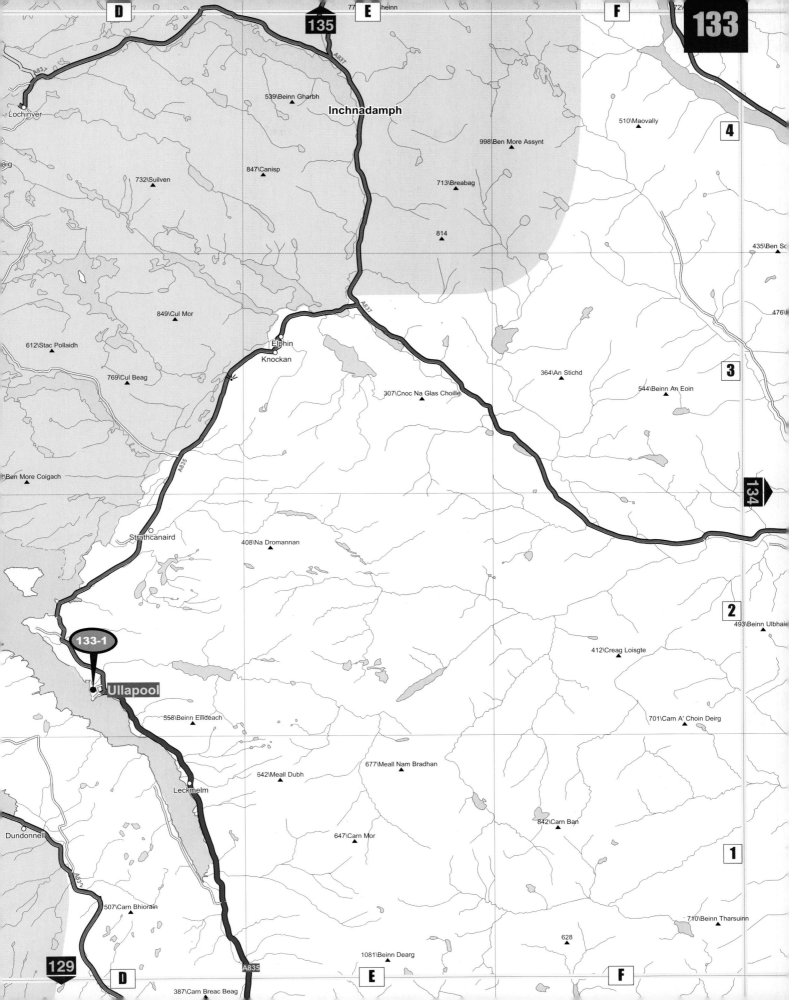

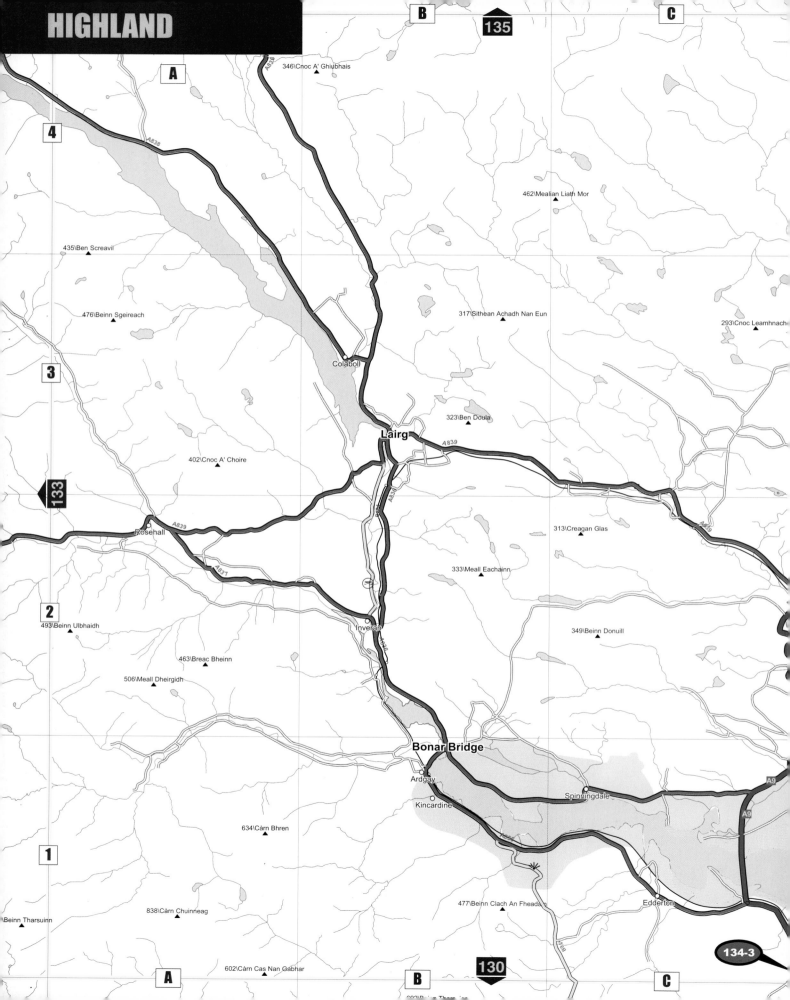

Cnoc Na Breun-Choille

388\Creag Nam Fiàdh

554\Creag Scalabsdale

Newport

Berriedale

4

416\Beinn Dubhain

401\Cnoc Na Maoile

337\Cnoc Na H-Innse Moire

404\Creag Thoraraidh

421\Cnoc Nan Crùbag Mór

624\Beinn Dhorain

591\Beinn Na Mèilich

Helmsdale

3

539\Col-Bheinn

A9

520\Ben Horn

446\Ben Lundie

378\Cagar Feosaig

134-1

Brora

Baddies

A9

Golspie

2

DUNROBIN CASTLE GARDENS 134-1
Golspie, Highland
Tel: 01408 633 177

MORANGIE GARDEN CENTRE 134-2
Morangie Road, Tain, Highland
Tel: 01862 893 164

SCOTSBURN GARDEN CENTRE 134-3
Scotsburn Road, Tain, Highland
Tel: 01862 892 377

Embo

Dornoch

1

Portmahomack

134-2

Tain

Inver

SCOTLAND

A

B

C

4

3

2

1

371\Sgribhis-Bheinn

297\Cnoc A Ghiubhais

300\Maovally

457\Fashven

Durness

423\Meall Meadhoi

485\Creag Riabach

468\Beinn Dearg Mhor

464\Meall Na Moine

331\Ghlas-Bheinn

489\Meall Na Cra

Balchreick

355\An Socach

521\Farveall

773\Beinn Spionnaidh

801\Cranstackie

Kinlochbervie

520\An Le

Rhiconich

908\Foinaven

786\Arkle

Scourie

A894

729\Sabhal Beag

721\Ben Stack

386\Ben Auskaird

333\Ben Screavie

800

796\Carn Dearg

757\Carn An Tionail

419\Ben Strome

Kinloch

8

680\Meall An Liath Mo

Culkein Drumbeg

Drumbeg

Nedd

Unapool

525\Beinn Aird Da Loch

613\Meall An Fheur Loch

776\Sail Ghorm

792\Beinn Leoid

809\Quinag

Bheinn 133

72\Cnoc A' Ghriama

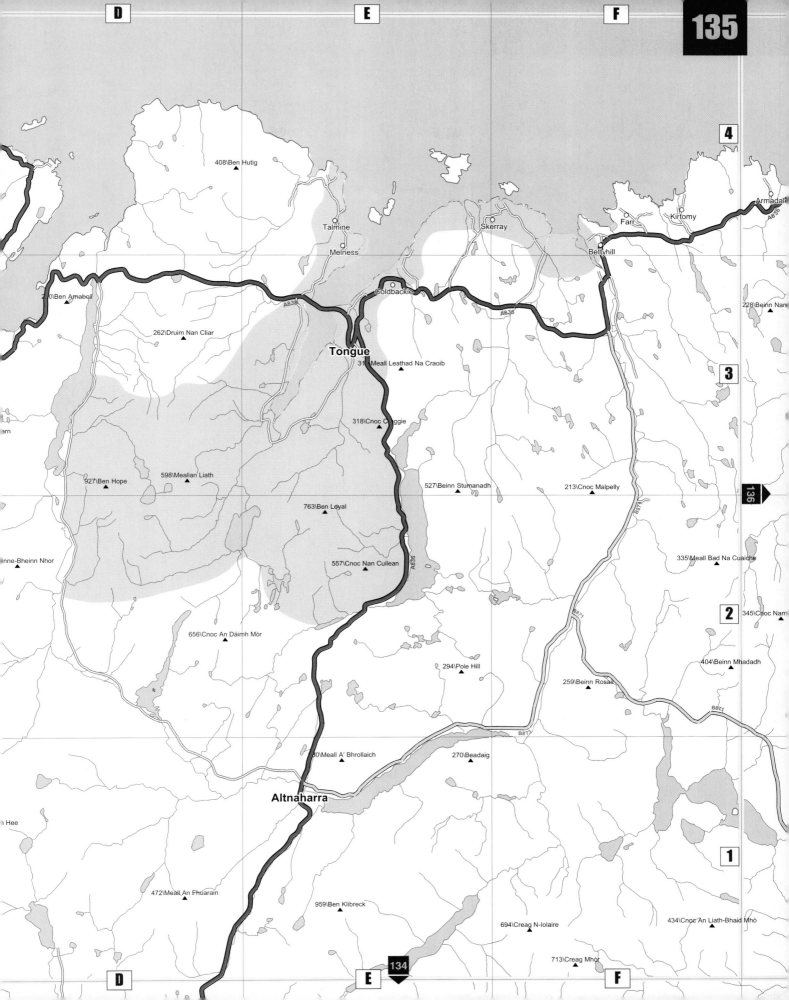

408\Ben Hutig ▲

Armadal

Talmine

Kirtomy

Skerray

Farr

Melness

Bettyhill

270\Ben Arnaboll ▲

Coldbackie

228\Beinn Nan

A838

A836

262\Druim Nan Cliar ▲

Tongue

31\Meall Leathad Na Craoib ▲

3

318\Cnoc Craggie ▲

927\Ben Hope ▲

598\Meallan Liath ▲

527\Beinn Stumanadh ▲

213\Cnoc Malpelly ▲

763\Ben Loyal ▲

335\Meall Bad Na Cuaiche ▲

inne-Bheinn Nhor

557\Cnoc Nan Cuilean ▲

A836

2 345\Cnoc Nam

656\Cnoc An Dàimh Mòr ▲

404\Beinn Mhadadh ▲

294\Pole Hill ▲

259\Beinn Rosail ▲

B871

B871

80\Meall A' Bhrollaich ▲

270\Beadaig ▲

B871

1

Altnaharra

472\Meall An Fhuarain ▲

959\Ben Klibreck ▲

434\Cnoc An Liath-Bhaid Mhò ▲

h Hee

694\Creag N-Iolaire ▲

713\Creag Mhor ▲

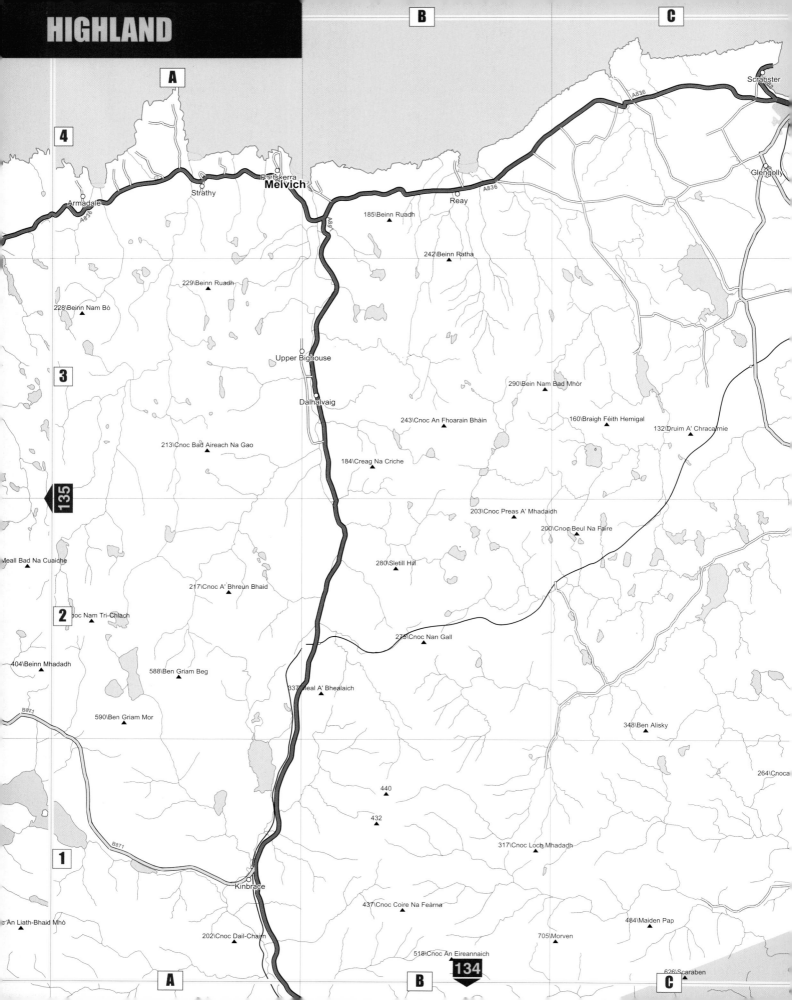

A

B

C

4

Scrabster

Glengolly

Armadale

Strathy

Portskerra

Melvich

Reay

A836

185\Beinn Ruadh

242\Beinn Ratha

229\Beinn Ruadh

228\Beinn Nam Bò

3

Upper Bighouse

290\Bein Nam Bad Mhòr

Dalhalvaig

243\Cnoc An Fhoarain Bhàin

160\Braigh Féith Hemigal

132\Druim A' Chracairnie

213\Cnoc Bad Aireach Na Gao

184\Creag Na Criche

135

203\Cnoc Preas A' Mhadaidh

200\Cnoc Beul Na Faire

Meall Bad Na Cuaiche

280\Sletill Hill

217\Cnoc A' Bhreun Bhaid

2

noc Nam Tri-Chlach

275\Cnoc Nan Gall

404\Beinn Mhadadh

588\Ben Griam Beg

348\Ben Alisky

337\Meal A' Bhealaich

590\Ben Griam Mor

264\Cnoca

B871

440

432

317\Cnoc Loch Mhadadh

1

B871

Kinbrace

437\Cnoc Coire Na Feàrna

484\Maiden Pap

An Liath-Bhaid Mhò

202\Cnoc Dail-Chairn

705\Morven

518\Cnoc An Eireannaich

626\Scaraben

A

B

134

C

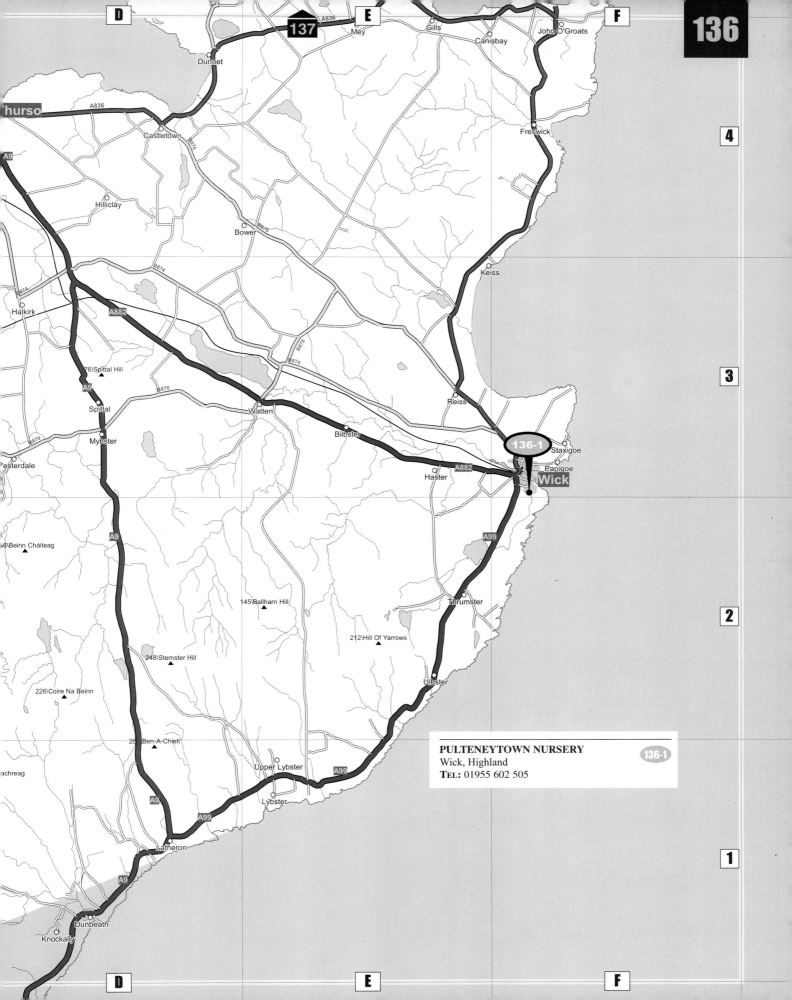

4

3

2

1

137

A836

Mey
Gills
Canisbay
John O'Groats

Dunnet

hurso
A836

Castletown

Freswick

A9

Hilliclay

B876

Bower
B876

Keiss

B874

Halkirk

A882

A9

76\Spittal Hill

Spittal

B870

Watten

B870

B874

Reiss

Bilbster

136-1

Staxigoe

A882

Mybster

Haster

Papigoe

Wick

esterdale

B870

6\Beinn Chàiteag

A9

A99

145\Ballharn Hill

Thrumster

212\Hill Of Yarrows

248\Stemster Hill

226\Coire Na Beinn

Ulbster

28\Ben-A-Chielt

Upper Lybster

A99

achreag

A9

A99

Lybster

Latheron

A9

PULTENEYTOWN NURSERY 136-1
Wick, Highland
Tel: 01955 602 505

Dunbeath

Knockally

ISLANDS

PLANTIECRUB GROWERS
Gott, Shetland
TEL: 01595 840 600
137-1

WELLPARK GARDEN CENTRE
Mill Street, Kirkwall, Orkney
TEL: 01856 874 203
137-2

WILLOWGLEN GARDEN CENTRE
Macauley Road, Stornoway, Western Isles
TEL: 01851 705 656
137-3

BALLALHEANAGH GARDENS
Glen Roy, Ionan, Isle of Man
TEL: 01624 861 875
137-4

TRESCO ABBEY GARDENS
Tresco, Isles of Scilly, Cornwall
TEL: 01720 424 105
137-5

JERSEY ZOOLOGICAL PARK
Les Augres Manor, Trinity, Jersey
TEL: 01534 860 000
137-6

ERIC YOUNG ORCHID FOUNDATION
Victoria Village, Trinity, Jersey
TEL: 01534 861 963
137-7

THE ART PARK
137-14
Sausmarez Manor, St Martins, Guernsey,
GY4 6SG
TEL: 01481 235 571
WEB: www.artparks.co.uk
The greatest variety of art in the open in Britain, set in a lush subtropical woodland garden with banana trees, tree ferns, bamboo groves, over 300 camellias, lillies, clematis, a couple of small lakes and stream. The bird-song is the loudest noise, it is so peaceful.
OPEN: Daily Apr-Dec, 10-5.
ENTRY COSTS: Adult £2.50, Children £2.00, OAPs £2.00, Disabled free.
SPECIALITIES: Exotic plants, Bamboos, Camelias, Palms, Sculptures.

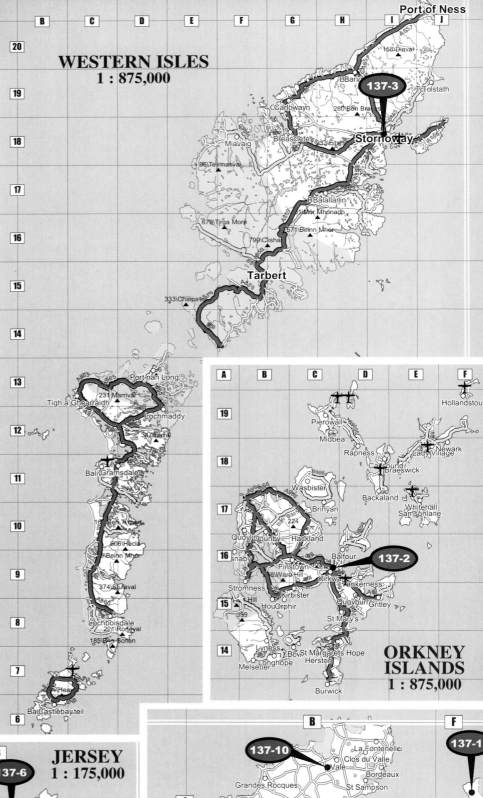

WESTERN ISLES
1 : 875,000

ORKNEY
ISLANDS
1 : 875,000

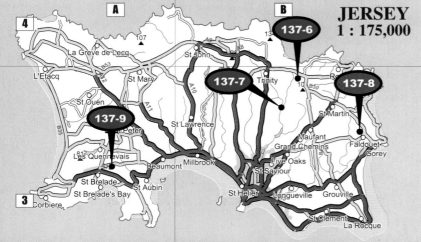

JERSEY
1 : 175,000

GUERNSEY
1 : 175,000

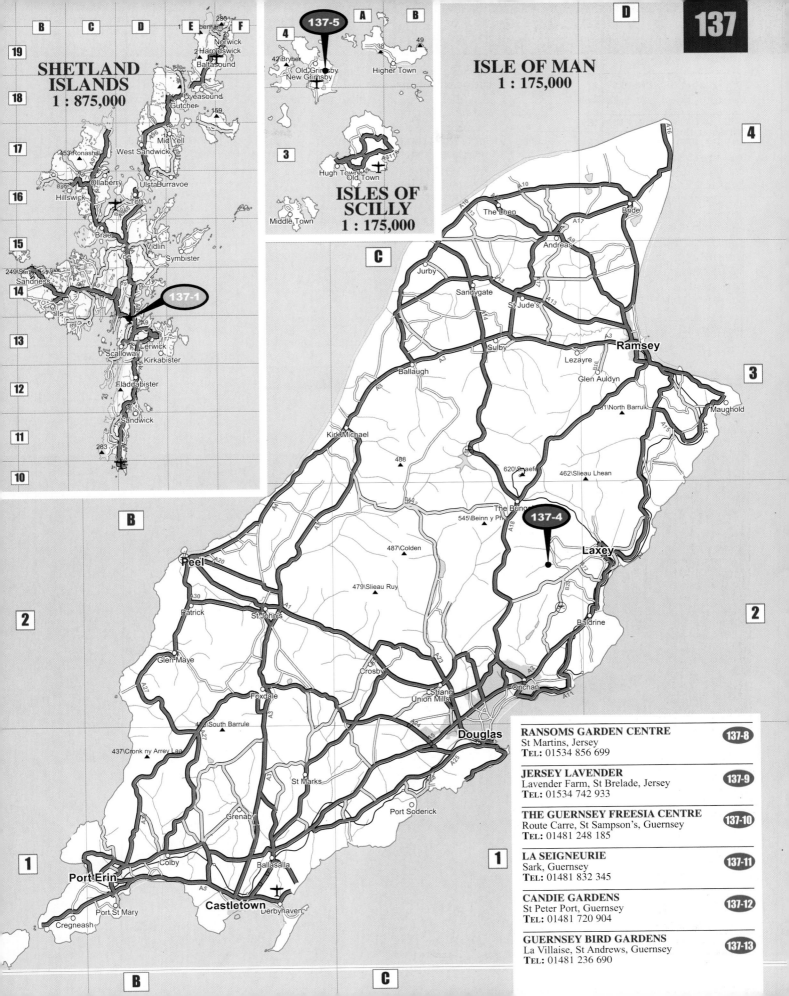

137

SHETLAND ISLANDS
1 : 875,000

Norwick
Haroldswick
Baltasound
Norwick
Uyeasound
Gutcher
159
Mid Yell
West Sandwick
453\Ronashill
Ollaberry
Hillswick
UlstaBurravoe
Toft
Brae
Vidlin
Voe
Symbister
249\Sandness Hill
Sandness
Walls
137-1
Scalloway
Lerwick
Kirkabister
Fladdabister
283
Sandwick

ISLES OF SCILLY
1 : 175,000

137-5
Bryher
Old Grimsby
New Grimsby
Higher Town
Hugh Town
Old Town
Middle Town

ISLE OF MAN
1 : 175,000

The Lhen
Bride
Andreas
Jurby
Sandygate
St Jude's
Ramsey
Sulby
Lezayre
Glen Auldyn
Ballaugh
31\North Barrule
Maughold
Kirk Michael
488
620\Snaefell
462\Slieau Lhean
137-4
545\Beinn y Phott
The Bungalow
Laxey
487\Colden
Peel
479\Slieau Ruy
Baldrine
Patrick
St John's
Glen Maye
Crosby
Foxdale
Strang
Union Mills
Onchan
448\South Barrule
437\Cronk ny Arrey Laa
St Marks
Douglas
Grenaby
Port Soderick
Colby
Ballasalla
Port Erin
Castletown
Port St Mary
Derbyhaven
Cregneash

BERKS · BUCKS · KENT · SURREY

○ GARDEN CENTRE   ● NURSERY & GARDEN CENTRE
○ NURSERY   ● GARDEN & NURSERY
○ GARDEN   ● WATER GARDEN SPECIALIST

BUTTERFIELDS NURSERY
Harvest Hill, Bourne End, Buckinghamshire
TEL: 01628 525 455

BOURNE END GARDEN CENTRE
Hedsor Road, Bourne End, Buckinghamshire
TEL: 01628 523 926

CLIVEDEN, NATIONAL TRUST
Taplow, Buckinghamshire
TEL: 01628 605 069

CHENIES AQUATICS
Wyevale Garden Centre, Farnham Royal,
Buckinghamshire
TEL: 01753 646 989

WYEVALE GARDEN CENTRE
Cedar Cottage, Slough, Berkshire
TEL: 01753 645 627

WILLIAM WOOD & SON
The Bishop Centre Shopping Village, Maidenhead,
Berkshire
TEL: 01628 605 454

MOOR GROWERS
Little Farm Nurseries, Maidenhead, Kent
TEL: 01628 634 275

**BRAYWICK HEATH NURSERY
& GARDEN CENTRE**
41 Braywick Road, Maidenhead, Berkshire
TEL: 01628 622 510

 **SQUIRE'S GARDEN CENTRE**
Maidenhead Road, Windsor, Berkshire, SL4 5UB
TEL: 01753 865 076
WEB: www.squiresgardencentres.co.uk
Wide range of quality plants, garden products, gifts and garden furniture. Awarded GCA Centre of Excellence.
OPEN: Mon-Sat 9-6, late nights spring, Sun 10.30-4.30.
SPECIALITIES: Bedding plants, Climbers, Roses, Bulbs, Shrubs.

WYEVALE GARDEN CENTRE
Dedworth Road, Windsor, Berkshire
TEL: 01753 841 791

LONG ORCHARD NURSERIES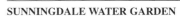
Oakley Green Road, Windsor, Berkshire
TEL: 01628 627 731

D. M. BOYER GARDEN SUPPLIES
Winkfield Lane, Windsor, Berkshire
TEL: 01344 882 532

MOSS END WATER GARDENS
Moss End Garden Centre, Bracknell, Berkshire
TEL: 01344 300 520

THE VALLEY GARDENS
Crown Estate Office, Windsor, Berkshire
TEL: 01753 860 222

OAK TREE NURSERY
Brock Hill, Bracknell, Berkshire
TEL: 01344 890 667

SUNNINGDALE WATER GARDEN
London Road, Windlesham, Surrey
TEL: 01344 625 599

WYEVALE GARDEN CENTRE
London Road, Windlesham, Surrey
TEL: 01344 621 411

HILLIER GARDEN CENTRE

138-17

London Road, Windlesham,
Surrey, GU20 6LN

TEL: 01344 623 166
WEB: www.hillier.co.uk

A nursery has been here since 1847. Now in addition to quality plants is a full range of sundries, furniture and all other garden requirements.
OPEN: Daily 9-5.30, Sun 10.30-4.30.
SPECIALITIES: Gifts, Greenhouses & sheds, Hardy plants, Trees, Shrubs.

BLOOMS OF DORNEY

138-19

Dorney Court, Dorney, Berkshire
TEL: 01628 669 999

Water Lily

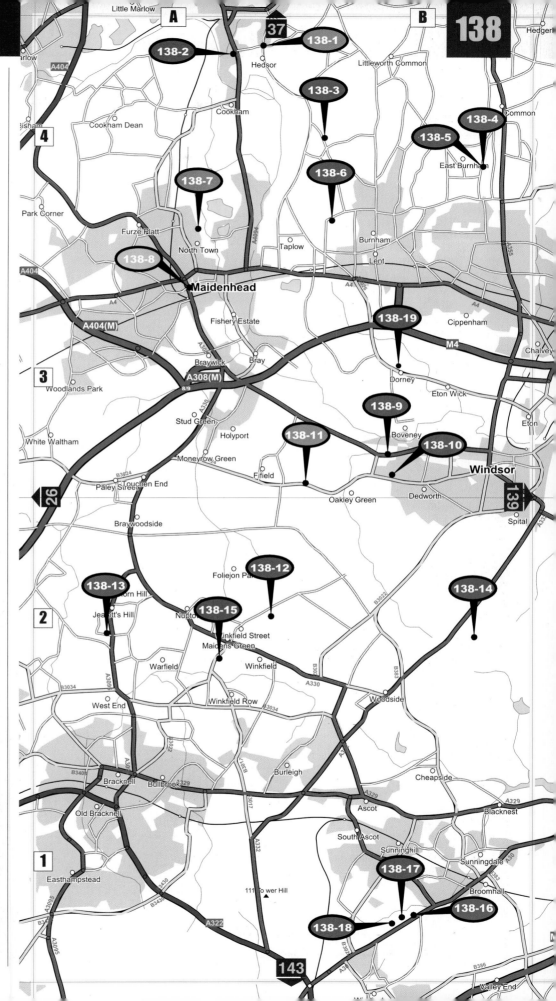

SPRINGBRIDGE NURSERIES 139-1
24-26 Oxford Road, Denham, Buckinghamshire
TEL: 01895 835 939

SHANE'S NURSERY 139-2
29 Oxford Road, Denham, Buckinghamshire
TEL: 01895 833 289

SLOUGH BOROUGH COUNCIL SPEEDWELL PLANT SALE 139-3
Wexham Nursery, Wexham Road, Slough, Berkshire, SL2 4HE
TEL: 01753 526 408

RHS Chelsea flower show award winning nursery, offers a full range of wholesale and retail quality plants, shrubs and trees.
OPEN: Mon-Fri 8-3, Sat 10-4, extended spring opening, phone for details. Closed Sun, Christmas, Boxing & New Year's day.
SPECIALITIES: Bedding plants, Bulbs, House plants, Shrubs, Trees.

LANGLEY PARK 139-4
Wexham, Slough, Berkshire
TEL: 01753 511 060

ALPA GARDEN & AQUATIC CENTRE 139-5
142-144 Swallow Street, Iver, Buckinghamshire
TEL: 01753 654 101

WYEVALE GARDEN CENTRE 139-6
Field Heath Road, Hillingdon, Middlesex
TEL: 01895 236 141

WOOD LANE NURSERY 139-7
Wood Lane, Iver, Bucks, SL0 0LG
TEL: 01753 653 168
EMAIL: enquiries@carpenders.co.uk
WEB: www.wood-lane-nursery.co.uk

Extensive range of plants, terracotta, stoneware, accessories, turf and seeds. Garden furniture, BBQ's and gifts. Delivery service. Friendly, expert advice.
OPEN: Mon-Sat 9-6. Sun 9.30-6.
SPECIALITIES: Climbers, Hardy plants, Perennials, Shrubs, Sundries.

J. C. ALLGROVE 139-8
The Nursery, Slough, Berkshire
TEL: 01753 520 155

JOHN TRAIN PLANTS 139-9
Harmondsworth Road, West Drayton, Middlesex
TEL: 020 8759 3010

AIRPORT AQUARIA 139-10
Heathrow Garden Centre, West Drayton, Middlesex
TEL: 020 897 2563

HEATHROW GARDEN CENTRE 139-11
Sipson Road, West Drayton, Middlesex
TEL: 020 8897 8893

BERKSHIRE GARDEN CENTRE 139-12
Sutton Lane, Slough, Berkshire
TEL: 01753 544 368

WYEVALE GARDEN CENTRE 139-13
Holloway Lane, West Drayton, Middlesex
TEL: 020 8897 6075

WATERLIFE 139-14
Bath Road, West Drayton, Middlesex
TEL: 01753 685 696

VERMEULEN'S GARDEN CENTRE 139-15
Horton Road, Staines, Middlesex
TEL: 01784 451 737

BULLDOG NURSERIES 139-16
Town Lane, Staines, Middlesex
TEL: 01784 254 545

WYEVALE GARDEN CENTRE 139-17
42 Wraysbury Road, Staines, Middlesex
TEL: 01784 482 146

P. J. S PALMS & EXOTICS 139-18
41 Salcombe Road, Ashford, Middlesex
TEL: 01784 250 181

H. J. PEARCEY & SONS 139-20
41 Clarence Street, Egham, Surrey
TEL: 01784 432 805

EGHAM GARDEN CENTRE 139-21
Vicarage Road, Egham, Surrey
TEL: 01784 433 388

MAYFLOWER NURSERIES 139-22
Thorpe Lea Road, Egham, Surrey
TEL: 01784 432 945

NOTCUTTS GARDEN CENTRE 139-23
Staines Road, Staines, Middlesex
TEL: 01784 460 832

PANTILES PLANT & GARDEN CENTRE 139-24
Almners Road, Chertsey, Surrey
TEL: 01932 872 195

SAVILL GARDEN 139-19
Windsor Great Park, Wick Lane, Englefield Green, Near Windsor, Surrey, TW20 0UU
TEL: 01753 847 518
EMAIL: savillgarden@crownestate.org.uk
WEB: www.savillgarden.co.uk

Magnificent landscaped 35-acre garden. Spectacular spring display in the woodland garden; sweeping summer herbaceous borders; formal rose beds; fiery autumn leaf colours; landscaped temperate house. Beauty at all seasons. Excellent gift shop, planteria and restaurant.
OPEN: Daily, Mar-Oct 10-6, Nov-Feb, 10-4. Closed 25/26 Dec.
ENTRY COSTS: Seasonal charges; Adult £5-£3, Children £2-£1, OAPs £4.50-£2.50.
SPECIALITIES: Rhododendrons and azaleas, Roses, Trees, Camellias, Ferns.

PLANTA VERA 139-25
Lyne Hill Nursery, Chertsey, Surrey
TEL: 01932 563 011

WOBURN HILL NURSERY 139-26
Woburn Hill, Weybridge, Surrey
TEL: 01932 821 066

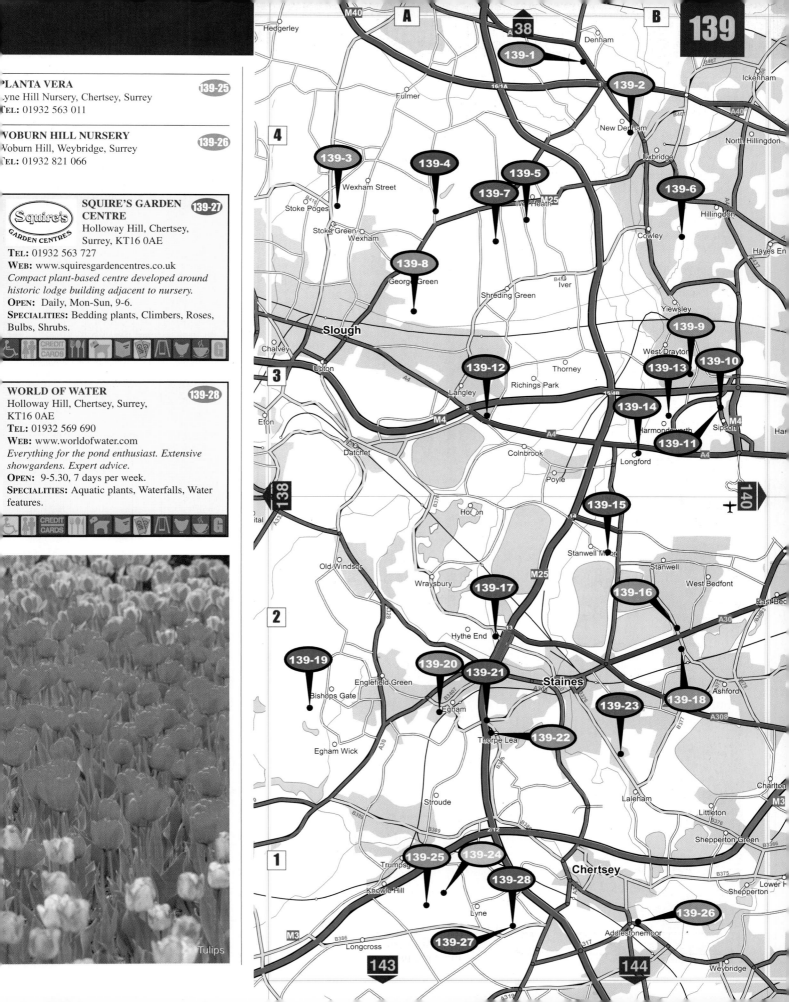

SQUIRE'S GARDEN CENTRE 139-27
Holloway Hill, Chertsey, Surrey, KT16 0AE
TEL: 01932 563 727
WEB: www.squiresgardencentres.co.uk
Compact plant-based centre developed around historic lodge building adjacent to nursery.
OPEN: Daily, Mon-Sun, 9-6.
SPECIALITIES: Bedding plants, Climbers, Roses, Bulbs, Shrubs.

WORLD OF WATER 139-28
Holloway Hill, Chertsey, Surrey, KT16 0AE
TEL: 01932 569 690
WEB: www.worldofwater.com
Everything for the pond enthusiast. Extensive showgardens. Expert advice.
OPEN: 9-5.30, 7 days per week.
SPECIALITIES: Aquatic plants, Waterfalls, Water features.

Tulips

LONDON · MIDDLESEX · SURREY

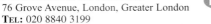

- ○ GARDEN CENTRE
- ○ NURSERY
- ○ GARDEN
- ● NURSERY & GARDEN CENTRE
- ● GARDEN & NURSERY
- ● WATER GARDEN SPECIALIST

PENSTEMONS BY COLOUR `140-1`
76 Grove Avenue, London, Greater London
TEL: 020 8840 3199

SPRINGBRIDGE NURSERIES `140-2`
2A Gordon Road, London, Greater London
TEL: 020 8997 4415

WYEVALE GARDEN CENTRE `140-3`
Windmill Lane, Osterley, Middlesex
TEL: 020 8847 2468

PANNELLS GARDEN CENTRE `140-4`
New Heston Road, Heston, Middlesex
TEL: 020 8570 4602

ROYAL BOTANIC GARDENS, KEW `140-5`
Kew, Richmond, Surrey
TEL: 020 8940 1171

WYEVALE GARDEN CENTRE `140-6`
Syon Park, Brentford, Middlesex
TEL: 020 8568 0134

SYON PARK `140-7`
Brentford, Middlesex
TEL: 020 8560 0881

KNELLER GARDEN SUPPLIES `140-8`
297 Whitton Dene, Isleworth, Middlesex
TEL: 020 8898 7494

ISABELLA PLANTATION `140-9`
Richmond Park, Richmond, Surrey
TEL: 020 8948 3209

MARBLE HILL HOUSE, ENGLISH HERITAGE `140-10`
Richmond Road, Twickenham, Middlesex
TEL: 020 8892 5115

LAKESIDE GARDEN CENTRE `140-11`
Bedfont Road, Feltham, Middlesex
TEL: 020 8844 2261

PETERSHAM NURSERIES `140-12`
Petersham Road, Richmond, Surrey
TEL: 020 8940 5230

HAM HOUSE, NATIONAL TRUST `140-13`
Ham, Richmond, Surrey
TEL: 020 8940 1950

THE PALM CENTRE `140-14`
Ham Central Nursery, Richmond, Surrey
TEL: 020 8255 6191

SQUIRE'S GARDEN CENTRE `140-15`
Sixth Cross Road, Twickenham,
Middlesex, TW2 5PA
TEL: 020 8977 9241
EMAIL: admin@squiresgardencentres.co.uk
WEB: www.squiresgardencentres.co.uk

Flagship of the Squire's group with a vast selection of quality plants and garden products. Judged Best Garden Centre in GCA 2001.
OPEN: Daily, Mon-Sat 9-6 (late nights spring), 10.30-4.30 Sun.
SPECIALITIES: Alpines, Bedding plants, Climbers Fruit & fruit trees, Garden & conservatory furniture.

ADRIAN HALL `140-16`
Hampstead Garden Centre, 161-163
Iverson Road, London, NW6 2RB
TEL: 020 7328 3208
A wide selection of products and plants for the London garden.
OPEN: All year; 9-6 Mon-Sat, 10-4 Sundays and bank holidays.

MARKS WATER GARDEN `140-17`
156 High Street, Teddington, Middlesex
TEL: 020 8943 9799

TEDDINGTON STATION GARDEN CENTRE `140-18`
Station Road, Teddington, Middlesex
TEL: 020 8943 5222

WATERHOUSE PLANTATION `140-19`
Bushy Park, Hampton, Surrey
TEL: 020 8979 1586

SQUIRE'S GARDEN CENTRE `140-22`
Halliford Road, Upper Halliford,
Shepperton, Middlesex, TW17 8RU
TEL: 01932 784 121
WEB: www.squiresgardencentres.co.uk
Extensive range of quality plants and garden products, hosts many horticultural shows, situated adjacent to Rose Nurseries. Awarded GCA Centre of Excellence.
OPEN: Daily, Mon-Sat 9-6 (late nights spring), Sun 10.30-4.30.
SPECIALITIES: Alpines, Bedding plants, Climbers, Fruit & fruit trees, Garden & conservatory furniture.

HAMPTON COURT PALACE
East Molesey, Surrey
Tel: 020 8781 9500
140-20

FUNKEY FISH
Squire's Garden Centre, Shepperton, Middlesex
Tel: 020 8897 2563
140-21

JUNGLE GARDEN & PET CENTRE
Fordbridge Road, Sunbury on Thames, Middlesex
Tel: 01932 772 136
140-23

HILL PARK ROSES
Woodstock Lane North, Surbiton, Surrey
Tel: 020 8398 0022
140-24

WOODSTOCK GARDEN CENTRE
Woodstock Lane North, Surbiton, Surrey
Tel: 020 8398 6040
140-25

GREEN FINGER HYDROPONICS
182 Hook Road, Surbiton, Surrey
Tel: 020 8255 8999
140-26

WYEVALE GARDEN CENTRE
Oaken Lane, Claygate, Surrey
Tel: 020 8398 0047
140-27

CHASE ORGANICS
Riverdene Estate, Hersham, Surrey
Tel: 01932 253 666
140-28

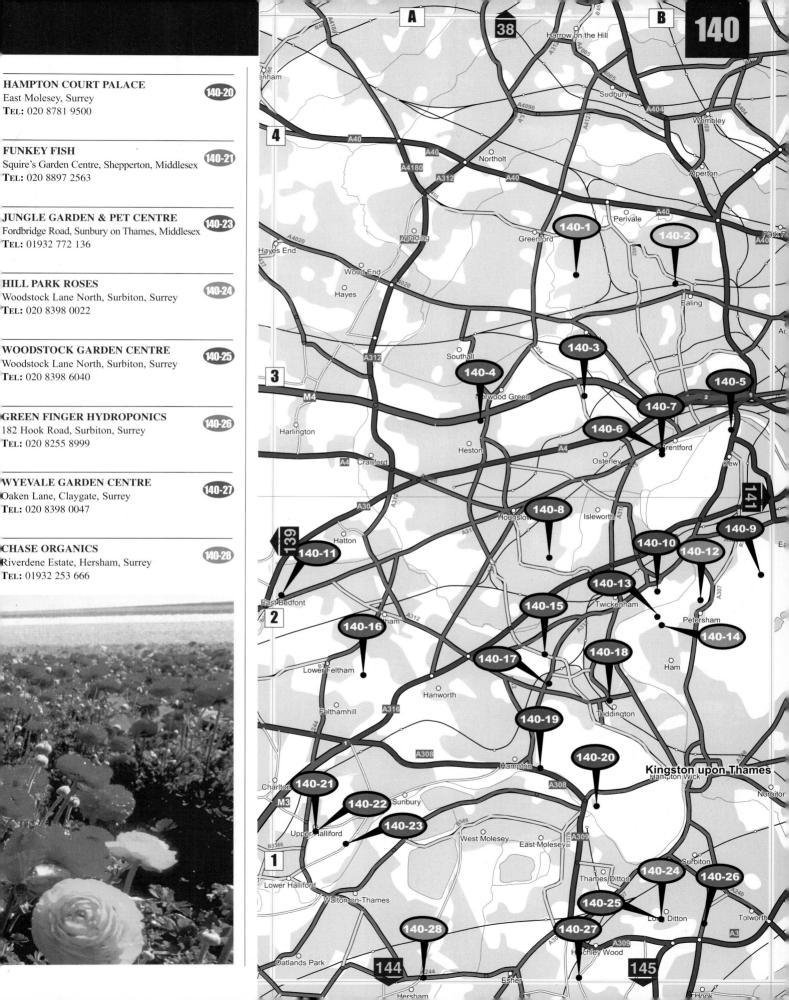

- GARDEN CENTRE
- NURSERY
- GARDEN
- NURSERY & GARDEN CENTRE
- GARDEN & NURSERY
- WATER GARDEN SPECIALIST

SPRINGFIELD PARK 141-1
Upper Clapton Road, London, Greater London
TEL: 020 8806 1826

GOLDERS HILL PARK 141-2
North End Way, London, Greater London
TEL: 020 8455 5183

THE GREENHOUSE 141-3
Birchen Grove, London, Greater London
TEL: 020 8905 9189

HILL GARDEN 141-4
Inverforth Close, London, Greater London
TEL: 020 8455 5183

GRANVILLE GARDEN CENTRE 141-5
170 Granville Road, London, Greater London
TEL: 020 8455 3654

ADRIAN HALL 141-6
Hampstead Garden Centre, 161-163
Iverson Road, London, NW6 2RB
TEL: 020 7328 3208
A wide selection of products and plants for the London garden.
OPEN: All year; 9-6 Mon-Sat, 10-4 Sundays and bank holidays.

NORTH ONE GARDEN CENTRE 141-7
25a Englefield Road, London, Greater London
TEL: 020 7923 3553

CULPEPPER COMMUNITY GARDEN 141-8
1 Cloudesley Road, London, Greater London
TEL: 020 7833 3951

CAMDEN GARDEN CENTRE 141-9
2 Barker Drive, St Pancras Way, Camden, London, NW1 0JW
TEL: 020 7485 8468
Exciting range of plants, containers, trellis and gardening products for gardens, balconies and window boxes. Delivery service and car park.
OPEN: Daily Apr-Sep, Mon-Sat 9-5.30, Sun 11-5; Oct-Mar, Mon-Sat 9-5, Sun 10-4.
SPECIALITIES: Alpines, Bedding plants, Climbers, Garden & conservatory furniture, Hardy plants.

LONDON ZOO 141-10
Regent's Park, London, Greater London
TEL: 020 7722 3333

GEFFRYE MUSEUM HERB GARDEN 141-11
Kingsland Road, London, Greater London
TEL: 020 7739 9893

REGENT'S PARK & QUEEN MARY`S ROSE GARDEN 141-12
Inner Circle, London, Greater London
TEL: 020 7298 2000

MUSEUM OF LONDON GARDEN 141-13
The Museum of London, London, Greater London
TEL: 020 7600 3699

DOCKLANDS GARDEN CENTRE 141-14
244-246 Ratcliffe Lane, London, Greater London
TEL: 020 7790 1146

KENSINGTON GARDENS 141-15
London, Greater London
TEL: 020 7298 2000

PIRELLI GARDEN 141-16
Victoria & Albert Museum, London, Greater London
TEL: 020 7942 2209

GINKGO GARDEN CENTRE 141-17
Ravenscourt Park, London, Greater London
TEL: 020 8563 7112

THE CHELSEA GARDENER 141-18
125 Sydney Street, London, Greater London
TEL: 020 7352 5656

ROYAL HOSPITAL, RANELAGH GARDENS 141-19
Royal Hospital Road, London, Greater London
TEL: 020 7730 0161

CHELSEA PHYSIC GARDEN 141-20
66 Royal Hospital Road, London, Greater London
TEL: 020 7352 5646

CHISWICK HOUSE, ENGLISH HERITAGE 141-21
Burlington Lane, London, Greater London
TEL: 020 8995 0508

FULHAM PALACE GARDEN CENTRE 141-22
Bishops Avenue, London, Greater London
TEL: 020 7736 3233

PARKSIDE NURSERY 141-23
Denmark Hill, London, Greater London
TEL: 020 7738 4240

DULWICH GARDEN CENTRE 141-24
20-22 Grove Vale, London, Greater London
TEL: 020 8299 1089

ADRIAN HALL 141-25
Putney Garden Centre, London, Greater London
TEL: 020 8789 9518

ADRIAN HALL 141-26
Sheen Garden Centre, East Sheen, Greater London
TEL: 020 8876 3648

CROXTED ROAD GARDEN CENTRE 141-27
Croxted Road, London, Greater London
TEL: 020 8674 4366

BROCKWELL PARK GARDENS 141-28
Brockwell Park, London, Greater London
TEL: 020 7926 0105

SHANNON'S 141-29
99-105 Stanstead Road, London, Greater London
TEL: 020 8291 1507

HORNIMAN GARDENS 141-30
Hornimans Drive, London, Greater London
TEL: 020 8699 8924

PATIO GARDEN CENTRE 141-31
100 Tooting Bec Road, London, Greater London
TEL: 020 8672 2251

CANNIZARO PARK 141-32
West Side Common, London, Greater London
TEL: 020 8946 7349

THE ROOKERY 141-33
Streatham Common South, London, Greater London
TEL: 020 8671 0994

THE SECRET GARDEN 141-34
70 Westow Street, London, Greater London
TEL: 020 8771 8200

MENDIP COTTAGE NURSERY 141-35
43 Copers Cope Road, Beckenham, Kent
TEL: 020 8658 6094

CRYSTAL PALACE PARK 141-36
Crystal Palace Road, London, Greater London
TEL: 020 8313 4407

GARDENERS WORLD 141-37
530 Kingston Road, London, Greater London
TEL: 020 8542 5678

CASTLE NURSERY 141-38
159 Elmers End Road, Beckenham, Kent
TEL: 020 8650 2899

MORDEN HALL PARK, NATIONAL TRUST 141-39
Morden Hall Road, Morden, Greater London
TEL: 020 8648 1845

CAPITAL GARDENS LTD MORDEN HALL GARDEN CENTRE 141-40
Morden Hall Road, Morden, Greater London
TEL: 020 8646 3002

PEACHPRINT 141-41
350 West Barnes Lane, New Malden, Greater London
TEL: 020 8942 0303

WYEVALE GARDEN CENTRE 141-42
Lower Morden Lane, Morden, Greater London
TEL: 020 8337 7781

AQUAJOY 141-43
31 Lower Morden Lane, Morden, Greater London
TEL: 020 8337 7373

J. DOBBE & SONS 141-44
Stonecot Nurseries, Sutton, Surrey
TEL: 020 8644 9412

EGMONT WATER GARDEN CENTRE 141-45
132 Tolworth Rise South, Surbiton, Surrey, KT5 9NJ
TEL: 020 8337 9605
Specialists in all water gardening including equipment and accessories. Also a large range of stoneware, alpines and shrubs.
OPEN: Daily, Mar-Aug, 7 days a week, Sep-Feb 6 days a week 10-5, closed Christmas & Boxing day.
SPECIALITIES: Alpines, Water features.

THOMMO'S FLOWERS 141-46
237 Sutton Common Road, Sutton, Surrey
TEL: 020 8288 1571

WYEVALE GARDEN CENTRE 141-47
Wickham Road, Croydon, Surrey
TEL: 020 8654 3720

NORTH CHEAM GARDEN CENTRE 141-48
583 London Road, Sutton, Surrey
TEL: 020 8337 2833

KENT · LONDON

- **GARDEN CENTRE**
- **NURSERY**
- **GARDEN**
- **NURSERY & GARDEN CENTRE**
- **GARDEN & NURSERY**
- **WATER GARDEN SPECIALIST**

MINI GARDEN CENTRE — 142-1
313b Cann Hall Road, London, Greater London
Tel: 020 8555 2132

FOREST FLOWERS & GARDEN CENTRE — 142-2
131 Forest Lane, London, Greater London
Tel: 020 8555 4299

WEST HAM PARK — 142-3
Upton Lane, London, Greater London
Tel: 020 8472 3584

BRIAN LAWLER — 142-4
65 The Shopping Hall, London, Greater London
Tel: 020 8472 7791

ROYS STORES — 142-5
45a Bostall Hill, London, Greater London
Tel: 020 8311 5212

ROYS STORES — 142-6
191 Sandyhill Road, London, Greater London
Tel: 020 8854 5368

BELVEDERE PET & GARDEN CENTRE — 142-7
6 Albert Road, Belvedere, Greater London
Tel: 01322 432 482

THE CITY GARDENER — 142-8
150 Long Lane, Bexleyheath, Kent
Tel: 020 8303 2838

THOMPSON'S PLANT & GARDEN CENTRE — 142-9
Shooters Hill, Welling, Kent
Tel: 020 8856 2933

WESTWOOD NURSERY — 142-10
65 Yorkland Avenue, Welling, Kent
Tel: 020 8301 0886

DANSON PARK — 142-11
Bexleyheath, Greater London
Tel: 020 8304 2631

HALL PLACE — 142-12
Bourne Road, Bexley, Kent
Tel: 01322 526 574

ELTHAM PALACE, ENGLISH HERITAGE — 142-13
Court Yard, London, Greater London
Tel: 020 8294 2548

BROADVIEW GARDENS — 142-14
Mottingham Lane, Tonbridge, Greater London
Tel: 020 8851 8793

PHOEBE'S GARDEN CENTRE — 142-15
Penerley Road, London, Greater London
Tel: 020 8698 4365

STUART'S NURSERIES — 142-16
North Cray Road, Sidcup, Kent
Tel: 020 8300 1933

HEATHSIDE NURSERY — 142-17
64 Leyton Cross Road, Dartford, Kent
Tel: 01322 224 482

ST. MARY'S NURSERY — 142-18
103 Birchwood Road, Dartford, Kent
Tel: 01322 667 883

WEATHERLEY FENCING & GARDEN CENTRE — 142-19
The Orchard, Sidcup, Kent
Tel: 020 8308 1316

THOMPSON'S PLANT & GARDEN CENTRE — 142-20
Perry Street, Chislehurst, Kent
Tel: 020 8300 1025

RUXLEY NURSERIES — 142-21
Maidstone Road, Sidcup, Kent
Tel: 020 8300 2515

RUXLEY MANOR GARDEN CENTRE — 142-22
Maidstone Road, Sidcup, Kent
Tel: 020 8300 0084

HARRINGTON'S NURSERY — 142-23
Silver Birches, Swanley, Kent
Tel: 01322 663 239

I. H. BEALE — 142-24
Swanley Village Road, Swanley, Kent
Tel: 01322 664 041

PRIORY GARDENS — 142-25
High Street, Orpington, Kent
Tel: 020 8464 3333

JUST BAMBOO — 142-26
109 Hayes Lane, Bromley, Kent
Tel: 020 8462 1800

KENT CACTI — 142-2
35 Rutland Way, Orpington, Kent
Tel: 01689 836 249

CONNOISSEURS' CACTI — 142-2
51 Chelsfield Lane, Orpington, Kent
Tel: 01689 837 781

MAYFIELD NURSERIES — 142-2
Chelsfield Lane, Orpington, Kent
Tel: 01689 876 602

WORLD OF KOI — 142-30
Bencewell Farm, Bromley, Kent
Tel: 020 8462 9479

EYNSFORD NURSERY — 142-3
Riverside, Dartford, Kent
Tel: 01322 864 439

KOI WATER BARN — 142-32
Lillys Farm, Orpington, Kent
Tel: 01689 878 161

WYEVALE GARDEN CENTRE — 142-33
Oakley Road, Bromley, Kent
Tel: 01689 859 419

LULLINGSTONE CASTLE — 142-34
Lullingstone Park, Eynsford, Kent
Tel: 01322 862 114

Queen Anne's Lace

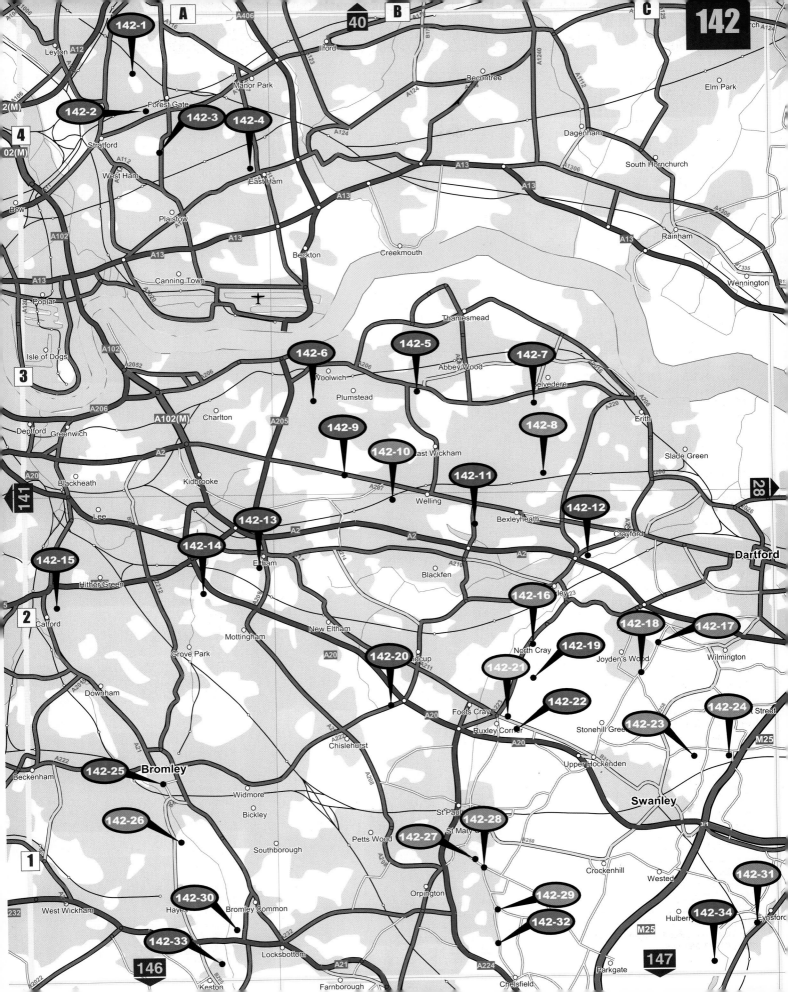

HAMPSHIRE · SURREY

- GARDEN CENTRE
- NURSERY
- GARDEN
- NURSERY & GARDEN CENTRE
- GARDEN & NURSERY
- WATER GARDEN SPECIALIST

THE PLANT CENTRE · 143-1
Bagshot Road, Chobham,
Surrey, GU24 8SJ
TEL: 01276 855 408

One of the finest ranges of plants for the amateur and professional gardener alike, always backed with expert advice.
OPEN: Daily, 8.30-6, Sun 10-4, closed Christmas & Boxing Day.
SPECIALITIES: Alpines, Climbers, Bedding plants, Garden & conservatory furniture, Hardy plants.

LINCLUDEN NURSERY · 143-2
Bisley Green, Woking, Surrey
TEL: 01483 797 005

SQUIRE'S GARDEN CENTRE · 143-3

Littlewick Road, Horsell,
Woking, Surrey, GU21 4XR
TEL: 01276 858 446
WEB: www.squiresgardencentres.co.uk
Wide, quality range of products from Squire's. Awarded GCA Centre of Excellence.
OPEN: Daily. Mon-Sat 9-6, Sun 10.30-4.30.
SPECIALITIES: Bedding plants, Climbers, Alpines, Fruit & fruit trees, Garden & conservatory furniture.

PENTANGLE WATER GARDENS & AQUARIA · 143-4
Botany Barns, Woking, Surrey
TEL: 01483 489 757

TOOBEES EXOTICS · 143-5
Blackhorse Road, Woking,
Surrey, GU22 0QT
TEL: 01483 797 534
EMAIL: bbpotter@compuserve.com
WEB: www.toobeesexotics.com
Specialists in South African and Madagascan succulents, plus selections of cacti, palms, cycads, carniverous air plants and other exotics. For mail order list SAE to:- 20 Inglewood, Woking, Surrey GU21 3HX.
OPEN: 12 Apr-30 Sep, 10-5, Thurs-Sun.
SPECIALITIES: South African & Madagascan succulents.

WYEVALE GARDEN CENTRE · 143-6
Egley Road, Woking, Surrey
TEL: 01432 276 568

BRIARWOOD NURSERIES · 143-7
Saunders Lane, Woking, Surrey
TEL: 01483 763 216

WOKING NURSERY · 143-8
99 Westfield Road, Woking, Surrey
TEL: 01483 725 646

SUTTON GREEN GARDEN NURSERY · 143-9
Guildford Road, Guildford, Surrey
TEL: 01483 232 366

ELM NURSERY · 143-10
Sutton Green Road, Guildford, Surrey
TEL: 01483 761 748

MERRIST WOOD PLANT CENTRE · 143-11
Merrist Wood College, Guildford, Surrey
TEL: 01483 235 122

TANGLEY GARDENS NURSERY · 143-12
Pitch Place, Guildford, Surrey
TEL: 01483 232 243

WOODLANDS FARM NURSERY · 143-13
The Green, Guildford, Surrey
TEL: 01483 235 536

OAKS NURSERY · 143-14
Foreman Road, Aldershot, Hampshire
TEL: 01252 285 90

LITTLE BROOK FUCHSIAS · 143-15
Ash Green Lane West, Aldershot, Surrey
TEL: 01252 329 731

GUILDFORD CASTLE GARDENS · 143-16
Castle Street, Guildford, Surrey
TEL: 01483 505 050

COMPTON NURSERY · 143-17
Compton, Guildford, Surrey
TEL: 01483 811 387

BADSHOT LEA GARDEN CENTRE · 143-18
Badshot Lea, Farnham, Surrey
TEL: 01252 333 666

ALDERWOOD NURSERIES · 143-19
Runfold St George, Farnham, Surrey
TEL: 01252 782 493

LITTLE ACRES NURSERY · 143-20
St Georges Road, Farnham, Surrey
TEL: 01252 782 942

SEALE NURSERIES · 143-21
Seale Lane, Seale, Farnham, Surrey,
GU10 1LD
TEL: 01252 782 410
EMAIL: ga@sealenurseries.demon.co.uk
WEB: www.sealenurseries.demon.co.uk

Family run, est. 1948, extensive selection of home-grown hardy plants. Speciality 'Seale Super Roses' uniquely container grown, ensuring unsurpassed quality.
OPEN: Daily, 9-5, closed Christmas week.
SPECIALITIES: Roses, Hedging, Shrubs, Herbaceous plants, Pelargoniums.

LOSELEY PARK · 143-22
Guildford, Surrey, GU3 1HS
TEL: 01483 304 440
EMAIL: enquiries@loseley-park.com
WEB: www.loseley-park.com

Loseley Walled Garden, based on a Gertrude Jekyll design, includes an award-winning rose garden, flower garden and a glorious moat walk. All set in the tranquil grounds of 16th century Loseley House.
OPEN: 7 May-30 Sep, Wed-Sun 11-5.
ENTRY COSTS (garden only): Adult £3, Children £1.50, Concession £2.50.
SPECIALITIES: Bedding plants, Climbers, Hardy plants, Pot plants, Roses.

HAZELBANK NURSERY · 143-23
Tilford Street, Farnham, Surrey
TEL: 01252 782 405

HIGHBANKS NURSERY · 143-24
Birtley Road, Guildford, Surrey
TEL: 01483 893 380

FRENSHAM GARDEN CENTRE · 143-25
The Reeds Road, Frensham, Farnham,
Surrey, GU10 3BP
TEL: 01252 792 545
EMAIL: info@frensham-gardencentre.co.uk
WEB: www.frensham.co.uk

Picturesque garden centre in mature woodland setting, offering full range of plants, sundries, furniture. Incorporating Frensham Coffee Shop & Camping World.
OPEN: Daily, Mon-Sat 9-5.30, Sun 10.30-4.30.
SPECIALITIES: Bedding plants, Climbers, Garden & conservatory furniture, Roses, Shrubs.

F. A. SECRETT · 143-26
Hurst Farm, Godalming, Surrey
TEL: 01483 426 633

BUSBRIDGE LAKES, WATERFOWL & GARDENS · 143-27
Busbridge Lakes, Godalming, Surrey
TEL: 01483 421 955

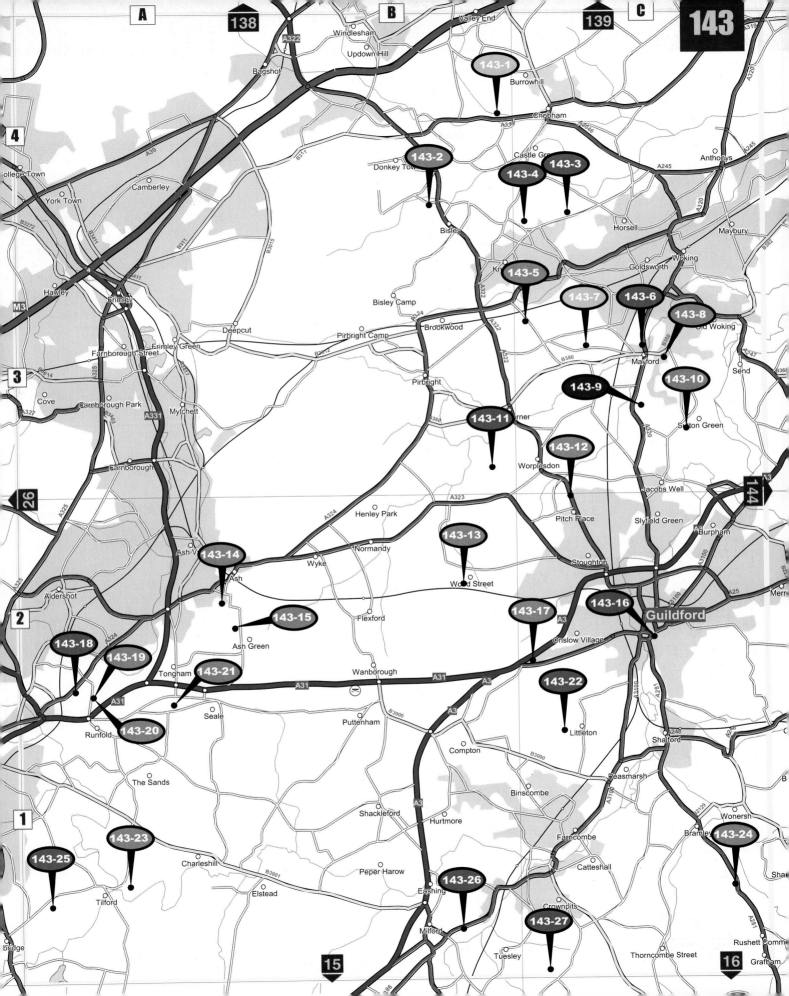

GARSONS 144-1
Winterdown Road, West End, Esher,
Surrey, KT10 8LS
TEL: 01372 460 181
EMAIL: mail@garson-farm.co.uk
WEB: www.garson-farm.co.uk

Large, modern garden centre with restaurant, PYO farm and farm shop selling local, fresh and specialist foods in traditional farm barns.
OPEN: Daily, summer 9-6, winter 9-5. Sun 11-5, closed Christmas & Boxing Day.
SPECIALITIES: Bedding plants, Climbers, Fruit & vegetables, Pot plants.

 ## SQUIRE'S GARDEN CENTRE 144-2
Burwood Road, Hersham, Surrey, KT12 4AR
TEL: 01932 247 579
WEB: www.squiresgardencentres.co.uk
New building and restaurant opened June 2000.
OPEN: Daily, 9-6 Mon-Sat, 10.30-4.30 Sun.
SPECIALITIES: Bedding plants, Climbers, Roses, Shrubs, Garden & Conservatory Furniture.

CLAREMONT LANDSCAPE GARDEN, NATIONAL TRUST 144-3
Portsmouth Road, Esher, Surrey
TEL: 01372 467 806

BOURNE VALLEY GARDEN CENTRE 144-4
Woodham Park Road,
Woodham Addlestone, Surrey
TEL: 01932 342 013

JACQUES CANN 144-5
Seven Hills Road, Walton on Thames, Surrey
TEL: 01932 844 575

F. W. CHARLES 144-6
33 The Avenue, Addlestone, Surrey
TEL: 01932 346 600

PAINSHILL LANDSCAPE GARDEN 144-7
Painshill Park, Cobham, Surrey
TEL: 01932 868 113

COBHAM PARK NURSERY 144-8
Plough Lane, Downside, Cobham, Surrey, KT11 3LT
TEL: 01932 863 933
Nursery in old walled garden, growing all own general stock, summer bedding and 600 varieties of herbaceous perennials and hardy ferns.
OPEN: 6 days a week, 10-5, closed Wed and Christmas Day.
SPECIALITIES: Bedding plants, Hardy plants, Pot plants, Shrubs.

SEYMOURS GARDEN & LEISURE CENTRE OF STOKE D'ABERNON 144-9
Stoke Road, Stoke D'Abernon, Cobham, Surrey, KT11 3PU
TEL: 01932 862 530
EMAIL: james@seymours-gardens.com
WEB: www.seymours-gardens.com

Well known centre offering service, value and quality. Plants, aquatics, landscape materials, furniture, house plants, restaurant and cafe terrace.
OPEN: Daily, Mon-Sat, 8.30-5.30. Sun 10.30-4.30, closed Christmas and Easter Sun.
SPECIALITIES: Aquatic plants, Furniture, Herbaceous plants, Pot plants, Shrubs.

WISLEY GARDEN, ROYAL HORTICULTURAL SOCIETY 144-10
Wisley, Woking, Surrey, GU23 6QB
TEL: 01483 224 234
WEB: www.rhs.org.uk
Whatever the season, RHS Garden Wisley demonstrates British gardening at its best with 240 acres of glorious garden.

OPEN: Daily Mon-Fri, 10-6 (or sunset), Sat-Sun 9-6 (or sunset), closed Christmas day. RHS Members only on Sun.
ENTRY COSTS: Adult £5, Children £2, Under 6 years Free, Group rate £4.

KAYTIE FISHER NURSERY 144-12
South End Cottage, Ockham, Surrey
TEL: 01483 282 304

LOWER ROAD NURSERY 144-14
Lower Road, Effingham, Surrey
TEL: 01372 459 841

DOBBE'S NURSERIES 144-15
Guildford Road, Great Bookham, Surrey
TEL: 01372 454 553

POLESDEN LACEY, NATIONAL TRUST 144-17
Dorking, Surrey
TEL: 01372 452 048

CEDAR NURSERY 144-11
Horsley Road, Cobham, Surrey, KT11 3JX
TEL: 01932 862 473
EMAIL: info@landscaping.co.uk
WEB: www.landscaping.co.uk

We grow a wide range of trees, shrubs and perennials. We also source specimen plants from Europe. Other services and products include plant sourcing, plant hire / exhibitions, exclusive Impruneta terracotta and classical garden structures.
OPEN: Mon-Sat, 9-5.30.
SPECIALITIES: Shrubs, Trees, Terracotta pots, Box hedges, Bamboos.

RIPLEY NURSERIES 144-13
Portsmouth Road, Ripley, Woking, Surrey, GU23 6EY
TEL: 01483 225 090
WEB: www.potsofplants.com

The nursery is one mile south of Wisley RHS, set in natural surroundings offering an extensive range of ornamental plants.
OPEN: Daily, closed Christmas and New Year's Day.
SPECIALITIES: Alpines, Bedding plants, Hardy plants, Water plants, Wild flowers.

 ## SQUIRE'S GARDEN CENTRE 144-16
Epsom Road, West Horsley, Leatherhead, Surrey, KT24 6AR
TEL: 01483 282 911
WEB: www.squiresgardencentres.co.uk
An extensive garden centre adjacent to plant nursery for the very freshest stock. Awarded GCA Centre of Excellence.
OPEN: Daily, Mon-Sat 9- 6, Sun 10.30-4.30.
SPECIALITIES: Alpines, Bedding plants, Climbers, Fruit & fruit trees, Garden & conservatory furniture.

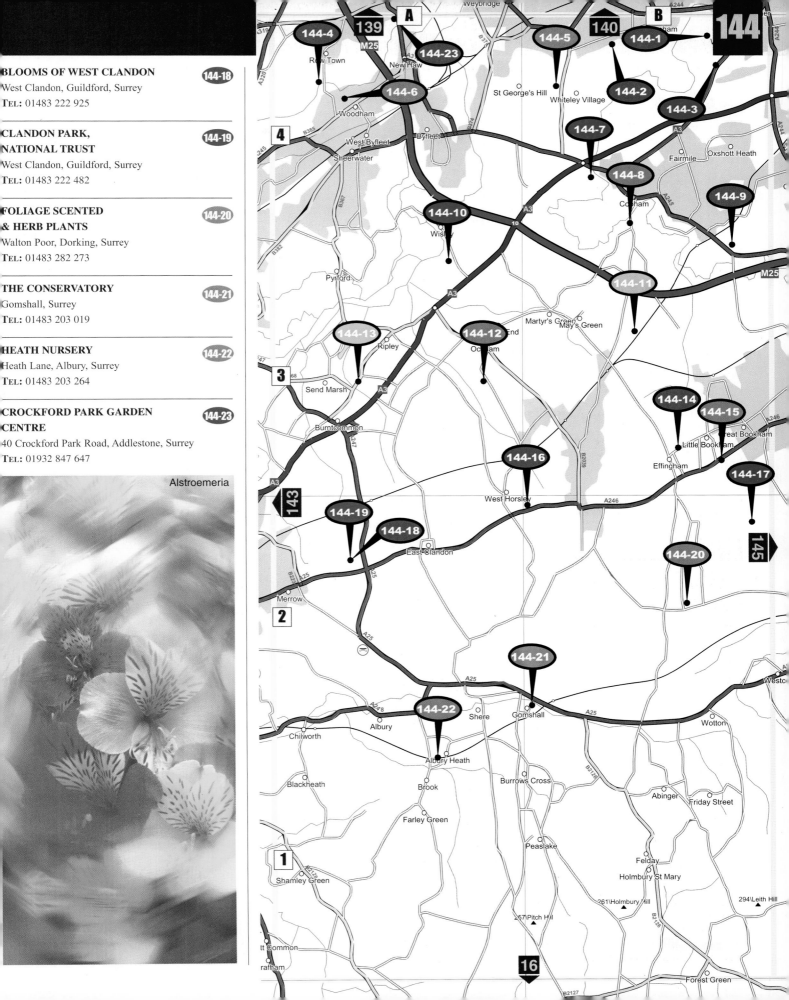

BLOOMS OF WEST CLANDON
144-18

West Clandon, Guildford, Surrey

TEL: 01483 222 925

CLANDON PARK, NATIONAL TRUST
144-19

West Clandon, Guildford, Surrey

TEL: 01483 222 482

FOLIAGE SCENTED & HERB PLANTS
144-20

Walton Poor, Dorking, Surrey

TEL: 01483 282 273

THE CONSERVATORY
144-21

Gomshall, Surrey

TEL: 01483 203 019

HEATH NURSERY
144-22

Heath Lane, Albury, Surrey

TEL: 01483 203 264

CROCKFORD PARK GARDEN CENTRE
144-23

40 Crockford Park Road, Addlestone, Surrey

TEL: 01932 847 647

Alstroemeria

RUSKIN GARDEN CENTRE
9 Ruskin Road, Carshalton, Surrey
TEL: 020 8669 8205

BRIAN HILEY
Telegraph Track, Wallington, Surrey
TEL: 020 8647 9679

WOODCOTE GREEN NURSERIES
Woodmansterne Lane, Wallington, Surrey
TEL: 020 8647 6838

CHESSINGTON GARDEN CENTRE
Leatherhead Road, Chessington, Surrey
TEL: 01372 725 638

FLITTON'S NURSERY & PLANT CENTRE
51 Woodmansterne Lane, Wallington, Surrey
TEL: 020 8647 5615

BARNES NURSERIES
46 Woodmansterne Lane, Wallington, Surrey
TEL: 020 8647 8213

MELBOURNE NURSERY
43 Woodmansterne Lane, Wallington, Surrey
TEL: 020 8647 2368

VERNON GERANIUM NURSERY
Cuddington Way, Sutton, Surrey
TEL: 020 8393 7616

WONDER NURSERIES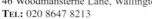
69 Lower Pillory Downs, Little Woodcote,
Carshalton, Surrey, SM5 4DD
TEL: 020 8668 3133

An old established nursery specialising in fuchsias, geraniums, universal pansies and bedding plants. Dogs allowed only on leads.
OPEN: Daily, summer 9-6, winter 9-4 (when clocks change) closed end of Nov till March.
SPECIALITIES: Bedding plants, Hanging baskets.

BEECHCROFT NURSERY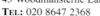
127 Reigate Road, Ewell,
Surrey, KT17 3DE
TEL: 020 8393 4265
EMAIL: sales@aylingsgardencentre.co.uk
A nursery growing a very wide range of conifers, alpines, heathers, perennials and winter bedding.
OPEN: Mon-Sat, 10-4. Closed Sun and Christmas-New Year week.
SPECIALITIES: Alpines, Conifers, Fuchsias, Heathers.

S. G. CLARKE MARKET GARDEN & NURSERY
23 Croydon Lane, Banstead,
Surrey, SM7 3BE
TEL: 020 8643 3836
Bedding plants, shrubs, farm shop with fruit, vegetables and flowers. Christmas trees.
OPEN: Farm shop open daily, Jun-Dec, 9-5. Nursery stock Apr-Dec, 9-5.
SPECIALITIES: Bedding plants, Shrubs, Trees, Vegetables.

ROCKHAM NURSERY
139 Reigate Road, Ewell, Surrey
TEL: 020 8394 2186

WILLOUGHBYS NURSERIES
Leatherhead Road, Oxshott, Surrey
TEL: 01372 842 434

A. J. DOBBE AND SONS
Bramley Nurseries, Ashtead, Surrey
TEL: 01372 273 924

MARSDEN GARDEN CENTRE
Pleasure Pit Road, Ashtead, Surrey
TEL: 01372 273 891

FARM LANE NURSERIES
Farm Lane, Ashtead, Surrey
TEL: 01372 274 400

MEARE CLOSE NURSERIES
Tadworth Street, Tadworth, Surrey
TEL: 01737 812 449

RUPERT BOWLBY
Gatton, Reigate, Surrey
TEL: 01737 642 221

BUCKLAND NURSERIES
Buckland, Reigate, Surrey
TEL: 01737 242 990

SQUIRE'S GARDEN CENTRE, HIGH TREES
Main Road, Buckland, Reigate, Surrey, RH2 9RE
TEL: 01737 247 217
WEB: www.squiresgardencentres.co.uk
A long-established garden centre offering friendly, expert advice and carrying a wide range of quality plants and gardening products.
OPEN: Daily, Mon-Sat 9-6, Sun 10.30-4.30.
SPECIALITIES: Bedding plants, Climbers, Roses, Bulbs, Shrubs.

HEATHFIELD NURSERIES
Flanchford Road, Reigate, Surrey
TEL: 01737 247 641

WYEVALE GARDEN CENTRE
Reigate Road, Dorking, Surrey
TEL: 01306 884 845

BLOOMS OF BETCHWORTH
Station Road, Betchworth, Surrey
TEL: 01737 842 099

CLAY LANE NURSERY
The Surrey Fuchsia Centre, Redhill, Surrey
TEL: 01737 823 307

REIGATE GARDEN CENTRE
143 Sandcross Lane, Reigate, Surrey
TEL: 01737 248 188

NUTFIELD NURSERIES
Crabhill Lane, Redhill, Surrey
TEL: 01737 823 277

HILLSIDE HARDY PLANT NURSERY
109 Horley Road, Redhill, Surrey
TEL: 01737 765 645

SUNNYACRES NURSERY
18 Reigate Road, Horley, Surrey
TEL: 01293 785 435

LANGSHOTT MANOR
Langshott, Gatwick, Surrey
TEL: 01293 786 680

ZIEGLERS ORNAMENTAL GARDEN STATUARY LTD
Village Street, Dorking, Surrey
TEL: 01306 631 287

Bearded Iris

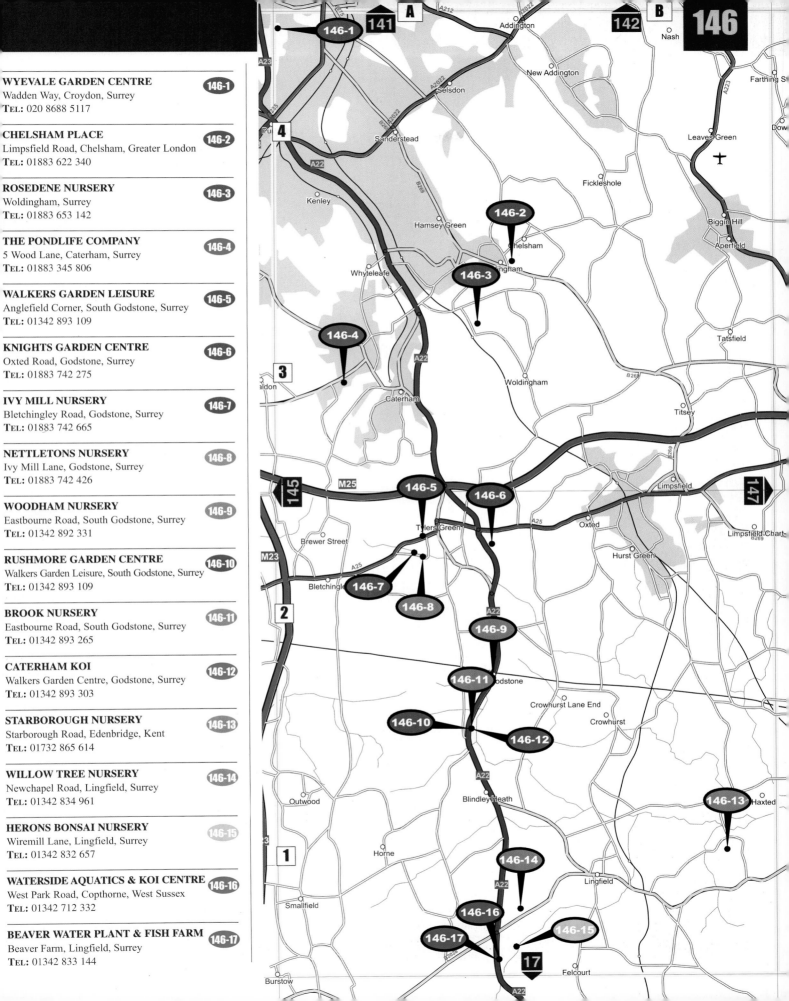

WYEVALE GARDEN CENTRE 146-1
Wadden Way, Croydon, Surrey
TEL: 020 8688 5117

CHELSHAM PLACE 146-2
Limpsfield Road, Chelsham, Greater London
TEL: 01883 622 340

ROSEDENE NURSERY 146-3
Woldingham, Surrey
TEL: 01883 653 142

THE PONDLIFE COMPANY 146-4
5 Wood Lane, Caterham, Surrey
TEL: 01883 345 806

WALKERS GARDEN LEISURE 146-5
Anglefield Corner, South Godstone, Surrey
TEL: 01342 893 109

KNIGHTS GARDEN CENTRE 146-6
Oxted Road, Godstone, Surrey
TEL: 01883 742 275

IVY MILL NURSERY 146-7
Bletchingley Road, Godstone, Surrey
TEL: 01883 742 665

NETTLETONS NURSERY 146-8
Ivy Mill Lane, Godstone, Surrey
TEL: 01883 742 426

WOODHAM NURSERY 146-9
Eastbourne Road, South Godstone, Surrey
TEL: 01342 892 331

RUSHMORE GARDEN CENTRE 146-10
Walkers Garden Leisure, South Godstone, Surrey
TEL: 01342 893 109

BROOK NURSERY 146-11
Eastbourne Road, South Godstone, Surrey
TEL: 01342 893 265

CATERHAM KOI 146-12
Walkers Garden Centre, Godstone, Surrey
TEL: 01342 893 303

STARBOROUGH NURSERY 146-13
Starborough Road, Edenbridge, Kent
TEL: 01732 865 614

WILLOW TREE NURSERY 146-14
Newchapel Road, Lingfield, Surrey
TEL: 01342 834 961

HERONS BONSAI NURSERY 146-15
Wiremill Lane, Lingfield, Surrey
TEL: 01342 832 657

WATERSIDE AQUATICS & KOI CENTRE 146-16
West Park Road, Copthorne, West Sussex
TEL: 01342 712 332

BEAVER WATER PLANT & FISH FARM 146-17
Beaver Farm, Lingfield, Surrey
TEL: 01342 833 144

GLENSIDE GARDEN CENTRE
Brittenden Parade, Orpington, Kent
TEL: 01689 855 557

POLHILL GARDEN CENTRE
London Road, Sevenoaks, Kent
TEL: 01959 534 212

THE NURSERY
Filstone Farm, Sevenoaks, Kent
TEL: 01959 534 362

COOLING'S NURSERIES
Rushmore Hill Nurseries, Sevenoaks, Kent
TEL: 01959 532 269

RANDLES HANGING BASKETS
Randles House, Knockholt, Kent
TEL: 01732 760 050

WYEVALE GARDEN CENTRE
Main Road, Sevenoaks, Kent
TEL: 01959 532 187

RIVER GARDEN NURSERIES
Troutbeck, Sevenoaks, Kent
TEL: 01959 525 588

WESTERHAM HEIGHTS NURSERY
Main Road, Westerham, Kent
TEL: 01959 571 545

SELECT GARDEN & PET CENTRE
Main Road, Sevenoaks, Kent
TEL: 01959 562 400

SQUERRYES COURT
Westerham, Kent
TEL: 01959 562 345

EMMETTS GARDEN, NATIONAL TRUST
Ide Hill, Sevenoaks, Kent
TEL: 01732 750 367

NEWLANDS NURSERY
Goathurst Common, Sevenoaks, Kent
TEL: 01732 750 591

CHARTWELL, NATIONAL TRUST
Westerham, Kent
TEL: 01732 866 368 / 01732 868 381

FRENCH STREET NURSERIES
Hosey Common Lane, Westerham, Kent
TEL: 01959 563 366

HEVER CASTLE & GARDENS 147-16
Edenbridge, Kent, TN8 7NG
TEL: 01732 865 224
EMAIL: mail@hevercastle.co.uk,
WEB: www.hevercastle.co.uk
13th century castle, childhood home of Anne Boleyn. Award winning gardens. Italian, Tudor, Rose gardens, Yew and water mazes, 110 metre herbaceous border, 35 acre lake.
OPEN: Daily 1 Mar-30 Nov, 11-5.
ENTRY COSTS: Castle & Gardens; Adult £8, Children (5-14) £4.40, Family (2 ad/2 child) £20.40, OAPs £6.80. Gardens only; Adult £6.30, Children (5-14) £4.20, Family £16.80, OAPs £5.40.
SPECIALITIES: Herbaceous plants, Maze, Ornaments, Rhododendrons and azaleas, Roses.

RING LODGE NURSERY
Main Road, Edenbridge, Kent
TEL: 01732 862 930

PENSHURST PLACE AND GARDENS 147-18
Penshurst, Tonbridge, Kent, TN11 8DG
TEL: 01892 870 307
EMAIL: enquiries@penshurstplace.com
WEB: www.penshurstplace.com

The gardens at Penshurst Place offer an abundance of variety in form, foliage and bloom throughout the year. From spring flowering bulbs, through fragrant summer roses and exuberant herbaceous borders to mellow orchard fruits. The garden ends in a vivid blaze of autumnal colour before winter starkness reveals its original shape and structure. There is also a woodland trail and a toy museum.
OPEN: 3 Mar-1 Apr, Sat & Sun. 1 Apr-31 Oct: daily. Grounds: 10:30-6, house: 12-5.
ENTRY COSTS: Adult £6 /£4.50, Children £4 /£3.50, Family £16/£13, OAPs £5.50/£4, Groups for House & Garden: £5.30. Garden season ticket: £25.
SPECIALITIES: Fruit & fruit trees, Herbaceous plants, Roses, Bulbs, Trees.

CHIDDINGSTONE CASTLE
Chiddingstone, Edenbridge, Kent
TEL: 01892 870 347

ROGER PLATTS GARDEN DESIGN & NURSERIES 147-19
Stick Hill, Edenbridge, Kent, TN8 5NH
TEL: 01732 863 318
EMAIL: plattsgdn@aol.com

Traditional nursery with emphasis on garden design. Interesting range of plants available, including a wide variety of hardy perennials.
OPEN: Daily, 9-5, closed Christmas & Boxing Day.
SPECIALITIES: Garden design & landscaping, Perennials, Roses, Shrubs, Trees.

Ranunculus

LARGE GARDEN

B & Q, Sainsbury Homebase, Great Mills, Focus-Do-It-All – they're now all part of our every day lives. You can buy garden furniture, plants and pesticides from all of them, but they also sell household goods and many other items. So whilst all of these stores are visited by many garden enthusiasts, they are available on most corners, and therefore our mapping will not be as essential as for the more specialist outlet. Below is a list, sorted by town, with the phone number should you need to call before visiting.

B&Q

Abingdon	01235 550 022
Airdrie	01236 433 357
Alfreton	01773 540 840
Altrincham	0161 928 4222
Ashford	01233 636 931
Aylesbury	01296 338 753
Aylesford	01732 870 470
Ayr	01292 886 644
Banbury	01295 273 372
Bangor	01248 370 258
Barnsley	01226 292 939
Barnstaple	01271 379 040
Barrow in Furness	01229 834 023
Basildon	01268 534 884
Bexhill-on-sea	01424 730 977
Birmingham	0121 789 7227
Bishop Auckland	01388 662 120
Bishopbriggs	0141 762 4556
Blackburn	01254 543 28
Blackburn	01253 798 111
Bognor Regis	01243 867 111
Bolton	01204 595 454
Boston	01205 355 877
Bournemouth	01202 534 131
Bournemouth	01202 297 631
Bradford	01274 688 327
Bradford	01274 668 309
Braintree	01376 347 313
Bridge of Don	01224 822 079
Bridgend	01656 768 611
Bridgwater	01278 428 118
Bridlington	01262 400 061
Brierley Hill	01384 572 772
Brighton	01273 679 926
Brislington	0117 977 9254
Bristol	0117 959 0621
Bristol	0117 951 0722
Bristol	01454 311 074
Burton upon Trent	01283 536 957
Bury	0161 764 8844
Bury St Edmunds	01284 706 316
Cambridge	01223 322 639
Cannock	01543 468 839
Cardiff	029 2039 5936
Carlisle	01228 548 814
Carmarthen	01267 238 007
Cheadle Hulme	0161 485 8807
Chelmsford	01245 495 678
Cheltenham	01242 572 525
Chester	01244 372 773
Chesterfield	01246 211 957
Chorley	01257 260 361
Christchurch	01202 473 536
Clacton-on-sea	01255 430 022
Colchester	01206 574 767
Coventry	024 7660 1600
Coventry	024 7665 2000
Crawley	01293 611 651
Crewe	01270 257 824
cricklewood	020 8450 1255
Cumbernauld	01236 724 714
Cwmbran	01633 877 323
Dagenham	020 8595 4116
Darlington	01325 480 812
Dartford	01322 223 878
Derby	01332 574 818
Derby	01332 203 090
Derby	01332 281 479
Dewsbury	01924 457 435
Douglas	01624 677 077
Dover	01304 240 373
Dundee	01382 623 175
Dundee	01382 500 950
Dunfermline	01383 621 058
East Shotton	01244 830 497
Eastbourne	01323 509 466
Eastleigh	023 8061 1219
Eastwood	01773 530 290
Edinburgh	0131 554 1464
Edinburgh	0131 455 7637
Edinburgh	0131 346 1563
Edinburgh	0131 557 1300
Ellesmere	0151 357 1414
Exeter	01392 444 645
Exmouth	01395 224 116
Falkirk	01324 636 152
Fareham	01489 582 855
Galashiels	01896 754 044
Gateshead	0191 488 8144
Gillingham	01634 263 983
Glasgow	0141 954 1565
Glastonbury	01458 835 618
Gloucester	01452 300 744
Gorseinon	01792 897 337
Grantham	01476 591 112
Gravesend	01474 536 534
Greenford	020 8575 7175
Grimsby	01472 267 602
Guildford	01483 304 881
Halifax	01422 348 421
Harlow	01279 453 738
Hartlepool	01429 272 229
Hastings	01424 441 133
Hayes	020 8848 1898
Hemel Hempstead	01442 216 644
Hengoed	01443 815 888
Hereford	01432 357 447
High Wycombe	01494 463 400
Hitchin	01462 455 253
Hogganfield	0141 770 8668
Hull	01482 565 160
Ilford	020 8554 6653
Inverness	01463 234 562
Ipswich	01473 232 823
Irvine	01294 471 909
Keighley	01535 611 057
Kettering	01536 482 431
Killingbeck	0113 249 4554
Kilmarnock	01563 570 222
Kirkcaldy	01592 267 208
Lancaster	01524 388 366
Leatherhead	01372 373 793
Leicester	01455 250 000
Leicester	0116 288 1360
Leigh	01942 608 521
Lincoln	01522 520 515
Liverpool	0151 254 2044
Liverpool	0151 523 0111
Llandudno	01492 878 181
London	020 8503 3576
London	020 8850 4411
London	020 7252 0657
London	020 8365 1699
London	020 8558 4817
London	020 8875 1052
London	020 8761 1236
London	020 8995 8028
London	020 8445 3696
London	020 8879 3322
Loughborough	01509 236 454
Lowestoft	01502 561 814
Luton	01582 728 821
Macclesfield	01625 616 729
Maidstone	01622 672 488
Manchester	0161 257 2839
Manchester	0161 832 2901
Manchester	0161 367 9095
Manchester	0161 865 8435
Manchester	0161 794 8411
Margate	01843 298 833
Merthyr Tydfil	01685 723 231
Milton Keynes	01908 648 511
Mitcham	020 8685 1551
Motherwell	01698 269 124
Mount Vernon	0141 778 8563
Neath	01639 635 001
Nelson	01282 698 008
New Haven	01273 515 818
New Malden	020 8336 0365
Newbury	01635 528 515
Newcastle Upon Tyne	0191 276 6496
Newcastle Upon Tyne	0191 271 3333
Newport	01983 821 281
Newport	01633 213 241
Newton Abbot	01626 369 177
Northallerton	01609 773 161
Northampton	01604 232 926
Northwich	01606 481 54
Nottingham	0115 926 3456
Nottingham	01623 620 171
Nottingham	01623 651 252
Oldham	0161 626 7623
Oxford	01865 749 339
Penrith	01768 890 777
Penzance	01736 330 712
Perth	01738 620 884
Peterborough	01733 561 206
Plymouth	01752 346 462
Pontypridd	01443 480 851
Portsmouth	023 9269 4751
Preston	01772 258 232
Reading	0118 931 2211
Redditch	01527 550 552
Redruth	01209 717 281
Renfrew	0141 885 2040
Rhyl	01745 338 369
Rochdale	01706 350 446
Rochester	01634 712 801
Rotherham	01709 829 081
Rutherglen	0141 647 1945
Salisbury	01722 332 299
Scarborough	01723 500 477
Selly Oak	0121 414 1710
Sheffield	0114 250 7685
Sheffield	0114 233 6330
Shiremoor	0191 251 3513
Shoreham-by-sea	01273 463 423
Shrewsbury	01743 448 696
Sidcup	020 8308 1844
Solihull	0121 733 1212
South Shields	0191 456 6218
Southampton	023 8078 8311
Southampton	023 8058 4724
Southend-on-Sea	01702 619 922
Southport	01704 500 085
St Austell	01726 730 14
St Helens	01744 451 594
Stafford	01785 253 377
Stanmore	020 8204 8181
Stevenage	01438 315 722
Stirling	01786 449 559
Stoke-on-Trent	01782 205 158
Stoke-on-Trent	01782 272 770
Stoke-on-Trent	01782 771 323
Stourbridge	01384 390 676
Sunderland	0191 521 1898
Swansea	01792 580 262
Swansea	01792 701 702
Swindon	01793 616 349
Tamworth	01827 281 888
Taunton	01823 444 429
Telford	01952 290 284
Tonbridge	01732 770 441
Torquay	01803 213 841
Wakefield	01924 377 988
Wallsend	0191 263 3330
Warrington	01925 571 747
Welwyn Garden City	01707 371 543
Wembley	020 8998 9019
West Bromwich	0121 525 1090
Weymouth	01305 778 103
Whitstable	01227 794 663
Widnes	0151 495 1668
Wigan	01942 323 030
Wisbech	01945 463 748
Workington	01900 685 85
Worksop	01909 531 127
Worthing	01903 821 104
Wrexham	01978 362 777
yeading	020 8841 3092
Yeovil	01935 429 147
York	01904 693 030
York	01904 611 000
St Peter Port	01481 713 018
St Helier	01534 636 500

B&Q WAREHOUSE

Aberdeen	01224 326 262
Ashton under Lyme	0161 371 0082
Basingstoke	01256 460 876
Blackpool	01253 594 234
Bristol	0117 960 2126
Bury	0161 763 1012
Canterbury	01227 760 066
Cardiff	029 2073 1200
Coseley	01902 408 783
Croydon	020 8649 9930
Darlington	01325 480 180
Doncaster	01302 787 382
Edinburgh	0131 657 2555
Enfield	020 88366 0366
Exeter	01392 413 506
Farnborough	01252 372 005
Glasgow	0141 621 2244
Glasgow	0141 949 1122
Halesowen	0121 550 9099
Havant	023 9247 6051
Hedge End	01489 799 711
Huddersfield	01484 455 004
Hull	01482 839 183
Leeds	0113 276 1761
Leicester	0116 253 2012
Liverpool	0151 427 4488
London	020 8591 7666
Luton	01582 429 293
Newcastle Upon Tyne	0191 274 3344
Norwich	01603 488 422
Nottingham	0115 986 4818
Oldham	0161 626 1769
Paisley	0141 889 9146
Poole	01202 685 516
Romford	01708 372 200
Slough	01753 571 333
Southampton	023 8074 0877
Stockport	0161 429 7117
Stockton on Tees	01642 670 022
Stratford-upon-Avon	01789 415 446
Sunderland	0191 567 1444
Sutton	020 8643 8933
Wallasey	0151 346 9698
Washington	0191 201 5711
Watford	01923 225 533
Wednesbury	0121 526 5555
West Thurrock	01708 680 331
Winwick	01925 245 522
York	01904 438 441

FOCUS DO IT ALL

Aberdare	01685 884 005
Aberdeen	01224 782 889
Airdrie	01236 765 458
Aldridge	01922 743 565
Alloa	01259 724 612
Andover	01264 338115
Arbroath	01241 870 600
Ashford	01233 503 974
Ashington	01670 852 570
Banbury	01295 275 642
Bangor	01248 370 037
Barnsley	01226 770 627
Bathgate	01506 632 912
Belper	01773 880 108
Benfleet	01268 759 666
Bishop Auckland	01388 608 918
Bishop's Stortford	01279 653 232
Blackburn	01254 573 05
Blackpool	01253 695 936
Blackpool	01253 408 070
Blantyre	01698 712 178
Bodmin	01208 765 00
Bolton	01204 361 414
Borehamwood	020 8207 5277
Bradford	01274 725 175
Bromborough	0151 334 4060
Bromsgrove	01527 575 540
Bulwell	01159 757 796
Burnley	01282 457 511
Burton upon Trent	01283 516 809
Cannock	01543 574 467
Canterbury	01227 780 105
Cardiff	029 2074 7494
Cardiff	029 2049 8780
Cardiff	029 20233 038
Carlisle	01228 511 171
Chester	01244 390 700
Chesterfield	01246 208 551
Clevedon	01275 340 032
Coalville	01530 814 663
Cobridge	01782 287 011
Colchester	01206 767 700
Consett	01207 580 606
Corby	01536 202 555
Cramlington	01670 717 777
Crewe	01270 252 522
Crowborough	01892 665 344
Darlaston	01922 720 730
Derby	01332 292 142
Dewsbury	01924 457 598
Didcot	01235 811 366
Doncaster	01302 768 447
Dudley	01384 242 186
Dunfermline	01383 623 888
Ebbw Vale	01495 304 567
Edinburgh	0131 448 2485
Epsom	01372 748 890
Flint	01352 731 515
Folkestone	01303 277 258
Formby	01704 878 658
Frome	01373 467 658
Gainsborough	01427 811 373
Glenrothes	01592 770 474
Grantham	01476 570 666
Great Yarmouth	01493 442 654
Grimsby	01472 240 169
Guiseley	01943 870 059
Halesowen	0121 550 9980
Halifax	01422 330 170
Hartlepool	01429 233 633
Hereford	01432 355 535
Hertford	01992 501 808
Hinckley	01455 251 089
Ilkeston	01159 443 990
Kettering	01536 410 144
Kettering	01536 412 447
Kidderminster	01562 748 402
Kilmarnock	01563 573 721
King's Lynn	01553 691 169
Leicester	01858 461 481
Lichfield	01543 416 121
Lincoln	01522 567 007
Littlehampton	01903 723 229
Liverpool	0151 486 5455
Liverpool	0151 256 7418
London	020 8208 4588
Loughborough	01509 236 414
Macclesfield	01625 426 610
Malvern	01684 577 911
Manchester	0161 688 6227
Middleton	0161 721 4421
Morecombe	01524 35 023
Newcastle Upon Tyne	0191 213 1633
Newport	01633 222 268
Nottingham	01602 700 588
Nuneaton	024 7634 4560
Oldham	0161 628 5819
Paignton	01803 528 810
Paisley	0141 848 9164
Pembroke Dock	01646 687 246
Penrith	01768 890 840
Peterborough	01733 320 910
Plymouth	01752 337 223
Plympton	01752 337 223
Pontefract	01977 602 323
Pontypridd	01443 843536
Port Talbot	01639 822 295
Rochdale	01706 524 010
Rotherham	01709 780 228
Rugby	01788 541 245
Rustington	01903 787 779
Scunthorpe	01724 849 883
Selby	01757 210 153
Shipley	01274 592 866
Shrewsbury	01743 367 222
South Shields	0191 454 6160
St Albans	01727 836 668
Stafford	01785 223 363
Stamford	01780 482 131
Stirchley	0121 459 8908
Stockport	0161 477 3961
Stoke On Trent	01782 287 011
Stoke-on-Trent	01782 744 045
Straiton	0131 448 2485
Sunderland	0191 567 0717
Swansea	01792 793 318
Swindon	01793 423 241
Tamworth	01827 65 213
Taplow	01628 666 434
Tavistock	01822 616 438
Telford	01952 291 023
Truro	01872 241 935
Tunbridge Wells	01892 510 225
Walsall	01922 720 730
Walton le Dale	01772 203 320
Warwick	01926 401 434
Washington	0191 419 1558
Whitehaven	01946 690 710
Widnes	0151 495 2050
Wigan	01942 824 848
Winnersh	0118 9770 184
Winsford	01606 862 983
Wolverhampton	01902 717 387
Yeovil	01935 432 100
York	01904 692 799

GREAT MILLS

Aberdeen	01224 276 766
Aberystwyth	01970 627 722
Aldershot	01252 334 252
Ashford	01784 256 761
Barnsley	01226 207 635
Barnstaple	01271 379 709
Bedford	01234 217 773
Beverley	01482 860 612
Bracknell	01344 862 343
Bradford	01274 617 028
Bridgwater	01278 426 530
Bristol	0117 977 9348
Bristol	0117 965 3127
Bristol	0117 960 3849
Bromley	020 8460 9969
Burton upon Trent	01283 539 080
Caerphilly	029 2086 7712
Cambridge	01223 362 000
Carmarthen	01267 235 257
Chesham	01494 778 383
Chester	01244 346 206
Chippenham	01249 659 203
Coulby Newham	01642 576 200
Darlington	01325 481 414
Daventry	01327 311 616
Devizes	01380 730 500
Doncaster	01302 730 014
Dumfries	01387 248 623
Edinburgh	0131 316 4553
Evesham	01386 446 684
Exeter	01392 496 633
Fareham	01329 823 133
Gloucester	01452 311 811
Goole	01405 726 600
Gravesend	01474 564 040
Hanley	01782 268 999
Harrogate	01423 524 181
Haverhill	01440 760 200
Horwich	01204 664 600
Huntingdon	01480 434 492
Inverness	01463 711 644
Ipswich	01473 610 823
Kendal	01539 729 977
Kingswinford	01384 401 951
Llanelli	01554 771 121
London	020 8523 1131
London	020 8316 6060
Longbridge	0121 478 1881
Lowestoft	01502 565 155
Macclesfield	01625 427 777
Maldon	01621 840 044
March	01354 661 661
Merthyr Tydfil	01685 723 488
Middlesbrough	01642 440 044
Milton Keynes	01908 282 330
Newark	01636 673 111
Newport	01633 896 236
Northampton	01604 416 002
Nottingham	0115 940 0830
Paisley	0141 848 1331
Paulton	01761 412 594
Peterborough	01733 897 677
Peterhead	01779 474 111
Poole	01202 733 032
Reading	0118 945 1566
Redruth	01209 612 010
Ruislip	020 8845 2372
Rushden	01933 418 558
Saltash	01752 848 069
Sheffield	0114 275 2756
Sheffield	0114 251 4050
Skipton	01756 798 899
Southampton	01489 789 333
Stoke-on-Trent	01782 711 880
Stroud	01453 753 636
Sudbury	01787 880 101
Taunton	01823 259 545
Thetford	01842 751 362

CENTRE GROUPS

Torquay	01803 617 317	Bristol	0117 960 6622	Eastleigh	023 80629 729	Inverness	01463 240 898	Southampton	023 80510 024
Trowbridge	01225 763 944	Broadheath	0161 929 7262	Edinburgh	0131 315 3530	Ipswich	01473 241 687	Southport	01704 500 490
Tunstall	01782 839 031	Broadstairs	01843 866 116	Edinburgh	0131 442 2633	Ipswich	01473 719 155	Newmarket	St Albans	01727 855 487
Twickenham	0208 943 3978	Bromborough	0151 334 0555	Edinburgh	0131 668 3663	Irvine	01294 277 912	Newport	01633 816 682	St Austell	01726 76 373
Uddingston	01698 810 606	Camberley	01276 685 408	Edinburgh	0131 448 2125	Isleworth	020 8847 3687	Newton Abbot	01626 331 959	Staines	01784 463 593
Walsall	01543 377 700	Cambridge	01223 360 888	Elgin	01343 548 641	King's Lynn	01553 769 179	Northampton	01604 407 830	Stevenage	01438 740 256
Walsall	01922 645 590	Cannock	01543 468 174	Enfield	020 8366 1490	Kirkcaldy	01592 641 561	Northampton	01604 755 217	Stockport	0161 480 8984
Warwick	01926 425 415	Canterbury	01227 456 881	Epsom	020 8393 5085	Leamington Spa	01926 330 161	Norwich	01603 628 731	Stockton on Tees	01642 678 822
West Drayton	01895 448 261	Cardiff	029 2048 6604	Exeter	01392 216 099	Leeds	0113 393 0296	Norwich	01603 789 573	Stratford Upon Avon	
Weston-Super-Mare		Cardiff	029 2059 9900	Falkirk	01324 624 953	Leeds	0113 235 0442	Nottingham	0115 941 3800		01789 414 885
	01934 412 326	Carlisle	01228 541 700	Fareham	01329 822 595	Leicester	0116 254 3155	Oldham	0161 628 7009	Sutton Coldfield	0121 313 1343
Witney	01993 778 981	Chaddesden Sidings		Farnborough	01329 822 595	Leighton Buzzard	01525 852 800	Orpington	01689 890 470	Sutton Coldfield	0121 354 7893
Worksop	01909 473 444		01332 280 680	Farnham	01252 717 180	Lincoln	01522 539 096	Oxford	01865 728 952	Sutton In Ashfield	01623 441 777
Yeovil	01935 422 116	Chatham	01634 200 200	Felixstowe	01394 670 192	Liverpool	0151 521 8692	Oxford	01865 749 660	Swansea	01792 473 240
		Cheltenham	01242 261 807	Feltham	020 8893 8361	Liverpool	0151 254 1049	Perth	01738 442 011	Swindon	01793 420 092
SAINSBURY'S HOMEBASE		Chester	01244 378 881	Folkestone	01303 243 566	Livingston	01506 414 666	Peterborough	01733 558 286	Swindon	01793 828 130
Hayes	020 8561 2450	Chesterfield	01246 230 538	Gateshead	0191 482 0077	Llandudno	01492 860 278	Pity Me	01913 832 455	Tamworth	01827 282 191
Abingdon	01235 521 004	Chichester	01243 532 221	Glasgow	0141 772 9899	London	020 7228 7666	Plymouth	01752 222 877	Taunton	01823 444 345
Accrington	01254 872 767	Chippenham	01249 444 748	Glasgow	0141 956 6575	London	020 8697 8511	Poole	01202 762 133	Telford	01952 261 800
Andover	01264 337 796	Christchurch	01202 487 890	Glasgow	0141 649 2120	London	020 8531 8129	Portlethen	01224 782 233	Tiverton	01884 258 693
Ashford	01233 503 051	Clacton-on-sea	01255 221 115	Glenrothes	01592 630 544	London	020 7435 3457	Portsmouth	023 9269 1217	Tonbridge	01732 771 288
Aylesbury	01296 394 495	Colchester	01206 866 644	Gloucester	01452 507 589	London	020 8858 3826	Portsmouth	023 9220 0197	Truro	01872 263 905
Aylesford	01622 715 071	Colchester	01206 563 297	Godalming	01483 414 609	London	020 8800 6673	Preston	01772 252 580	Tunbridge Wells	01892 511 775
Ayr	01292 610 063	Coventry	024 7671 6271	Great Yarmouth	01493 652 137	London	020 7200 7500	Preston	01772 720 828	Tunbridge Wells	01892 546 566
Barnstaple	01271 323 087	Coventry	024 7660 2120	Greenock	01475 783 132	London	020 7603 6397	Rayleigh	01268 745 555	Upton	0151 604 1277
Barrow in Furness		Crawley	01293 534 040	Grimsby	01472 355 966	London	020 8856 9122	Reading	01189 323 110	Wakefield	01924 367 367
	01229 813 303	Crayford	01322 556 658	Guildford	01483 538 735	London	020 8543 0026	Reading	01189 571 331	Waltham Cross	01992 629 276
Basildon	01268 534 921	Croydon	020 8667 1088	Hamilton	01698 426 336	London	020 8203 9312	Redditch	01527 637 88	Walton on Thames	
Basildon	01268 550 656	Croydon	020 8689 5503	Harlow	01279 451 144	London	020 8361 1235	Reigate	01737 247 661		01932 254 429
Basingstoke	01256 355 658	Cwmbran	01633 872 637	Harlow	01279 431 885	London	020 8343 9790	Richmond	020 8392 9979	Warley	0121 544 9088
Bath	01225 339 225	Dagenham	020 8517 0838	Harrow	020 8424 2130	London	020 8778 0950	Rochdale	01706 860 656	Warrington	01925 231 088
Bedford	01234 340 014	Darlington	01325 359 426	Hatfield	01707 269 025	London	020 8679 8284	Rochford	01702 549 525	Washington	0191 415 5722
Bedworth	024 7664 3231	Dartford	01322 277 126	Havant	023 92492 739	London	020 8527 4355	Romford	01708 730 131	Watford	01923 247 565
Berwick upon Tweed		Daybrook	0115 967 9713	Hemel Hempstead		London	020 8875 1426	Rotherham	01709 780 400	Wellingborough	01933 441 212
	01289 330 939	Derby	01332 291 102		01442 258 490	London	020 8451 5666	Rugby	01788 551 967	Weston-Super-Mare	
Bicester	01869 320 265	Doncaster	01302 325 806	Hemel Hempstead		London	020 8944 1044	Salisbury	01722 422 050		01934 515 817
Biggleswade	01767 312 870	Dover	01304 826 537		01442 212 596	Loughborough	01509 237 622	Scunthorpe	01724 848 396	Wigan	01942 230 345
Birmingham	0121 443 3513	Droitwich	01905 795 553	Hereford	01432 278 906	Luton	01582 491 165	Sevenoaks	01732 455 928	Winchester	01962 840 054
Birmingham	0121 414 1144	Dumbarton	01389 734 071	Herne Bay	01227 740 221	Maidstone	01622 761 542	Sheffield	0114 255 4634	Wishaw	01698 359 191
Bishop's Stortford	01279 657 627	Dumfries	01387 257 188	Hessle	01482 506 055	Manchester	0161 872 4074	Sheffield	0114 261 9150	Woking	01483 799 525
Blackpool	01253 341 274	Dundee	01382 828 681	High Wycombe	01494 465 016	Milton Keynes	01908 609 069	Shoreham By Sea		Worcester	01905 763 021
Bolton	01204 364 825	Dunfermline	01383 620 920	High Wycombe	01628 810 333	New Malden	020 8336 0202		01273 871 403	Worcester	01905 755 551
Boston	01205 357 337	Dunstable	01582 472 028	Horsham	01403 217 653	New Malden	020 8336 0202	Shrewsbury	01743 464 016	Worcester	01905 429 426
Bracknell	01344 483 868	East Dereham	01362 691 032	Hove	01273 729 637	Newbury	01635 529 102	Sleaford	01529 414 475	Yealdon	0113 239 1313
Bradford	01274 614 712	East Grinstead	01342 302 087	Huddersfield	01484 451 693	Newcastle Under Lyme		Slough	01753 511 120	York	01904 690 997
Bridge of Don	01224 703 884	East Kilbride	01355 245 330	Huntingdon	01480 411 327		01782 711 277	Solihull	0121 733 8690	York	01904 643 803
Bridgend	01656 648 548	Eastbourne	01323 431 012	Ilford	020 8503 8284	Newcastle Under Lyme		South Ruislip	020 8841 6730		
							01782 617 755	Southampton	01489 789 709		

ASSOCIATIONS, CLUBS AND SOCIETIES

We have assembled the web sites of a number of the groups and societies with whom we have come into contact. It is by no means comprehensive, but we hope over time to make it so, so please let us know of any gardening association, club or society that may be of interest to others.

African Violet Society of America	www.avsa.org
Alpine Garden Society	www.alpinegardensociety.org
American Bamboo Society	www.bamboo.org/abs
American Horticultural Society	www.aha.org
American Rose Society	www.ars.org
Bonsai Club International	www.bonsai-bci.com
Botanical Society of Scotland	www.rbge.org.uk
British and European Geranium Society	www.fitzjohn.linkuk.co.uk/
British Association of Landscape Industries	www.bali.co.uk
British Cactus & Succulent Society	www.cactus-mall.com/bcss
British Ecological Society	www.demon.co.uk/bes
British Hosta & Hermocallis Society	www.casarocca.com/bhhs/html
British Mycological Society	www.ulst.ac.uk/faculty/sciences/bms
British Pelargonium and Geranium Society	www.homeusers.prestel.co.uk
Butterfly Conservation	www.butterflyconversation.org.uk
Commercial Horticultural Association	www.ukexenet.co.uk/hort/cha/
Cyclamen Society	www.cyclamen.@denney.demon.co.uk
Delphinium Society	www.delphinium.demon.co.uk
Devon Gardens Trust	www.devon-gardens@lineone.net
Flora and Fauna International	www.ffi.org.uk
Flowers and Plants Association	www.flowers.org.uk
Garden Centres Association	www.gca.org.uk
Garden History Society	www.gardenhistorysociety.org
Hardy Orchid Society	www.drover.demon.co.uk/HOS
Heather Society	www.users.zetnet.co.uk/heather
Hebe Society	www.gwynfryn.demon.co.uk/hebesoc/
Henry Doubleday Research Association	www.hdra.org.uk
Herb Society	www.herbsociety.co.uk
Horticultural Research International	www.hri.ac.uk
Horticultural Trades Association	www.martex.net/hta.co.uk
International Plant Propogators Society	www.ipps.org
International Violet Association	www.sweetviolets.com
International Camellia Society	www.med-rz.uni-sb.de/med-fak/physiol2/camellia/home
Linnean Society of London	www.linnean.org.uk
London Historic Parks & Gardens Trust	www.btinternet.com/~gardenstrust/
Museum of Garden History	www.compulink.co.uk/museumgh
National Tree Club of the Arboricultural Association	www.trees.org.uk
Northern Horticultural Society	www.harlowcarr.fsnet.co.uk
Old Lawnsmowers Club	www.artizan.demon.co.uk/olc
Ramblers Association	www.ramblers.org.uk
Royal National Rose Society	www.roses.co.uk/harkness/rnrs.rnrs.htm
Saxifrage Society	www.skydanver.demon.co.uk/saxifrage
Scottish Rhododendron Society	www.hammondsrhodies@compuserve.com
Scottish Rock Garden Club	www.SRGC.org.uk
Society of Floristry	www.dryden.co.uk/society.of.floristry
Surrey Gardens Trust	www.surreyweb.org.uk/surrey-gardens-trust
The Cottage Garden Society	www.alfresco.demon.co.uk/cgs
The Hardy Plant Society	www.hardy-plant.org.uk
The National Council for the Conservation of Plants and Gardens	www.nccpg.org.uk
The National Gardens Scheme	www.ngs.org.uk
The Nerine and Amaryllid Society	www.nerine-amaryllid.demon.co.uk
Welsh Historic Gardens Trust	www.gardenofwales.org.uk/historic/

GARDENERS' ATLAS

Sourcing: We originally contacted more than 5,000 companies sourced from the Yellow Pages Business Database and sent every outlet an entry form and map to identify their precise location. We mailed reminders and duplicate entry forms but there were a few outlets whose completed forms were not returned by the deadline. Where companies did not manage to respond in time, we took informed decisions based upon the company name, source information and postcode, and included them where appropriate.

Locations were mapped using GeoConcept software; the post code provides coordinates which gives accuracy to the nearest 100 metres. We have also called all entries.

Every outlet had the opportunity to be listed in one of three ways; *a company name only, a full listing with box and a full listing with colour photograph.* The latter two listings incurred a charge. For further information please contact the **Gardeners' Atlas** on 01603 633 808 or by emailing info@gardenersatlas.co.uk.

HAVE WE MISSED ANYONE?

To ensure the **Gardeners' Atlas** is as up to date and accurate as possible we would like to hear about anywhere we've missed.

Please copy and complete the form below and send it to:

The Gardeners' Atlas,
Grosvenor House, 112 Prince of Wales Road,
Norwich, Norfolk NR1 1NS
Or email: info@gardenersatlas.co.uk
Or fax us on: 01603 632 808

. . . .

NAME OF LOCATION _____

Garden ☐ Garden centre ☐ Nursery ☐ Water garden specialist ☐

Other (please specify) _____

ADDRESS _____
_____

TOWN _____

COUNTY _____ POSTCODE _____

TELEPHONE NUMBER (if known) _____

Please tick this box if you are the manager or owner of the outlet ☐

MR/MRS/MISS NAME _____

ADDRESS _____
_____

TOWN _____

COUNTY _____ POSTCODE _____

EMAIL _____

INDEX
BY OUTLET NAME

INDEX
BY OUTLET TYPE

GARDEN & NURSERY

NURSERY

GAZETTEER

Avebury 24 C3
Aveley 28 A4
Avening 35 A1
Averham 70 B3
Aveton Gifford 7 A4
Aviemore 125 E3
Avington 25 A3
Avoch 130 C2
Avon 12 B1
Avon Dassett 49 A2
Avonbridge 111 B3
Avonmouth 23 A4
Avonwick 3 D1
Awliscombe 10 A1
Awre 34 D2
Awsworth 69 A2
Axbridge 22 D2
Axford 25 C1
Axford 24 D3
Axminster 10 B1
Axmouth 5 B4
Aycliffe 96 D2
Aydon 101 B1
Aylburton 34 C2
Aylesbeare 4 C4
Aylesbury 37 B3
Aylesby 82 A4
Aylesford 28 B2
Aylmerton 73 A2
Aylsham 73 A1
Aylton 46 B1
Aylworth 35 C3
Aymestrey 45 D3
Aynho 36 D4
Ayot St Lawrence 38 B3
Ayr 104 D2
Aysgarth 90 B3
Ayshford 9 D2
Ayston 59 D2
Aythorpe Roding 40 B3
Ayton 113 D2
Azerley 90 D1
Babbs Green 39 B3
Babcary 11 A3
Babington 23 C1
Babraham 51 C2
Babworth 80 C1
Backaland 13 D1
Backford 66 B4
Backies 134 D2
Backwell 23 A3
Baconsthorpe 73 A1
Bacton 34 A4
Bacton 73 B1
Bacton 52 D3
Bacup 84 B1
Badachro 128 F4
Badbury 24 D4
Badby 49 B3
Badcaul 133 C1
Baddesley Clinton 48 A4
Baddesley Ensor 58 A2
Badger 56 B2
Badgeworth 35 A3
Badgworth 22 D1
Badicaul 123 F4
Badingham 53 B3
Badlesmere 29 C2
Badluachrach 133 C2
Badsey 47 C1
Badsworth 80 A4
Badwell Ash 52 C4
Bagber 11 C2
Bagby 91 A2
Bagillt 75 C1
Baginton 48 B4
Baglan 32 E1
Bagley 66 B1
Bagmore 26 A1
Bagnall 67 C3
Bagot 46 B4
Bagshot 27 A2
Bagstone 23 B4
Bagworth 58 C3
Bagwy Llydiart 34 A4
Baile Mor 114 B3
Bainbridge 90 B3
Bainshole 132 A1
Bainton 60 B3
Bainton 86 D3
Baintown 117 D1
Bakewell 68 B4
Bala 65 C1
Balbeggie 117 B3
Balblair 130 C3
Balchreick 135 A3
Balcombe 17 A4
Baldersby 90 E2
Baldersby St James 90 E2
Balderstone 83 D2
Baldinnie 117 D2
Baldock 51 A1
Baldovie 117 D4
Baldrine 137 D2
Baldslow 19 B2
Bale 72 D1
Baledgarno 117 C3
Balerno 112 A2
Balfield 122 A3
Balfour 13 D16
Balfron 110 B4
Balgonar 111 C4
Balgracie 98 A1
Balgray 117 D4
Balintore 130 D4
Balivanich 13 C10
Balk 91 A2
Balkholme 86 C1
Ballachulish 119 E2
Ballantrae 98 B3
Ballasalla 137 B1
Ballater 126 D1
Ballaugh 137 C3
Ballchraggan 130 C4
Ballevullin 118 A1
Ballidon 68 B3
Ballindean 117 C3
Ballinger Common 37 C2
Ballingham 34 B4
Ballingry 117 B1
Ballinluig 121 A1
Ballintuim 121 B2
Balloch 130 C2
Ballochroy 108 E1
Balls Cross 16 A3
Ballygrant 108 C2
Balmacara 123 F4
Balmaclellan 98 F2
Balmaha 109 E4
Balmalcolm 117 C2
Balmedie 127 D3
Balmore 110 B3
Balmullo 117 D3
Balnaguard 121 A1
Balnain 125 A4
Balquhidder 116 A3
Balsall Common 48 A4
Balscote 49 A1
Balsham 51 D2
Baltersan 98 D1
Baltonsborough 11 A4
Balvicar 114 F2
Balvraid 123 F3
Bamber Bridge 83 C1
Bamber's Green 40 B4
Bamburgh 107 E3
Bamford 79 A1
Bampton 95 B1
Bampton 36 B2
Bampton 9 C3
Banbury 49 A1
Bancffosfelem 32 C3
Banchory 127 B1
Bancycapel 32 C3
Bancyfelin 32 B3
Banff 132 A3
Bangor 64 E4
Bangor-is-y-coed 66 B2
Banham 62 B1
Bank 13 A2
Bankend 99 D1
Bankfoot 117 A4
Bankglen 104 F1
Banks 83 B1
Banningham 73 A1
Bannister Green 40 C3
Banstead 27 D2
Banton 110 C3
Banwell 22 D2
Bapchild 29 B2
Bapton 12 A4
Bar Hill 51 B3
Barbaraville 130 C4
Barbon 89 C2
Barbrook 21 C1
Barby 49 B4
Barcheston 48 A1
Barcombe 17 B2
Barcombe Cross 17 B2
Barden 90 C3
Bardfield Saling 40 C4
Bardney 71 A4
Bardon 58 C3
Bardowie 110 B3
Bardsea 88 D1
Bardsey 85 B3
Bardwell 52 C4
Barewood 45 D2
Barford 62 B3
Barford 48 A3
Barford St John 36 C4
Barford St Martin 12 B4
Barford St Michael 36 C4
Barfrestone 30 B1
Bargoed 33 D2
Barham 50 D4
Barham 30 A1
Barham 53 A2
Barholm 60 B3
Barkby 59 B3
Barkby Thorpe 59 B3
Barkestone-le-Vale 70 B1
Barkham 26 B3
Barking 52 D2
Barking Tye 52 D2
Barkisland 84 D1
Barkston 70 C2
Barkston Ash 85 C2
Barkway 51 B1
Barlaston 67 B2
Barlavington 16 A2
Barlborough 80 A1
Barlestone 58 C3
Barley 51 B1
Barley 84 B2
Barleythorpe 59 C3
Barling 41 B1
Barlings 81 C1
Barlow 79 B1
Barlow 86 B1
Barlow 101 C1
Barmby Moor 86 C3
Barmby on the Marsh 86 B1
Barmouth 54 A4
Barmpton 96 D1
Barmston 87 B4
Barnack 60 A3
Barnard Castle 96 B1
Barnard Gate 36 C3
Barnardiston 52 A2
Barnburgh 80 A3
Barnby 63 C1
Barnby Dun 80 B4
Barnby in the Willows 70 C3
Barnby Moor 80 C2
Barnet 39 A1
Barnetby le Wold 81 C4
Barney 72 C1
Barnham 52 B4
Barnham 15 B1
Barnham Broom 62 B3
Barningham 90 C4
Barningham 52 C4
Barnoldby le Beck 82 A3
Barns Green 16 B3
Barnsley 35 C2
Barnsley 79 B3
Barnstaple 8 E4
Barnston 40 B3
Barnston 75 D1
Barnstone 70 A1
Barnt Green 47 B4
Barnton 77 A1
Barnwell All Saints 60 A1
Barnwell St Andrew 60 A1
Barr 98 C4
Barrapoll 118 A1
Barrasford 101 A2
Barrhead 110 A1
Barrhill 98 C3
Barrington 51 B2
Barrington 10 C3
Barripper 1 C4
Barrmill 109 E1
Barrow 35 A4
Barrow 84 A2
Barrow 59 D4
Barrow 11 C4
Barrow 52 A3
Barrow Burn 107 B1
Barrow Gurney 23 A3
Barrow Haven 87 A1
Barrow upon Soar 59 A4
Barrow-upon-Humber 87 A1
Barrowby 70 C1
Barrowden 59 D2
Barrow-in-Furness 88 C1
Barrowford 84 B2
Barry 117 E4
Barry 22 B3
Barsby 59 B3
Barsham 63 B1
Barston 48 A4
Bartestree 46 A1
Barthol Chapel 127 C4
Bartholomew Green 40 C3
Barthomley 67 A3
Bartley 13 A2
Bartlow 51 D1
Barton 51 B2
Barton 66 B3
Barton 35 C4
Barton 76 A4
Barton 83 C2
Barton 90 D4
Barton Bendish 61 C3
Barton Hartshorn 37 A4
Barton in Fabis 69 B1
Barton in the Beans 58 C3
Barton Mills 52 A4
Barton Seagrave 50 B4
Barton St David 11 A4
Barton Stacey 25 B1
Barton Town 9 A4
Barton Waterside 87 A1
Barton-le-Clay 38 B4
Barton-le-Street 91 C1
Barton-le-Willows 86 B4
Barton-on-the-Heath 36 A4
Barton-upon-Humber 87 A1
Barway 51 D4
Barwell 58 C2
Barwick 8 E2
Barwick 11 A2
Barwick in Elmet 85 C2
Baschurch 55 C4
Bascote 49 A3
Bashall Eaves 83 D3
Basildon 25 C4
Basildon 40 C1
Basingstoke 26 A1
Baslow 79 A1
Bason Bridge 22 C1
Bassenthwaite 94 E2
Bassingbourn 51 B1
Bassingham 70 C3
Bassingthorpe 70 D1
Bassus Green 39 A4
Baston 60 B3
Bastwick 63 B4
Batchworth 38 A1
Batcombe 11 B1
Batcombe 11 B4
Bath 23 C3
Bathampton 23 C3
Bathealton 9 D3
Batheaston 23 C3
Bathford 23 C3
Bathgate 111 B2
Bathley 70 B3
Bathpool 2 F3
Bathway 23 B1
Batley 85 A1
Batsford 48 A1
Battersby 91 B4
Battisford Tye 52 D2
Battle 19 A2
Battle 33 C4
Battlesbridge 41 A1
Battleton 9 C3
Baughton 47 A1
Baughurst 25 C2
Baulking 36 B1
Baumber 82 A1
Baunton 35 B2
Baverstock 12 A4
Bawburgh 62 C3
Bawdeswell 62 B4
Bawdrip 10 B4
Bawdsey 53 B1
Bawtry 80 C2
Baxterley 58 B2
Baycliff 88 D1
Baydon 25 A4
Bayford 39 A2
Bayford 11 C3
Baylham 52 D2
Bayston Hill 55 D3
Bayton 46 B4
Bayworth 36 C2
Beachampton 50 A1
Beachamwell 61 C3
Beacon 10 A1
Beacon's Bottom 37 B1
Beaconsfield 37 C1
Beadlam 91 C2
Beadlow 50 D1
Beadnell 107 E3
Beaford 8 E2
Beal 86 A1
Beal 107 D4
Bealsmill 3 A3
Beaminster 11 A1
Beamish 96 C4
Beamsley 84 D3
Beanacre 24 A3
Beanley 107 D2
Beardon 3 B4
Beare 9 C1
Beare Green 27 C1
Bearley 48 A3
Bearpark 96 C3
Bearsden 110 A2
Bearsted 29 A2
Bearstone 67 A2
Beattock 99 D4
Beauchamp Roding 40 B2
Beaufort 33 D3
Beaulieu 13 A1
Beauly 130 A2
Beaumaris 74 D1
Beaumont 100 A1
Beaumont 42 B4
Beaumont 137 A3
Beausale 48 A4
Beaworthy 8 D1
Bebington 75 D1
Beccles 63 B1
Becconsall 83 B1
Beck Row 52 A4
Beck Side 88 D2
Beckbury 56 B2
Beckering 81 D1
Beckermet 88 B4
Beckfoot 94 D4
Beckford 47 B1
Beckhampton 24 C3
Beckingham 70 C3
Beckingham 81 A2
Beckington 23 C1
Beckley 19 B3
Beckley 36 D3
Beckwithshaw 85 A4
Bedale 90 D3
Bedchester 11 D2
Beddingham 18 A2
Bedfield 53 A3
Bedford 50 C2
Bedham 16 A3
Bedingfield 53 A4
Bedingfield Street 53 A3
Bedlam 85 A4
Bedlam Lane 29 A1
Bedlington 102 A3
Bedlinog 33 C2
Bedmond 38 B2
Bednall 57 A4
Bedrule 106 D2
Bedstone 45 D4
Bedwas 33 D1
Bedwellty 33 D2
Bedworth 58 B1
Beeby 59 B3
Beech 14 B4
Beech 67 B2
Beechingstoke 24 C2
Beedon 25 B4
Beedon Hill 25 B4
Beeford 87 B4
Beeley 68 B4
Beelsby 82 A3
Beenham 25 C3
Beer 5 A4
Beer 10 C4
Beesands 7 B4
Beesby 82 C1
Beeson 7 B4
Beeston 50 D2
Beeston 66 C3
Beeston 62 A4
Beeston 69 B1
Beeston Regis 73 A2
Beeswing 99 C2
Beetham 89 B2
Beetham 10 B2
Beetley 62 A4
Begbroke 36 C3
Begelly 31 E2
Beguildy 45 B4
Beighton 63 B3
Beighton Hill 68 C3
Beith 109 E1
Belaugh 63 A4
Belbroughton 47 A4
Belchalwell 11 C2
Belchalwell Street 11 C2
Belchamp Otten 52 B1
Belchamp St Paul 52 B1
Belchamp Walter 52 B1
Belchford 82 A1
Belford 107 D3
Bell Busk 84 B4
Bell End 47 B4
Bell o' th' Hill 66 C2
Belleau 82 B1
Bellerby 90 C3
Bellingdon 37 C2
Bellingham 101 A3
Bellochantuy 103 D3
Bellows Cross 12 B2
Bells Yew Green 18 B4
Bellshill 110 C1
Bellside 111 A1
Belluton 23 B2
Belmont 77 A4
Belper 68 C2
Belper Lane End 68 C3
Belsay 101 C2
Belses 106 C2
Belsford 3 D1
Belsize 38 A2
Belstead 53 A1
Belstone 3 C4
Beltingham 100 E1
Beltoft 81 A3
Belton 58 C4
Belton 81 A4
Belton 70 C2
Belton 63 C2
Belton 59 C2
Belvoir 70 B1
Bembridge 7 B4
Bempton 92 C1
Benacre 63 C1
Benderloch 115 A4
Benenden 19 B4
Benhall Street 53 C3
Beningbrough 86 A4
Benington 39 A4
Benington 71 C2
Benllech 74 C1
Benniworth 82 A1
Benson 37 A1
Bentley 87 A2
Bentley 26 B1
Bentley 52 D1
Benton 9 A4
Bentpath 100 A3
Bentwichen 9 A4
Bentworth 14 B4
Benvie 117 C4
Benville 11 A1
Benwick 60 D1
Beoley 47 C4
Bepton 15 B3
Berden 40 A4
Bere Alston 3 B2
Bere Ferrers 3 B2
Bere Regis 6 A4
Berea 31 B4
Bergh Apton 63 A2
Berinsfield 36 D1
Berkeley 34 C2
Berkhamsted 38 A2
Berkley 23 C1
Berkswell 48 A4
Bernisdale 128 C2
Berrick Prior 37 A1
Berrick Salome 37 A1
Berrier 95 A2
Berriew 55 A2
Berrington 55 D3
Berrington 46 A3
Berrow 22 C1
Berrynarbor 21 B1
Bersham 66 A2
Berwick 18 A1
Berwick Bassett 24 C3
Berwick Hill 102 A2
Berwick St James 12 B4
Berwick St John 12 A3
Berwick-upon-Tweed 113 E1
Bescaby 70 B1
Besford 47 A1
Bessacarr 80 B3
Bessingby 92 C1
Bessingham 73 A1
Besthorpe 62 B2
Besthorpe 70 B4
Beswick 87 A3
Betchworth 27 D1
Bethel 64 D4
Bethel 64 C4
Bethersden 20 A4
Bethesda 64 E4
Bethesda 31 E3
Bethlehem 32 E4
Betley 67 A2
Betteshanger 30 B1
Bettiscombe 10 C1
Bettisfield 66 B1
Bettws 33 E1
Bettws Bledrws 44 B2
Bettws Cedewain 55 A2
Bettws Evan 43 D2
Bettws-Newydd 34 A2
Bettyhill 135 F4
Betws 21 E4
Betws Gwerfil Goch 65 D2
Betws-y-coed 65 B3
Betws-yn-Rhos 75 A1
Beulah 43 D2
Beulah 44 E2
Bevercotes 80 C1
Beverley 87 A2
Beverstone 35 A1
Bewcastle 100 C2
Bewdley 46 C4
Bewerley 90 C1
Bewholme 87 B3
Bexhill 19 A2
Beyton 52 C3
Bibury 35 C2
Bicester 36 D4
Bickenhill 58 A1
Bicker 71 B2
Bickerstaffe 76 A3
Bickerton 85 C3
Bickford 56 C3
Bickington 4 A3
Bickleigh 9 C2
Bickleigh 3 B2
Bickley 92 A3
Bickley Moss 66 C2
Bicknacre 41 A2
Bicknoller 9 D4
Bicknor 29 A2
Bicton 55 C4
Bicton 55 B1
Biddenden 19 B4
Biddenham 50 C2
Biddestone 24 A3
Biddisham 22 D2
Biddlesden 49 C1
Biddulph 67 B3
Biddulph Moor 67 B3
Bidford-on-Avon 47 C2
Bideford 8 D3
Bielby 86 C3
Bierley 7 A3
Bierton 37 B3
Bigbury 7 A4
Bigbury-on-Sea 7 B4
Bigby 81 C4
Biggar 105 D4
Biggin 68 B2
Biggin 68 A3
Biggin 86 A2
Biggin Hill 27 E2
Biggleswade 50 D1
Bighton 14 A4
Biglands 94 F4
Bignor 16 A2
Bigrigg 94 C1
Bilbrook 9 D4
Bilbrough 86 A3
Bilbster 136 E3
Bildershaw 96 C2
Bildeston 52 C2
Billericay 40 C1
Billesdon 59 B2
Billesley 47 C2
Billingborough 71 A1
Billinge 76 B3
Billingford 62 B4
Billingford 53 A4
Billingham 97 A2
Billinghay 71 A3
Billingley 80 A3
Billingshurst 16 B3
Billingsley 56 B1
Billington 37 C4
Billington 84 A2
Billockby 63 B3
Billy Row 96 C3
Bilsborrow 83 C2
Bilsby 82 C1
Bilsham 16 A1
Bilsington 20 B4
Bilsthorpe 70 A4
Bilton 85 C3
Binbrook 82 A2
Binfield Heath 26 B4
Bingfield 101 B2
Bingham 70 A2
Bingham's Melcombe 11 C1
Bingley 84 D2
Binham 72 C2
Binley 25 B2
Binstead 15 A4
Binton 47 C2
Bintree 62 B4
Birch 41 B3
Birch Cross 68 A1
Birch Green 41 B3
Birch Green 47 A2
Birch Vale 78 B2
Birch Wood 10 B2
Bircham Newton 72 A1
Birchanger 40 A4
Bircher 46 A3
Birchgrove 17 B4
Birchgrove 32 E1
Birchley Heath 58 B2
Birchover 68 B4
Bircotes 80 C2
Birdbrook 52 A1
Birdforth 91 A1
Birdham 15 A1
Birdingbury 49 A4
Birdlip 35 A3
Birds Edge 79 A4
Birds Green 40 B2
Birdsall 91 D1
Birdsgreen 56 B1
Birdsmoorgate 10 C1
Birgham 107 A4
Birkby 90 E4
Birkenhead 75 D2
Birkenshaw 85 A1
Birkhill 117 D4
Birkin 86 A1
Birley 45 D2
Birling 28 B2
Birlingham 47 B1
Birmingham 57 B1
Birnam 117 A4
Birness 127 D4
Birstall 59 A3
Birstwith 85 A4
Birtley 45 D4
Birtley 101 A2
Birtley 96 C4
Birts Street 46 C1
Biscathorpe 82 A2
Bish Mill 9 A3
Bisham 26 B4
Bishampton 47 B2
Bishop Auckland 96 C2
Bishop Burton 87 A2
Bishop Middleham 96 D2
Bishop Monkton 90 E1
Bishop Norton 81 C2
Bishop Sutton 23 B2
Bishop Thornton 85 A4
Bishop Wilton 86 C4
Bishop's Castle 55 B1
Bishop's Caundle 11 C2
Bishop's Cleeve 35 B4
Bishop's Frome 46 B2
Bishop's Green 40 B3
Bishop's Itchington 48 B3
Bishop's Norton 35 A4
Bishop's Nympton 9 A3
Bishop's Offley 67 A1
Bishop's Stortford 40 A3
Bishop's Sutton 14 A4
Bishop's Tachbrook 48 B3
Bishop's Waltham 14 A2
Bishop's Wood 56 C3
Bishopbridge 81 C2
Bishops Cannings 24 B2
Bishops Lydeard 10 A3
Bishopsbourne 30 A1
Bishopsteignton 4 B3
Bishopston 32 D1
Bishopstone 37 B2
Bishopstone 18 A1
Bishopstone 45 D1
Bishopstone 12 B3
Bishopstone 24 D4
Bishopstrow 24 A1
Bishopswood 10 B2
Bishopthorpe 86 A3
Bishopton 96 D1
Bishopton 110 A2
Bishton 22 D4
Bishton 57 A4
Bisley 35 A2
Bisley 27 A2
Bissoe 1 D4
Bisterne 12 B1
Bitchfield 70 D1
Bittadon 21 B1
Bittaford 3 D1
Bitterley 46 A4
Bitteswell 59 A1
Bitton 23 B3
Blaby 59 A2
Black Bourton 36 B2
Black Callerton 102 A2
Black Dog 9 B2
Black Notley 40 C3
Black Torrington 8 D1
Blackawton 4 A1
Blackborough 9 D2
Blackborough End 61 C4
Blackbrook 68 C2
Blackbrook 67 A2
Blackburn 127 C3
Blackburn 111 B2
Blackburn 83 D1
Blackdown 10 C1
Blacker Hill 79 B3
Blackfield 13 B1
Blackford 116 E2
Blackford 22 D1
Blackfordby 58 B4
Blackhall Colliery 97 A3
Blackheath 53 C4
Blackheath 27 B1
Blackhill 132 E1
Blackland 9 B4
Blackmill 21 E4
Blackmoor 15 A4
Blackmoor 23 A2
Blackmoorfoot 78 C4
Blackmore 40 B2
Blackmore End 40 C4
Blackness 111 C3
Blacknest 26 B1
Blacko 84 B3
Blackpool 7 B4
Blackpool 83 A2
Blackridge 111 B2
Blackrod 77 A4
Blackshaw Head 84 C1
Blacksnape 84 A1
Blackstone 17 A2
Blackthorn 37 A3
Blackthorpe 52 C3
Blackwall 68 B3
Blackwater 1 D4
Blackwater 10 B2
Blackwaterfoot 103 F3
Blackwell 95 A4
Blackwell 68 A4
Blackwell 69 A3
Blackwell 48 A1
Blackwell 47 B4

Blackwood	33	D1
Blackwood	105	B4
Bladnoch	93	D4
Bladon	36	C3
Blaen-y-Coed	32	B4
Blaen-y-cwm	33	D3
Blaen-y-cwm	33	B1
Blaenannerch	43	D2
Blaenau Ffestiniog	65	A2
Blaenavon	33	E2
Blaenffos	43	C1
Blaengarw	33	B1
Blaengwrach	33	A2
Blaengwynfi	33	B1
Blaenpennal	44	B3
Blaenplwyf	44	B4
Blaenporth	43	D2
Blaenwaun	32	A4
Blagdon	23	A2
Blagdon Hill	10	A2
Blaich	119	D4
Blaina	33	D2
Blairingone	116	E1
Blairgowrie	121	C1
Blairlogie	116	D1
Blairmore	109	C3
Blair Atholl	120	E3
Blaisdon	34	D3
Blakedown	47	A4
Blakemere	45	D1
Blakeney	34	C2
Blakeney	72	D2
Blakenhall	67	A2
Blakesley	49	C2
Blanchland	96	A4
Bland Hill	85	A4
Blandford Forum	11	D1
Blandford St Mary	11	D1
Blanefield	110	B3
Blankney	70	D3
Blantyre	110	C1
Blaston	59	C2
Blatherwycke	60	A2
Blawith	88	D3
Blaxhall	53	C3
Blaxton	80	C3
Blaydon	102	A1
Bleadon	22	C2
Blean	30	A3
Bleasby	70	A3
Bleasdale	83	C3
Bleddfa	45	B4
Bledington	36	A4
Bledlow	37	B2
Blencarn	95	C2
Blencogo	94	E4
Blendworth	14	B2
Blennerhasset	94	E3
Bletchingdon	36	D3
Bletchingley	27	E1
Bletchley	37	C4
Bletchley	66	D1
Bletherston	31	D3
Bletsoe	50	C3
Blewbury	25	C4
Blickling	73	A1
Blidworth	69	B3
Blidworth Bottoms	69	B3
Blindcrake	94	E3
Blindley Heath	27	E1
Blisland	2	E3
Bliss Gate	46	C4
Blissford	12	C2
Blisworth	49	C2
Blithbury	57	B4
Blo Norton	52	D4
Blockley	48	A1
Blofield	63	A3
Blore	67	A1
Blore	68	A3
Bloxham	49	A1
Bloxholm	70	D3
Bloxworth	6	A4
Blubberhouses	85	A4
Blue Anchor	22	A1
Blue Bell Hill	28	B2
Blundeston	63	C2
Blunham	50	D2
Blunsdon St Andrew	35	C1
Bluntington	47	A4
Bluntisham	51	B4
Blyborough	81	B2
Blyford	53	C4
Blymhill	56	B3
Blyth	80	C2
Blyth	102	B3
Blyth Bridge	105	E4
Blythburgh	53	C4
Blyton	81	B2
Bo'ness	111	B3
Boarhills	117	E2
Boarhunt	14	A2
Boarstall	37	A3
Boat of Garten	125	E3
Boath	130	B4
Bobbing	29	A3
Bobbington	56	B1
Boddam	132	E1
Boddington	35	A4
Bodedern	74	B1
Bodelwyddan	75	B1
Bodenham	46	A2
Bodenham	12	C3
Bodenham Moor	46	A2
Bodewryd	74	B2
Bodfari	65	D4
Bodffordd	74	C1
Bodfuan	64	C2
Bodham	73	A2
Bodicote	49	A1
Bodinnick	2	E1
Bodmin	2	D2
Bodsham Green	29	C1
Bogbrae	132	D1
Bognor Regis	15	B1
Bogue	98	F3
Bohortha	1	E3
Bolam	96	C2
Bolberry	7	A4
Boldre	13	A1
Boldron	96	A1
Bole	81	A2
Bolehill	68	C3
Bolham	9	C2
Bolham Water	10	A2
Bolingey	2	B1
Bollington	78	B1
Bolney	17	A3
Bolnhurst	50	D3
Bolsover	69	A4
Bolsterstone	79	A3
Boltby	91	A2
Bolton	95	C2
Bolton	113	A2
Bolton	86	C3
Bolton	107	D1
Bolton	77	B4
Bolton Abbey	84	D4
Bolton le Sands	89	B1
Bolton Low Houses	94	F3
Bolton Percy	86	A2
Boltonfellend	100	C2
Boltongate	94	E3
Bolventor	2	E3
Bonar Bridge	134	B1
Bonby	81	C4
Boncath	43	D1
Bonchester Bridge	106	D1
Bondleigh	8	E1
Bonds	83	C3
Boningale	56	C2
Bonkle	111	A1
Bonnington	20	B4
Bonnyrigg	112	B2
Bonnyton	117	C4
Bonsall	68	C3
Bont-Dolgadfan	54	C2
Bontnewydd	44	B3
Bontnewydd	64	D3
Bontuchel	65	D3
Bonvilston	22	A3
Boode	8	D4
Boohay	4	B1
Booley	55	D4
Boosbeck	97	C1
Boose's Green	41	A4
Boot	88	C4
Booth	86	B1
Boothby Graffoe	70	D3
Boothby Pagnell	70	D1
Boothstown	77	B3
Bootle	88	B3
Bootle	75	D3
Boraston	46	B4
Bordeaux	137	B4
Borden	29	A2
Bordon	15	A4
Boreham	40	C2
Boreham	24	A1
Boreham Street	19	A2
Borehamwood	38	B1
Boreland	99	E3
Borgh	13	B6
Borgue	93	F4
Borley	52	B1
Borness	93	F4
Boroughbridge	91	A1
Borough Green	28	A2
Borrowash	69	A1
Borrowby	91	A3
Borrowstoun	111	B3
Borth	54	A1
Borth-y-Gest	64	E1
Borve	128	C2
Borve	13	B6
Borwick	89	B1
Bosbury	46	B1
Boscastle	2	E4
Boscombe	12	C4
Bosham	15	A1
Bosherston	31	D1
Bosley	67	B4
Bosoughan	2	C2
Bossall	86	B4
Bossiney	2	D4
Bossingham	30	A1
Bossington	21	E1
Bostock Green	66	D4
Boston	71	C2
Boston Spa	85	C3
Boswinger	1	F4
Botany Bay	39	A2
Botesdale	52	D4
Bothal	102	A3
Bothampstead	25	C4
Bothamsall	80	C1
Bothel	94	E3
Bothwell	110	C1
Botley	38	A2
Botley	14	A2
Botolph Claydon	37	A4
Botolphs	16	B2
Bottesford	70	B2
Bottisham	51	D3
Bottomcraig	117	D3
Bottoms	84	C1
Botusfleming	3	A2
Botwnnog	64	B1
Boughton	50	A3
Boughton	61	C2
Boughton	70	A4
Boughton Aluph	29	C1
Boughton Lees	29	C1
Boughton Street	29	C2
Bouldon	55	D1
Boulmer	107	E1
Bourn	51	B2
Bourne	60	B4
Bourne End	50	B1
Bourne End	38	A2
Bournheath	47	B4
Bournemouth	6	C4
Bourton	11	C4
Bourton	24	D4
Bourton	56	A2
Bourton	24	B3
Bourton-on-the-Water	36	A3
Bousd	118	C2
Bouth	88	D2
Boveridge	12	B2
Bovingdon	38	A2
Bow	9	A1
Bow Brickhill	50	B1
Bow Street	54	A1
Bowburn	96	D3
Bowcombe	6	F4
Bowd	4	C4
Bowden	106	C3
Bowden Hill	24	B3
Bowdon	77	B2
Bower	136	E4
Bower's Row	85	C1
Bowerchalke	12	A3
Bowershall	111	C4
Bowes	96	A1
Bowgreave	83	C3
Bowley	46	A2
Bowlhead Green	15	B4
Bowling	110	A3
Bowmanstead	88	D3
Bowmore	108	B1
Bowness-on-Solway	99	E1
Bowriefauld	122	A1
Bowsden	107	C4
Box	24	A3
Boxford	25	B3
Boxford	52	C1
Boxgrove	15	B2
Boxted	41	B4
Boxted	52	B2
Boxted Cross	41	B4
Boxted Heath	41	B4
Boxworth	51	B3
Boyden Gate	30	A3
Boyndie	132	A3
Boynton	92	C1
Boyton	3	A4
Boyton	53	C2
Boyton	12	A4
Boyton Cross	40	B2
Boyton End	52	A1
Bozeat	50	B3
Brabourne	29	C1
Brabourne Lees	20	B4
Bracadale	128	B1
Braceborough	60	A3
Bracebridge Heath	70	D4
Braceby	70	D1
Bracewell	84	B3
Brackenfield	68	C3
Brackletter	119	E4
Brackley	49	B1
Bracknell	27	A3
Braco	116	D2
Bracon Ash	62	C2
Bradbourne	68	B3
Bradbury	96	D2
Bradden	49	C2
Bradenham	37	B1
Bradenstoke	24	B4
Bradfield	25	C3
Bradfield	9	D2
Bradfield	42	B4
Bradfield	73	B1
Bradfield	79	A2
Bradfield Combust	52	C3
Bradfield Green	66	D3
Bradfield Heath	42	B4
Bradfield St Clare	52	C3
Bradfield St George	52	C3
Bradford	8	C2
Bradford	85	A2
Bradford Abbas	11	B2
Bradford Leigh	24	A2
Bradford Peverell	5	E4
Bradford-on-Avon	24	A2
Bradley	68	B2
Bradley	26	A1
Bradley	82	A3
Bradley	56	C4
Bradley	47	B3
Bradley in the Moors	68	A2
Bradmore	69	B1
Bradninch	9	C1
Bradnop	67	C3
Bradpole	5	D4
Bradshaw	84	D1
Bradstone	3	A3
Bradwall Green	67	A4
Bradwell	79	A1
Bradwell	41	A4
Bradwell Waterside	41	B2
Bradwell-on-Sea	41	B2
Bradworthy	8	C2
Braegrum	117	A3
Braehead	111	B1
Braemar	126	B1
Brafferton	96	D1
Brafferton	91	A1
Bragbury End	39	A3
Braidwood	105	B4
Brailsford	68	B2
Braintree	40	C4
Braiseworth	53	A4
Braishfield	13	A3
Braithwaite	94	E2
Bramcote	58	C1
Bramdean	14	A3
Bramerton	63	A3
Bramfield	39	A3
Bramfield	53	C4
Bramford	53	A2
Bramhall	78	A2
Bramham	85	C3
Bramhope	85	A3
Bramley	26	A2
Bramley	80	A2
Bramley	27	B1
Bramling	30	A2
Brampford Speke	9	C1
Brampton	51	A4
Brampton	95	C2
Brampton	81	A1
Brampton	80	A3
Brampton	63	B1
Brampton	100	C1
Brampton Abbotts	34	C4
Brampton Ash	59	C1
Bramshall	68	A1
Bramshaw	12	C2
Bramshott	15	A4
Bramwell	10	C3
Bran End	40	B4
Branault	118	F3
Brancaster	72	A2
Brancaster Staithe	72	B2
Brancepeth	96	C3
Brandesburton	87	B3
Brandeston	53	B3
Brandiston	62	C4
Brandon	96	C3
Brandon	70	C2
Brandon	61	D1
Brandon	49	A4
Brandon Parva	62	B3
Brandsby	91	B1
Brandy Wharf	81	C3
Bransbury	25	B1
Bransby	81	B1
Branscombe	5	A4
Bransford	46	C2
Bransgore	12	C1
Bransley	46	B4
Branston	70	B1
Branston	70	D4
Branston	58	A4
Branston Booths	70	D4
Brant Broughton	70	C3
Brantham	52	D1
Branthwaite	94	D2
Branthwaite	94	F3
Brantingham	86	D1
Branton	107	D2
Branton	80	C3
Branton Green	85	C4
Branxton	107	B3
Brassington	68	B3
Brasted	27	F2
Bratoft	71	D4
Brattleby	81	B1
Bratton	24	A1
Bratton Clovelly	3	B4
Bratton Fleming	8	E4
Bratton Seymour	11	B3
Braughing	39	B4
Braunston	49	B3
Braunston	59	C3
Braunton	8	D4
Brawby	91	D2
Bray Shop	3	A3
Braybrooke	59	C1
Brayford	9	A4
Braythorn	85	A3
Brayton	86	A2
Breachwood Green	38	B4
Breadsall	68	C2
Breadstone	34	D2
Breage	1	C3
Breamore	12	C2
Brean	22	C2
Brearton	85	B4
Breaston	69	A1
Brechfa	32	C4
Brechin	122	B2
Breckles	62	A2
Brecon	33	C4
Brede	19	B3
Bredenbury	46	B2
Bredfield	53	B2
Bredgar	29	A2
Bredon	47	A1
Bredon's Norton	47	B1
Bredwardine	45	C1
Breighton	86	B2
Breinton	46	A1
Bremhill	24	B3
Brendon	21	C1
Brenfield	109	A3
Brent Eleigh	52	C2
Brent Knoll	22	C1
Brent Mill	3	D1
Brent Pelham	40	A4
Brentingby	59	C4
Brentwood	40	B1
Brenzett	20	A3
Brereton Green	67	A4
Bressingham	62	B1
Bretby	58	B4
Bretford	49	A4
Bretforton	47	C1
Bretherton	83	C1
Brettenham	62	A1
Brettenham	52	C2
Bretton	66	B4
Brewood	56	C3
Briantspuddle	6	A4
Brickendon	39	B2
Bricklehampton	47	B1
Bride	137	D4
Bridekirk	94	D2
Bridestowe	3	B4
Bridford	4	A4
Bridge	1	C4
Bridge	30	A2
Bridge Hewick	90	E1
Bridge of Allan	116	D1
Bridge of Cally	121	C1
Bridge of Canny	127	A1
Bridge of Dee	99	A1
Bridge of Earn	117	B2
Bridge of Orchy	115	D4
Bridge of Weir	109	E2
Bridge Sollers	45	D1
Bridge Street	52	B2
Bridgehampton	11	A3
Bridgend	108	B2
Bridgend	111	C3
Bridgend	21	E4
Bridgend of Lintrathen	121	D2
Bridgerule	8	B1
Bridgetown	9	C4
Bridgnorth	56	B2
Bridgham	62	A1
Bridgwater	10	B4
Bridlington	92	C1
Bridport	5	D4
Bridstow	34	C4
Brierfield	84	B2
Brierley	34	C3
Brierley	80	A4
Brig o'Turk	116	A1
Brigg	81	C4
Briggate	73	B1
Briggswath	92	A4
Brigham	94	D2
Brigham	87	A4
Brighouse	84	D1
Brighstone	6	F3
Brighthampton	36	B2
Brightley	8	E1
Brightling	19	A3
Brightlingsea	42	A3
Brighton	17	B1
Brightons	111	B3
Brightwalton	25	B4
Brightwell	53	B1
Brightwell Baldwin	37	A1
Brightwell Upperton	37	A1
Brightwell-cum-Sotwell	36	D1
Brignall	96	B1
Brigsley	82	A3
Brigsteer	89	B3
Brigstock	59	D1
Brill	37	A3
Brilley	45	C2
Brimfield	46	A3
Brimfield Cross	46	A3
Brimington	80	A1
Brimley	4	A3
Brimpsfield	35	B3
Brimpton	25	C3
Brimscombe	35	A2
Brimstage	75	D1
Brind	86	C2
Brindle	83	D1
Brineton	56	B3
Brington	50	D4
Briningham	72	D1
Brinkhill	82	B1
Brinkley	51	D2
Brinklow	49	A4
Brinkworth	24	B4
Brinscall	83	D1
Brinsley	69	A2
Brinton	72	D1
Brinyan	13	C1
Brisley	62	A4
Brissenden Green	20	A4
Bristol	23	B3
Briston	72	D1
Britford	12	C3
Brithdir	33	D2
Brithdir	54	B4
British Legion Village	28	B2
Briton Ferry	32	E1
Britwell Salome	37	A1
Brixham	4	B1
Brixton	3	C1
Brixton Deverill	11	D4
Brixworth	50	A4
Brize Norton	36	B2
Broad Alley	47	A3
Broad Blunsdon	35	C1
Broad Campden	48	A1
Broad Carr	84	D1
Broad Chalke	12	A3
Broad Green	41	A4
Broad Green	52	B3
Broad Green	46	C2
Broad Haven	31	C3
Broad Hinton	24	C4
Broad Laying	25	B2
Broad Marston	47	C2
Broad Oak	19	B3
Broad Oak	18	B3
Broad Oak	34	B3
Broad Street	19	B2
Broad Street	29	A2
Broad Town	24	C4
Broad's Green	40	C3
Broadbottom	78	B2
Broadbridge	15	A1
Broadclyst	9	C1
Broadford	123	E4
Broadford Bridge	16	B3
Broadhembury	9	D1
Broadhempston	4	A2
Broadland Row	19	B3
Broadmayne	5	F4
Broadmoor	31	E2
Broadoak	10	C1
Broadstone	55	D1
Broadwas	46	C2
Broadway	31	C3
Broadway	10	B2
Broadway	47	C1
Broadwell	36	A4
Broadwell	36	A2
Broadwell	49	A3
Broadwindsor	10	C1
Broadwood Kelly	8	E1
Broadwoodwidger	3	A4
Brockamin	46	C2
Brockbridge	14	A3
Brockhall	49	C3
Brockham	27	C1
Brockhampton	35	B4
Brockhampton	34	C4
Brockholes	78	C4
Brocklesby	81	D4
Brockley	23	A3
Brockley	52	B4
Brockley Green	52	A2
Brockley Green	52	B2
Brockton	55	B3
Brockton	55	B1
Brockton	55	D2
Brockton	67	B1
Brockweir	34	B2
Brockworth	35	A3
Brocton	57	A4
Brodick	104	A3
Brodsworth	80	B4
Brogaig	128	C3
Brokenborough	35	A1
Brokerswood	24	A1
Brome	53	A4
Brome Street	53	A4
Bromeswell	53	B2
Bromfield	94	E4
Bromfield	46	A4
Bromham	50	C2
Bromham	24	B3
Bromley	56	B2
Bromley	27	E3
Brompton	90	E3
Brompton	92	A2
Brompton Ralph	9	D4
Brompton Regis	9	C4
Brompton-on-Swale	90	D4
Bromsberrow	46	C1
Bromsberrow Heath	34	D4
Bromsgrove	47	B4
Bromyard	46	B2
Bronant	44	B3
Brongest	43	E2
Bronington	66	C2
Bronllys	45	B1
Bronwydd	32	B4
Bronygarth	66	A1
Brook	12	C2
Brook	13	A3
Brook	29	C1
Brook Hill	12	C2
Brook Street	40	B1
Brook Street	20	A4
Brooke	63	A2
Brooke	59	C3
Brookhouse Green	67	B4
Brookhouses	78	B2
Brookland	20	A3
Brookmans Park	39	A2
Brookthorpe	35	A3
Brookwood	27	A2
Broom	50	D1
Broom	47	C2
Broom Hill	80	A3
Broom Hill	47	A4
Broome	63	A2
Broome	55	C1
Broome	47	A4
Broomedge	77	B2
Broomfield	10	A4
Broomfleet	86	D1
Broomhaugh	101	B1
Broomhill	102	A4
Brora	134	E3
Broseley	56	A2
Brotherlee	95	E3
Brotherton	85	C1
Brotton	97	C1
Brough	86	D1
Brough	70	B3
Brough	95	D1
Brough Sowerby	95	D1
Broughton	105	D3
Broughton	50	B1
Broughton	51	A4
Broughton	66	A4
Broughton	13	A4
Broughton	83	C2
Broughton	81	B4
Broughton	84	C3
Broughton	91	D1
Broughton	50	A4
Broughton	49	A1
Broughton	67	A1
Broughton	21	E3
Broughton Astley	59	A2
Broughton Green	47	B3
Broughton Hackett	47	A2
Broughton Mills	88	C3
Broughton Poggs	36	A2
Broughton-in-Furness	88	C2
Brown Candover	14	A4
Brown Edge	67	B3
Brownhills	117	E2
Brownhills	57	B3
Browninghill Green	25	C2
Brownsham	8	B3
Brownston	3	D1
Broxa	92	A3
Broxburn	113	B3
Broxburn	111	C3
Broxted	40	B4
Broxwood	45	D2
Bruichladdich	108	A2
Bruisyard	53	B3
Bruisyard Street	53	B3
Brund	68	A4
Brundall	63	A3
Brundish	53	B4
Brundish Street	53	B4
Brunthwaite	84	D3
Bruntingthorpe	59	A1
Brunton	117	C3
Brunton	107	E2
Brunton	24	D2
Brushford	9	C3
Brushford Barton	9	A2
Bruton	11	B4
Bryanston	11	D2
Brydekirk	99	E2
Bryn	33	A1
Bryn Gates	77	A3
Bryn Saith Marchog	65	D3
Bryn-coch	32	E2
Bryn-Henllan	43	B1
Bryn-mawr	64	B1
Brynaman	32	E3
Brynberian	43	C1
Bryncir	64	D2
Bryncroes	64	B1
Bryncrug	54	A3
Bryneglwys	65	E2
Brynford	75	C1
Bryngwran	74	B1
Bryngwyn	34	A2
Bryngwyn	45	B2
Brynhoffnant	43	E2
Brynmawr	33	D3
Brynmenyn	21	E4
Brynna	21	E4
Brynsadler	22	A4
Brynsiencyn	64	D4
Bubbenhall	48	B4
Bubwith	86	B2
Buchanty	116	E3
Buchany	116	C1
Buchlyvie	110	B4
Buck's Cross	8	C3
Buck's Mills	8	C3
Buckabank	95	A4
Buckden	50	D3
Buckden	90	B2
Buckenham	63	B3
Buckerell	10	A1
Buckfast	3	D2
Buckfastleigh	3	D2
Buckhaven	117	D1
Buckholt	34	B3
Buckhorn Weston	11	C3
Buckie	131	D3
Buckie	13	C3
Buckingham	49	C1
Buckland	37	C3
Buckland	7	A4
Buckland	47	C1
Buckland	51	B1
Buckland	36	B1
Buckland	27	D1
Buckland Brewer	8	C3
Buckland Dinham	23	C1
Buckland Filleigh	8	D2
Buckland in the Moor	3	D3
Buckland Monachorum	3	B2
Buckland Newton	11	B1
Buckland Ripers	5	E3
Buckland St Mary	10	B2
Buckland-Tout-Saints	7	A4
Bucklebury	25	C3
Bucklerheads	117	D4
Bucklers Hard	13	B1
Bucklesham	53	B1
Buckley	66	A4
Buckminster	59	D4
Bucknall	71	A4
Bucknell	36	D4
Bucknell	45	D4
Bucks Green	16	B4
Buckton	92	C1
Buckton	107	D4
Buckworth	50	D4
Budbrooke	48	A3
Budby	69	B4
Budd's Titson	8	B1
Bude	8	B1
Budge's Shop	3	A1
Budleigh Salterton	4	C3
Budock Water	1	D3
Buerton	66	D2
Bugbrooke	49	C3
Bugle	2	D1
Bugthorpe	86	C4
Buildwas	56	A3
Builth Wells	45	A2
Bulbridge	12	B4
Bulford	24	D1
Bulkeley	66	C3
Bulkington	58	C1

Place	Page	Grid
Crostwick	63	A4
Crouch Hill	11	C2
Croucheston	12	B3
Croughton	36	D4
Crovie	132	B3
Crow Edge	79	A3
Crow Hill	34	C4
Crowan	1	C3
Crowborough	18	A4
Crowcombe	10	A4
Crowdecote	68	A4
Crowell	37	B2
Crowfield	53	A3
Crowhurst	19	A2
Crowhurst	27	E1
Crowland	60	C3
Crowland	52	D4
Crowlas	1	B3
Crowle	81	A4
Crowle	47	A2
Crowle Green	47	A2
Crown Corner	53	B4
Crownthorpe	62	B3
Crows-an-Wra	1	A3
Crowthorne	26	B3
Crowton	76	B1
Croxdale	96	C3
Croxden	68	A2
Croxton	51	A3
Croxton	81	D4
Croxton	72	C1
Croxton	61	D1
Croxton Kerrial	70	B1
Croy	130	D2
Croy	110	C3
Croyde	8	D4
Croydon	51	B2
Croydon	27	E3
Cruckmeole	55	C3
Cruckton	55	C3
Cruden Bay	132	E1
Crudgington	56	A4
Crudwell	35	B1
Crug-y-byddar	55	A1
Crumlin	33	D1
Crumplehorn	2	F1
Crundale	29	C1
Crunwear	31	E3
Crux Easton	25	B2
Crwbin	32	C3
Cryers Hill	37	C1
Crymmych	43	C1
Crynant	33	A2
Cubert	2	B1
Cublington	37	B4
Cublington	45	D1
Cuckfield	17	A3
Cucklington	11	C3
Cuckney	69	B4
Cuddesdon	36	D2
Cuddington	37	B3
Cuddington	66	D4
Cuddington Heath	66	C2
Cudham	27	F2
Cudworth	79	B4
Cudworth	10	C2
Cuffley	39	A2
Culbokie	130	B3
Culcheth	77	A2
Culford	52	B4
Culgaith	95	C2
Culham	36	D1
Culkein Drumbeg	135	A1
Culkerton	35	B1
Cullen	131	E3
Cullingworth	84	D2
Culloden	130	C2
Cullompton	9	D2
Culm Davy	10	A2
Culmington	55	D1
Culmstock	9	D2
Culross	111	B4
Culroy	104	D1
Culsalmond	127	A4
Cultercullen	127	C4
Culverstone Green	28	A2
Culverthorpe	70	D2
Culworth	49	B2
Cumberworth	82	C1
Cuminestown	132	B2
Cummertrees	99	E1
Cummingston	131	B4
Cummingston	13	A4
Cumnock	104	F2
Cumnor	36	C2
Cumrew	95	B4
Cumwhinton	95	A4
Cumwhitton	95	B4
Cundall	91	A1
Cupar Muir	117	D2
Curbar	79	A1
Curbridge	14	A2
Curbridge	36	B2
Curdridge	14	A2
Curdworth	58	A2
Curland	10	B2
Cumbernauld	110	C3
Cupar	117	D2
Curridge	25	B3
Currie	112	A2
Curry Mallet	10	B3
Curry Rivel	10	C3
Curtisden Green	19	A4
Curtisknowle	3	D1
Cury	1	C2
Cushnie	126	E3
Cusop	45	C1
Cutcombe	9	C4
Cutsdean	35	C4
Cutthorpe	79	B1
Cuxton	28	B3
Cuxwold	81	D3
Cwm	75	B1
Cwm Crawnon	33	D3
Cwm Morgan	43	D1
Cwm-cou	43	D1
Cwm-Llinau	54	C3
Cwm-y-glo	32	D3
Cwm-y-glo	64	E4
Cwmafan	33	A1
Cwmaman	33	C2
Cwmbach	32	A4
Cwmbach	45	B1
Cwmbach	33	C2
Cwmbach Llechrhyd	45	A2
Cwmbran	33	E1
Cwmcarn	33	D1
Cwmcarvan	34	B2
Cwmdare	33	B2
Cwmdu	33	D4
Cwmduad	32	B4
Cwmfelin	33	A1
Cwmfelin	33	C2
Cwmfelin Boeth	31	E3
Cwmfelinfach	33	D1
Cwmffrwd	32	B3
Cwmgiedd	33	A3
Cwmgorse	32	E2
Cwmhiraeth	43	E1
Cwmllynfell	32	E3
Cwmpengraig	43	E1
Cwmsychbant	44	A2
Cwmtillery	33	D2
Cwmystwyth	44	D4
Cwrt-newydd	44	A2
Cylibebyll	32	E2
Cymer	33	A1
Cynghordy	44	D1
Cynonville	33	A1
Cynwyd	65	D2
Cynwyl Elfed	32	B4
Dacre	95	A2
Dacre	85	A4
Daddry Shield	95	E3
Dadford	49	C1
Dadlington	58	C2
Daglingworth	35	B2
Dagnall	38	A3
Dailly	98	C4
Dainton	4	A2
Dairsie	117	D2
Dalbeattie	99	B1
Dalby	91	C1
Dalcapon	121	A2
Dalcrue	117	A3
Dalditch	4	C4
Dale	69	A2
Dale	31	B2
Dalgety Bay	112	A3
Dalginross	116	D3
Dalguise	121	A1
Dalhalvaig	136	B3
Dalham	52	A3
Dalkeith	112	B2
Dallas	131	B2
Dallas	13	A2
Dallinghoo	53	B2
Dallington	18	B3
Dalmally	115	C3
Dalmellington	104	E1
Dalmeny	112	A3
Dalry	109	D1
Dalrymple	104	D1
Dalserf	111	A1
Dalston	95	A4
Dalswinton	99	C3
Dalton	99	D2
Dalton	90	C4
Dalton	91	A2
Dalton	101	C2
Dalton Piercy	97	A2
Dalton-in-Furness	88	C1
Dalton-le-Dale	97	A4
Dalton-on-Tees	90	E4
Dalveich	116	B3
Dalwhinnie	120	C4
Damerham	12	B2
Damgate	63	B3
Danbury	41	A2
Danby	91	C4
Danby Wiske	90	E3
Dane Street	29	C2
Danebridge	67	C4
Danehill	17	B3
Daresbury	76	B1
Darfield	80	A3
Dargate	29	C2
Darite	2	F2
Darley	85	A4
Darley Bridge	68	B4
Darley Dale	68	B4
Darley Green	48	A4
Darleyhall	38	B4
Darlingscott	48	A1
Darlington	96	D1
Darowen	54	C2
Darracott	8	B2
Darracott	8	D4
Darras Hall	101	C2
Darrington	85	C1
Darsham	53	C4
Darshill	23	B1
Dartford	27	F3
Dartington	4	A2
Dartmouth	4	A1
Darvel	104	F3
Darwen	83	D1
Datchet	27	B4
Datchworth	39	A3
Dauntsey	24	B4
Dauntsey Green	24	B4
Dava	131	A1
Davenham	66	D4
Daventry	49	B3
Davidstow	2	E4
Davington	100	A4
Daviot	127	B4
Daviot	130	C1
Dawesgreen	27	D1
Dawlish	4	B3
Dawlish Warren	4	B3
Dawn	74	F1
Daylesford	36	A4
Deal	30	C1
Dean	94	D2
Dean	21	C1
Dean	3	D2
Dean	13	B4
Dean	14	A3
Dean	36	B4
Dean Bottom	28	A3
Dean Prior	3	D2
Deanburnhaugh	106	B1
Deancombe	3	D2
Deane	25	C1
Deanhead	78	C4
Deanland	12	A3
Deanraw	101	A1
Deanscales	94	D2
Deanshanger	50	A1
Dearham	94	D3
Debach	53	B2
Debden	40	B4
Debenham	53	A3
Deblin's Green	47	A2
Deddington	36	C4
Dedham	42	A4
Deene	59	D2
Deenethorpe	59	D2
Deeping St Nicholas	60	C4
Deerhurst	35	A4
Defford	47	A1
Defynnog	33	B4
Deganwy	74	F1
Deighton	90	E4
Deighton	86	B3
Deiniolen	64	E4
Delabole	2	D4
Delamere	66	C4
Dell Quay	15	A1
Dembleby	70	D2
Den of Lindores	117	C2
Denaby	80	A3
Denbigh	65	D4
Denbury	4	A2
Denby	69	A2
Denby Dale	79	A4
Denchworth	36	B1
Denford	50	C4
Dengie	41	B2
Denham	27	B4
Denham	52	A3
Denham	53	A4
Denham Green	38	A1
Denholm	106	C2
Denholme	84	D2
Denmead	14	B2
Dennington	53	B3
Denny	111	A3
Dennyloanhead	111	A3
Densole	30	A1
Denston	52	A2
Denstone	68	A2
Denstroude	29	C2
Dent	89	D2
Denton	60	B1
Denton	78	A2
Denton	30	A1
Denton	70	C1
Denton	84	D3
Denton	50	A3
Denton	63	A1
Denver	61	B2
Denwick	107	E1
Deopham	62	B2
Deopham Green	62	B2
Deptford	12	A4
Derby	68	C1
Derbyhaven	137	B1
Dereham	62	A3
Deri	33	D2
Derringstone	30	A1
Derrington	56	C4
Derry Hill	24	B3
Dersingham	72	A1
Dervaig	118	E1
Derwen	65	D3
Derwenlas	54	B2
Desborough	59	C1
Desford	58	C3
Deskford	131	E3
Detling	29	A2
Devauden	34	B1
Devizes	24	B2
Devonside	116	E1
Devoran	1	D4
Dewlish	11	C1
Dewsbury	85	A1
Deytheur	55	B4
Dial Post	16	B3
Dibden	13	B2
Dickleburgh	62	C1
Didbrook	35	C4
Didcot	36	D1
Diddington	50	D3
Diddlebury	55	D1
Didling	15	A3
Digby	70	D3
Diggle	78	B4
Dihewyd	44	A2
Dilham	63	A4
Dilhorne	67	C2
Dillington	50	D3
Dilston	101	B1
Dilton	24	A1
Dilton Marsh	24	A1
Dilwyn	45	D2
Dinas	64	B1
Dinas	43	B1
Dinas-Mawddwy	54	C4
Dinder	23	A1
Dinedor	46	A1
Dingestow	34	A2
Dingley	59	C1
Dingwall	130	B3
Dinnington	80	B2
Dinnington	10	C2
Dinnington	102	A2
Dinorwic	64	E4
Dinton	37	B3
Dinton	12	A4
Dinworthy	8	B2
Dippertown	3	B4
Diptford	3	D1
Dipton	96	C4
Dirleton	113	A3
Dirt Pot	95	E4
Diseworth	58	C4
Dishforth	90	E1
Disley	78	B2
Diss	62	B1
Distington	94	D2
Ditchburn	107	D2
Ditcheat	11	B4
Ditchingham	63	A1
Ditchling	17	B2
Ditteridge	24	A3
Dittisham	4	A1
Ditton	28	B2
Ditton Green	51	D3
Ditton Priors	56	A1
Dixton	35	B4
Dixton	34	B3
Dobcross	78	B3
Dobwalls	2	F2
Doccombe	4	A4
Docker	89	B1
Docking	72	A1
Docklow	46	A3
Dockray	95	A1
Dod's Leigh	67	C1
Dodd's Green	66	D2
Doddinghurst	40	B2
Doddington	60	D1
Doddington	29	B2
Doddington	70	C4
Doddington	107	C3
Doddiscombsleigh	4	A4
Dodford	49	B3
Dodford	47	B4
Dodington	23	C4
Dodington	10	A4
Dodleston	66	B4
Dodworth	79	B3
Dog Village	9	C1
Dogdyke	71	B3
Dogmersfield	26	B2
Dolanog	54	E3
Dolbenmaen	64	D2
Dolfach	54	D2
Dolfor	54	E1
Dolgarrog	65	A4
Dolgellau	54	B4
Dollar	116	E1
Dolphin	75	C1
Dolphinholme	83	C4
Dolphinton	105	D4
Dolton	8	E2
Dolwen	74	F1
Dolwyddelan	65	A3
Domgay	55	B4
Doncaster	80	B3
Donhead St Andrew	11	D3
Donhead St Mary	11	D3
Doniford	22	A1
Donington	71	B1
Donington on Bain	82	A1
Donisthorpe	58	B3
Donnington	36	A4
Donnington	55	D3
Donyatt	10	B2
Dorchester	36	D1
Dorchester	5	E4
Dordon	58	A2
Dores	130	B1
Dorking	27	C1
Dormington	46	B1
Dormston	47	B3
Dorney	27	A4
Dornie	124	A4
Dornoch	134	D1
Dornock	99	E1
Dorridge	48	A4
Dorrington	70	D3
Dorrington	55	D3
Dorrington	67	A2
Dorsington	47	C2
Dorstone	45	C1
Dorton	37	A3
Douglas	137	C1
Douglas	105	B3
Douglas Water	105	B3
Douglastown	121	E1
Doulting	23	B1
Dounby	13	B1
Doune	116	C1
Dousland	3	B2
Dove Holes	78	C1
Dovenby	94	D2
Dover	30	B1
Doverdale	47	A3
Doveridge	68	A1
Dowally	121	A1
Dowdeswell	35	B3
Dowland	8	E2
Down Ampney	35	C1
Down Hatherley	35	A4
Down St Mary	9	A1
Down Thomas	3	B1
Downderry	3	A1
Downe	27	F2
Downend	35	A1
Downgate	2	F2
Downgate	3	A3
Downham	61	A1
Downham	40	C1
Downham	84	A3
Downham Market	61	B3
Downhead	11	A3
Downhead	23	B1
Downholme	90	C3
Downside	27	C2
Downton	6	D4
Downton	12	C3
Downton on the Rock	45	D4
Dowsby	71	A1
Doynton	23	C3
Draethen	22	B4
Draffan	105	B4
Drakeholes	80	C2
Drakemyre	109	D1
Drakes Broughton	47	B2
Draughton	84	C3
Draughton	50	A4
Drax	86	B1
Draycote	49	A4
Draycott	48	A1
Draycott	23	A1
Draycott in the Clay	68	A1
Draycott in the Moors	67	C2
Drayton	59	C2
Drayton	62	C3
Drayton	49	A1
Drayton	36	C1
Drayton	10	C3
Drayton	47	A4
Drayton Bassett	58	A2
Drayton Beauchamp	37	C3
Drayton Parslow	37	B4
Dreen Hill	31	C3
Drefach	43	E1
Drefach	32	C3
Drefach	44	A2
Drellingore	20	D4
Drem	113	A3
Drewsteignton	3	D4
Driby	82	B1
Driffield	35	C2
Driffield	87	A4
Drift	1	A3
Drigg	88	B4
Drighlington	85	A1
Drimnin	118	F2
Drimpton	10	C1
Drinkstone	52	C3
Drinkstone Green	52	C3
Drointon	67	C1
Droitwich	47	A3
Dron	117	B2
Dronfield	79	B1
Drongan	104	E2
Dronley	117	C4
Droop	11	C2
Droxford	14	A3
Droylsden	78	A3
Druid	65	D2
Druidston	31	C3
Drum	117	A1
Drumbeg	135	A1
Drumburgh	100	A1
Drumburn	94	B4
Drumclog	104	F4
Drumeldrie	117	D1
Drumelzier	105	E3
Drumleaning	94	F4
Drumlithie	122	C4
Drumnadrochit	125	A4
Drummuir	131	D1
Drunzie	117	B2
Dry Doddington	70	C2
Dry Drayton	51	B3
Drybeck	95	C1
Drybridge	104	D3
Drybrook	34	C3
Dryburgh	106	D3
Drym	1	C3
Drymen	110	A4
Drynoch	123	C4
Dryton	56	A3
Ducklington	36	B2
Duddington	60	A2
Duddlestone	10	B3
Duddlewick	56	A1
Duddo	107	C4
Duddon	66	C4
Dudleston	66	A2
Dudley	102	A2
Dudley	57	A1
Duffield	68	C2
Duffryn	33	A1
Dufftown	131	C1
Duffus	131	B3
Dufton	95	C2
Duggleby	92	A1
Duirinish	123	F4
Duisky	119	D4
Duke Street	52	D1
Dukinfield	78	B3
Dulcote	23	A1
Dulford	9	D1
Dull	120	E1
Dullingham	51	D3
Dulnain Bridge	125	E4
Duloe	2	F1
Dulverton	9	C3
Dumbarton	109	E3
Dumbleton	47	B1
Dumfries	99	C2
Dummer	25	C1
Dun	122	B2
Dunan	109	C2
Dunan	123	D4
Dunbar	113	B3
Dunbeath	136	D1
Dunbeg	115	A4
Dunblane	116	D1
Dunbog	117	C2
Duncanstone	126	E4
Dunchideock	4	A4
Dunchurch	49	A4
Duncow	99	C3
Duncrievie	117	B2
Duncton	15	B2
Dundee	117	D4
Dundon	11	A4
Dundonald	104	D3
Dundonnell	133	D1
Dundraw	94	E4
Dundrennan	94	A4
Dundry	23	A3
Dunecht	127	B2
Dunfermline	111	C4
Dunfield	35	C1
Dunham	81	A1
Dunham Town	77	B2
Dunham-on-the-Hill	76	B1
Dunhampton	47	A3
Dunholme	81	C1
Dunino	117	E2
Dunipace	111	A3
Dunkeld	121	B1
Dunkerton	23	C2
Dunkeswell	10	A2
Dunkeswick	85	B3
Dunkirk	23	C4
Dunkirk	29	C2
Dunlappie	122	B3
Dunley	46	C4
Dunmore	111	B4
Dunnet	136	D4
Dunnichen	122	A1
Dunning	117	A2
Dunnington	87	B3
Dunnington	86	B3
Dunnockshaw	84	B1
Dunoon	109	C3
Dunragit	98	B1
Duns	113	C1
Duns Tew	36	C4
Dunsby	71	A1
Dunscore	99	B3
Dunsdale	97	B1
Dunsden Green	26	B4
Dunsdon	8	B2
Dunsfold	16	A4
Dunsford	4	A4
Dunshalt	117	C2
Dunsley	97	E1
Dunsmore	37	C2
Dunsop Bridge	83	D3
Dunstable	38	A3
Dunstall	58	A4
Dunstan	107	E2
Dunster	21	E1
Dunston	70	D4
Dunston	62	C2
Dunston	57	A4
Dunstone	3	C1
Dunstone	3	D3
Dunswell	87	A2
Dunsyre	105	D4
Dunterton	3	A3
Duntisbourne Abbots	35	B2
Duntisbourne Rouse	35	B2
Duntish	11	B1
Duntocher	110	A3
Dunton	37	B4
Dunton	72	B1
Dunton Bassett	59	A1
Dunure	104	C2
Dunvant	32	D1
Dunvegan	128	A2
Dunwich	53	D4
Durgan	1	D3
Durham	96	D3
Durisdeer	105	C1
Durleigh	10	B4
Durley	14	A2
Durley	24	D2
Durlock	30	B2
Durmgley	121	E1
Durness	135	C4
Duror	119	D2
Durrington	24	C1
Durris	127	B1
Dursley	34	D1
Dursley Cross	34	D3
Durston	10	B3
Durweston	11	D2
Duthil	125	E4
Dutton	76	B1
Duxford	51	C2
Duxford	36	B2
Dwygyfylchi	74	E1
Dwyran	64	D4
Dyce	127	C3
Dyffryn Ardudwy	54	A4
Dyke	60	B4
Dyke	130	E3
Dykehead	121	E2
Dymchurch	20	B4
Dymock	34	D4
Dyrham	23	C3
Dyserth	75	B1
Eagland Hill	83	B3
Eagle	70	C4
Eaglesfield	94	D2
Eaglesfield	99	E2
Eaglesham	110	B1
Eakring	70	A4
Ealand	81	A4
Ealing	27	C4
Eals	95	C4
Eamont Bridge	95	B2
Earby	84	B3
Eardington	56	B1
Eardisland	45	D3
Eardisley	45	C2
Eardiston	55	C4
Eardiston	46	C4
Earith	51	B4
Earl Soham	53	A3
Earl Sterndale	68	A4
Earl's Croome	47	A1
Earley	26	B3
Earls Barton	50	B3
Earls Colne	41	A4
Earls Common	47	B3
Earlsferry	117	E1
Earlston	106	C4
Earlswood	47	C4
Earnley	15	A1
Earsdon	102	A4
Earsham	63	A1
Eartham	15	B2
Easby	91	B4
Easdale	114	F2
Easebourne	15	B3
Easenhall	49	A4
Eashing	27	A1
Easington	37	A2
Easington	97	A3
Easington	87	D1
Easington	97	D1
Easington Colliery	97	A3
Easingwold	91	B1
Eassie and Nevay	121	D1
East Aberthaw	22	A3
East Allington	7	A4
East Anstey	9	B3
East Ashey	7	A4
East Ayton	92	B2
East Barkwith	81	D1
East Barming	28	B2
East Beckham	73	A2
East Bergholt	52	D1
East Bilney	62	A4
East Boldon	102	B1
East Boldre	13	A1
East Bradenham	62	A3
East Brent	22	C1
East Bridgford	70	A2
East Buckland	9	A4
East Budleigh	4	C4
East Butterwick	81	A3
East Calder	111	C2
East Carleton	62	C2
East Carlton	59	C1
East Chiltington	17	B2
East Chisenbury	24	C1
East Clandon	27	B1
East Coker	11	A2
East Compton	23	B1
East Cottingwith	86	B3
East Cowes	13	B1
East Cowick	86	B1
East Cowton	90	E4
East Cranmore	23	B1
East Creech	6	B3
East Dean	18	B1
East Dean	34	C3
East Dean	12	C3
East Dean	15	B2
East Down	21	B1
East Drayton	81	A1
East End	19	B4
East End	36	C3
East Everleigh	24	D2
East Farleigh	28	B2
East Farndon	59	B1
East Ferry	81	A3
East Garston	25	A4
East Goscote	59	B3
East Grafton	24	D2
East Grimstead	12	C3
East Grinstead	17	B4
East Guldeford	20	A3
East Haddon	49	C3
East Hagbourne	36	D1
East Halton	87	B1
East Hanney	36	C1
East Hanningfield	40	C2
East Hardwick	85	C1
East Harling	62	A1
East Harlsey	91	A4
East Harptree	23	A2
East Harting	15	A3
East Hatch	12	A3
East Hatley	51	A2
East Haven	117	F4
East Heckington	71	A2
East Hedleyhope	96	B3
East Hendred	36	C1
East Heslerton	92	A2
East Hewish	22	D3
East Hoathly	18	A2
East Holme	6	A4
East Horrington	23	B1
East Huntspill	22	C1
East Ilsley	25	B4

East Keal 71 C4
East Kennett 24 C3
East Keswick 85 B3
East Kilbride 110 B1
East Kirkby 71 C4
East Knighton 6 A4
East Knoyle 11 D4
East Kyloe 107 D4
East Lambrook 10 C3
East Langdon 30 B1
East Lavington 15 B2
East Layton 90 D4
East Leake 69 B1
East Lockinge 36 C1
East Lound 81 A3
East Lulworth 6 A3
East Lutton 92 A1
East Marden 15 A2
East Markham 81 A1
East Marton 84 B3
East Meon 14 B3
East Mersea 42 A3
East Morden 6 A4
East Morton 84 D3
East Ness 91 C2
East Norton 59 C2
East Orchard 11 D2
East Peckham 28 B1
East Pennard 11 B4
East Portlemouth 7 A4
East Prawle 7 B3
East Preston 16 A1
East Pulham 11 C2
East Putford 8 C2
East Quantoxhead 22 B1
East Rainton 96 D4
East Ravendale 82 A3
East Raynham 61 D4
East Rigton 85 B3
East Rudham 72 B1
East Runton 73 A2
East Ruston 73 B1
East Saltoun 113 A2
East Shefford 25 A3
East Stockwith 81 A2
East Stoke 6 A4
East Stour 11 C3
East Stowford 8 E3
East Stratton 14 A4
East Studdal 30 B1
East Taphouse 2 E2
East Thirston 102 A4
East Tilbury 28 B4
East Tisted 14 B4
East Torrington 81 D1
East Tuddenham 62 B3
East Tytherley 13 A3
East Tytherton 24 B3
East Village 9 B1
East Wall 55 D2
East Walton 61 C4
East Week 3 D4
East Wellow 13 A3
East Wemyss 117 C1
East Williamston 31 E2
East Winch 61 C4
East Winterslow 12 C4
East Wittering 15 A1
East Woodburn 101 A3
East Woodhay 25 B2
East Worldham 15 A4
East Wretham 62 A1
East Youlstone 8 B2
Eastbourne 18 B1
Eastbridge 53 C3
Eastburn 84 C3
Eastbury 25 A4
Eastby 84 C4
Eastchurch 29 B3
Eastcombe 35 A2
Eastcote 49 C2
Eastcote 48 A4
Eastcott 24 B2
Eastcourt 35 B1
Eastcourt 24 D2
Eastend 41 B1
Easter Compton 23 A4
Easterton 24 B2
Eastfield 111 B2
Eastfield 92 B2
Eastgate 96 A3
Eastgate 62 C4
Easthampton 45 D3
Easthope 55 D2
Easthorpe 41 B3
Eastington 9 A2
Eastington 35 C3
Eastington 34 D2
Eastleach Martin 36 A2
Eastleach Turville 36 A2
Eastleigh 8 D3
Eastleigh 13 B3
Eastling 29 B2
Eastnor 46 C1
Eastoft 81 A4
Easton 50 D4
Easton 100 A1
Easton 3 D4
Easton 5 E2
Easton 14 A4
Easton 70 C1
Easton 62 C3
Easton 23 A1
Easton 53 B3
Easton 24 A3
Easton Grey 35 A1
Easton Maudit 50 B3
Easton on the Hill 60 A3
Easton Royal 24 D2
Eastrea 60 C2
Eastriggs 100 A1
Eastrington 86 C1
Eastry 30 B2
Eastville 71 C3
Eastwell 70 B1
Eastwick 40 A3
Eastwood 69 A2
Eastwood 84 C1
Eathorpe 49 A4
Eaton 66 C4
Eaton 67 B4
Eaton 70 B1
Eaton 80 C1
Eaton 36 C2
Eaton 55 D1
Eaton Bray 38 A3
Eaton Green 38 A3
Eaton Hastings 36 A1
Eaton Mascott 55 D3
Eaton Socon 50 D3
Eaton upon Tern 56 A4
Ebberston 92 A2
Ebbesborne Wake 12 A3
Ebbw Vale 33 D2
Ebchester 96 B4
Ebford 4 B4
Ebnal 66 C2
Ebrington 48 A1
Ebsworthy Town 3 B4
Ecchinswell 25 B2
Ecclefechan 99 E2
Eccles 107 A4
Eccles 77 B3
Eccles 28 B2
Eccleshall 67 B1
Ecclesmachan 111 C3
Eccleston 66 B4
Eccleston 76 B4
Echt 127 B2
Eckford 107 A2
Eckington 80 A1
Eckington 47 A1
Ecton 50 A3
Edale 78 C2
Edburton 17 A2
Edderton 134 C1
Eddleston 106 A4
Edenbridge 27 F1
Edenfield 84 A1
Edenhall 95 B2
Edenham 60 A4
Edensor 68 B4
Edenthorpe 80 C3
Edern 64 B2
Edgcott 37 A4
Edgcott 9 B4
Edge 35 A2
Edge 55 C3
Edgefield 72 D1
Edgefield Green 72 D1
Edgeworth 35 B2
Edgmond 56 B4
Edgton 55 C1
Edgworth 77 B4
Edinbane 128 B2
Edinburgh 112 B3
Edingale 58 A3
Edingley 70 A3
Edingthorpe 73 B1
Edingthorpe Green 73 B1
Edington 101 C3
Edington 10 C4
Edington 24 A2
Edington Burtle 22 D1
Edingworth 22 D2
Edith Weston 59 D3
Edithmead 22 C1
Edlesborough 38 A3
Edlingham 107 D1
Edlington 71 B4
Edmondsham 12 B2
Edmondsley 96 C4
Edmondthorpe 59 D4
Edmundbyers 96 A4
Ednam 107 A3
Edrom 113 D1
Edstaston 66 C1
Edstone 48 A3
Edwinstowe 70 A4
Edworth 51 A1
Edwyn Ralph 46 B3
Edzell 122 B3
Efail Isaf 22 A4
Efail-fach 33 A1
Efailnewydd 64 C1
Efailwen 31 E4
Efenechtyd 65 D3
Effingham 27 C2
Efford 9 C1
Egerton 77 B4
Egerton 29 B1
Eggesford 9 A2
Eggington 37 C4
Egginton 68 B1
Eggleston 96 A2
Egham 27 B3
Egleton 59 D3
Eglingham 107 D2
Egloshayle 2 D3
Egloskerry 2 F4
Eglwys Cross 66 C2
Eglwysbach 65 B4
Eglwyswrw 43 C1
Egmanton 70 A4
Egremont 88 B4
Egton 91 D4
Egton Bridge 91 D4
Eight Ash Green 41 B4
Elan Village 44 E3
Elberton 34 C1
Elcombe 24 C4
Eldersfield 34 D4
Elderslie 110 A2
Eldon 96 C2
Elford 58 A3
Elgin 131 B3
Elgol 123 D3
Elham 30 A1
Elie 117 E1
Elim 74 B2
Eling 13 A2
Elkesley 80 C1
Elkstone 35 B3
Elland 84 D1
Ellary 108 F3
Ellastone 68 A2
Ellel 83 C4
Ellemford 113 C1
Ellen's Green 16 B4
Ellenhall 67 B1
Ellerbeck 91 A3
Ellerby 97 D1
Ellerdine Heath 56 A4
Ellerker 86 D1
Ellerton 86 B2
Ellerton 90 D3
Ellesborough 37 B2
Ellesmere 66 B1
Ellesmere Port 76 A1
Ellingham 63 B2
Ellingham 107 E2
Ellingstring 90 D2
Ellington 50 D4
Ellington 102 B4
Ellington Thorpe 50 D4
Elliots Green 23 C1
Ellisfield 26 A1
Ellistown 58 C3
Ellon 127 D4
Ellonby 95 A3
Elloughton 86 D1
Ellwood 34 C2
Elm 61 A3
Elmbridge 47 A3
Elmdon 51 C1
Elmdon 58 A1
Elmhurst 57 B3
Elmley Castle 47 B1
Elmley Lovett 47 A4
Elmore 34 D3
Elmore Back 34 D3
Elmsett 52 D2
Elmstead Market 42 A4
Elmstone 30 B2
Elmstone Hardwicke 35 A4
Elmswell 87 A4
Elmswell 52 C3
Elmton 80 A1
Elphin 133 E3
Elphinstone 112 C2
Elrig 93 D4
Elrington 101 A1
Elsdon 101 B4
Elsenham 40 A4
Elsfield 36 D2
Elsham 81 C4
Elsing 62 B4
Elslack 84 C3
Elsrickle 105 D4
Elstead 27 A1
Elsted 15 A3
Elsthorpe 60 A4
Elston 70 B2
Elstone 9 A2
Elstow 50 C2
Elstree 38 B1
Elstronwick 87 C2
Elswick 83 B2
Elsworth 51 B3
Elterwater 88 D4
Eltisley 51 A3
Elton 60 B2
Elton 76 A1
Elton 68 B4
Elton 97 A1
Elton 45 D4
Elton 70 B2
Eltringham 101 C1
Elvanfoot 105 C2
Elvaston 69 A1
Elveden 61 D1
Elvington 30 B1
Elvington 86 B3
Elwick 97 A2
Elworth 67 A4
Elworthy 9 D4
Ely 61 A1
Emberton 50 B2
Embleton 107 E2
Embo 134 D2
Emborough 23 B1
Embsay 84 C4
Emley 79 A4
Emmington 37 B2
Emneth 61 A3
Emneth Hungate 61 A3
Empingham 59 D3
Empshott 15 A4
Emsworth 15 A1
Enborne Row 25 B2
Endmoor 89 B2
Endon 67 C3
Enfield 39 B1
Enford 24 C1
Engine Common 23 C4
Englefield 26 A3
Englesea-brook 67 A3
English Bicknor 34 C3
English Frankton 66 B1
Englishcombe 23 C2
Enmore 10 B4
Ennerdale Bridge 94 D1
Ensdon 55 C4
Ensis 8 E3
Enstone 36 B4
Enville 56 C1
Epney 34 D3
Epperstone 70 A2
Epping 40 A2
Epping Green 40 A2
Epping Upland 40 A2
Eppleby 96 C1
Epsom 27 D2
Epwell 48 B1
Epworth 81 A3
Erbistock 66 B2
Eridge Green 18 B4
Eriswell 52 A4
Erlestoke 24 B2
Ermington 3 C1
Erpingham 73 A1
Errogie 125 B3
Errol 117 C3
Erskine 110 A2
Erwarton 53 A1
Erwood 45 A1
Eryholme 90 E4
Eryrys 65 E3
Escomb 96 C2
Escrick 86 B3
Esgairgeiliog 54 B3
Esh 96 C3
Esh Winning 96 C3
Esher 27 C3
Eshott 102 A4
Eskadale 130 A1
Eskdale Green 88 C4
Eskdalemuir 100 A4
Esprick 83 B2
Essendine 60 A3
Essendon 39 A2
Essington 57 A3
Eston 97 B1
Etal 107 C4
Etchilhampton 24 C2
Etchingham 19 A3
Etchinghill 20 C4
Eton 27 A4
Eton Wick 27 A4
Ettersgill 95 E2
Ettington 48 A2
Etton 60 B3
Etton 87 A3
Ettrick 106 A1
Ettrickbridge 106 B2
Etwall 68 B1
Euston 52 C4
Euxton 83 C1
Evanton 130 B3
Evedon 71 A2
Evenjobb 45 C3
Evenley 49 B1
Evenlode 36 A4
Evercreech 11 B4
Everingham 86 C3
Everleigh 24 D2
Eversholt 38 A4
Evershot 11 A1
Eversley 26 B2
Eversley Cross 26 B2
Everthorpe 86 D2
Everton 51 A2
Everton 80 C2
Evertown 100 B2
Evesbatch 46 B2
Evesham 47 B2
Ewden Village 79 B3
Ewelme 37 A1
Ewen 35 B1
Ewenny 21 E4
Ewerby 71 A2
Ewesley 101 C4
Ewhurst 16 B4
Ewhurst Green 16 B4
Ewloe 66 A4
Eworthy 8 D1
Ewshot 26 B1
Ewyas Harold 34 A4
Exbourne 8 E1
Exbury 13 B1
Exebridge 9 C3
Exelby 90 E2
Exeter 4 B4
Exford 9 B4
Exfordsgreen 55 C3
Exhall 47 C2
Exhall 58 B1
Exlade Street 26 A4
Exminster 4 B4
Exmouth 4 B3
Exning 51 D3
Exton 4 B4
Exton 14 A3
Exton 59 D3
Exton 9 C4
Eyam 79 A1
Eydon 49 B2
Eye 60 C2
Eye 46 A3
Eye 53 A4
Eyemouth 113 E2
Eyeworth 51 A2
Eyhorne Street 29 A2
Eyke 53 B2
Eynsford 27 F3
Eynsham 36 C2
Eype 5 C4
Eythorne 30 B1
Eyton 46 A3
Eyton 55 C3
Eyton 55 C4
Eyton 55 C1
Eyton on Severn 56 A3
Eyton upon the Weald Moors 56 A4
Faccombe 25 B2
Faceby 91 A4
Fachwen 54 E4
Fadmoor 91 C3
Failand 23 A3
Failsworth 78 A3
Fair Oak Green 26 A2
Fairbourne 54 A3
Fairburn 85 C1
Fairfield 47 B4
Fairford 35 C2
Fairgirth 94 B4
Fairlie 109 D1
Fairlight 19 B2
Fairmile 9 D1
Fairnilee 106 B3
Fairoak 67 A1
Fairseat 28 A2
Fairstead 40 C3
Fairwarp 18 A3
Fairy Cross 8 C3
Fakenham 72 C1
Fakenham Magna 52 C4
Fala 112 C2
Fala Dam 112 C2
Faldingworth 81 C2
Faldouet 137 B3
Falfield 34 C1
Falkenham 53 B1
Falkirk 111 A3
Falkland 117 C2
Fallin 111 A4
Falloden 107 E2
Fallowfield 101 B1
Falmer 17 B2
Falmouth 1 E3
Falstone 100 E3
Fancott 38 A4
Fangdale Beck 91 B3
Fangfoss 86 C4
Far End 88 D3
Far Green 34 D2
Far Sawrey 89 A3
Far Thorpe 82 A1
Farcet 60 C2
Fareham 14 A1
Farewell 57 B3
Faringdon 36 B1
Farington 83 C1
Farlam 100 C1
Farleigh Hungerford 23 C2
Farleigh Wallop 26 A1
Farlesthorpe 82 C1
Farleton 89 B2
Farley 68 A2
Farley 12 C3
Farley Green 52 A2
Farley Green 27 B1
Farley Hill 26 B3
Farleys End 34 D3
Farlington 91 B1
Farlow 56 A1
Farmborough 23 B2
Farmcote 35 C4
Farmers 44 B1
Farmington 35 C3
Farmoor 36 C2
Farnachty 131 D3
Farnborough 25 B4
Farnborough 27 A2
Farnborough 49 A2
Farndish 50 B3
Farndon 66 B3
Farndon 70 B3
Farnell 122 B2
Farnham 40 A4
Farnham 85 B4
Farnham 53 C3
Farnham 26 B1
Farnham Common 27 A4
Farnley 85 A3
Farnley Tyas 79 A4
Farnsfield 70 A3
Farnworth 77 B3
Farr 135 F4
Farringdon 4 C4
Farrington Gurney 23 B2
Farthinghoe 49 B1
Farthingstone 49 B2
Fasnacloich 119 D1
Fauldhouse 111 B1
Faulkbourne 41 A3
Faulkland 23 C2
Fauls 66 D1
Faversham 29 C2
Fawdington 91 A1
Fawdon 107 C2
Fawkham Green 28 A3
Fawler 36 B3
Fawley 25 B4
Fawley 26 B4
Fawley 13 B1
Faxfleet 86 D1
Faygate 17 A4
Fazeley 58 A2
Fearby 90 D2
Fearnan 120 D1
Fearnmore 128 E3
Featherstone 57 A3
Featherstone 85 C1
Feckenham 47 B3
Feering 41 A3
Feetham 90 B3
Felbrigg 73 A2
Felcourt 27 E1
Felin gwm Isaf 32 C4
Felin gwm Uchaf 32 C4
Felindre 32 D3
Felindre 43 E1
Felindre 55 A1
Felindre 32 D2
Felindre Farchog 43 C1
Felixkirk 91 A2
Felixstowe 53 B1
Felixstowe Ferry 53 B1
Felling 102 B1
Felmersham 50 C3
Felmingham 73 B1
Felsham 52 C3
Felsted 40 C3
Felthorpe 62 C4
Felton 46 A2
Felton 102 A4
Felton Butler 55 C4
Feltwell 61 C1
Fen Ditton 51 C3
Fen Drayton 51 B4
Fen Street 62 A2
Fence 84 B2
Fence 80 A2
Fencote 90 E3
Fendike Corner 71 D3
Feniscowles 83 D1
Feniton 9 D1
Fenny Bentley 68 B3
Fenny Bridges 9 D1
Fenny Compton 49 A2
Fenny Drayton 58 B2
Fenstanton 51 B4
Fenstead End 52 B2
Fenton 51 B4
Fenton 95 B4
Fenton 81 A1
Fenton 70 C3
Fenton 81 A1
Fenton 107 C3
Fenwick 104 E4
Fenwick 107 D4
Fenwick 101 C2
Fenwick 80 B4
Feock 1 E4
Ferndale 33 B1
Fernham 36 B1
Fernhill Heath 47 A3
Fernhurst 15 B3
Fernilee 78 B1
Ferrensby 85 B4
Ferring 16 B1
Ferryden 122 C2
Ferryhill 96 D2
Ferryside 32 B2
Fersfield 62 B1
Fetterangus 132 D2
Fettercairn 122 B3
Fewston 85 A4
Ffair Rhos 44 C3
Ffairfach 32 D3
Ffestiniog 65 A2
Fforest 32 D2
Ffostrasol 43 E2
Ffrith 66 A3
Ffynnongroew 75 C1
Fickleshole 27 E2
Fiddington 35 A4
Fiddington 10 A4
Fiddleford 11 C2
Fiddlers Green 2 B1
Field 67 C1
Field Broughton 89 A2
Field Dalling 72 D2
Fifehead Neville 11 C2
Fifehead St Quinton 11 C2
Fifield 27 A4
Fifield 36 A3
Figheldean 24 C1
Filby 63 B3
Filey 92 C2
Filgrave 50 B2
Filkins 36 A2
Filleigh 9 A3
Filleigh 9 A2
Fillingham 81 B2
Fimber 86 D4
Fincham 61 C3
Finchdean 15 A2
Finchingfield 40 C4
Findern 68 C1
Findhorn 131 A3
Findochty 131 D3
Findon 127 D1
Finedon 50 B4
Fingal Street 53 A4
Finghall 90 D3
Fingringhoe 42 A3
Finmere 37 A4
Finningham 52 D4
Finningley 80 C3
Finstall 47 B4
Finsthwaite 89 A3
Finstock 36 B3
Fintry 110 B4
Finzean 127 A1
Fionnphort 114 B3
Fir Tree 96 B3
Firbank 89 C3
Firbeck 80 B2
Firby 90 D2
Firby 91 D1
Firsby 71 D4
Fishbourne 7 A4
Fishburn 96 D2
Fishcross 111 B4
Fisherton 104 C2
Fisherton de la Mere 12 A4
Fishguard 43 A1
Fishlake 80 C4
Fishtoft 71 C2
Fishtoft Drove 71 C2
Fiskerton 70 D4
Fiskerton 70 B3
Fittleton 24 C1
Fittleworth 16 A3
Fitz 55 C4
Fitzhead 10 A3
Fitzwilliam 80 A4
Five Ashes 18 B3
Five Bells 22 A1
Five Oak Green 28 A1
Five Oaks 137 B3
Fivehead 10 C3
Fladbury 47 B2
Flagg 68 A4
Flamborough 92 D1
Flamstead 38 A3
Flansham 15 B1
Flasby 84 C4
Flash 67 C4
Flaunden 38 A2
Flawith 91 A1
Flax Bourton 23 A3
Flaxby 85 C4
Flaxley 34 C3
Flaxpool 10 A4
Flaxton 86 B4
Fleckney 59 B2
Flecknoe 49 B3
Fledborough 70 B4
Fleet 26 B2
Fleet 60 D4
Fleet Hargate 60 D4
Fleetwood 83 A3
Flemingston 22 A3
Flempton 52 B4
Fletchertown 94 E3
Fletching 17 B3
Flexford 27 A1
Flimby 94 D2
Flimwell 19 A4
Flint 75 D1
Flintham 70 B2
Flinton 87 C2
Flitcham 72 A1
Flitton 50 C1
Flitwick 50 C1
Flixborough 81 B4
Flixton 92 B2
Flixton 63 A1
Flockton 79 A4
Flockton Green 79 A4
Flookburgh 89 A1
Flordon 62 C2
Flore 49 C3
Flowton 52 D2
Flushing 1 E3
Fluxton 4 C4
Flyford Flavell 47 B2
Fobbing 28 B4
Fochabers 131 C3
Fockerby 86 C1
Foddington 11 A4
Foel 54 D3
Foggathorpe 86 C2
Fogo 107 A4
Fole 67 C1
Folke 11 B2
Folkestone 20 C4
Folkingham 70 D1
Folkington 18 B1
Folksworth 60 B1
Folkton 92 B2
Follifoot 85 B3
Folly Gate 8 E1
Fonthill Bishop 12 A4
Fonthill Gifford 11 D4
Fontmell Magna 11 D2
Fontwell 15 B2
Foolow 79 A1
Forcett 96 C1
Ford 37 B2
Ford 80 A1
Ford 8 C3
Ford 7 B4
Ford 35 C4
Ford 107 C3
Ford 9 D3
Ford 68 A3
Ford 16 A1
Ford 24 A3
Ford End 40 C3
Ford Street 10 A3
Fordcombe 18 A4
Fordell 112 A4
Forden 55 A2
Forder Green 4 A2
Fordham 51 D4
Fordham 41 B4
Fordham 61 B2
Fordingbridge 12 B2
Fordon 92 B1
Fordoun 122 C3
Fordstreet 41 B4
Fordyce 131 E3
Foremark 68 C1
Forest Becks 84 A3
Forest Chapel 67 C4
Forest Green 27 C1
Forest Hill 36 D2
Forest Mill 111 B4
Forest Row 17 B4
Forestside 15 A2
Forfar 121 E1
Forgandenny 117 A2
Forgie 131 D2
Formby 75 D4
Forncett End 62 C2

Forncett St Mary	62	C2
Forncett St Peter	62	C2
Fornham All Saints	52	B3
Fornham St Martin	52	B3
Forres	131	A3
Forsbrook	67	C2
Fort Augustus	124	E2
Forteviot	117	A2
Forth	111	B1
Forthampton	35	A4
Fortingall	120	D1
Forton	25	B1
Forton	83	C3
Forton	55	C4
Forton	10	B2
Forton	56	B4
Fortrose	130	C2
Fortuneswell	5	E3
Fort William	119	E3
Fosbury	25	A2
Foscot	36	A3
Fosdyke	71	C1
Foss	120	E2
Fossebridge	35	C3
Foston	68	B1
Foston	59	A2
Foston	70	C2
Foston	91	C1
Foston on the Wolds	87	B4
Fotherinhay	60	A2
Foul End	58	A2
Foulden	113	E1
Foulridge	84	B3
Foulsham	62	B4
Fountainhall	106	B4
Four Ashes	52	C4
Four Crosses	55	B4
Four Elms	27	F1
Four Forks	10	A4
Four Gotes	61	A4
Four Lanes	1	D4
Four Marks	14	B4
Four Mile Bridge	74	A1
Four Oaks	58	A1
Four Roads	32	C2
Four Throws	19	B4
Fovant	12	A3
Fowey	2	E1
Fowlhall	28	B1
Fowlis	117	C4
Fowlis Wester	116	E3
Fowlmere	51	B2
Fownhope	46	B1
Foxcote	23	C2
Foxdale	137	B2
Foxearth	52	B1
Foxfield	88	C2
Foxhole	2	D1
Foxholes	92	B1
Foxley	62	B4
Foxt	67	C2
Foxton	51	B2
Foxton	59	B1
Foxton	91	A3
Foxwood	46	B4
Foy	34	C4
Foyers	125	A3
Fraddon	2	C1
Fradley	58	A3
Fradswell	67	C1
Fraisthorpe	87	B4
Framfield	18	A3
Framingham Earl	63	A2
Framingham Pigot	63	A3
Framlingham	53	B3
Frampton	11	B1
Frampton	71	C2
Frampton Mansell	35	A2
Frampton on Severn	34	D2
Framsden	53	A3
Frances Green	83	D2
Frankby	75	D2
Frankley	57	A1
Frankton	49	A4
Frant	18	B4
Fraserburgh	132	D3
Frating	42	A4
Frating Green	42	A4
Freathy	3	A1
Freckenham	52	A4
Freckleton	83	B1
Freeby	59	C4
Freefolk	25	B1
Freeland	36	C3
Freethorpe Common	63	B3
Freiston	71	C2
Fremington	8	D4
Fremington	90	C3
Freshford	23	C2
Freshwater	6	E4
Fressingfield	53	B4
Freswick	136	F4
Fretherne	34	D2
Frettenham	63	A4
Freuchie	117	C1
Freystrop	31	C3
Friday Bridge	61	A3
Fridaythorpe	86	D4
Friesthorpe	81	C1
Frieston	70	C2
Frieth	37	B1
Frilford	36	C1
Frilsham	25	C3
Fring	72	A1
Fringford	36	D4
Frinsted	29	B2
Frinton-on-Sea	42	B3
Friockheim	122	B1
Frisby on the Wreake	59	B4
Friskney	71	D3
Friston	18	B1
Friston	53	C3
Fritchley	68	C3
Fritham	12	C2
Frithelstock	8	D3
Frithelstock Stone	8	D3
Frithville	71	C3
Frittenden	19	B4
Frittiscombe	7	B4
Fritton	63	B2
Fritton	62	C2
Fritwell	36	D4
Frizington	94	D1
Frocester	34	D2
Frodesley	55	D2
Frodsham	76	B1
Frog End	51	B2
Frog Pool	46	C3
Froggatt	79	A1
Froghall	67	C2
Frogmore	7	B4
Frognall	60	B3
Frogwell	3	A2
Frolesworth	59	A1
Frome	23	C1
Frome St Quintin	11	B1
Fromes Hill	46	B2
Fron Isaf	66	A2
Fron-goch	65	C2
Froncysyllte	66	A2
Frosterley	96	A3
Froxfield	25	A3
Froxfield Green	14	B3
Fulbeck	70	C3
Fulbourn	51	C2
Fulbrook	36	A3
Fulford	10	A3
Fulford	67	C2
Fulking	17	A2
Full Sutton	86	C4
Fuller Street	40	C3
Fulletby	82	A1
Fullready	48	B2
Fulmer	27	B4
Fulnetby	81	D1
Fulstow	82	B3
Fulwell	36	B4
Fundenhall	62	C2
Furley	10	B1
Furnace	115	B1
Furness Vale	78	B1
Furneux Pelham	40	A4
Furzley	13	A2
Fyfield	40	B2
Fyfield	25	A1
Fyfield	36	C2
Fyfield	24	C3
Fyfield	24	D2
Fylingthorpe	92	A4
Fyning	15	A3
Fyvie	132	B1
Gaddesby	59	B3
Gaddesden Row	38	A3
Gaer	33	D3
Gaer-llwyd	34	A1
Gaerwen	64	D4
Gailes	104	D3
Gailey	56	C3
Gainford	96	C1
Gainsborough	81	A2
Gainsford End	52	A1
Gairloch	128	F4
Gairlochy	119	E4
Gaitsgill	95	A4
Galashiels	106	C3
Galgate	83	C4
Galhampton	11	B4
Gallowfauld	121	E1
Galmpton	7	A4
Galphay	90	D1
Galston	104	E3
Gamblesby	95	C3
Gamlingay	51	A2
Gamston	80	C1
Ganllwyd	54	B4
Ganstead	87	B2
Ganthorpe	91	C1
Ganton	92	B2
Garboldisham	62	A1
Gardeners Green	26	B3
Gardenstown	132	B3
Gare Hill	11	C4
Garelochhead	109	D4
Garford	36	C1
Garforth	85	C2
Gargrave	84	C4
Gargunnock	110	C4
Garlic Street	62	C1
Garlieston	93	E4
Garlinge Green	29	C2
Garlogie	127	B2
Garmond	132	B2
Garmouth	131	C3
Garmston	56	A3
Garn-Dolbenmaen	64	D2
Garras	1	D2
Garrigill	95	D3
Garrochtrie	93	B3
Garsdale Head	89	D3
Garsdon	35	B1
Garshall Green	67	C1
Garsington	36	D2
Garstang	83	C3
Garth	66	A2
Garth	44	E2
Garth Penrhyncoch	54	A1
Garth Row	89	B3
Garthmyl	55	A2
Garthorpe	59	C4
Gartmore	116	A1
Gartness	111	A2
Gartness	110	A4
Gartocharn	110	A4
Garton	87	C2
Garton-on-the-Wolds	87	A4
Garvald	113	B2
Garvan	119	D4
Garve	129	E3
Garvestone	62	B3
Garway	34	A4
Gasper	11	C4
Gastard	24	A3
Gasthorpe	62	A1
Gaston Green	40	A3
Gatcombe	6	F4
Gate Helmsley	86	B4
Gateforth	86	A1
Gatehouse	100	E3
Gatehouse of Fleet	93	F4
Gateley	62	A4
Gatenby	90	E3
Gateshead	102	A1
Gateside	110	A1
Gateside	117	B2
Gatley	78	A2
Gatton	27	D2
Gaulby	59	B2
Gauldry	117	D3
Gautby	81	D1
Gavinton	113	C1
Gawcott	37	A4
Gawsworth	67	B4
Gawthrop	89	C2
Gawthwaite	88	D2
Gaydon	48	B2
Gayhurst	50	A2
Gayle	90	A3
Gayles	90	C4
Gayton	49	C2
Gayton	61	C4
Gayton	67	C1
Gayton le Marsh	82	B2
Gayton Thorpe	61	C4
Gazeley	52	A3
Gedding	52	C3
Geddinge	30	B1
Geddington	59	D1
Gedney	60	D4
Gedney Broadgate	60	D4
Gedney Drove End	71	D1
Gedney Dyke	71	C1
Gedney Hill	60	D3
Geeston	60	A3
Geldeston	63	B2
Gelli Gynan	65	E3
Gellifor	65	E4
Gelligaer	33	D1
Gellilydan	65	A2
Gellywen	32	A4
Gelston	99	B1
Gelston	70	C2
Gembling	87	B4
Gentleshaw	57	B3
George Green	27	B4
George Nympton	9	A3
Georgeham	8	D4
Germansweek	3	B4
Gerrards Cross	38	A1
Gerrick	97	C1
Geuffordd	55	A3
Gifford	113	A2
Giggleswick	84	A4
Gilcrux	94	D3
Gildersome	85	A1
Gildingwells	80	B2
Gileston	22	A3
Gilfach Goch	33	B1
Gilfachrheda	43	E3
Gilgarran	94	D2
Gillamoor	91	C3
Gilling East	91	B2
Gillingham	29	A3
Gilling West	90	D4
Gillingham	11	C3
Gillingham	63	B2
Gilmerton	116	D3
Gilmonby	96	A1
Gilmorton	59	A1
Gilsland	100	D1
Gilwern	33	E3
Gimingham	73	B1
Gipping	52	D3
Gipsey Bridge	71	B3
Girsby	90	E4
Girton	51	B3
Girton	70	B4
Girvan	98	B4
Gisburn	84	B3
Gisleham	63	C1
Gislingham	52	D4
Gissing	62	C1
Gittisham	10	A1
Gladestry	45	B2
Gladsmuir	112	C3
Glais	32	E2
Glaisdale	91	D4
Glamis	121	E1
Glan-y-don	75	C1
Glanaman	32	E3
Glandford	72	D2
Glandwr	31	E4
Glandyfi	54	B2
Glanton	107	D1
Glanvilles Wootton	11	B2
Glapthorn	60	A1
Glasbury	45	B1
Glascwm	45	B2
Glasfryn	65	C3
Glasgow	110	B2
Glasinfryn	64	E4
Glasserton	93	D3
Glassford	105	A4
Glasshouse	34	D3
Glasshouses	90	D1
Glasson	100	A1
Glasson	83	B4
Glassonby	95	B3
Glasterlaw	122	B1
Glaston	59	D2
Glastonbury	11	A4
Glatton	60	B1
Glazebrook	77	B2
Glazebury	77	A3
Glazeley	56	B1
Gleaston	88	D1
Gledrid	66	A1
Glemsford	52	B2
Glen Auldyn	137	D3
Glen Maye	137	B2
Glenbarr	103	D3
Glenboig	110	C2
Glenborrodale	118	F2
Glenbuck	105	A3
Glencaple	99	C2
Glencarse	117	B3
Glencoe	119	E2
Glencraig	112	A4
Glendaruel	109	B3
Glendevon	116	E1
Glendoick	117	B3
Gleneagles	116	E2
Glenelg	123	F3
Glenfarg	117	B2
Glenfinnan	119	C4
Glengolly	136	C4
Glenholm	105	D3
Glenkindie	126	D3
Glenluce	98	C1
Glenmavis	110	C2
Glenmore	128	C1
Glenridding	95	A1
Glenrothes	117	C1
Glentham	81	C2
Glentrool Village	98	D2
Glentworth	81	B2
Glenurquhart	130	C3
Glenwhilly	98	B2
Glewstone	34	B3
Glinton	60	B3
Glooston	59	C2
Glossop	78	B2
Gloucester	35	A3
Glusburn	84	C3
Gluvian	2	C2
Glyn Ceiriog	65	E2
Glyn-Neath	33	A2
Glynarthen	43	E2
Glyncorrwg	33	A2
Glynde	18	A2
Glyndyfrdwy	65	E2
Glyntawe	33	A3
Glynteg	43	E1
Gnosall	56	C4
Goadby	59	C2
Goadby Marwood	70	B1
Goatacre	24	B4
Goathill	11	B2
Goathland	91	D4
Goathurst	10	B4
Gobowen	66	A1
Goddard's Green	19	B4
Godmanchester	51	A4
Godmanstone	11	B1
Godney	23	A1
Godolphin Cross	1	C3
Godre'r-graig	32	E2
Godshill	7	A3
Goetre	33	E2
Goff's Oak	39	B2
Gofilon	33	E3
Goginan	54	B1
Golan	64	D2
Golant	2	E1
Golberdon	3	A2
Golborne	77	A3
Goldcliff	22	D4
Golden Green	28	A1
Golden Pot	26	A1
Goldhanger	41	B2
Goldsborough	97	D1
Goldsborough	85	B4
Goldsithney	1	B3
Goldthorpe	80	A3
Goldworthy	8	C3
Gollanfield	130	D2
Golspie	134	D2
Gomeldon	12	C4
Gomshall	27	C1
Gonalston	70	A2
Good Easter	40	B3
Gooderstone	61	C2
Goodleigh	8	E4
Goodmanham	86	D3
Goodnestone	29	C2
Goodnestone	30	B2
Goodrich	34	B3
Goodshaw Fold	84	A1
Goodworth Clatford	25	A1
Goole	86	C1
Goom's Hill	47	B2
Goonbell	2	A1
Goonhavern	2	B1
Goonvrea	2	A1
Goose Green	42	B4
Goose Green	42	B4
Goose Green	23	B3
Goosey	36	B1
Goosnargh	83	C2
Goostrey	67	A4
Gordon	106	D4
Gordonstown	132	B1
Gorebridge	112	B2
Gores	24	C2
Gorey	137	B3
Goring	25	C4
Gorran	1	F4
Gorran Haven	1	F4
Gorsedd	75	C1
Gorseinon	32	D1
Gorsgoch	44	A2
Gorslas	32	D3
Gorsley	34	C4
Gorstello	66	B4
Gorsty Hill	68	A1
Gosbeck	53	A2
Gosberton	71	B1
Gosfield	41	A4
Gosforth	88	B4
Gosforth	102	A1
Gospel End	56	C2
Gosport	14	A1
Gossington	34	D2
Gotham	69	B1
Gotherington	35	B4
Gotton	10	B3
Goudhurst	19	A4
Goulceby	82	A1
Gourdon	122	D3
Gourock	109	D3
Goveton	7	A4
Gowdall	86	B1
Gowerton	32	D1
Gowkhall	111	C4
Goxhill	87	B3
Goxhill	87	B1
Graffham	15	B2
Grafham	50	D4
Grafham	27	B1
Grafton	85	C4
Grafton	36	A2
Grafton	55	C4
Grafton	47	B1
Grafton Flyford	47	B2
Grafton Regis	50	A2
Grafton Underwood	59	D1
Graig	65	B4
Graig-fechan	65	E3
Grain	29	A4
Grainsby	82	A3
Grainthorpe	82	B3
Grampound Road	2	C1
Granborough	37	B4
Granby	70	B1
Grand Chemins	137	B3
Grandborough	49	A3
Grandes Rocques	137	B4
Grange	94	F1
Grange Moor	79	A4
Grange Villa	96	C4
Grange-over-Sands	89	A2
Grangemouth	111	B3
Gransmoor	87	B4
Granston	43	A1
Grantchester	51	C2
Grantham	70	C1
Grantown-on-Spey	126	A4
Grantshouse	113	C2
Grasby	81	D3
Grasmere	88	D4
Grasscroft	78	B3
Grassington	84	C4
Grassmoor	69	A4
Grassthorpe	70	B4
Grateley	25	A1
Graveley	51	A3
Graveley	39	A4
Graveney	29	C2
Gravesend	28	A3
Grayingham	81	B3
Grayrigg	89	B3
Grays	28	A4
Grayshott	15	B4
Grayswood	15	B4
Grazeley	26	A3
Greasbrough	80	A3
Greasley	69	A2
Great Addington	50	B4
Great Alne	47	C3
Great Altcar	75	D3
Great Amwell	39	B3
Great Asby	95	C1
Great Ayton	97	B1
Great Badminton	23	C4
Great Bardfield	40	C4
Great Barford	50	D2
Great Barrington	36	A3
Great Barrow	66	C4
Great Barton	52	C3
Great Barugh	91	D2
Great Bavington	101	B3
Great Bealings	53	A2
Great Bedwyn	24	D3
Great Bentley	42	A3
Great Bircham	72	A1
Great Blakenham	52	D2
Great Blencow	95	A2
Great Bolas	56	A4
Great Bosullow	1	A3
Great Bourton	49	A2
Great Bowden	59	C1
Great Bradley	52	A2
Great Braxted	41	A3
Great Bricett	52	D2
Great Brickhill	37	C4
Great Bridgeford	67	B1
Great Brington	49	C3
Great Bromley	42	A4
Great Broughton	94	D2
Great Budworth	77	A1
Great Burdon	96	D1
Great Busby	91	B4
Great Carlton	82	B2
Great Casterton	60	A3
Great Chart	29	B1
Great Chatfield	24	A2
Great Chatwell	56	B4
Great Chesterford	51	C1
Great Cheverell	24	B2
Great Chishill	51	B1
Great Clifton	94	D2
Great Cowden	87	C3
Great Coxwell	36	A1
Great Cransley	50	A4
Great Cressingham	61	D2
Great Crosthwaite	94	F2
Great Cubley	68	B2
Great Dalby	59	C3
Great Dunham	61	D4
Great Dunmow	40	B4
Great Durnford	12	B4
Great Easton	40	B4
Great Easton	59	C2
Great Eccleston	83	B2
Great Ellingham	62	B2
Great Elm	23	C1
Great Englebourne	4	A1
Great Everdon	49	B3
Great Eversden	51	B2
Great Finborough	52	D3
Great Fransham	62	A3
Great Gaddesden	38	A3
Great Gidding	60	B1
Great Givendale	86	C4
Great Glemham	53	B3
Great Glen	59	B2
Great Gonerby	70	C2
Great Gransden	51	A2
Great Green	51	A1
Great Green	52	C3
Great Habton	91	D2
Great Hale	71	A2
Great Hallingbury	40	A3
Great Harrowden	50	B4
Great Harwood	84	A2
Great Haseley	37	A2
Great Hatfield	87	B3
Great Haywood	57	A4
Great Heck	86	A1
Great Henny	52	B1
Great Hinton	24	A2
Great Hockham	62	A2
Great Holland	42	B3
Great Horkesley	41	B4
Great Hormead	39	B4
Great Horwood	37	B4
Great Houghton	50	A3
Great Houghton	80	A3
Great Hucklow	79	A1
Great Kelk	87	B4
Great Kimble	37	B2
Great Kingshill	37	C1
Great Langdale	88	D4
Great Langton	90	E3
Great Leighs	40	C3
Great Limber	81	D4
Great Linford	50	A1
Great Livermere	52	B4
Great Lumley	96	D4
Great Malvern	46	C2
Great Maplestead	52	B1
Great Massingham	61	D4
Great Milton	37	A2
Great Missenden	37	C2
Great Mongeham	30	B1
Great Moulton	62	C1
Great Musgrave	95	D1
Great Ness	55	C4
Great Oak	34	A2
Great Oakley	42	B4
Great Offley	38	B4
Great Ormside	95	D1
Great Orton	94	F4
Great Ouseburn	85	C4
Great Oxendon	59	B1
Great Paxton	51	A3
Great Plumpton	83	B2
Great Plumstead	63	A3
Great Ponton	70	C1
Great Preston	85	C1
Great Raveley	60	C1
Great Rissington	36	A3
Great Rollright	36	B4
Great Ryburgh	72	C1
Great Ryle	107	C1
Great Ryton	55	D3
Great Saling	40	C4
Great Salkeld	95	B3
Great Sampford	51	D1
Great Saughall	66	B4
Great Shefford	25	A3
Great Shelford	51	C2
Great Smeaton	90	E4
Great Snoring	72	C1
Great Somerford	24	B4
Great Soudley	67	A1
Great Stainton	96	D1
Great Stambridge	41	B1
Great Steeping	71	D4
Great Strickland	95	B2
Great Stukeley	51	A4
Great Sturton	82	A1
Great Swinburne	101	B2
Great Tew	36	C4
Great Tey	41	B4
Great Torrington	8	D3
Great Tosson	101	B4
Great Totham	41	A3
Great Totham	41	A3
Great Urswick	88	D1
Great Wakering	41	B1
Great Waldingfield	52	C1
Great Walsingham	72	C1
Great Waltham	40	C3
Great Warley	40	B1
Great Washbourne	47	B1
Great Wenham	52	D1
Great Whittington	101	B2
Great Wigborough	41	B3
Great Wilbraham	51	D3
Great Wishford	12	B4
Great Witcombe	35	A3
Great Wolford	48	A1
Great Wratting	52	A2
Great Wymondley	39	A4
Great Wyrley	57	A3
Great Yarmouth	63	C3
Great Yeldham	52	A1
Greatford	60	B3
Greatgate	68	A2
Greatham	97	A2
Greatham	15	A4
Greatham	16	A2
Greatworth	49	B1
Green End	39	B4
Green End	39	B4
Green End	58	A1
Green Hammerton	85	C4
Green Ore	23	A1
Greenock	109	D3
Green Quarter	89	A4
Green Street	40	A3
Green Street	47	A2
Green Street Green	28	A3
Green Tye	40	A3
Greenfield	50	C1
Greenfield	75	C1
Greenfield	78	B3
Greengairs	111	A2
Greenhalgh	83	B2
Greenham	9	D3
Greenhaugh	100	E3
Greenhill	99	D2
Greenholm	104	F3
Greenhow Hill	84	D4
Greenlaw	107	A4
Greenlea	99	D2
Greenloaning	116	D2
Greenodd	88	D2
Greens Norton	49	C2
Greenside	101	C1
Greenstead Green	41	A4
Greenway	10	B3
Greenwich	27	E4
Greet	35	B4
Greete	46	A4
Greetham	71	B4
Greetham	59	D3
Greetland	84	D1
Greinton	10	C4
Grenaby	137	B1
Grendon	50	B3
Grendon Underwood	37	A3
Gresford	66	A3
Gresham	73	A2
Gressenhall	62	A4
Gressenhall Green	62	A4
Gressingham	89	B1
Greta Bridge	96	B1
Gretna	100	A1
Gretna Green	100	A1
Gretton	59	D2
Grewelthorpe	90	D2
Greys Green	26	A4
Greysouthen	94	D2
Greystoke	95	A2
Greystone	122	A1
Greywell	26	A1
Griff	58	B1
Grimeford Village	77	A4
Grimethorpe	80	A4
Grimley	47	A3
Grimoldby	82	B2
Grimpo	66	B1
Grimsargh	83	D2
Grimscott	8	B2
Grimsthorpe	60	A4
Grimston	59	B4
Grimston	61	C4
Grimstone	5	E4
Grimstone End	52	C4
Grindale	92	C1
Grindleford	79	A1
Grindleton	84	A3
Grindley Brook	66	C2
Grindlow	79	A1
Grindon	68	A3
Gringley on the Hill	81	A2
Grinsdale	100	B1
Grinshill	55	D4
Grinton	90	C3
Grimsby	82	A4
Gristhorpe	92	C2
Griston	62	A2
Grittenham	24	B4
Grittleton	24	A4
Grizebeck	88	D2
Grizedale	88	D3
Groby	59	A3
Groes	65	D4
Groes-faen	22	A4
Groes-Wen	22	B4
Groesffordd Marli	75	A1
Gronant	75	B1
Groombridge	18	A4
Grosmont	34	A4
Grosmont	91	D4
Groton	52	C1
Grouville	137	B3
Grove	81	A1
Grove	36	C1

Hirnant 54 E4
Hirst Courtney 86 A1
Hirwaun 33 B2
Hiscott 8 E3
Histon 51 C3
Hitcham 52 C2
Hitcham Causeway 52 C2
Hitchin 38 B4
Hittisleigh 9 A1
Hive 86 C2
Hixon 57 A4
Hoaden 30 B2
Hoarwithy 34 B4
Hoath 30 A3
Hobarris 45 C4
Hobson 96 C4
Hoby 59 B4
Hockering 62 B3
Hockerton 70 A3
Hockley 41 A1
Hockley Heath 47 C4
Hockliffe 38 A4
Hockwold cum Wilton 61 C1
Hockworthy 9 D3
Hoddesdon 39 B2
Hoddlesden 84 A1
Hoddom Mains 99 E2
Hodgeston 31 D2
Hodnet 66 D1
Hodsall Street 28 A2
Hodsock 80 B2
Hodson 24 D4
Hodthorpe 80 B1
Hoe 62 A4
Hogben's Hill 29 C2
Hoggeston 37 B4
Hoggrill's End 58 A2
Hoghton 83 D1
Hognaston 68 B3
Hogsthorpe 71 D4
Holbeach 60 D4
Holbeach Drove 60 D3
Holbeach Hurn 71 C1
Holbeach St Johns 60 D4
Holbeach St Mark's 71 C1
Holbeach St Matthew 71 C1
Holbeck 80 B1
Holberrow Green 47 B3
Holbeton 3 C1
Holbrook 68 C2
Holbrook 53 A1
Holbury 13 B1
Holcombe 4 B3
Holcombe 23 B1
Holcombe Rogus 9 D3
Holcot 50 A4
Holden 84 A3
Holdenby 49 C3
Holdgate 55 D1
Holdingham 70 D2
Holditch 10 B1
Hole 8 C1
Holford 22 B1
Holker 89 A2
Holkham 72 C2
Hollacombe 8 C1
Holland Fen 71 B3
Hollesley 53 C1
Hollingdon 37 C4
Hollington 68 B2
Hollington 68 A2
Hollins Green 77 B2
Hollinsclough 68 A4
Hollocombe 8 E2
Holloway 68 C3
Hollowell 49 C4
Holly Green 47 A1
Hollybush 33 D2
Hollybush 104 D2
Hollybush 46 C1
Hollym 87 D1
Holmbridge 78 C3
Holmbury St Mary 27 C1
Holme 60 B1
Holme 89 B2
Holme 90 E2
Holme 70 B3
Holme 78 C3
Holme Chapel 84 B1
Holme Green 86 A3
Holme Hale 61 D3
Holme Lacy 46 A1
Holme Marsh 45 C2
Holme next the Sea 72 A2
Holme on the Wolds 86 D3
Holme Pierrepont 70 A2
Holme St Cuthbert 94 D4
Holmes Chapel 67 A4
Holmesfield 79 B1
Holmeswood 76 A4
Holmewood 69 A4
Holmpton 87 D1
Holmrook 88 B4
Holne 3 D2
Holnest 11 B2
Holnicote 21 E1
Holsworthy 8 C1
Holsworthy Beacon 8 C2
Holt 12 A1
Holt 24 A2
Holt 47 A3
Holt 66 B3
Holt 72 D2
Holt End 47 C4
Holt Heath 47 A3
Holtby 86 B4
Holton 11 B3
Holton 53 C4
Holton cum Beckering 81 D1
Holton le Clay 82 A3
Holton le Moor 81 C3
Holton St Mary 52 D1
Holwell 11 C2
Holwell 38 B4
Holwell 59 B4
Holwell 36 A2
Holwick 95 E2
Holyhead 74 A1
Holy Island 107 D4
Holybourne 14 B4
Holymoorside 68 C4
Holystone 101 B4
Holytown 110 C1
Holywell 51 B4
Holywell 2 B1
Holywell 11 B1
Holywell 75 C1
Holywell Lake 9 D3
Holywell Row 52 A4
Holywood 99 C3
Homer 56 A2
Homer Green 75 D3
Homersfield 63 A1
Homington 12 B3
Honey Tye 52 C1
Honeybourne 47 C1
Honeychurch 8 E1
Honeystreet 24 C2
Honiley 48 A4
Honing 73 B1
Honingham 62 B3
Honington 70 C2
Honington 52 C4
Honington 48 A1
Honiton 10 A1
Honley 78 C4
Hoo 29 A3
Hoo Green 77 B1
Hooe 19 A2
Hook 26 A2
Hook 28 A3
Hook 31 D3
Hook 24 C4
Hook Norton 36 B4
Hooke 11 A1
Hookway 9 B1
Hooton Levitt 80 B2
Hooton Pagnell 80 A4
Hooton Roberts 80 A3
Hope 79 A1
Hope 7 A4
Hope 66 A3
Hope 46 B4
Hope 68 A3
Hope Bowdler 55 D2
Hope End Green 40 B3
Hope Mansell 34 C3
Hope under Dinmore 46 A2
Hopeman 131 B4
Hopeman 13 A4
Hopesay 55 C1
Hopperton 85 C4
Hopstone 56 B2
Hopton 57 A4
Hopton 52 C4
Hopton Cangeford 55 D1
Hopton Castle 45 D4
Hopton on Sea 63 C2
Hopton Wafers 46 B4
Hoptonheath 45 D4
Hopwas 58 A3
Hopwood 47 B4
Horam 18 B2
Horbling 71 A1
Hordley 66 B1
Horham 53 A4
Horkesley Heath 41 B4
Horkstow 81 C4
Horley 49 A1
Horley 27 D1
Hornblotton Green 11 B4
Hornby 89 C1
Hornby 90 E4
Hornby 90 D3
Horncastle 71 B4
Horncliffe 113 E1
Horndean 107 B4
Horndean 14 B2
Horndon 3 B3
Horndon on the Hill 28 B4
Horne 27 E1
Horner 21 E1
Horning 63 A4
Horninghold 59 C2
Horningsea 51 C3
Horningsham 11 D4
Horningtoft 62 A4
Horns Cross 8 C3
Hornsea 87 C3
Hornton 49 A2
Horrabridge 3 B2
Horridge 3 D3
Horringer 52 B3
Horrocksford 84 A3
Horsebridge 3 A3
Horsebridge 13 A4
Horsebridge 55 C3
Horseheath 51 D2
Horsehouse 90 B2
Horseman's Green 66 B2
Horsey 63 B4
Horsey 10 B4
Horsford 62 C4
Horsham 16 B4
Horsham 46 C3
Horsham St Faith 62 C4
Horsington 71 A4
Horsington 11 C3
Horsley 68 C2
Horsley 35 A1
Horsley 101 A4
Horsley 101 C1
Horsley Woodhouse 69 A2
Horsmonden 19 A4
Horspath 36 D2
Horstead 63 A4
Horsted Keynes 17 B3
Horton 27 B3
Horton 37 C3
Horton 12 A2
Horton 23 C4
Horton 84 B3
Horton 50 A2
Horton 56 A4
Horton 10 B2
Horton 67 C3
Horton 21 A4
Horton 24 C2
Horton Green 66 B3
Horton in Ribblesdale 89 D1
Horton Kirby 28 A3
Horton-cum-Studley 36 D3
Horwich 77 A4
Horwood 8 D3
Hose 70 A1
Hosh 116 D3
Hotham 86 D2
Hothfield 29 B1
Hoton 59 A4
Hott 100 E3
Hough 67 A3
Hough-on-the-Hill 70 C2
Hougham 70 C2
Houghton 51 A4
Houghton 13 A4
Houghton 31 D2
Houghton 16 A2
Houghton Conquest 50 C1
Houghton Green 20 A3
Houghton le Spring 96 D4
Houghton on the Hill 59 B3
Houghton St Giles 72 C1
Hound Green 26 A2
Houndslow 106 D4
Hounslow 27 C3
Hounslow Green 40 B3
Houses Hill 79 A4
Houston 109 E2
Hove 17 A1
Hoveringham 70 A2
Hoveton 63 A4
Hovingham 91 C1
How Caple 34 C4
How Mill 95 B4
Howden 86 C1
Howden-le-Wear 96 C2
Howe 90 E2
Howe 63 A2
Howe Green 40 C2
Howe Street 40 C3
Howe Street 52 A1
Howegreen 41 A2
Howell 71 A2
Howey 45 A3
Howgate 112 B1
Howick 107 E2
Howle 56 B4
Howle 96 B2
Howle Hill 34 C3
Howlett End 51 D1
Howley 10 B2
Hownam 107 A2
Howsham 81 C3
Howsham 86 B4
Howtel 107 B3
Howwood 109 E1
Hoxne 53 A4
Hoylake 75 C2
Hoyland Nether 79 B3
Hoyland Swaine 79 A3
Huby 85 A3
Huby 91 B1
Hucking 29 A2
Hucknall 69 B3
Huddersfield 78 C4
Huddington 47 B3
Hudswell 90 C4
Huggate 86 D4
Hugh Town 137 A3
Hughley 55 D2
Huish 8 D2
Huish 24 C2
Hulcott 37 C3
Hull 87 B1
Hulland 68 B2
Hullavington 24 A4
Hullbridge 41 A1
Hulme 67 C2
Hulme End 68 A3
Hulme Walfield 67 B4
Hulver Street 63 B1
Hulverstone 6 F4
Humberston 82 A3
Humbie 112 C2
Humbleton 87 C2
Humby 70 D1
Hume 107 A4
Humshaugh 101 A2
Huncote 59 A2
Hunderthwaite 96 A1
Hundleby 71 C4
Hundleton 31 C2
Hundon 52 A2
Hundred End 83 B1
Hundred House 45 A2
Hungarton 59 B3
Hungerford 9 D4
Hungerford 25 A3
Hungerford Newtown 25 A3
Hungerstone 45 D1
Hunmanby 92 C2
Hunningham 48 B3
Hunsdon 39 B3
Hunsingore 85 C4
Hunsonby 95 C3
Hunstanton 72 A2
Hunstanworth 96 A4
Hunston 52 C4
Hunston 15 B1
Hunstrete 23 B2
Hunsworth 85 A1
Hunterston 67 A2
Huntham 10 B3
Huntingdon 51 A4
Huntingfield 53 B4
Huntington 66 B4
Huntington 45 C2
Huntington 57 A3
Huntley 34 D3
Huntly 131 E1
Hunton 13 B4
Hunton 28 B1
Hunton 90 D3
Huntscott 21 E1
Huntsham 9 C3
Huntshaw 8 D3
Huntspill 22 C1
Huntstile 10 B4
Huntworth 10 B4
Hunwick 96 C2
Hunworth 72 D1
Hurdcott 12 C4
Hurley 58 A2
Hurley Common 58 A2
Hurlford 104 E3
Hurn 12 B1
Hursley 13 B3
Hurst 26 B3
Hurst Green 19 A3
Hurst Green 83 D2
Hurstbourne Priors 25 B1
Hurstbourne Tarrant 25 A2
Hurstley 45 D2
Hurstpierpoint 17 A2
Hurstwood 84 B2
Hurworth Place 90 E4
Hurworth-on-Tees 90 E4
Husthwaite 91 B1
Huttoft 82 C1
Hutton 113 D1
Hutton 87 A4
Hutton 83 C1
Hutton 22 D2
Hutton Bonville 90 E4
Hutton Buscel 92 B2
Hutton Conyers 90 E1
Hutton Cranswick 87 A3
Hutton End 95 A3
Hutton Henry 97 A3
Hutton Lowcross 97 B1
Hutton Magna 96 B1
Hutton Roof 95 A3
Hutton Roof 89 B2
Hutton Rudby 91 A4
Hutton Sessay 91 A1
Hutton Wandesley 86 A3
Hutton-le-Hole 91 C3
Huxley 66 C4
Hycemoor 88 B3
Hyde 78 B2
Hyde Heath 37 C2
Hyde Lea 56 C4
Hyssington 55 B2
Hythe 20 C4
Hythe 13 B2
Hythe End 27 B3
Ibberton 11 C2
Ible 68 B3
Ibsley 12 B2
Ibstock 58 C3
Ibstone 37 B1
Ibthorpe 25 A2
Iburndale 92 A4
Ibworth 25 C2
Ickburgh 61 D2
Ickford 37 A2
Ickham 30 A2
Ickleford 38 B4
Ickleton 51 C1
Icklingham 52 A4
Ickornshaw 84 C3
Ickwell Green 50 D2
Icomb 36 A4
Idbury 36 A3
Iddesleigh 8 E2
Ide 4 B4
Ide Hill 27 F1
Ideford 4 B3
Iden 20 A3
Iden Green 19 A4
Idless 1 E4
Idlicote 48 B1
Idmiston 12 C4
Idridgehay 68 C2
Idrigill 128 B3
Idstone 24 D4
Iford 17 B2
Ifton 34 B1
Ightfield 66 D2
Ightham 28 A2
Iken 53 C2
Ilam 68 A3
Ilchester 11 A3
Ilderton 107 C2
Ilford 10 C2
Ilfracombe 21 A1
Ilkeston 69 A2
Ilkley 84 D3
Ilketshall St Andrew 63 B1
Ilketshall St Margaret 63 A1
Illand 2 F3
Illey 57 A1
Illogan 1 C4
Illston on the Hill 59 B2
Ilmer 37 B2
Ilmington 48 A1
Ilminster 10 C2
Ilsington 4 A3
Ilston 32 D1
Ilton 90 D2
Ilton 10 C2
Immingham 81 D4
Immingham Dock 81 D4
Ince 76 A1
Ince Blundell 75 D3
Ince-in-Makerfield 77 A3
Inchnadamph 133 E4
Inchture 117 C3
Indian Queens 2 C1
Ingatestone 40 B2
Ingbirchworth 79 A3
Ingestre 57 A4
Ingham 81 B1
Ingham 73 C1
Ingham 52 B4
Ingham Corner 73 C1
Ingleby 68 C1
Ingleby Arncliffe 91 A4
Ingleby Greenhow 91 B4
Ingleigh Green 8 E2
Inglesbatch 23 C2
Inglesham 36 A1
Ingleton 96 C1
Ingleton 89 D1
Inglewhite 83 C2
Ingoe 101 B2
Ingoldisthorpe 72 A1
Ingoldsby 70 D1
Ingram 107 C2
Ingrave 40 B1
Ingst 34 C1
Ingthorpe 60 A3
Ingworth 73 A1
Inkberrow 47 B3
Inkpen 25 A2
Innellan 109 C2
Innerleithen 106 A3
Innermessan 98 B1
Innerwick 113 C3
Insch 127 A4
Insh 125 D2
Inskip 83 B2
Instow 8 D4
Inver 134 D1
Inver 121 B1
Inver-boyndie 132 A3
Inveralligin 128 F3
Inverallochy 132 D3
Inveran 134 B2
Inveraray 115 C2
Inverasdale 133 A1
Inverbervie 122 D3
Invergarry 124 D2
Invergordon 130 C3
Invergowrie 117 C4
Inverie 123 F2
Inverinate 124 B3
Inverkeilor 122 B1
Inverkeithing 112 A3
Inverkeithny 132 A2
Inverkip 109 D2
Inverkirkaig 133 C4
Invermoriston 124 E3
Inverness 130 C1
Inversanda 119 C2
Inveruglas 115 E2
Inverurie 127 B3
Inwardleigh 8 E1
Inworth 41 A3
Iping 15 B3
Ipplepen 4 A2
Ipsden 26 A4
Ipstones 67 C3
Ipswich 53 A1
Irby in the Marsh 71 D4
Irby upon Humber 82 A3
Irchester 50 B3
Ireby 94 F3
Ireby 89 C1
Ireland 50 D1
Ireleth 88 C2
Ireshopeburn 95 E3
Ireton Wood 68 C2
Irlam 77 B2
Irnham 70 D1
Ironbridge 56 A3
Ironville 69 A3
Irstead 63 B4
Irthington 100 C1
Irthlingborough 50 B4
Irton 92 B2
Irvine 104 D4
Isfield 18 A2
Isham 50 B4
Isington 26 B1
Isle Abbotts 10 C3
Isle of Whithorn 93 E3
Isleham 51 D4
Isleornsay 123 E3
Isley Walton 58 C4
Islington 27 E4
Islip 50 C4
Islip 36 D3
Isombridge 56 A3
Itchen Abbas 14 A4
Itchen Stoke 14 A4
Itchingfield 16 B3
Itteringham 73 A1
Itton 9 A1
Itton 34 B1
Ivegill 95 A3
Iver 27 B4
Iver Heath 27 B4
Iveston 96 B4
Ivinghoe 37 C3
Ivinghoe Aston 37 C3
Ivington 46 A2
Ivington Green 45 D2
Ivybridge 3 C1
Ivychurch 20 B3
Iwade 29 B3
Iwerne Minster 11 D2
Ixworth 52 C4
Ixworth Thorpe 52 C4
Jack-in-the-Green 9 D1
Jackton 110 B1
Jacobstow 8 B1
Jacobstowe 8 E1
Jameston 31 D1
Jarrow 102 B1
Jasper's Green 40 C4
Jaywick 42 B3
Jedburgh 106 D2
Jeffreston 31 E2
Jemimaville 130 C3
Jerbourg 137 B4
Jevington 18 B1
Jockey End 38 A3
John O'Groats 136 F4
Johnby 95 A2
Johnshaven 122 C3
Johnston 31 C3
Johnstone 110 A2
Joppa 44 B3
Jordanston 31 C4
Jurby 137 C3
Kaber 95 D1
Kames 109 B2
Kea 1 E4
Keal Cotes 71 C4
Kearsley 77 B3
Kearsley 101 B2
Kearstwick 89 C2
Kedington 52 A2
Kedleston 68 C2
Keelby 81 D4
Keele 67 A2
Keelham 84 D2
Keeston 31 C3
Keevil 24 A2
Kegworth 69 A1
Kehelland 1 C4
Keig 127 A3
Keighley 84 D2
Keir Mill 99 B4
Keisley 95 D2
Keiss 136 E3
Keith 131 D2
Keithtown 130 A2
Kelbrook 84 B3
Kelby 70 D2
Keld 90 A4
Kelfield 86 A2
Kelham 70 B3
Kelhead 99 E2
Kellamergh 83 B1
Kellas 117 D4
Kellaton 7 B4
Kelling 72 D2
Kellington 86 A1
Kelloe 96 D3
Kelly 3 A3
Kelmarsh 50 A4
Kelmscot 36 A2
Kelsale 53 C3
Kelsall 66 C4
Kelshall 51 B1
Kelsick 94 E4
Kelso 107 A3
Kelstedge 68 C4
Kelstern 82 A2
Kelston 23 C3
Kelty 112 A4
Kelvedon 41 A3
Kelvedon Hatch 40 B1
Kelynack 1 A3
Kemback 117 D2
Kemberton 56 B3
Kemble 35 B1
Kemerton 47 B1
Kemeys Commander 33 E2
Kemnay 127 B3
Kempley 34 C4
Kempley Green 34 C4
Kempsey 47 A2
Kempsford 36 A1
Kempston 50 C2
Kemsing 28 A2
Kenardington 20 A4
Kenchester 45 D1
Kencot 36 A2
Kendal 89 B3
Kenfig 21 D4
Kenilworth 48 B4
Kenley 55 D2
Kenmore 120 E1
Kenn 4 B4
Kenn 22 D3
Kennacraig 108 F2
Kennerleigh 9 B2
Kennet 111 B4
Kennethmont 126 E4
Kennett 52 A4
Kennford 4 B4
Kenninghall 62 B1
Kennington 36 D2
Kennoway 117 D1
Kenny 10 B2
Kennyhill 61 C1
Kennythorpe 91 D1
Kensworth 38 A3
Kent's Green 34 D4
Kent's Oak 13 A3
Kentallen 119 D2
Kentchurch 34 A4
Kentford 52 A3
Kentisbury 21 B1
Kentmere 89 A4
Kenton 4 B3
Kenton 53 A3
Kepwick 91 A3
Kerris 1 A3
Kerry 55 A1
Kerrycroy 109 C2
Kersall 70 A4
Kersey 52 C1
Kerswell Green 47 A2
Kessingland 63 C1
Kestle 1 F4
Kestle Mill 2 C1
Keswick 62 C3
Keswick 94 F2
Ketsby 82 B1
Ketteringham 62 C3
Kettins 117 C4
Kettlebaston 52 C2
Kettleburgh 53 B3
Kettering 50 B4
Kettleshulme 78 B1
Kettlesing 85 A4
Kettlesing Bottom 85 A4
Kettlestone 72 C1
Kettlethorpe 81 A1
Kettlewell 90 B1
Ketton 60 A3
Kewstoke 22 C2
Kexby 81 B2
Kexby 86 B3
Key Green 67 B4
Key Street 29 A3
Keyham 59 B3
Keyhaven 6 E4
Keyingham 87 C1
Keynsham 23 B3
Keysoe 50 C3
Keysoe Row 50 D3
Keyston 50 C4
Keyworth 69 B1
Kibblesworth 96 C4
Kibworth Beauchamp 59 B2
Kibworth Harcourt 59 B2
Kidderminster 47 A4
Kidlington 36 C3
Kidmore End 26 A4
Kidsgrove 67 B3
Kidwelly 32 B2
Kielder 100 D4
Kiells 108 C2
Kilbarchan 109 E2
Kilberry 108 E2
Kilbirnie 109 E1
Kilburn 68 C2
Kilburn 91 B2
Kilby 59 B2
Kilchattan 109 C1
Kilchoan 118 E2
Kilchrenan 115 B3
Kilconquhar 117 E1
Kilcot 34 D4
Kilcreggan 109 D3
Kildale 91 B4
Kildary 130 C4
Kildrummy 126 E3
Kildwick 84 C3
Kilfinan 109 A3
Kilgwrrwg Common 34 B1
Kilham 87 A4
Kilkenneth 118 A1
Kilkenzie 103 D2
Kilkhampton 8 B2
Killamarsh 80 A1
Killearn 110 A4
Killerby 96 C1
Killerton 9 C1
Killichonan 120 C2
Killiecrankie 121 A2
Killin 116 B4
Killinghall 85 B4
Killington 89 C3
Kilmacolm 109 E2
Kilmany 117 D3
Kilmarnock 104 E4
Kilmartin 114 F1
Kilmaurs 104 D4
Kilmelford 115 A2
Kilmersdon 23 C1
Kilmeston 14 A3
Kilmichael 103 D2
Kilmington 10 B1
Kilmington 11 C4
Kilmington Common 11 C4
Kilmorack 130 A1
Kilmun 109 C3
Kiln Pit Hill 96 A4
Kilndown 19 A4
Kilninver 114 F3
Kilnsea 82 B4
Kilnsey 90 B1
Kilnwick 87 A3
Kilpeck 34 A4
Kilpin 86 C1
Kilrenny 117 E1
Kilsby 49 B4
Kilspindie 117 B3
Kilstay 93 B3
Kilsyth 110 C3
Kiltarlity 130 A1
Kilton 97 C1
Kilton Thorpe 97 C1
Kilve 22 B1

Kilvington	70	B2
Kilwinning	104	C4
Kimberley	62	B3
Kimblesworth	96	C4
Kimbolton	50	D3
Kimbolton	46	A3
Kimcote	59	A1
Kimmeridge	6	A3
Kimpton	25	A1
Kimpton	38	B3
Kinbrace	136	A1
Kinbuck	116	D1
Kincardine	134	B1
Kincardine	111	B4
Kincardine O'Neil	127	A1
Kincraig	125	D2
Kindallachan	121	A1
Kineton	35	C4
Kineton	48	B2
Kinfauns	117	B3
Kingsbridge	7	A4
King's Cliffe	60	A2
King's Coughton	47	C3
King's Lynn	61	B4
King's Mills	137	B4
King's Nympton	9	A3
King's Pyon	45	D2
King's Somborne	13	A4
King's Stag	11	C2
King's Stanley	35	A2
King's Sutton	49	A1
King's Walden	38	B4
Kingarth	109	C1
Kingcoed	34	A2
Kingford	8	B1
Kingham	36	A4
Kinghorn	112	B4
Kinglassie	117	B1
Kingoldrum	121	D2
Kings Caple	34	B4
Kings Langley	38	A2
Kings Meaburn	95	C1
Kings Newnham	49	A4
Kings Ripton	51	A4
Kings Weston	23	A4
Kingsand	3	B1
Kingsbarns	117	F2
Kingsbridge	9	C4
Kingsbury	58	A2
Kingsclere	25	C2
Kingscote	35	A1
Kingscott	8	D2
Kingsdon	11	A3
Kingsdown	30	C1
Kingsdown	23	C3
Kingseat	112	A4
Kingsey	37	B2
Kingsfold	16	B4
Kingshall Street	52	C3
Kingsheanton	8	E4
Kingskerswell	4	A2
Kingsland	45	D3
Kingsley	76	B1
Kingsley	15	A4
Kingsley	67	C2
Kingsley Green	15	B4
Kingsmuir	122	A1
Kingsnorth	20	A4
Kingsthorne	34	B4
Kingston	51	B2
Kingston	3	A3
Kingston	7	B4
Kingston	11	C2
Kingston	6	B3
Kingston	6	F3
Kingston	30	A1
Kingston Blount	37	B2
Kingston Lisle	36	B1
Kingston on Soar	69	A1
Kingston on Spey	131	C3
Kingston Russell	5	D4
Kingston Seymour	22	D3
Kingston upon Thames	27	C3
Kingstone	45	D1
Kingstone	10	C2
Kingstone	68	A1
Kingswood	37	A3
Kingswood	34	D1
Kingswood	9	D4
Kingswood	48	A4
Kingthorpe	81	D1
Kington	34	C1
Kington	47	B2
Kington	45	C2
Kington Langley	24	A4
Kington Magna	11	C3
Kington St Michael	24	A4
Kingussie	125	C2
Kingweston	11	A4
Kinkell Bridge	116	E2
Kinlet	56	B1
Kinloch	135	C1
Kinloch	123	C2
Kinloch	121	C1
Kinloch Hourn	124	A2
Kinloch Rannoch	120	D2
Kinlochbervie	135	B3
Kinlocheil	119	D4
Kinlochewe	129	B3
Kinlochlaggan	125	A1
Kinlochleven	119	E2
Kinlochmoidart	119	A3
Kinloss	131	A3
Kinnaird	121	A2
Kinneff	122	D4
Kinnerley	55	B4
Kinnersley	45	C2
Kinnersley	47	A1
Kinnerton	45	C3
Kinnesswood	117	B1
Kinninvie	96	B1
Kinoulton	70	A1
Kinross	117	B1
Kinrossie	117	B4
Kinsham	45	D3
Kinsham	47	B1
Kinsley	80	A4
Kintbury	25	A3
Kintessack	130	E3
Kintillo	117	B2
Kinton	45	D4
Kinton	55	C4
Kintore	127	B3
Kintra	114	B3
Kintraw	114	F1
Kinver	56	C1
Kippax	85	C2
Kippen	110	B4
Kippford or Scaur	94	B4
Kipping's Cross	18	B4
Kirby Bedon	63	A3
Kirby Bellars	59	B4
Kirby Cane	63	B2
Kirby Grindalythe	92	A1
Kirby Hill	90	C4
Kirby Hill	91	A1
Kirby Knowle	91	A2
Kirby le Soken	42	B3
Kirby Misperton	91	D2
Kirby Muxloe	59	A3
Kirby Row	63	B2
Kirby Sigston	91	A3
Kirby Underdale	86	C4
Kirby Wiske	90	E2
Kirdford	16	A3
Kirk Bramwith	80	C4
Kirk Deighton	85	C3
Kirk Hammerton	85	C4
Kirk Ireton	68	B3
Kirk Langley	68	C2
Kirk Michael	137	C3
Kirk Sandall	80	B4
Kirk Smeaton	80	B4
Kirk Yetholm	107	B3
Kirkandrews	93	F4
Kirkbampton	94	F4
Kirkbean	99	C1
Kirkbride	94	E4
Kirkburn	87	A4
Kirkburton	79	A4
Kirkby	81	C2
Kirkby	76	A3
Kirkby	91	B4
Kirkby Fleetham	90	E3
Kirkby in Ashfield	69	A3
Kirkby Lonsdale	89	C2
Kirkby Malham	84	B4
Kirkby Mallory	58	C2
Kirkby Malzeard	90	D1
Kirkby on Bain	71	B4
Kirkby Overblow	85	B3
Kirkby Thore	95	C2
Kirkby Underwood	70	D1
Kirkby Wharf	86	A2
Kirkby-in-Furness	88	C2
Kirkbymoorside	91	C2
Kirkcaldy	112	B4
Kirkcambeck	100	C2
Kirkcolm	98	A2
Kirkconnel	105	A1
Kirkcowan	98	D1
Kirkcudbright	94	A4
Kirkgunzeon	99	B1
Kirkham	83	B2
Kirkham	91	D1
Kirkhamgate	85	B1
Kirkharle	101	B3
Kirkhaugh	95	C4
Kirkheaton	101	B2
Kirkheaton	79	A4
Kirkhill	130	B1
Kirkinner	93	D4
Kirkintilloch	110	B3
Kirkland	94	D1
Kirkland	99	B3
Kirkleatham	97	B1
Kirklevington	91	A4
Kirklington	90	E2
Kirklington	70	A3
Kirklinton	100	B1
Kirkliston	112	A3
Kirkmabreck	93	E4
Kirkmaiden	93	B3
Kirkmichael	121	B2
Kirkmichael	104	D1
Kirkmuirhill	105	B4
Kirknewton	107	B3
Kirknewton	111	C2
Kirkoswald	95	B3
Kirkoswald	104	C1
Kirkpatrick	99	C3
Kirkpatrick Durham	99	B2
Kirkpatrick-Fleming	100	A2
Kirksanton	88	C2
Kirkstead	71	A4
Kirkstile	100	B3
Kirkthorpe	85	B1
Kirkton	99	C3
Kirkton of Glenbuchat	126	D3
Kirkton of Logie Buchan	127	D4
Kirkton of Menmuir	122	A2
Kirkton of Rayne	127	B4
Kirkton of Skene	127	B2
Kirkton of Strathmartine	117	D4
Kirktown of Bourtie	127	B4
Kirkwhelpington	101	B3
Kirmington	81	D4
Kirmond le Mire	81	D2
Kirriemuir	121	E2
Kirstead Green	63	A2
Kirtlebridge	100	A2
Kirtling	52	A3
Kirtling Green	52	A2
Kirtlington	36	C3
Kirtomy	135	F4
Kirton	127	A3
Kirton	71	B2
Kirton	70	A4
Kirton	53	B1
Kirton in Lindsey	81	B3
Kishorn	128	F1
Kislingbury	49	C3
Kittisford	9	D3
Kivernoll	34	B4
Knaith	81	A2
Knaplock	9	B4
Knapp	10	B3
Knapton	86	A3
Knapton	92	A2
Knapton	73	B1
Knapwell	51	B3
Knaresborough	85	B4
Knarsdale	95	C4
Knayton	91	A3
Knebworth	39	A3
Kneesall	70	A4
Kneesworth	51	B1
Kneeton	70	A2
Knenhall	67	B2
Knightcote	49	A2
Knightley	56	C4
Knighton	11	B2
Knighton	45	C4
Knighton	22	B1
Knighton	67	A2
Knighton	67	A1
Knightwick	46	C2
Knill	45	C3
Knipton	70	B1
Kniveton	68	B3
Knock	95	C2
Knockally	136	D1
Knockan	133	E3
Knockholt	27	F2
Knockholt Pound	27	F2
Knockin	55	B4
Knocknain	98	A1
Knodishall	53	C3
Knole	11	A3
Knolton	66	B2
Knook	24	B1
Knossington	59	C3
Knott End-on-Sea	83	B3
Knotting	50	C3
Knotting Green	50	C3
Knottingley	85	C1
Knowbury	46	A4
Knowehead	98	F3
Knowl Hill	26	B4
Knowle	9	B1
Knowle	9	C2
Knowle	4	C3
Knowle	21	E1
Knowle	48	A4
Knowle Green	83	D2
Knowle St Giles	10	B2
Knowsley	76	A3
Knowstone	9	B3
Knox Bridge	19	B4
Knucklas	45	C4
Knuston	50	B3
Knutsford	77	B1
Krumlin	78	C4
Kuggar	1	D2
Kyleakin	123	F4
Kyle of Lochalsh	123	F4
Kylerhea	123	F3
Kynnersley	56	A4
Kyrewood	46	B3
L'Eree	137	A4
L'Etacq	137	A4
La Fontenelle	137	B4
La Greve de Lecq	137	A4
La Rocque	137	B3
La Villette	137	B4
Laceby	82	A3
Lacey Green	37	B2
Lach Dennis	67	A4
Lackford	52	B4
Lackford Green	52	B4
Lacock	24	A3
Ladbroke	49	A3
Laddingford	28	B1
Ladock	2	C1
Lady Hall	88	C2
Ladybank	117	C2
Ladykirk	107	B4
Ladywood	47	A3
Lagavulin	103	B4
Laggan	125	B1
Laide	133	B1
Lairg	134	B3
Lake	12	B4
Lakenheath	61	C1
Lakesend	61	A2
Laleston	21	D4
Lamancha	112	A1
Lamas	63	A4
Lamberhurst	19	A4
Lamberhurst Down	19	A4
Lambley	70	A2
Lambley	100	D1
Lambourn	25	A4
Lambourne End	40	A1
Lambs Green	17	A4
Lamerton	3	B3
Lamesley	102	A1
Lamington	105	C3
Lamlash	104	A3
Lamonby	95	A3
Lamorna	1	A2
Lampeter	44	B2
Lampeter Velfrey	31	E3
Lamphey	31	D2
Lamplugh	94	D1
Lamport	50	A4
Lamyatt	11	B4
Lanark	105	B4
Lancaster	83	C4
Lanchester	96	C4
Lancing	16	B1
Landbeach	51	C3
Landcross	8	D3
Landimore	32	C1
Landkey Town	8	E4
Landrake	3	A2
Landscove	4	A2
Landulph	3	B2
Lane	2	B1
Lane End	37	B1
Lane End Waberthwaite	88	B3
Lane Ends	68	B1
Lane Head	96	B1
Laneast	2	F4
Laneham	81	A1
Lanehead	95	E3
Langar	70	A1
Langbank	109	E3
Langbar	84	D3
Langcliffe	90	A1
Langdale End	92	A3
Langdyke	117	C1
Langenhoe	42	A3
Langford	50	D1
Langford	9	D1
Langford	41	A2
Langford	70	B3
Langford	36	A2
Langford Budville	9	D3
Langford End	50	D2
Langham	52	D1
Langham	72	D2
Langham	59	C3
Langham	52	C4
Langho	84	A2
Langholm	100	B3
Langley	13	B1
Langley	39	A4
Langley	101	A1
Langley	48	A3
Langley Burrell	24	B3
Langley Park	96	C3
Langley Street	63	B2
Langley Upper Green	51	C1
Langold	80	B2
Langore	2	F4
Langport	10	C3
Langrick	71	B2
Langridge	23	C3
Langrigg	94	E4
Langrish	14	B3
Langsett	79	A3
Langstone	34	A1
Langthorne	90	D3
Langthorpe	90	E1
Langthwaite	90	B4
Langtoft	92	B1
Langtoft	60	B3
Langton	96	C1
Langton	71	B4
Langton	71	C4
Langton	91	D1
Langton by Wragby	81	D1
Langton Herring	5	E3
Langton Matravers	6	B3
Langtree	8	D2
Langwathby	95	B2
Langworth	81	C1
Lanivet	2	D2
Lank	2	E3
Lanlivery	2	E1
Lanner	1	D4
Lanreath	2	E1
Lansallos	2	E1
Lanteglos	2	E3
Lanteglos Highway	2	E1
Lanton	106	D2
Lanton	107	C3
Lapford	9	A2
Laphroaig	103	B4
Lapley	56	C3
Lapworth	48	A4
Larbert	111	A3
Largoward	117	E2
Largs	109	D1
Larkhall	110	C1
Larkhill	24	C1
Larling	62	A1
Lartington	96	A1
Lasham	26	A1
Lask Edge	67	B3
Lastingham	91	C3
Latchingdon	41	A2
Latchley	3	A3
Latebrook	67	B3
Lathbury	50	B1
Latheron	136	D1
Latimer	38	A2
Latteridge	23	B4
Latton	35	C1
Lauder	106	C4
Laugharne	32	A3
Laughton	59	B1
Laughton	81	A3
Laughton	70	D1
Laughton	18	A2
Laughton-en-le-Morthen	80	B2
Launcells	8	B1
Launceston	3	A4
Launton	36	D4
Laurencekirk	122	C3
Laurieston	99	A1
Lavendon	50	B2
Lavenham	52	C2
Lavernock	22	B3
Laversdale	100	C1
Laverton	47	C1
Laverton	90	D1
Laverton	23	C2
Lavister	66	B3
Law	111	A1
Lawers	116	C4
Lawford	42	A4
Lawford	10	A4
Lawhitton	3	A3
Lawkland	89	D1
Lawrenny	31	D2
Lawshall	52	B2
Laxey	137	D2
Laxfield	53	B4
Laxton	86	C1
Laxton	59	D2
Laxton	70	A4
Laycock	84	C2
Layer Breton	41	B3
Layer Marney	41	B3
Layham	52	D1
Laytham	86	C2
Laythes	94	F4
Lazonby	95	B3
Leamington Spa	48	B3
Le Bourg	137	B4
Le Villocq	137	B4
Lea	68	C3
Lea	34	C3
Lea	81	A2
Lea	55	C1
Lea	24	B4
Lea Marston	58	A2
Leaden Roding	40	B3
Leadenham	70	C3
Leadgate	96	B4
Leadhills	105	B2
Leafield	36	B3
Leake Common Side	71	C3
Lealholm	91	D4
Leamington Hastings	49	A3
Leasgill	89	B2
Leasingham	70	D2
Leasingthorne	96	C2
Leatherhead	27	C2
Leathley	85	A3
Leaton	55	D4
Leavenheath	52	C1
Leavening	86	C4
Leaves Green	27	E2
Lebberston	92	B2
Lechlade	36	A2
Leck	89	C2
Leckford	13	A4
Leckhampstead	25	B3
Leckhampstead	49	C1
Leckhampstead Thicket	25	B4
Leckmelm	133	D1
Leconfield	87	A3
Ledburn	37	C3
Ledbury	46	C1
Ledgemoor	45	D2
Ledsham	85	C1
Ledston	85	C1
Ledwell	36	C4
Lee	21	A1
Lee Brockhurst	66	C1
Lee-on-the-Solent	14	A1
Leebotwood	55	D2
Leece	88	D1
Leeds	29	A2
Leeds	85	B2
Leedstown	1	C3
Leek	67	C3
Leek Wootton	48	B4
Leeming	90	E3
Leeming Bar	90	E3
Lees	68	B1
Leesthorpe	59	C3
Leeswood	66	A3
Leetown	117	B3
Legbourne	82	B2
Legerwood	106	D4
Legsby	81	D2
Leicester	59	A3
Leigh	11	B2
Leigh	35	A4
Leigh	77	A3
Leigh	28	A1
Leigh	27	D1
Leigh	35	C1
Leigh	46	C2
Leigh Delamere	24	A4
Leigh Green	20	A4
Leigh Sinton	46	C2
Leigh upon Mendip	23	B1
Leigh Woods	23	A3
Leighterton	35	A1
Leighton	55	B3
Leighton	56	A3
Leighton Buzzard	37	C4
Leinthall Earls	45	D3
Leinthall Starkes	45	D4
Leintwardine	45	D4
Leire	59	A1
Leiston	53	C3
Leitfie	121	D1
Leitholm	107	A4
Lelant	1	B4
Lelley	87	C2
Lem Hill	46	C4
Lenchwick	47	B2
Lendalfoot	98	B3
Lenham	29	B1
Lenham Heath	29	B1
Lennel	107	B4
Lennoxtown	110	B3
Lenton	70	D1
Leochel-Cushnie	126	E2
Leominster	46	A3
Leppington	86	C4
Lepton	79	A4
Lerryn	2	E1
Les Quartiers	137	B4
Les Quennevais	137	A3
Lesbury	107	E1
Leslie	127	A4
Leslie	117	C1
Lesmahagow	105	B4
Lesnewth	2	E4
Lessingham	73	C1
Lessonhall	94	E4
Leswalt	98	A1
Letchworth	39	A4
Letcombe Bassett	25	A4
Letcombe Regis	25	A4
Letham	122	A1
Letham	117	C2
Letheringham	53	B3
Letheringsett	72	D2
Letterston	31	C4
Letton	45	C2
Letty Green	39	A3
Letwell	80	B2
Leuchars	117	D3
Levedale	56	C4
Leven	87	B3
Leven	117	D1
Levens	89	B2
Levens Green	39	B4
Leverington	61	A3
Leverton	71	C2
Levington	53	A1
Levisham	91	D3
Lew	36	B2
Lewannick	2	F3
Lewdown	3	B4
Lewes	17	B2
Leweston	31	C4
Lewknor	37	A1
Lewson Street	29	B2
Lewtrenchard	3	B4
Lexworthy	10	B4
Ley Hill	38	A2
Leybourne	28	B2
Leyburn	90	C3
Leygreen	38	B4
Leyland	83	C1
Leys	117	C4
Leysdown-on-Sea	29	C3
Leysmill	122	B1
Leysters	46	A3
Lezant	3	A3
Lezayre	137	C3
Lhanbryde	131	C3
Libanus	33	B4
Libberton	105	C4
Lichfield	57	B3
Lickey	47	B4
Lickey End	47	B4
Lickfold	15	B3
Liddesdale	119	B2
Liddington	24	D4
Lidgate	52	A3
Lidlington	50	C1
Liff	117	C4
Lifton	3	A4
Liftondown	3	A4
Lighthorne	48	B2
Lilbourne	49	B4
Lilleshall	56	B4
Lilley	38	B4
Lilliesleaf	106	C2
Lillingstone Dayrell	49	C1
Lillingstone Lovell	49	C1
Lillington	11	B2
Lilstock	22	B1
Lime Street	35	A4
Limekilns	111	C3
Limerstone	6	F3
Limington	11	A3
Limpenhoe	63	B3
Limpley Stoke	23	C2
Limpsfield	27	E2
Limpsfield Chart	27	E1
Linby	69	B3
Linchmere	15	B4
Lincoln	70	D4
Lincomb	47	A4
Lindal in Furness	88	D1
Lindale	89	A2
Lindford	15	A4
Lindley Green	85	A3
Lindridge	46	B4
Lindsell	40	B4
Lindsey	52	C2
Lindsey Tye	52	C2
Lingdale	97	C1
Lingen	45	D3
Lingfield	27	E1
Lingwood	63	B3
Linkend	35	A4
Linkenholt	25	A2
Linkinhorne	3	A3
Linley	55	C2
Linley Green	46	B2
Linleygreen	56	A2
Linlithgow	111	B3
Linstead Parva	53	B4
Linstock	100	B1
Linthwaite	78	C4
Lintlaw	113	D1
Lintmill	131	E3
Linton	51	D2
Linton	58	B4
Linton	34	C4
Linton	28	B1
Linton	84	C4
Linton	85	C3
Linton Hill	34	C4
Linton-on-Ouse	85	C4
Linwood	81	D2
Linwood	110	A2
Liphook	15	A4
Liscombe	9	B4
Liskeard	2	F2
Liss	15	A3
Lissett	87	B4
Lissington	81	D1
Litcham	61	D4
Litchborough	49	C2
Litchfield	25	B2
Litlington	51	A1
Litlington	18	A1
Little Abington	51	C2
Little Addington	50	B4
Little Alne	47	C3
Little Amwell	39	B3
Little Asby	89	D4
Little Aston	57	B2
Little Ayton	91	B4
Little Baddow	41	A2
Little Badminton	23	C4
Little Bampton	94	F4
Little Bardfield	40	B4
Little Barningham	73	A1
Little Barrington	36	A3
Little Bavington	101	B2
Little Bedwyn	25	A3
Little Bentley	42	A4
Little Berkhamsted	39	A2
Little Birch	34	B4
Little Blencow	95	A2
Little Bognor	16	A3
Little Bolehill	68	C3
Little Bollington	77	B2
Little Bourton	49	A1
Little Bradley	52	A2
Little Brampton	55	C1
Little Brechin	122	B2
Little Brickhill	37	C4
Little Brington	49	C3
Little Bromley	42	A4
Little Broughton	94	D2
Little Budworth	66	D4
Little Burstead	40	C1
Little Bytham	60	A4
Little Casterton	60	A3
Little Cawthorpe	82	B1
Little Chart	29	B1
Little Chesterford	51	C1
Little Cheverell	24	B2
Little Chishill	51	B1
Little Clacton	42	B3
Little Clifton	94	D2
Little Comberton	47	B1
Little Compton	36	A4
Little Cornard	52	C1
Little Cowarne	46	B2
Little Coxwell	36	B1
Little Crakehall	90	D3
Little Cressingham	61	D2
Little Crosby	75	D3
Little Cubley	68	B1
Little Dalby	59	C3
Little Dewchurch	34	B4
Little Ditton	52	A3
Little Driffield	87	A4
Little Dunham	61	D3
Little Dunkeld	121	B1
Little Dunmow	40	B3
Little Durnford	12	B4
Little Eaton	68	C2
Little Ellingham	62	A2
Little Everdon	49	B3
Little Faringdon	36	A2
Little Fencote	90	E3
Little Fenton	86	A2
Little Fransham	62	A3
Little Gaddesden	38	A3
Little Gorsley	34	C4
Little Gransden	51	A2
Little Green	23	C1
Little Grimsby	82	B2
Little Hadham	40	A4
Little Hale	71	A2
Little Hallingbury	40	A3
Little Harrowden	50	B4
Little Haseley	37	A2
Little Hatfield	87	B3
Little Haven	31	C3
Little Hay	57	B2
Little Haywood	57	A4
Little Hereford	46	A4
Little Horkesley	41	B4
Little Hormead	39	B4
Little Horwood	37	B4
Little Houghton	50	A3
Little Houghton	80	A3
Little Hucklow	79	A1
Little Hutton	91	A1
Little Keyford	23	C1
Little Kimble	37	B2
Little Kineton	48	B2
Little Kingshill	37	C2
Little Langdale	88	D4
Little Langford	12	B4
Little Leigh	77	A1
Little Lever	77	B4
Little Linford	50	A1
Little Load	11	A3
Little London	25	A1
Little London	26	A2
Little Longstone	68	B4

Little Malvern 46 C1
Little Maplestead 52 B1
Little Marcle 46 B1
Little Marlow 37 C1
Little Massingham 61 D4
Little Melton 62 C3
Little Mill 33 E2
Little Milton 36 D2
Little Missenden 37 C2
Little Musgrave 95 D1
Little Ness 55 C4
Little Newcastle 31 D4
Little Newsham 96 B1
Little Norton 11 A2
Little Oakley 42 B4
Little Oakley 59 D1
Little Onn 56 C4
Little Orton 95 A4
Little Packington 58 A1
Little Paxton 50 D3
Little Petherick 2 C3
Little Plumstead 63 A3
Little Ponton 70 C1
Little Preston 49 B2
Little Raveley 60 C1
Little Ribston 85 B4
Little Rissington 36 A3
Little Rollright 36 B4
Little Ryburgh 72 C1
Little Salkeld 95 B3
Little Sampford 51 D1
Little Saughall 66 B4
Little Saxham 52 B3
Little Sessay 91 A1
Little Singleton 83 B2
Little Snoring 72 C1
Little Sodbury 23 C4
Little Somerford 24 B4
Little Soudley 67 A1
Little Stainton 96 D1
Little Stanney 76 A1
Little Staughton 50 D3
Little Steeping 71 D4
Little Stonham 52 D3
Little Stretton 59 B2
Little Stretton 55 C2
Little Strickland 95 B1
Little Stukeley 51 A4
Little Swinburne 101 B2
Little Tew 36 B4
Little Tey 41 B4
Little Thetford 51 C4
Little Thorpe 97 A3
Little Thurlow Green 52 A2
Little Torrington 8 D2
Little Town 83 D2
Little Urswick 88 D1
Little Wakering 41 B1
Little Walden 51 D1
Little Waldingfield 52 C2
Little Walsingham 72 C1
Little Weighton 87 A2
Little Wenham 52 D1
Little Wenlock 56 A3
Little Whitefield 7 A4
Little Wilbraham 51 C3
Little Witcombe 35 A3
Little Witley 46 C3
Little Wittenham 36 D1
Little Wolford 48 A1
Little Wymington 50 B3
Little Wymondley 39 A4
Little Wyrley 57 A3
Little Yeldham 52 B1
Littleborough 78 B4
Littleborough 81 A1
Littlebourne 30 A2
Littlebredy 5 E4
Littlebury 51 C1
Littlebury Green 51 C1
Littledean 34 C3
Littleham 8 D3
Littleham 4 C3
Littlehampton 16 A1
Littlehempston 4 A2
Littleport 61 B1
Littlethorpe 59 A2
Littlethorpe 90 E1
Littleton 66 B4
Littleton 13 B4
Littleton 11 A4
Littleton Drew 24 A4
Littleton-on-Severn 34 C1
Littletown 96 D3
Littleworth 36 B1
Littleworth 47 A2
Litton 79 A1
Litton 90 A1
Litton 23 B2
Litton Cheney 5 D4
Liverpool 75 D2
Liversedge 85 A1
Liverton 4 A3
Liverton 97 C1
Livingston 111 C2
Livingston Village 111 C2
Lixton 3 D1
Lixwm 65 E4
Lizard 1 D1
Llanaelhaearn 64 C2
Llanafan 44 C4
Llanallgo 74 C2
Llanarmon Dyffryn
Ceiriog 65 E1
Llanarmon-yn-Ial 65 E3
Llanarth 43 E3
Llanarth 34 A3
Llanarthne 32 C3
Llanasa 75 B1
Llanbadarn Fynydd 45 A4
Llanbadoc 34 A2
Llanbeder 34 A1
Llanbedr 64 E1
Llanbedr 33 E3
Llanbedr-Dyffryn-Clwyd 65 E3
Llanbedr-y-Cennin 65 A4
Llanbedrgoch 74 C1
Llanbedrog 64 C1
Llanberis 64 E3
Llanbethery 22 A3
Llanbister 45 A4
Llanboidy 32 A4
Llanbradach 33 D1
Llanbrynmair 54 D2
Llancadle 22 A3
Llancarfan 22 A3
Llancloudy 34 B3
Llandanwg 64 E1
Llanddanielfab 64 D4
Llanddarog 32 C3
Llanddeiniol 44 B4
Llandderfel 65 C1
Llanddeusant 74 B2
Llanddew 33 C4
Llanddewi 32 C1
Llanddewi Brefi 44 C2
Llanddewi Rhydderch 34 A3
Llanddewi Velfrey 31 E3
Llanddewi Ystradenni 45 A4
Llanddoget 65 B4
Llanddona 74 D1
Llanddowror 32 A3
Llanddulas 75 A1
Llanddwywe 54 A4
Llanddyfnan 74 C1
Llandefaelog-Trer-Graig 33 D4
Llandefalle 45 A1
Llandegfan 74 D1
Llandegla 65 E3
Llandegley 45 B3
Llandegveth 33 E1
Llandeilo 32 D4
Llandeilo Graban 45 A1
Llandeloy 31 C4
Llandenny 34 A2
Llandevaud 34 A1
Llandevenny 22 D4
Llandinam 54 E1
Llandissilio 31 E3
Llandogo 34 B2
Llandough 21 E3
Llandovery 44 C1
Llandow 21 E3
Llandre 44 C1
Llandre 54 A1
Llandre Isaf 31 E4
Llandrindod Wells 45 A3
Llandrillo 65 D1
Llandrinio 55 B4
Llandudno 74 F1
Llandudno Junction 74 F1
Llandudwen 64 B1
Llandulas 44 D1
Llandwrog 64 D3
Llandybie 32 D3
Llandyfaelog 32 B3
Llandyfriog 43 E1
Llandygai 64 E4
Llandygwydd 43 D1
Llandyrnog 65 D4
Llandyssil 55 A2
Llandysul 43 E1
Llanedeyrn 22 B4
Llanegryn 54 A3
Llanegwad 32 C3
Llaneilian 74 C2
Llanelian-yn-Rhos 74 F1
Llanelidan 65 D3
Llanelieu 45 B1
Llanellen 33 E3
Llanelli 32 C2
Llanelltyd 54 B4
Llanelwedd 45 A2
Llanenddwyn 54 A4
Llanengan 64 B1
Llanerchymedd 74 B2
Llanerfyl 54 E3
Llanfachraeth 74 B1
Llanfachreth 54 B4
Llanfaelog 74 B1
Llanfaelrhys 64 B1
Llanfaethlu 74 B2
Llanfair 64 E1
Llanfair Caereinion 54 E3
Llanfair Clydogau 44 B2
Llanfair P G 64 D4
Llanfair Talhaiarn 65 C4
Llanfair Waterdine 45 C4
Llanfair-is-gaer 64 D4
Llanfair-y-Cwmwd 64 D4
Llanfair-yn-Neubwll 74 A1
Llanfairfechan 74 E1
Llanfairynghornwy 74 B2
Llanfallteg 31 E3
Llanfallteg West 31 E3
Llanfarian 44 B4
Llanfechain 55 A4
Llanfechell 74 B2
Llanferres 65 E3
Llanfihangel Glyn Myfyr 65 C3
Llanfihangel Nant Bran 44 E1
Llanfihangel Rhydithon 45 B3
Llanfihangel yn Nhowyn 74 B1
Llanfihangel-ar-Arth 44 A1
Llanfihangel-y-
Creuddyn 44 C4
Llanfihangel-y-traethau 64 E1
Llanfihangel-yng-
Ngwynfa 54 E4
Llanfilo 33 D4
Llanfoist 33 E3
Llanfor 65 C1
Llanfrechfa 33 E1
Llanfrynach 33 C4
Llanfwrog 65 D3
Llanfwrog 74 A2
Llanfyllin 55 A4
Llanfynydd 32 D4
Llanfynydd 66 A3
Llanfyrnach 32 A4
Llangadfan 54 E3
Llangadog 32 E4
Llangadwaladr 64 C4
Llangaffo 64 D4
Llangammarch Wells 44 E2
Llangan 21 E4
Llangarron 34 B3
Llangathen 32 D3
Llangattock 33 D3
Llangattock Lingoed 34 A3
Llangedwyn 55 A4
Llangefni 74 C1
Llangeinor 33 B1
Llangeitho 44 B3
Llangeler 43 E1
Llangelynin 54 A3
Llangendeirne 32 C3
Llangennech 32 D2
Llangennith 32 C1
Llangian 64 B1
Llangloffan 31 C4
Llanglydwen 31 E4
Llangoed 74 D1
Llangollen 65 E2
Llangolman 31 E4
Llangors 33 D4
Llangower 65 C1
Llangranog 43 E2
Llangristiolus 74 C1
Llangrove 34 B3
Llangunllo 45 B4
Llangunnor 32 C3
Llangurig 54 D1
Llangwm 65 C2
Llangwm 34 A2
Llangwm 31 D2
Llangwm-isaf 34 A2
Llangwnnadl 64 B1
Llangwyryfon 44 B4
Llangybi 44 B2
Llangybi 64 D2
Llangybi 34 A1
Llangynhafal 65 E4
Llangynidr 33 D3
Llangynin 32 A3
Llangynog 32 B3
Llangynog 65 D1
Llangynwyd 33 A1
Llanhamlach 33 C4
Llanharan 21 E4
Llanharry 22 A4
Llanhennock 34 A1
Llanhilleth 33 D2
Llanidloes 54 D1
Llaniestyn 64 B1
Llanigon 45 B1
Llanilid 21 E4
Llanina 43 E3
Llanishen 34 B2
Llanllechid 64 E4
Llanllowell 34 A1
Llanllugan 54 E2
Llanllwch 32 B3
Llanllwni 44 A1
Llanllyfni 64 D3
Llanmadoc 32 C1
Llanmaes 21 E3
Llanmartin 34 A1
Llanmiloe 32 A2
Llannefydd 65 C4
Llannon 32 C2
Llannor 64 C1
Llanon 44 A3
Llanover 33 E2
Llanpumsaint 32 B4
Llanrhaeadr-ym-
Mochnant 65 E1
Llanrhidian 32 C1
Llanrhychwyn 65 B4
Llanrhyddlad 74 B2
Llanrhystud 44 A4
Llanrian 31 B4
Llanrothal 34 B3
Llanrug 64 D4
Llanrwst 65 B4
Llansadurnen 32 A2
Llansadwrn 32 E4
Llansadwrn 74 D1
Llansaint 32 B2
Llansanffraid Glan
Conwy 74 F1
Llansannan 65 C4
Llansantffraed 33 D4
Llansantffraed-
Cwmdeuddwr 44 E3
Llansantffraed-in-Elvel 45 A2
Llansantffraid 44 A3
Llansantffraid-ym-
Mechain 55 A4
Llansawel 44 B1
Llansilin 65 E1
Llansoy 34 A2
Llanspyddid 33 C4
Llanstadwell 31 C2
Llansteffan 32 B3
Llanteg 31 E2
Llanthewy Skirrid 33 E3
Llanthony 33 E4
Llantilio Pertholey 33 E3
Llantilio-Crossenny 34 A3
Llantrisant 34 A1
Llantrisant 22 A4
Llantrithyd 22 A3
Llantwit Fardre 22 A4
Llantwit Major 21 E3
Llanuwchllyn 65 B1
Llanvaches 34 A1
Llanvair Discoed 34 A1
Llanvapley 34 A3
Llanvetherine 34 A3
Llanvihangel Crucorney 33 E3
Llanwddyn 54 E4
Llanwenog 44 A2
Llanwern 34 A1
Llanwinio 32 A4
Llanwnda 64 D3
Llanwnda 43 A1
Llanwnnen 44 A2
Llanwnog 54 E2
Llanwrda 32 E4
Llanwrin 54 C3
Llanwrthwl 44 E3
Llanwrtyd Wells 44 D2
Llanyblodwel 55 B4
Llanybri 32 B3
Llanybydder 44 A1
Llanycefn 31 E4
Llanychaer Bridge 43 B1
Llanymawddwy 54 D4
Llanymynech 55 B4
Llanynghenedl 74 B1
Llanynis 44 E2
Llanynys 65 D4
Llanyre 45 A3
Llanystumdwy 64 D2
Llanywern 33 C4
Llawhaden 31 D3
Llawryglyn 54 D1
Llay 66 A3
Llechrhyd 33 C2
Llechryd 43 D1
Llechylched 74 B1
Lledrod 44 B4
Llithfaen 64 C2
Lloc 75 C1
Llowes 45 B1
Llwydcoed 33 B2
Llwydiarth 54 E4
Llwyncelyn 44 A3
Llwyndafydd 43 E2
Llwyngwril 54 A3
Llwynmawr 65 E1
Llwynypia 33 B1
Llynclys 55 B4
Llynfaes 74 B1
Llys-y-fran 31 D4
Llysfaen 75 A1
Llyswen 45 B1
Llysworney 21 E3
Llywel 33 A4
Loan 111 B3
Loanhead 112 B2
Loaningfoot 94 C4
Loans 104 D3
Lochailort 119 B4
Lochaline 119 A1
Lochans 93 A4
Locharbriggs 99 C3
Lochawe 115 C3
Lochbuie 114 D3
Lochcarron 129 A1
Lochdon 114 E4
Lochdonhead 114 E4
Lochearnhead 116 B3
Lochfoot 99 C2
Lochgair 109 A4
Lochgelly 112 A4
Lochgilphead 109 A4
Lochgoilhead 115 D1
Lochinver 133 D4
Lochmaben 99 D3
Lochore 117 B1
Lochranza 109 A1
Lochwinnoch 109 E1
Lockengate 2 D2
Lockerbie 99 E3
Lockeridge 24 C3
Locking 22 D2
Lockington 87 A3
Lockton 91 D3
Loddington 59 C2
Loddington 50 A4
Loddiswell 7 A4
Loddon 63 B2
Lode 51 C3
Loders 5 D4
Lofthouse 85 B1
Lofthouse Gate 85 B1
Loftus 97 C1
Logan 104 F2
Loggerheads 67 A1
Logie 117 D3
Logie Coldstone 126 D2
Logie Pert 122 B2
Logierait 121 A1
Logierieve 127 C4
Login 31 E4
Lolworth 51 B3
Londesborough 86 D3
London 27 D4
London Apprentice 2 D1
London Colney 38 B2
Londonthorpe 70 C2
Long Ashton 23 A3
Long Bank 46 C4
Long Bredy 5 D4
Long Buckby 49 C3
Long Clawson 70 A1
Long Compton 56 C4
Long Compton 36 B4
Long Crendon 37 A2
Long Crichel 12 A2
Long Duckmanton 69 A4
Long Eaton 69 A1
Long Green 66 C4
Long Green 35 A4
Long Hanborough 36 C3
Long Itchington 49 A3
Long Marston 37 C3
Long Marston 85 C3
Long Marston 47 C2
Long Marton 95 C2
Long Melford 52 B2
Long Newnton 35 A1
Long Newton 113 A2
Long Preston 84 B4
Long Riston 87 B3
Long Stratton 62 C2
Long Street 50 A2
Long Sutton 26 B1
Long Sutton 61 A4
Long Sutton 11 A3
Long Thurlow 52 D4
Long Waste 56 A4
Long Whatton 58 C4
Longbenton 102 A2
Longborough 36 A4
Longbridge Deverill 11 D4
Longburton 11 B2
Longcliffe 68 B3
Longcombe 4 A1
Longcot 36 B1
Longden 55 C3
Longdon 57 B3
Longdon 47 A1
Longdon Green 57 B3
Longdown 4 A4
Longdowns 1 D3
Longfield 28 A3
Longford 68 B2
Longford 35 A3
Longford 66 D1
Longford 56 B4
Longforgan 117 C3
Longformacus 113 B1
Longframlington 101 C4
Longham 12 B1
Longham 62 A4
Longhirst 102 A3
Longhope 34 C3
Longhorsley 101 C4
Longhoughton 107 E2
Longley 84 D1
Longleys 121 D1
Longmorn 131 C3
Longnewton 96 D1
Longney 34 D3
Longniddry 112 C3
Longnor 55 D2
Longparish 25 B1
Longridge 83 D2
Longridge 111 B2
Longriggend 111 A2
Longrock 1 B3
Longsdon 67 A4
Longside 132 D2
Longstanton 51 B3
Longstowe 51 A2
Longthwaite 95 A2
Longton 83 C1
Longtown 33 E4
Longtown 100 B2
Longueville 137 B3
Longwick 37 B2
Longwitton 101 C3
Longworth 36 B2
Longyester 113 A2
Looe 2 F1
Loosley Row 37 B2
Lopen 10 C2
Loppington 66 C1
Lornty 121 C1
Loscoe 69 A2
Lossiemouth 131 C4
Lostock Gralam 77 A1
Lostock Green 77 A1
Lostwithiel 2 E1
Lothersdale 84 C3
Loughborough 59 A4
Loughton 56 A1
Lound 60 A4
Lound 80 C2
Lound 63 C2
Lount 58 B4
Louth 82 B2
Love Clough 84 A1
Lover 12 C3
Loversall 80 B3
Loves Green 40 B2
Loveston 31 E2
Lovington 11 B4
Low Ackworth 80 A4
Low Bentham 89 C1
Low Borrowbridge 89 C4
Low Bradfield 79 A2
Low Bradley 84 C3
Low Burnham 81 A3
Low Crosby 100 B1
Low Dinsdale 96 D1
Low Eggborough 86 A1
Low Ellington 90 D2
Low Ham 10 C4
Low Hesket 95 A4
Low Hill 47 A4
Low Hutton 91 D1
Low Marnham 70 B4
Low Mill 91 C3
Low Moorsley 96 D4
Low Mowthorpe 92 A1
Low Newton 89 A2
Low Row 100 D1
Low Row 90 B3
Low Santon 81 B4
Low Tharston 62 C2
Low Worsall 91 A4
Low Wray 89 A4
Lowdham 70 A2
Lower Aisholt 10 A4
Lower Ansty 11 C1
Lower Apperley 35 A4
Lower Assendon 26 B4
Lower Beeding 17 A3
Lower Benefield 60 A1
Lower Bentley 47 B3
Lower Boddington 49 A2
Lower Brailes 48 B1
Lower Broadheath 47 A3
Lower Caldecote 50 D2
Lower Chapel 45 A1
Lower Chicksgrove 12 A4
Lower Chute 25 A2
Lower Cumberworth 79 A4
Lower Dean 50 C4
Lower Diabaig 128 F3
Lower Down 55 B1
Lower Dunsforth 91 A1
Lower End 50 B1
Lower Eythorne 30 B1
Lower Failand 23 A3
Lower Froyle 26 B1
Lower Gabwell 4 B2
Lower Gravenhurst 50 D1
Lower Hergest 45 C2
Lower Langford 22 D2
Lower Largo 117 D1
Lower Lydbrook 34 C3
Lower Lye 45 D3
Lower Machen 33 D1
Lower Merridge 10 A4
Lower Moor 47 B2
Lower Morton 34 C1
Lower Nazeing 39 B2
Lower Penn 56 C2
Lower Peover 77 B1
Lower Pond Street 51 C1
Lower Quinton 48 A2
Lower Roadwater 9 D4
Lower Seagry 24 B4
Lower Shelton 50 C1
Lower Shiplake 26 B4
Lower Shuckburgh 49 A3
Lower Slaughter 36 A4
Lower Stanton St Quintin 24 A4
Lower Stoke 29 A4
Lower Stone 34 C1
Lower Stow Bedon 62 A2
Lower Street 11 D1
Lower Street 73 B1
Lower Street 52 D2
Lower Sundon 38 A4
Lower Swanwick 13 B2
Lower Swell 36 A4
Lower Town 3 D3
Lower Tysoe 48 B2
Lower Upcott 4 A3
Lower Upham 14 A3
Lower Vexford 9 D4
Lower Weare 22 D2
Lower Westmancote 47 B1
Lower Whitley 77 A1
Lower Wield 14 B4
Lower Withington 67 B4
Lower Woodford 12 B4
Lowesby 59 B3
Lowestoft 63 C2
Loweswater 94 E1
Lowick 60 A1
Lowick 107 C4
Lowick Green 88 D2
Lowsonford 48 A3
Lowther 95 B2
Lowthorpe 87 A4
Lowton 10 A3
Loxbeare 9 C2
Loxhill 16 A4
Loxhore 8 E4
Loxhore Cott 8 E4
Loxley 48 A2
Loxton 22 D2
Loxwood 16 A4
Luccombe 21 E1
Luccombe Village 7 A3
Lucker 107 D3
Luckett 3 A3
Luckington 24 A4
Luckwell Bridge 9 C4
Lucton 45 D3
Ludborough 82 A3
Ludbrook 3 D1
Ludchurch 31 E3
Luddenden 84 C1
Luddenden Foot 84 C1
Luddesdown 28 B3
Luddington 81 A4
Luddington 48 A2
Ludford 82 A2
Ludford 46 A4
Ludgershall 37 A3
Ludgershall 24 D1
Ludgvan 1 B3
Ludham 63 B4
Ludlow 46 A4
Ludney 10 C2
Ludwell 11 D3
Ludworth 96 D3
Luffincott 3 A4
Lugar 104 F2
Lugton 109 E1
Lugwardine 46 A1
Lulham 45 D1
Lullington 58 A3
Lullington 23 C1
Lulsgate Bottom 23 A3
Lulsley 46 C2
Lumb 84 B1
Lumb 84 C1
Lumby 85 C2
Lumphanan 127 A2
Lumphinnans 112 A4
Lumsden 126 E3
Lunan 122 B1
Lunanhead 122 A1
Luncarty 117 A3
Lund 87 A3
Lund 86 B2
Lundie 117 C4
Lunsford's Cross 19 A2
Lunt 75 D3
Luppitt 10 A2
Lupridge 3 D1
Lupton 89 B2
Lurgashall 15 B3
Lurley 9 C2
Luscombe 4 A1
Luss 109 E4
Lusta 128 A2
Lustleigh 4 A3
Luston 46 A3
Luthermuir 122 B3
Luthrie 117 C3
Luton 9 D1
Luton 4 B3
Luton 38 B3
Lutterworth 59 A1
Lutton 3 C1
Lutton 3 D2
Lutton 61 A4
Lutton 60 B1
Luxborough 9 C4
Luxulyan 2 D1
Lybster 136 E1
Lydbury North 55 C1
Lydd 20 B3
Lydden 30 B1
Lydden 30 B3
Lyddington 59 D2
Lyde Green 26 A2
Lydeard St Lawrence 10 A4
Lydford 3 B4
Lydford on Fosse 11 A4
Lydgate 84 B1
Lydham 55 B1
Lydiard Millicent 24 C4
Lydiate Ash 47 B4
Lydney 34 C2
Lydstep 31 E1
Lye Green 48 A3
Lye's Green 24 A1
Lyford 36 C1
Lyme Regis 5 B4
Lyminge 20 C4
Lymm 77 A2
Lympne 20 B4
Lympsham 22 C2
Lympstone 4 B4
Lynch Green 62 C3
Lyndhurst 13 A2
Lyndon 59 D3
Lyne 27 B3
Lyne of Skene 127 B2
Lyneal 66 B1
Lyneham 36 B3
Lyneham 24 B4
Lyng 62 B4
Lyng 10 B3
Lynsted 29 B2
Lynton 21 C1
Lyon's Gate 11 B1
Lyonshall 45 C2
Lytchett Matravers 12 A1
Lytchett Minster 6 B4
Lytham St Anne's 83 A1
Lythe 97 D1
Mabe Burnthouse 1 D3
Mablethorpe 82 C2
Macclesfield 78 A1
Macduff 132 B3
Machen 33 D1
Machrihanish 103 D2
Machynlleth 54 B2
Mackworth 68 C1
Macmerry 112 C2
Maddiston 111 B3
Madeley 67 A2
Madingley 51 B3
Madley 45 D1
Madresfield 46 C2
Madron 1 A3
Maen-y-groes 43 E3
Maenclochog 31 E4
Maendy 22 A4
Maentwrog 65 A2
Maer 67 A2
Maerdy 33 B1
Maesbrook 55 B4
Maesbury Marsh 55 B4
Maesllyn 43 E1
Maesmynis 45 A2
Maesteg 33 A1
Maesybont 32 D3
Maesycwmmer 33 D1
Maggieknockater 131 C2
Maggots End 40 A4
Maghull 76 A3
Maiden Bradley 11 C4
Maiden Head 23 A3
Maiden Newton 11 B1
Maiden Wells 31 D2
Maidencombe 4 B2
Maidenhayne 10 B1

Maidenhead 27 A4
Maidens 104 C1
Maidenwell 82 B1
Maidford 49 B2
Maidstone 28 B2
Maidwell 50 A4
Mainsforth 96 D2
Mainsriddle 94 C4
Mainstone 55 B1
Maisemore 35 A3
Makeney 68 C2
Malborough 7 A4
Maldon 41 A2
Malham 84 B4
Mallaig 123 E1
Malltraeth 64 C4
Mallwyd 54 C3
Malmesbury 24 B4
Malmsmead 21 D1
Malpas 66 C2
Malpas 1 E4
Maltby 97 A1
Maltby 80 B2
Maltby le Marsh 82 C1
Malting Green 41 B3
Maltman's Hill 29 B1
Malton 91 D1
Malvern Wells 46 C1
Mamble 46 B4
Mamhilad 33 E2
Manaccan 1 D2
Manafon 54 E2
Manaton 3 D3
Manby 82 B2
Mancetter 58 B2
Manchester 78 A3
Mancot 66 A4
Manea 61 A1
Manfield 96 C1
Manley 66 C4
Manmoel 33 D2
Manningford Bruce 24 C2
Manningtree 42 A4
Manorbier 31 D1
Manorbier Newton 31 D2
Manorowen 43 A1
Mansell Gamage 45 D1
Mansell Lacy 45 D2
Mansfield 69 B4
Manston 11 D2
Manswood 12 A2
Manthorpe 60 A4
Manton 81 B3
Manton 59 D3
Manuden 40 A4
Maperton 11 B3
Maplebeck 70 A4
Mapledurham 26 A4
Mapledurwell 26 A1
Maplehurst 16 B3
Maplescombe 28 A2
Mapleton 68 B2
Mapperley 69 A2
Mapperton 11 A1
Mappleton 87 C3
Mapplewell 79 B4
Mappowder 11 C1
Marazanvose 2 B1
Marazion 1 B3
Marbury 66 C2
March 60 D2
Marcham 36 C1
Marchamley 66 D1
Marchington 68 A1
Marchwiel 66 B2
Marchwood 13 A2
Marcross 21 E3
Marden 46 A2
Marden 28 B1
Marden 24 C2
Marden Thorn 28 B1
Mareham le Fen 71 B4
Mareham on the Hill 71 B4
Marehill 16 A3
Maresfield 18 A3
Marford 66 B3
Margaret Marsh 11 D3
Margaretting 40 C2
Margaretting Tye 40 C2
Margate 30 C3
Margnaheglish 104 A3
Margrove Park 97 C1
Marham 61 C3
Marhamchurch 8 B1
Marholm 60 B2
Mariansleigh 9 A3
Maristow 3 B2
Mark 98 B1
Mark 22 D1
Mark Cross 18 A2
Mark Cross 18 B4
Markbeech 27 F1
Markby 82 C1
Market Bosworth 58 C3
Market Deeping 60 B3
Market Drayton 66 D1
Market Harborough 59 B1
Market Lavington 24 B2
Market Overton 59 D4
Market Rasen 81 D2
Market Stainton 82 A1
Market Weston 52 C4
Market Weighton 86 D3
Markfield 58 C3
Markham 33 D2
Markham Moor 80 C1
Markington 90 E1
Marks Tey 41 B4
Marksbury 23 B2
Markyate 38 A3
Marlborough 24 D3
Marlcliff 47 C2
Marldon 4 A2
Marlesford 53 B3
Marlingford 62 C3
Marloes 31 B2
Marlow 26 B4
Marnhull 11 C3
Marple 78 B2
Marr 80 B3
Marrick 90 C3
Marsden 78 C4
Marsh Baldon 36 D2
Marsh Chapel 82 B3
Marsh Gibbon 37 A4
Marsh Green 27 F1
Marsh Lane 80 A1
Marsh Street 21 E1
Marsham 62 C4
Marshbrook 55 C1
Marshfield 23 C3
Marshfield 22 C4
Marshland St James 61 A3
Marshwood 10 C1
Marske 90 C4
Marske-by-the-Sea 97 C1
Marston 45 D3
Marston 70 C2
Marston 67 B1
Marston 24 B2
Marston Magna 11 B3
Marston Meysey 35 C1
Marston Moretaine 50 C1
Marston on Dove 68 B1
Marston St Lawrence 49 B1
Marston Stannett 46 A2
Marston Trussell 59 B1
Marstow 34 B3
Marten 25 A2
Marthall 77 B1
Martham 63 B4
Martin 12 B3
Martin 30 B1
Martin 71 A3
Martin 71 B4
Martinhoe 21 C1
Martinstown 5 E4
Martlesham 53 B2
Martletwy 31 D3
Martley 46 C3
Martock 10 C3
Marton 67 B4
Marton 87 B2
Marton 81 A1
Marton 97 B1
Marton 85 C4
Marton 91 C2
Marton 55 B2
Marton 49 A4
Martyr's Green 27 C2
Marwood 8 E4
Mary Tavy 3 B3
Maryburgh 130 A2
Maryculter 127 C1
Marykirk 122 B3
Maryport 93 B3
Maryport 94 D3
Marystow 3 B3
Marywell 127 A1
Marywell 122 B1
Masham 90 D2
Mastin Moor 80 A1
Matching Tye 40 A3
Matfen 101 B2
Mathern 34 B1
Mathon 46 C2
Mathry 31 C4
Matlask 73 A1
Matlock 68 C3
Mattersey 80 C2
Mattishall 62 B3
Mattishall Burgh 62 B3
Mauchline 104 E3
Maud 132 C2
Maufant 137 B3
Maugersbury 36 A4
Maughold 137 D3
Maulden 50 C1
Maulds Meaburn 95 C1
Maunby 90 E2
Maundown 9 D3
Mautby 63 C3
Mavesyn Ridware 57 B4
Mavis Enderby 71 C4
Mawbray 94 D4
Mawdesley 76 B4
Mawdlam 21 D4
Mawgan 1 D2
Mawgan Porth 2 C2
Mawla 1 D4
Mawnan 1 D3
Mawnan Smith 1 D3
Maxey 60 B3
Maxstoke 58 A1
Maxworthy 2 F4
Maybole 104 C1
Mayfield 18 B3
Mayfield 112 C2
Mayfield 68 A2
Maypole Green 63 B2
Maypole Green 52 C3
Meadgate 23 B2
Meadle 37 B2
Meadwell 3 A3
Mealrigg 94 E4
Meare 22 D1
Mearns 110 B1
Mears Ashby 50 A3
Measham 58 B3
Meathop 89 A2
Meavy 3 B2
Medbourne 59 C2
Meden Vale 69 B4
Medmenham 26 B4
Medomsley 96 B4
Meerbrook 67 C3
Meesden 40 A4
Meeth 8 E2
Meeting House Hill 73 B1
Meidrim 32 A3
Meifod 55 A3
Meigle 121 D1
Meikleour 117 B4
Meinciau 32 C3
Melbourn 51 B1
Melbourne 58 B4
Melbourne 86 C3
Melbury Abbas 11 D3
Melbury Bubb 11 B1
Melbury Osmond 11 A2
Melchbourne 50 C3
Melcombe Bingham 11 C1
Meldon 3 C4
Meldon 101 C3
Meldreth 51 B2
Melin-y-wig 65 D2
Melkinthorpe 95 B2
Melkridge 100 E1
Melksham 24 A2
Melling 89 C1
Melling 76 A3
Mellis 52 D4
Mellor 78 B2
Mellor 83 D2
Mellor Brook 83 D2
Mells 23 C1
Melmerby 95 C3
Melmerby 90 C2
Melmerby 90 E2
Melness 135 E4
Melplash 11 A1
Melrose 106 C3
Melsonby 90 D4
Meltham 78 C4
Melton 87 A1
Melton 53 B2
Melton Constable 72 D1
Melton Mowbray 59 C4
Melton Ross 81 C4
Melvaig 133 A1
Melverley 55 B4
Melvich 136 A4
Membury 10 B1
Memsie 132 D3
Memus 121 E2
Menai Bridge 64 E4
Mendham 63 A1
Mendlesham 52 D3
Mendlesham Green 52 D3
Menheniot 2 F2
Mennock 105 B1
Menston 85 A3
Menstrie 116 D1
Mentmore 37 C3
Meonstoke 14 A3
Meopham 28 A3
Mepal 61 A1
Meppershall 50 D1
Mere 77 B1
Mere 11 D4
Mere Brow 83 B1
Mereclough 84 B2
Mereworth 28 A2
Meriden 58 A1
Merrion 31 C1
Merriott 10 C2
Merrymeet 2 F2
Merther 1 E4
Merthyr Cynog 44 E1
Merthyr Mawr 21 D4
Merthyr Tydfil 33 C2
Merthyr Vale 33 C2
Merton 8 D2
Merton 62 A2
Meshaw 9 A3
Messing 41 B3
Messingham 81 B3
Metfield 63 A1
Metherell 3 A2
Metheringham 70 D4
Methil 117 D1
Methley 85 C1
Methlick 132 C1
Methven 117 A3
Methwold 61 C2
Mettingham 63 B1
Metton 73 A1
Mevagissey 1 F4
Mexborough 80 A3
Mey 136 E4
Meyllteyrn 64 B1
Meysey Hampton 35 C2
Michaelchurch 34 B4
Michaelchurch Escley 45 C1
Michaelston-le-Pit 22 B3
Michaelstone-y-Fedw 22 C4
Michaelstow 2 E3
Micheldever 14 A4
Micheldever Station 25 C1
Mickfield 53 A3
Mickle Trafford 66 B4
Micklebring 80 B2
Mickleby 97 D1
Micklefield 85 C2
Mickleham 27 C2
Mickleton 96 A2
Mickleton 48 A1
Mickletown 85 C1
Mickley 90 D2
Mickley Square 101 C1
Mid Calder 111 C2
Mid Lavant 15 B2
Middle Aston 36 C4
Middle Barton 36 C4
Middle Claydon 37 A4
Middle Duntisbourne 35 B2
Middle Handley 80 A1
Middle Kames 109 A4
Middle Mayfield 68 A2
Middle Rasen 81 D2
Middle Stoke 29 A3
Middle Town 137 A3
Middle Tysoe 48 B1
Middle Wallop 13 A4
Middle Winterslow 12 C4
Middlebie 99 E2
Middlebridge 120 E3
Middleham 90 C2
Middlehill 24 A3
Middlehope 55 D1
Middlemarsh 11 B2
Middlesbrough 97 A1
Middleshaw 89 B3
Middlesmoor 90 C1
Middlestone 96 C2
Middlestown 79 A4
Middleton 68 B4
Middleton 68 C3
Middleton 52 B1
Middleton 78 A3
Middleton 25 B1
Middleton 46 A4
Middleton 84 D3
Middleton 91 D2
Middleton 59 C1
Middleton 61 C4
Middleton 101 C3
Middleton 46 A4
Middleton 53 C3
Middleton 32 B1
Middleton 58 A2
Middleton Cheney 49 A1
Middleton on the Hill 46 A3
Middleton on the Wolds 86 D3
Middleton Scriven 56 A1
Middleton St George 96 D1
Middleton Stoney 36 D4
Middleton Tyas 90 D4
Middleton-in-Teesdale 96 A2
Middleton-on-Sea 15 B1
Middletown 55 B3
Middlewich 67 A4
Middlewood 2 F3
Middlewood 45 C1
Middlezoy 10 C4
Midford 23 C2
Midgham 25 C3
Midgley 84 C1
Midgley 79 A4
Midhopestones 79 A3
Midhurst 15 B3
Midlem 106 C3
Midsomer Norton 23 B2
Milborne Port 11 B3
Milborne St Andrew 11 C1
Milborne Wick 11 B3
Milbourne 101 C2
Milbourne 35 B1
Milburn 95 C2
Milbury Heath 34 C1
Milby 91 A1
Milcombe 49 A1
Milden 52 C2
Mildenhall 52 A4
Mildenhall 24 D3
Mileham 62 A4
Milesmark 111 C4
Milfield 107 C3
Milford 68 C2
Milford 57 A4
Milford 27 A1
Milford Haven 31 C2
Milford on Sea 6 E4
Milkwall 34 C2
Mill Brow 78 B2
Mill End 26 B4
Mill End 39 B4
Mill Green 51 D2
Mill Green 40 B2
Mill Green 60 C4
Mill Green 52 C1
Mill Green 53 A3
Mill Meece 67 B1
Mill Street 52 D4
Milland 15 A3
Millbrex 132 C1
Millbridge 26 B1
Millbrook 50 C1
Millbrook 3 B1
Millbrook 137 B3
Millcorner 19 B3
Milldale 68 A3
Miller's Dale 78 C1
Millerhill 112 B2
Millhalf 45 C2
Millhouse 109 A2
Millhouse Green 79 A3
Millington 86 C3
Millom 88 C2
Millport 109 C1
Millthrop 89 C3
Milltown 100 A2
Milltown 8 E4
Milnathort 117 B1
Milngavie 110 B3
Milnrow 78 A4
Milnthorpe 89 B2
Milson 46 B4
Milstead 29 B2
Milston 24 D1
Milton 51 C3
Milton 100 C1
Milton 93 C4
Milton 99 B2
Milton 68 C1
Milton 130 C4
Milton 80 C1
Milton 36 C1
Milton 31 D2
Milton 11 A3
Milton 110 A3
Milton Abbas 11 C1
Milton Abbot 3 A3
Milton Bryan 38 A4
Milton Clevedon 11 B4
Milton Combe 3 B2
Milton Damerel 8 C2
Milton Ernest 50 C2
Milton Green 66 B3
Milton Hill 36 C1
Milton Keynes 50 B1
Milton of Balgonie 117 C1
Milton of Campsie 110 B3
Milton on Stour 11 C3
Milton-under-Wychwood 36 A3
Milverton 10 A3
Milwich 67 C1
Minchinhampton 35 A2
Minehead 21 E1
Minera 66 A3
Minety 35 B1
Minffordd 64 E2
Miningsby 71 C4
Minions 2 F2
Minllyn 54 C3
Minnigaff 98 D1
Minskip 90 E1
Minstead 13 A2
Minsted 15 B3
Minster 29 B3
Minster 30 B3
Minster Lovell 36 B3
Minsterley 55 C3
Minsterworth 34 D3
Minterne Magna 11 B1
Minting 81 D1
Mintlaw 132 D2
Minto 106 C2
Minton 55 C1
Mirfield 85 A1
Miserden 35 B2
Miskin 22 A4
Misson 80 C2
Misterton 59 A1
Misterton 81 A2
Misterton 10 C2
Mistley 42 A4
Mitchel Troy 34 B2
Mitcheldean 34 C3
Mitchell 2 C1
Mitford 102 A3
Mithian 2 B1
Mixbury 49 B1
Mobberley 77 B1
Mobberley 67 C2
Moccas 45 D1
Mochdre 54 E1
Mochrum 93 D4
Mockbeggar 28 B1
Mockerkin 94 D2
Modbury 3 D1
Moddershall 67 B1
Moelfre 74 C2
Moelfre 65 E1
Mogerhanger 50 D2
Moffat 105 D1
Moira 58 B4
Molash 29 C1
Mold 66 A4
Molehill Green 40 B4
Molland 9 B3
Mollington 66 B4
Mollington 49 A2
Monewden 53 B3
Moniaive 99 B3
Monikie 117 E4
Monimail 117 C2
Monk Fryston 86 A1
Monk Sherborne 25 C2
Monk Soham 53 A3
Monkhide 46 B1
Monkhill 100 A1
Monkhopton 56 A2
Monkland 45 D3
Monkleigh 8 D3
Monknash 21 E3
Monkokehampton 8 E1
Monks Eleigh 52 C2
Monks Heath 78 A1
Monks Horton 20 B4
Monks Kirby 58 C1
Monksilver 9 D4
Monksthorpe 71 D4
Monkswood 33 E2
Monkton 30 B3
Monkton 104 D3
Monkton Deverill 11 D4
Monkton Farleigh 23 C3
Monkton Wyld 10 B1
Monkwood 14 B4
Monmouth 34 B3
Monnington on Wye 45 D1
Monreith 93 D3
Mont Saint 137 B4
Montacute 11 A2
Montford 55 C4
Montgarrie 126 E3
Montgarswood 104 E3
Montgomery 55 A2
Montrose 122 C2
Monxton 25 A1
Monyash 68 A4
Monymusk 127 A3
Monzie 116 D3
Moodiesburn 110 C2
Moor Monkton 86 A4
Moorby 71 B4
Moore 76 B2
Moorends 80 C4
Moorgreen 69 A2
Moorhouse 94 F4
Moorhouse 70 B4
Moorlinch 10 C4
Moorsholm 97 C1
Moorside 11 C3
Moorswater 2 F2
Moortown 81 C3
Morborne 60 B2
Morchard Bishop 9 A2
Morcombelake 5 C4
Morcott 59 D2
Morden 11 D1
Mordiford 46 A1
Mordon 96 D2
More 55 B2
Morebath 9 C3
Morebattle 107 A2
Morecambe 83 B4
Moreleigh 3 D1
Moresby 94 C1
Morestead 14 A3
Moreton 5 F4
Moreton 40 A2
Moreton 46 A3
Moreton 37 A2
Moreton Corbet 55 D4
Moreton Jeffries 46 B2
Moreton Morrell 48 B2
Moreton Pinkney 49 B2
Moreton Say 66 D1
Moreton Valence 34 D2
Moreton-in-Marsh 36 A4
Moretonhampstead 3 D4
Morland 95 C2
Morley 78 A1
Morley 69 A2
Morley 85 A1
Morley Green 78 A1
Morley St Botolph 62 B2
Morningside 111 A1
Morpeth 102 A3
Morrey 57 B4
Morston 72 D2
Mortehoe 21 A1
Morthen 80 A2
Mortimer 26 A3
Mortimer West End 26 A2
Morton 69 A3
Morton 55 B4
Morton-on-Swale 90 E3
Morvah 1 A3
Morville 56 A2
Morwenstow 8 B2
Mosborough 80 A1
Moseley 47 A3
Moss 80 B4
Moss Edge 83 B3
Moss Side 75 D4
Moss-side 130 D2
Mossat 126 E3
Mossblown 104 D2
Mossley 78 B3
Mosstodloch 131 C3
Mossy Lea 76 B4
Mosterton 10 C1
Mostyn 75 C1
Motcombe 11 D3
Mothecombe 7 B4
Motherby 95 A2
Motherwell 110 C1
Mottisfont 13 A3
Mottistone 6 F4
Mottram in Longdendale 78 B3
Mottram St Andrew 78 A1
Mouldsworth 66 C4
Moulin 121 A2
Moulsford 25 C4
Moulsoe 50 B1
Moulton 66 D4
Moulton 60 C4
Moulton 90 D4
Moulton 50 A3
Moulton 52 A3
Moulton 22 A3
Moulton Chapel 60 C4
Moulton Seas End 71 C1
Mount 2 E2
Mount Ambrose 1 D4
Mount Bures 41 B4
Mount Hawke 1 D4
Mount Lothian 112 B1
Mount Pleasant 68 C2
Mount Pleasant 52 A2
Mount Tabor 84 D1
Mountain 84 D2
Mountain Ash 33 C2
Mountfield 19 A3
Mountjoy 2 C1
Mountnessing 40 B1
Mounton 34 B1
Mountsorrel 59 A3
Mousehole 1 B3
Mouswald 99 D2
Mowsley 59 B1
Moy 130 C1
Moy 120 A4
Moylgrove 43 C1
Muasdale 103 D4
Much Cowarne 46 B2
Much Dewchurch 34 B4
Much Hadham 39 B3
Much Hoole 83 C1
Much Marcle 34 C4
Much Wenlock 56 A2
Muchalls 127 C1
Muchelney 10 C3
Muchelney Ham 10 C3
Muchlarnick 2 F1
Mucklestone 67 A1
Muckton 82 B1
Muddiford 8 E4
Mudford 11 A3
Mudford Sock 11 A3
Mugeary 128 C1
Mugginton 68 C2
Muir of Fowlis 126 E3
Muir of Ord 130 A2
Muirdrum 117 E4
Muirhead 117 C4
Muirhead 117 C1
Muirhead 110 C2
Muirhouses 111 C3
Muirkirk 105 A3
Muirton 116 E2
Muker 90 A3
Mulbarton 62 C2
Mullion 1 C2
Mullion Cove 1 C2
Mumby 82 C1
Munderfield Row 46 B2
Mundesley 73 B1
Mundford 61 D2
Mundham 63 A2
Mundon Hill 41 A2
Mungrisdale 95 A2
Munlochy 130 B2
Munsley 46 B1
Munslow 55 D1
Murchington 3 D4
Murcott 36 D3
Murrow 60 D3
Mursley 37 B4
Murthly 117 A4
Murton 95 D1
Murton 96 D4
Murton 86 B3
Murton 107 C4
Musbury 5 B4
Musselburgh 112 B3
Muston 70 B2
Muston 92 C2
Mustow Green 47 A4
Mutehill 94 A4
Mutford 63 C1
Muthill 116 D2
Mybster 136 D3
Myddfai 32 E4
Myddle 55 D4
Mydroilyn 44 A2
Mylor 1 E3
Mylor Bridge 1 E3
Mynachlog ddu 31 E4
Myndtown 55 C1
Mynydd-bach 34 B1
Mytholmroyd 84 C1
Myton-on-Swale 91 A1
Naburn 86 A3
Nackington 30 A2
Nacton 53 A1
Nafferton 87 A4
Nailsbourne 10 A3
Nailsea 23 A3
Nailstone 58 C3
Nailsworth 35 A2
Nairn 130 D2
Nannerch 65 E4
Nanpantan 59 A4
Nanpean 2 C1
Nanstallon 2 D2
Nant Peris 64 E3
Nant-y-moel 33 B1
Nanternis 43 E3
Nantgaredig 32 C3
Nantglyn 65 D4
Nantmel 45 A3
Nantmor 64 E2
Nantwich 66 D3
Nantyglo 33 D2
Naphill 37 B1
Napleton 47 A2
Napton on the Hill 49 A3
Narberth 31 E3
Narborough 59 A2
Narborough 61 C3
Nasareth 64 D3
Naseby 49 C4
Nash 50 A1
Nash 22 C4
Nash 46 B4
Nash's Green 26 A1
Nassington 60 A2
Nateby 89 D4
Nateby 83 B3
Natland 89 B3
Naughton 52 D2
Naunton 35 C4
Naunton 47 A1
Naunton Beauchamp 47 B2
Navenby 70 D3
Navestock 40 A1
Navestock Side 40 B1
Nawton 91 C2
Nayland 52 C1
Nazeing 39 B2
Near Cotton 68 A2
Near Sawrey 89 A3
Neasham 90 E4
Neath 32 E1
Neatham 15 A4
Neatishead 63 A4

Nebo 44 B3
Nebo 65 B3
Nebo 64 D3
Nebo 74 C2
Necton 61 D3
Nedd 135 A1
Nedging 52 C2
Nedging Tye 52 D2
Needham 62 C1
Needham Market 52 D2
Needingworth 51 B4
Neen Savage 46 B4
Neen Sollars 46 B4
Neenton 56 A1
Nefyn 64 B2
Neilston 110 A1
Nelson 33 C1
Nelson 84 B2
Nemphlar 105 B4
Nempnett Thrubwell 23 A2
Nenthead 95 D3
Nenthorn 106 D3
Nercwys 65 E4
Nesbit 107 C3
Nesfield 84 D3
Neston 75 D1
Neston 24 A3
Netchwood 56 A2
Nether Alderley 78 A1
Nether Broughton 59 B4
Nether Cerne 11 B1
Nether Compton 11 B2
Nether Dallachy 131 D3
Nether Exe 9 C1
Nether Haugh 80 A3
Nether Headon 81 A1
Nether Heage 68 C3
Nether Heyford 49 C3
Nether Langwith 69 B4
Nether Moor 68 C4
Nether Padley 79 A1
Nether Poppleton 86 A4
Nether Silton 91 A3
Nether Stowey 10 A4
Nether Wallop 13 A4
Nether Wasdale 88 C4
Nether Whitacre 58 A2
Nether Winchendon 37 A3
Netheravon 24 C1
Netherbury 11 A1
Netherby 85 B3
Netherend 34 C2
Netherfield 19 A3
Netherhampton 12 B4
Netherhay 10 C1
Netherseal 58 B3
Netherthong 78 C4
Netherton 107 C1
Netherton 56 B1
Netherton 79 B4
Nethertown 88 A4
Nethertown 57 B4
Netherwitton 101 C3
Nethy Bridge 125 E3
Netley 13 B2
Netley Marsh 13 A2
Nettlebed 26 A4
Nettlecombe 11 A1
Nettleden 38 A2
Nettleham 81 C1
Nettlestone 7 B4
Nettleton 81 D3
Nettleton 24 A4
Netton 12 B4
Nevern 43 C1
Nevill Holt 59 C2
New Abbey 99 C1
New Aberdour 132 C3
New Addington 27 E2
New Alresford 14 A4
New Alyth 121 D1
New Ash Green 28 A3
New Barn 28 A3
New Bewick 107 D2
New Bolingbroke 71 B3
New Brancepeth 96 C3
New Buckenham 62 B1
New Crofton 79 B4
New Cross 10 C3
New Deer 132 C2
New Edlington 80 B3
New Ellerby 87 B2
New End 47 C3
New Galloway 98 F2
New Gilston 117 D2
New Grimsby 137 A4
New Holkham 72 B2
New Holland 87 A1
New Houghton 69 A4
New Houghton 72 B1
New Hutton 89 B3
New Inn 44 A1
New Lanark 105 B4
New Leeds 132 D2
New Luce 98 B1
New Marske 97 B1
New Mill 79 A4
New Mills 2 C1
New Mills 78 B2
New Mills 54 E2
New Milton 12 C1
New Mistley 42 B4
New Moat 31 D4
New Pitsligo 132 C2
New Quay 43 E3
New Rackheath 63 A3
New Radnor 45 B3
New Romney 20 B3
New Scone 117 B3
New Sharlston 85 B1
New Stevenston 110 C1
New Town 11 D3
New Town 12 A3
New Town 112 C2
New Tredegar 33 D2
New Trows 105 B4
New Waltham 82 A3
New Wimpole 51 B2
New Winton 112 C2
New York 71 B3
Newark-on-Trent 70 B3
Newarthill 111 A1
Newbattle 112 B2
Newbiggin 95 B2
Newbiggin 95 B4
Newbiggin 95 C2
Newbiggin 95 E2
Newbiggin 90 B2
Newbiggin-by-the-Sea 102 B3
Newbiggin-on-Lune 89 D4
Newbigging 121 D1
Newbigging 117 E4
Newbigging 105 D4
Newbold on Avon 49 A4
Newbold on Stour 48 A2
Newbold Pacey 48 B3
Newbold Verdon 58 C3
Newborough 60 C3
Newborough 64 C4
Newborough 57 B4
Newbourne 53 B1
Newbridge 112 A3
Newbridge 33 D1
Newbridge 1 A3
Newbridge 99 C2
Newbridge 6 F4
Newbridge Green 47 A1
Newbridge on Wye 45 A3
Newbrough 101 A1
Newbuildings 9 B1
Newburgh 127 D4
Newburgh 117 C2
Newburgh 76 B4
Newburgh Priory 91 B2
Newbury 23 C1
Newbury 25 B3
Newby 95 C1
Newby 84 B3
Newby 97 B1
Newby 89 D1
Newby Bridge 89 A2
Newby East 100 C1
Newby West 95 A4
Newby Wiske 90 E3
Newcastle 34 A3
Newcastle 55 B1
Newcastle Emlyn 43 D1
Newcastleton 100 C3
Newcastle-under-Lyme 67 B2
Newcastle upon Tyne 102 A1
Newchapel 43 D1
Newchurch 20 B4
Newchurch 34 A1
Newchurch 45 B2
Newchurch 57 B4
Newcraighall 112 B2
Newdigate 27 C1
Newent 34 D4
Newfield 96 C2
Newgale 31 C4
Newgate Street 39 A2
Newhall 66 D2
Newhaven 18 A1
Newholm 92 A4
Newick 17 B3
Newington 29 A3
Newington 20 C4
Newington 36 D1
Newland 34 B2
Newland 86 B1
Newland 9 B4
Newland 46 C2
Newlyn 1 B3
Newlyn East 2 B1
Newmains 111 A1
Newmarket 51 D3
Newmill 106 B1
Newmill 131 D2
Newmillerdam 79 B4
Newmills 34 B2
Newney Green 40 B2
Newnham 34 C3
Newnham 26 A2
Newnham 51 A1
Newnham 29 B2
Newnham 49 B3
Newnham 46 B4
Newport 86 D2
Newport 51 C1
Newport 33 E1
Newport 34 D1
Newport 43 B1
Newport 6 F4
Newport 56 B4
Newport Pagnell 50 B1
Newport-on-Tay 117 D3
Newquay 2 B2
Newsham 83 C2
Newsham 90 C4
Newsholme 86 B1
Newstead 106 C3
Newstead 69 B3
Newstead 107 D3
Newthorpe 85 C2
Newton 51 A1
Newton 61 A4
Newton 51 C2
Newton 66 C3
Newton 88 C1
Newton 69 A3
Newton 33 E4
Newton 46 A2
Newton 84 A3
Newton 70 D1
Newton 59 D1
Newton 61 D4
Newton 70 A2
Newton 101 B1
Newton 9 D4
Newton 57 A4
Newton 52 C1
Newton 111 C3
Newton 49 B4
Newton Abbot 4 A2
Newton Arlosh 94 E4
Newton Aycliffe 96 C2
Newton Bewley 97 A2
Newton Blossomville 50 B2
Newton Bromswold 50 C3
Newton Burgoland 58 B3
Newton by Toft 81 C2
Newton Ferrers 3 A2
Newton Ferrers 7 B4
Newton Flotman 62 C2
Newton Harcourt 59 B2
Newton Kyme 85 C3
Newton Longville 37 B4
Newton Morrell 90 D4
Newton Mountain 31 D2
Newton on Ouse 86 A4
Newton on Trent 81 A1
Newton Poppleford 4 C4
Newton Purcell 37 A4
Newton Reigny 95 B2
Newton Solney 58 B4
Newton St Cyres 9 B1
Newton St Faith 62 C4
Newton St Loe 23 C3
Newton St Petrock 8 C2
Newton Stacey 13 B4
Newton Stewart 98 D1
Newton Toney 12 C4
Newton Tracey 8 D3
Newton under Roseberry 97 B1
Newton upon Derwent 86 B3
Newton Valence 14 B4
Newton Wamphray 99 D4
Newton with Scales 83 B2
Newton-by-the-Sea 107 E2
Newton-le-Willows 77 A3
Newton-le-Willows 90 D3
Newton-on-Rawcliffe 91 D3
Newton-on-the-Moor 107 E1
Newtongrange 112 B2
Newtonhill 127 C1
Newtonloan 112 B2
Newtonmore 125 C1
Newtown 54 E2
Newtown 66 D2
Newtown 67 B3
Newtown 94 D4
Newtown 100 C1
Newtown 9 D1
Newtown 9 A3
Newtown 34 C2
Newtown 14 A2
Newtown 34 B4
Newtown 6 F4
Newtown 107 C2
Newtown 55 C4
Newtown 66 C1
Newtown 11 D3
Newtown Linford 59 A3
Newtyle 117 C4
Neyland 31 D2
Nicholashayne 9 D2
Nicholaston 32 C1
Nidd 85 B4
Nigg 130 D4
Nightcott 9 C3
Ninebanks 95 D4
Nineveh 46 B3
Ninfield 19 A2
Ningwood 6 F4
Nisbet 106 D2
Nisbet Hill 113 C1
No Man's Heath 66 C2
No Man's Heath 58 B3
Nocton 70 D4
Noke 36 D3
Nolton 31 C3
Nolton Haven 31 C3
Nomansland 9 B2
Nomansland 12 C2
Noneley 66 C1
Nonington 30 B1
Nook 89 B2
Norbury 66 C2
Norbury 68 A2
Norbury 55 C2
Norbury 56 B4
Norchard 47 A4
Nordelph 61 B2
Nordley 56 B2
Norham 107 B4
Norland Town 84 D1
Norley 76 B1
Norleywood 13 A1
Norman's Green 9 D1
Normanby 81 B4
Normanby 81 C2
Normanby 91 C2
Normanby le Wold 81 D2
Normandy 27 A1
Normanton 70 B2
Normanton 70 C2
Normanton 70 A3
Normanton 85 B1
Normanton le Heath 58 B3
Normanton on Soar 59 A4
Normanton on Trent 70 B4
North Anston 80 B2
North Aston 36 C4
North Baddesley 13 B3
North Ballachulish 119 D2
North Barrow 11 B3
North Berwick 113 A4
North Boarhunt 14 A2
North Bovey 3 D4
North Brentor 3 B3
North Brewham 11 C4
North Buckland 8 D4
North Burlingham 63 B3
North Cadbury 11 B3
North Carlton 81 B1
North Carlton 80 B2
North Cave 86 D2
North Cerney 35 B2
North Charlton 107 E2
North Cheriton 11 B3
North Chideock 5 C4
North Cliffe 86 D2
North Cockerington 82 B2
North Common 17 B3
North Cotes 82 B3
North Cove 63 C1
North Cowton 90 E4
North Crawley 50 B1
North Creake 72 B2
North Curry 10 B3
North Dalton 86 D3
North Deighton 85 C3
North Duffield 86 B2
North Elham 30 A1
North Elmham 62 A4
North Elmsall 80 A4
North End 40 C3
North End 12 B2
North Erradale 133 A1
North Fambridge 41 A1
North Frodingham 87 B3
North Gorley 12 C2
North Green 53 B3
North Grimston 91 D1
North Hayling 14 B1
North Hill 2 F3
North Huish 3 D1
North Hykeham 70 C4
North Kelsey 81 C3
North Killingholme 81 D4
North Kilvington 91 A2
North Kilworth 59 A1
North Kyme 71 A3
North Landing 92 D1
North Lee 37 B2
North Leigh 36 C3
North Lopham 62 B1
North Luffenham 59 D3
North Marden 15 A2
North Marston 37 B4
North Middleton 112 C1
North Molton 9 A4
North Moreton 36 D1
North Muskham 70 B3
North Newbald 86 D2
North Newington 49 A1
North Newnton 24 C2
North Newton 10 B4
North Nibley 34 D1
North Ormsby 82 A2
North Otterington 90 E3
North Owersby 81 C2
North Perrott 11 A2
North Petherton 10 B4
North Petherwin 2 F4
North Pickenham 61 D3
North Pool 7 B4
North Poorton 11 A1
North Quarme 9 C4
North Queensferry 112 A3
North Radworthy 9 A4
North Rauceby 70 D2
North Reston 82 B1
North Rigton 85 B3
North Rode 67 B4
North Scarle 70 B4
North Shoebury 29 B4
North Side 60 C2
North Somercotes 82 B3
North Stainley 90 E2
North Stifford 28 A4
North Stoke 25 C4
North Stoke 23 C3
North Stoke 16 A2
North Street 26 A3
North Street 29 C2
North Sunderland 107 E3
North Tamerton 8 C1
North Tawton 9 A1
North Thoresby 82 A3
North Tidworth 24 D1
North Town 8 D2
North Town 23 A1
North Tuddenham 62 B3
North Walsham 73 B1
North Waltham 25 C1
North Weald Basset 40 A2
North Wheatley 81 A2
North Widcombe 23 A2
North Willingham 81 D2
North Wingfield 69 A4
North Witham 59 D4
North Wootton 11 B2
North Wootton 61 B4
North Wootton 23 A1
North Wraxall 24 A3
Northall 37 C3
Northallerton 90 E3
Northam 8 D3
Northampton 50 A3
Northampton 47 A3
Northaw 39 A2
Northay 10 B2
Northborough 60 B3
Northbourne 30 B1
Northchapel 15 B3
Northcott 3 A4
Northend 49 A2
Northill 50 D2
Northington 14 A4
Northlands 71 C3
Northleach 35 C3
Northleigh 10 A1
Northlew 8 D1
Northmoor 36 C2
Northmuir 121 E2
Northop 66 A4
Northop Hall 66 A4
Northorpe 81 B3
Northorpe 71 B1
Northowram 84 D1
Northrepps 73 B2
Northway 10 A3
Northwich 77 A1
Northwold 61 C2
Northwood 66 C1
Northwood Green 34 D3
Norton 18 A1
Norton 35 A4
Norton 91 D1
Norton 49 B3
Norton 45 C3
Norton 80 B4
Norton 56 B2
Norton 52 C3
Norton 15 B1
Norton 24 A4
Norton 47 A2
Norton 47 B2
Norton Bavant 24 A1
Norton Bridge 67 B1
Norton Canes 57 A3
Norton Canon 45 D2
Norton Disney 70 C3
Norton Fitzwarren 10 A3
Norton Hawkfield 23 B3
Norton Heath 40 B2
Norton in Hales 67 A2
Norton Lindsey 48 A3
Norton Little Green 52 C3
Norton Malreward 23 B3
Norton St Philip 23 C2
Norton Wood 45 D2
Norton-Juxta-Twycross 58 B3
Norton-le-Clay 91 A1
Norwell 70 B4
Norwell Woodhouse 70 A4
Norwich 62 C3
Norwood Hill 27 D1
Noseley 59 C2
Noss Mayo 7 B4
Nosterfield 90 E2
Notgrove 35 C3
Notter 3 A2
Nottingham 69 B2
Notton 79 B4
Notton 24 A3
Noutard's Green 46 C3
Nox 55 C3
Nuffield 26 A4
Nun Monkton 86 A4
Nunburnholme 86 C3
Nuneaton 58 B2
Nunkeeling 87 B3
Nunney 23 C1
Nunnington 91 C2
Nunwick 90 E1
Nursling 13 A2
Nutbourne 15 A1
Nutbourne 16 A3
Nutfield 27 D1
Nuthampstead 51 B1
Nuthurst 16 B3
Nutley 18 A3
Nyewood 15 A3
Nymet Rowland 9 A2
Nymet Tracey 9 A1
Nympsfield 34 D2
Oad Street 29 A2
Oadby 59 B2
Oak Cross 8 D1
Oakamoor 68 A2
Oakdale 33 D1
Oake 10 A3
Oaken 56 C2
Oakenclough 83 C3
Oakenshaw 96 C3
Oakenshaw 85 A1
Oaker Side 68 C4
Oakford 44 A3
Oakford 9 C3
Oakham 59 D3
Oakhill 23 B1
Oakington 51 B3
Oakle Street 34 D3
Oakley 50 C2
Oakley 37 A3
Oakley 111 C4
Oakley 25 C1
Oakley 53 A4
Oakridge 35 A2
Oaksey 35 B1
Oakthorpe 58 B3
Oakwoodhill 16 B4
Oare 29 C2
Oare 21 D1
Oare 24 C2
Oasby 70 D2
Oath 10 C3
Oathlaw 122 A2
Oban 115 A3
Obley 45 C4
Occold 53 A4
Ochiltree 104 E2
Ockbrook 69 A1
Ockham 27 B2
Ockle 118 F3
Ockley 16 B4
Ocle Pychard 46 B2
Odcombe 11 A2
Oddingley 47 A3
Oddington 36 D3
Odell 50 B3
Odiham 26 B1
Odsey 51 A1
Odstock 12 B3
Odstone 58 C3
Offchurch 48 B3
Offenham 47 C2
Offham 17 B2
Offham 28 A2
Offord Cluny 51 A3
Offord Darcy 51 A3
Offton 52 D2
Offwell 10 A1
Ogbourne Maizey 24 D3
Ogbourne St Andrew 24 D3
Ogbourne St George 24 D3
Ogle 101 C2
Oglet 76 A1
Ogmore 21 D4
Ogmore Vale 33 B1
Ogmore-by-Sea 21 D3
Okeford Fitzpaine 11 C2
Okehampton 8 E1
Old 50 A4
Old Alresford 14 A4
Old Basing 26 A2
Old Bewick 107 D2
Old Bolingbroke 71 C4
Old Brampton 68 C4
Old Buckenham 62 B2
Old Burghclere 25 B2
Old Byland 91 B2
Old Church Stoke 55 B2
Old Cleeve 22 A1
Old Clipstone 69 B4
Old Dailly 98 C4
Old Dalby 59 B4
Old Deer 132 D2
Old Edlington 80 B3
Old Ellerby 87 B2
Old Forge 34 B3
Old Grimsby 137 A4
Old Hunstanton 72 A2
Old Hurst 51 A4
Old Hutton 89 B3
Old Kilpatrick 110 A3
Old Langho 84 A2
Old Leake 71 C3
Old Malton 91 D1
Old Milverton 48 B3
Old Newton 52 D3
Old Radnor 45 C3
Old Rayne 127 A4
Old Romney 20 B3
Old Sodbury 23 C4
Old Somerby 70 C1
Old Stratford 50 A1
Old Town 89 C2
Old Town 137 A3
Old Warden 50 D1
Old Weston 50 D4
Old Windsor 27 B3
Old Wives Lees 29 C2
Oldberrow 47 C3
Oldbury 56 B2
Oldbury 58 B2
Oldbury on the Hill 35 A1
Oldbury-on-Severn 34 C1
Oldcastle 33 E4
Oldcotes 80 B2
Oldfield 47 A3
Oldford 23 C1
Oldhall Green 52 C2
Oldham 78 A3
Oldhamstocks 113 C2
Oldmeldrum 127 B4
Oldmill 3 A3
Oldmixon 22 C2
Oldstead 91 B2
Oldwall 100 C1
Oldwalls 32 C1
Ollerton 77 B1
Ollerton 70 A4
Ollerton 56 A4
Olney 50 B2
Olveston 23 B4
Ombersley 47 A3
Ompton 70 A4
Onchan 137 C2
Onecote 68 A3
Onibury 45 D4
Onich 119 D2
Onllwyn 33 A2
Onneley 67 A2
Onston 77 A1
Opinan 128 F4
Orby 71 D4
Orchard Portman 10 B3
Orcheston 24 C1
Orcop 34 B4
Orcop Hill 34 B4
Ordhead 127 A2
Ordie 126 D2
Ordiequish 131 C2
Ordley 101 B1
Orford 53 C2
Organford 6 B4
Orleton 46 A3
Orleton 46 C3
Orlingbury 50 B4
Ormesby St Margaret 63 C4
Ormesby St Michael 63 C4
Ormiston 112 C2
Ormskirk 76 A4
Orpington 27 F3
Orrell 76 B3
Orsett 28 A4
Orslow 56 B4
Orston 70 B2
Orton 89 C4
Orton 50 A4
Orton 56 C2
Orton-on-the-Hill 58 B3
Orwell 51 B2
Osbaldeston 83 D2
Osbaston 58 C3
Osbaston 55 B4
Osbournby 70 D2
Oscroft 66 C4
Osgathorpe 58 C4
Osgodby 81 C2
Osgodby 86 B2
Osgodby 92 B2
Osmaston 68 B2
Osmington 5 F3
Osmington Mills 5 F3
Osmotherley 91 A3
Ossett 85 B1
Ossington 70 B4
Oswaldkirk 91 C2
Oswaldtwistle 84 A1
Oswestry 66 A1
Otford 27 F2
Othery 10 C4
Otley 53 A2
Otley 85 A3
Otter Ferry 109 A4
Otterbourne 13 B3
Otterburn 84 B4
Otterburn 101 A4
Otterham 2 E4
Otterhampton 22 C1
Otterton 4 C4
Ottery 3 B3
Ottery St Mary 9 D1
Ottringham 87 C1
Oughtibridge 79 B2
Oughtrington 77 B2
Oulston 91 B1
Oulton 94 F4
Oulton 73 A1
Oulton 67 B1
Oulton Street 73 A1
Oundle 60 A1
Ousby 95 C3
Ousden 52 A3
Ousefleet 86 C1
Ouston 96 C4
Out Rawcliffe 83 B3
Outgate 89 A4
Outhgill 89 D4
Outhill 47 C3
Outlane 78 C4
Outwell 61 A3
Outwood 27 E1
Outwoods 56 B4
Ouzlewell Green 85 B1
Over 51 B4
Over Compton 11 B2
Over Haddon 68 B4
Over Kellet 89 B1
Over Kiddington 36 C3
Over Norton 36 B4
Over Peover 77 B1
Over Silton 91 A3
Over Stowey 10 A4
Over Wallop 13 A4
Over Whitacre 58 A1
Over Worton 36 C4
Overbury 47 B1
Overcombe 5 F3
Overseal 58 B4
Oversland 29 C2
Overstone 50 A3
Overstrand 73 B2
Overthorpe 49 A1
Overton 25 C1
Overton 83 B4
Overton 86 A4
Overton 46 A4
Overton 21 A4
Overton 79 A4
Overton 66 B2
Overtown 89 C1
Overtown 111 A1
Oving 37 B3
Oving 15 B1
Ovingham 101 C1
Ovington 96 B1
Ovington 52 A1
Ovington 14 A4
Ovington 62 A2
Ovington 101 C1
Ower 13 A2
Owlswick 37 B2
Owmby 81 C3
Owmby 81 C2
Owslebury 14 A3
Owston 59 C3
Owston 80 B4
Owston Ferry 81 A3
Owstwick 87 C2
Owthorne 87 D1
Owthorpe 70 A1
Oxborough 61 C2
Oxbridge 11 A1
Oxcombe 82 A1
Oxen End 40 C4

Place	Pg	Grid	Place	Pg	Grid	Place	Pg	Grid
Oxen Park	88	D2	Peel	137	B2	Peper Harow	27	A1
Oxenholme	89	B3	Peene	20	C4	Peplow	56	A4
Oxenhope	84	C2	Pegswood	102	A3	Perlethorpe	70	A4
Oxenpill	22	D1	Peldon	41	B3	Perranporth	2	B1
Oxenton	35	B4	Pelsall	57	A3	Perranuthnoe	1	B3
Oxenwood	25	A4	Pelton	96	C4	Perranwell	1	D4
Oxford	36	D2	Pelynt	2	F1	Perranzabuloe	2	B1
Oxhill	48	B2	Pembrey	32	C2	Pershall	67	B1
Oxley Green	41	B3	Pembridge	45	D3	Pershore	47	B2
Oxley's Green	19	A3	Pembroke	31	D2	Pertenhall	50	D3
Oxnam	107	A2	Pembroke Dock	31	D2	Perth	117	A3
Oxnead	62	C4	Pembury	18	B4	Perthy	66	B1
Oxspring	79	A3	Pen Rhiwfawr	32	E3	Perton	46	B1
Oxted	27	C1	Pen-bont Rhydybeddau	54	B1	Peter Tavy	3	B3
Oxton	113	A1	Pen-ffordd	31	D4	Peter's Green	38	B3
Oxton	86	A3	Pen-rhiw	43	D1	Peterborough	60	B2
Oxton	70	A3	Pen-twyn	34	B2	Peterchurch	45	C1
Oxwich	21	A4	Pen-y-bont	55	A4	Peterculter	127	C2
Oxwich Green	21	A4	Pen-y-bont-fawr	54	A4	Peterhead	132	E2
Oyne	127	A4	Pen-y-bryn	43	C1	Peterlee	97	A3
Packington	58	B4	Pen-y-clawdd	34	A2	Petersfield	15	A3
Padanaram	121	E1	Pen-y-coedcae	33	C1	Peterstone Wentlooge	22	C4
Padbury	37	A4	Pen-y-cwn	31	C4	Peterstow	34	B4
Paddlesworth	28	B2	Pen-y-Garnedd	54	E4	Petham	30	A1
Paddlesworth	20	C4	Pen-y-graig	64	B1	Petherwin Gate	2	F4
Paddock Wood	28	B1	Pen-y-stryt	65	E3	Petrockstow	8	D2
Padiham	84	A2	Penallt	34	B3	Pett	19	B2
Padside	85	A4	Penally	31	E2	Pettaugh	53	A3
Padstow	2	C3	Penalt	34	B4	Pettinain	105	C4
Padworth	25	C3	Penarth	22	B3	Pettistree	53	B2
Pagham	15	B1	Penbryn	43	D2	Petton	9	D3
Paglesham	41	B1	Pencader	44	A1	Petworth	16	A3
Paignton	4	B2	Pencaitland	112	C2	Pevensey	18	B1
Painscastle	45	B2	Pencarnisiog	74	B1	Pewsey	24	D2
Painshawfield	101	C1	Pencarreg	44	A2	Phepson	47	B3
Painsthorpe	86	C4	Pencelli	33	C4	Philham	8	B3
Painswick	35	A2	Penclawdd	32	D1	Phillack	1	B1
Painter's Forstal	29	B2	Pencoed	21	E4	Philleigh	1	E4
Paisley	110	A3	Pencombe	46	B2	Philpstoun	111	C3
Pakenham	52	C3	Pencraig	34	B3	Phoenix Green	26	B2
Paley Street	27	A4	Pencraig	65	D1	Pica	94	D1
Palgrave	52	D4	Pendeen	1	A3	Pickford	58	B1
Pallington	5	F4	Penderyn	33	B2	Pickering	91	D2
Palnackie	99	B1	Pendine	32	A2	Pickhill	90	E2
Palnure	98	E1	Pendlebury	77	B3	Picklescott	55	C2
Palterton	69	A4	Pendleton	84	A2	Pickmere	77	A1
Pamber End	25	C2	Pendock	34	D4	Pickney	10	A3
Pamber Heath	25	C2	Pendoggett	2	D3	Pickup Bank	84	A1
Pamphill	12	A1	Pendoylan	22	A4	Pickwell	60	A3
Pampisford	51	C2	Penegoes	54	B2	Pickworth	60	A3
Panbride	117	E4	Pengam	33	D1	Pickworth	70	D1
Pancrasweek	8	B1	Pengelly	2	D4	Picton	66	B4
Pandy	33	E4	Pengrugla	1	F4	Picton	91	A4
Pandy Tudur	65	B4	Penhallow	2	B1	Piddinghoe	18	A1
Panfield	40	C4	Penhalvean	1	D4	Piddington	50	A2
Pangbourne	26	A4	Penhow	34	A1	Piddington	37	A3
Pangdean	17	A2	Penicuik	112	B1	Piddlehinton	11	C1
Pannal	85	B3	Peniel	33	A3	Piddletrenthide	11	C1
Pant	55	B4	Penistone	79	A3	Pidley	51	B4
Pant Glas	64	D2	Penkridge	57	A3	Pilham	81	B2
Pant-ffrwyth	21	E4	Penlean	8	B1	Pillaton	3	A2
Pant-y-dwr	44	E4	Penley	66	B2	Pilleth Hersey	48	B2
Pant-y-mwyn	65	C1	Penllyn	21	E4	Pillerton Priors	48	B2
Pantasaph	75	C1	Penmachno	65	B3	Pilley	13	A1
Pantglas	54	C2	Penmaenmawr	74	E1	Pilley	79	B3
Panton	81	D1	Penmaenpool	54	B4	Pilling	83	B3
Panxworth	63	A3	Penmark	22	A3	Pilning	23	A4
Papcastle	94	D2	Penmorfa	64	E2	Pilsbury	68	A4
Papigoe	136	F3	Penmynydd	74	C1	Pilsdon	10	C1
Papplewick	69	B3	Penn Street	37	C1	Pilsley	68	B4
Papworth Everard	51	A3	Pennal	54	B2	Pilsley	69	A4
Par	2	D1	Pennan	132	C3	Pilson Green	63	B3
Parbold	76	B4	Pennant	54	C2	Piltdown	18	A3
Parbrook	11	A4	Pennard	32	D1	Pilton	60	A1
Parc	65	B1	Pennerley	55	C2	Pilton	59	D2
Parc Seymour	34	A1	Pennorth	33	C4	Pilton	11	B4
Pardshaw	94	D2	Penny Bridge	88	D2	Pimperne	11	D2
Parham	53	B3	Penny Hill	71	C1	Pinchbeck	60	C4
Park	100	D1	Pennymoor	9	B2	Pinley Green	48	A3
Park Corner	37	A1	Penparc	43	D2	Pinn	4	C4
Park Street	38	B2	Penperlleni	33	E2	Pinvin	47	B2
Parkend	34	C2	Penpoll	2	E1	Pinwherry	98	C3
Parkgate	99	D3	Penponds	1	C4	Pinxton	69	A3
Parkgate	27	D1	Penpont	99	B4	Pipe and Lyde	46	A1
Parkham	8	C3	Penrherw-pal	43	E2	Pipewell	59	C1
Parkmill	32	D1	Penrhiwceiber	33	C1	Pirbright	27	A2
Parr Bridge	77	B3	Penrhiwllan	43	E1	Pirnmill	103	F4
Parracombe	21	C1	Penrhos	64	C1	Pirton	38	B4
Parson Drove	60	D3	Penrhos	34	A3	Pirton	47	A2
Partington	77	B2	Penrhyn Bay	74	F1	Pishill	37	A1
Partney	71	C4	Penrhyncoch	54	A1	Pistyll	64	C2
Parton	94	F4	Penrhyndeudraeth	64	E2	Pitcairngreen	117	A3
Parton	94	C1	Penrice	32	C1	Pitcaple	127	B4
Parton	99	A2	Penrith	95	B2	Pitch Green	37	B2
Partridge Green	16	B3	Penrose	2	C2	Pitch Place	15	B4
Parwich	68	B3	Penruddock	95	A2	Pitchcombe	35	A2
Paston	73	B1	Penryn	1	D3	Pitchcott	37	B3
Patchway	23	B4	Pensarn	75	A1	Pitchford	55	D3
Pateley Bridge	90	C1	Pensax	46	C4	Pitcombe	11	B4
Path of Condie	117	A2	Penselwood	11	C4	Pitlessie	117	C2
Pathhead	112	C2	Pensford	23	B2	Pitlochry	121	A4
Patna	104	D1	Pensham	47	B1	Pitmedden	127	C4
Patney	24	C2	Penshaw	96	D4	Pitney	10	C3
Patrick	137	B2	Penshurst	27	F1	Pitscottie	117	D2
Patrick Brompton	90	D3	Pensilva	2	F2	Pitsford	50	A3
Patrington	87	D1	Pentewan	1	F4	Pitt	9	D2
Patterdale	95	A1	Pentir	64	C1	Pittenweem	117	E1
Pattingham	56	C2	Pentlow	52	B2	Pittington	96	D3
Pattishall	49	C2	Pentney	61	C3	Pitton	12	C4
Pattiswick Green	41	A4	Penton Mewsey	25	A1	Pittulie	132	D3
Paulerspury	49	C2	Pentonbridge	100	A1	Pity Me	96	C4
Paull	87	B1	Pentre	55	C4	Plains	111	A2
Paulton	23	B2	Pentre Berw	74	C1	Plaish	55	D2
Pauperhaugh	101	C4	Pentre Hodrey	45	C4	Plaistow	68	C3
Pavenham	50	C2	Pentre Llanrhaeadr	65	D4	Plaistow	16	A4
Pawlett	22	C1	Pentre Meyrick	21	E3	Plaitford	13	A3
Paxford	48	A1	Pentre-bach	33	B4	Plas Cymyran	74	A1
Paxton	113	E1	Pentre-celyn	65	E3	Plastow Green	25	C2
Payhembury	9	D1	Pentre-celyn	54	C4	Platt	28	A2
Paythorne	84	B3	Pentre-cwrt	43	E1	Plawsworth	96	C4
Peacehaven	17	B1	Pentre-Gwenlais	32	E2	Plaxtol	28	A2
Peak Forest	78	C1	Pentre-tafarn-y-fedw	65	B4	Play Hatch	26	B4
Peakirk	60	B3	Pentrebach	33	C2	Playford	53	A2
Pease Pottage	17	A4	Pentredwr	65	E2	Playing Place	1	E4
Peaseland Green	62	B4	Pentrefelin	64	D2	Playley Green	34	D4
Peasemore	25	B4	Pentrefoelas	65	B3	Plealey	55	C3
Peasenhall	53	C4	Pentregat	43	D2	Plean	111	A4
Peaslake	27	C1	Pentrich	68	C3	Pleasance	117	B2
Peasmarsh	19	B3	Pentridge Hill	12	A2	Pleasington	83	D1
Peat Inn	117	D2	Pentyrch	22	A4	Pleasley	69	A4
Peathill	132	D3	Penwithick	2	D1	Plemstall	66	B4
Peatling Parva	59	A1	Penybanc	32	D4	Pleshey	40	C3
Pebmarsh	52	B1	Penybont	45	A3	Plockton	123	F4
Pebworth	47	C2	Penycae	66	A2	Plowden	55	C1
Pecket Well	84	C1	Penyffordd	66	A4	Ploxgreen	55	C1
Peckforton	66	C3	Penygraig	33	B3	Pluckley	29	B1
Peckleton	58	C2	Penygroes	32	D3	Pluckley Thorne	29	B1
Pedlinge	20	C4	Penygroes	64	D3	Plumbland	94	E3
Pedwell	10	C4	Penywaun	33	B2			
Peebles	106	A4	Penzance	1	B3			
			Peopleton	47	B2			

Place	Pg	Grid	Place	Pg	Grid	Place	Pg	Grid
Plumley	77	B1	Porthtowan	1	D4	Puncknowle	5	D4
Plumpton	95	B3	Porthyrhyd	32	C3	Purfleet	28	A4
Plumpton	17	B2	Portington	86	C2	Puriton	22	C1
Plumpton	49	B2	Portinscale	94	F2	Purleigh	41	A2
Plumpton Green	17	B2	Portishead	23	A3	Purley	10	C2
Plumstead	73	A1	Portknockie	131	E3	Purse Caundle	11	B2
Plumtree	69	B1	Portlethen	127	C1	Purtington	10	C2
Plungar	70	B1	Portloe	1	F4	Purton	34	C2
Plurenden	20	A4	Portmahomack	134	E1	Purton	34	C2
Plush	11	C1	Portmellon	1	F4	Purton	35	C1
Plwmp	43	E2	Portnacroish	119	C1	Purton Stoke	35	C1
Plymouth	3	B1	Portnahaven	108	A1	Pusey	36	B1
Plympton	3	C1	Porton	12	C4	Putley	46	B1
Plymtree	9	D1	Portpatrick	93	A4	Putloe	34	D2
Pockley	91	C2	Portreath	1	C4	Puttenham	27	A1
Pocklington	86	C3	Portree	128	C1	Puxley	50	A1
Podimore	11	A3	Portscatho	1	E3	Puxton	22	D1
Podington	50	B3	Portskerra	136	A4	Pwll	32	C2
Podmore	67	A1	Portskewett	34	B1	Pwll-du	33	E3
Pointon	71	A1	Portslade-by-Sea	17	A1	Pwll-glas	65	D3
Polbain	133	C3	Portsmouth	14	B1	Pwll-y-glaw	33	A1
Polbathic	3	A1	Portsoy	132	A3	Pwllgloyw	45	A1
Polbeth	111	C2	Portway	47	C4	Pwllheli	64	C1
Polebrook	60	A1	Portwrinkle	3	A1	Pwllmeyric	34	B1
Polesworth	58	A2	Postbridge	3	C3	Pye Bridge	69	A3
Polglass	133	C3	Postcombe	37	A2	Pye Corner	40	A3
Polgooth	1	F4	Postling	20	C4	Pyecombe	17	A2
Poling	16	A1	Postwick	63	A3	Pyle	21	D4
Polkerris	2	D1	Potsgrove	37	C4	Pyleigh	10	A4
Pollington	86	A1	Pott Shrigley	78	B1	Pylle	11	B4
Polmassick	1	F4	Potter Brompton	92	B2	Pymore	61	A1
Polmont	111	B3	Potter Heigham	63	B4	Pyrford	27	B2
Polnish	119	B4	Potterhanworth	70	D4	Pytchley	50	B4
Polperro	2	F1	Potterhanworth Booths	70	D4	Pyworthy	8	C1
Polruan	2	E1	Potterne	24	B2	Quabbs	55	A1
Polstead	52	C1	Potterne Wick	24	B2	Quadring	71	B1
Poltimore	9	C1	Potters Bar	39	A4	Quainton	37	B3
Polton	112	B2	Potters Crouch	38	B2	Quarley	24	D1
Polwarth	113	C1	Potters Marston	58	C2	Quarndon	68	C2
Polyphant	2	F3	Potterspury	50	A1	Quarrington	70	D2
Polzeath	2	C3	Potterton	127	D3	Quarrington Hill	96	D3
Pomathorn	112	B1	Potto	91	A4	Quarter	110	C1
Pondersbridge	60	C2	Potton	51	A2	Quatford	56	B1
Ponsanooth	1	D4	Poughill	8	B2	Quatt	56	B1
Ponsworthy	3	D3	Poughill	9	B2	Quebec	96	C3
Pont Robert	54	E3	Poulner	12	A1	Queen Adelaide	61	B1
Pont-faen	44	E1	Poulshot	24	B2	Queen Camel	11	B3
Pont-Nedd-Fechan	33	B2	Poulton	35	C2	Queen Charlton	23	B3
Pont-rhyd-y-fen	33	A1	Poulton-le-Fylde	83	A2	Queen Oak	11	C4
Pont-y-pant	65	A3	Pound Green	18	A3	Queensferry	66	A4
Pontantwn	32	C3	Poundffald	32	D1	Queenhill	47	A1
Pontardawe	32	E2	Poundon	37	A4	Queensbury	84	D2
Pontarddulais	32	D2	Poundsgate	3	D3	Queenzieburn	110	C3
Pontarsais	32	C4	Poundstock	8	B1	Quendon	40	A4
Pontblyddyn	66	A4	Povey Cross	27	D1	Queniborough	59	B3
Pontefract	85	C1	Powburn	107	D2	Quenington	35	C2
Ponteland	102	A3	Powderham	4	B4	Quethiock	3	A2
Ponterwyd	54	B1	Powfoot	99	E1	Quidenham	62	B1
Pontesbury	55	C3	Powhill	94	F4	Quidhampton	12	B4
Pontesford	55	C3	Powick	47	A2	Quinton	50	A2
Pontfadog	66	A2	Powmill	117	A1	Quither	3	B3
Pontfaen	43	B1	Poxwell	5	F4	Quoditch	8	C1
Pontgarreg	43	E2	Poyle	27	B4	Quorndon	59	A4
Ponthenry	32	C2	Poynings	17	A2	Rachub	64	E4
Ponthir	33	E1	Poyntington	11	B3	Rackenford	9	B3
Ponthirwaun	43	D1	Poynton	78	A1	Rackham	16	A2
Pontllanfraith	33	D1	Poynton Green	55	D4	Rackheath	63	A4
Pontlliw	32	D2	Poys Street	53	C4	Radbourne	68	C1
Pontlyfni	64	D3	Praa Sands	1	C3	Radcliffe	77	B4
Pontrhydfendigaid	44	C3	Prees	66	C1	Radcliffe	102	A4
Pontrhydygroes	44	C3	Prees Green	66	C1	Radcliffe on Trent	70	A2
Pontrilas	34	A4	Preesall	83	A3	Radclive	49	C1
Ponts Green	19	A2	Pren-gwyn	44	A2	Radford Semele	48	B3
Pontshaen	44	A2	Prendwick	107	C1	Radlett	38	B2
Pontshill	34	C3	Prenteg	64	E2	Radley	36	D1
Pontsticill	33	C3	Prescot	76	B2	Radley Green	40	B2
Pontwelly	43	E1	Prescott	9	D2	Radnage	37	B1
Pontyates	32	C2	Prestatyn	75	B1	Radstock	23	B2
Pontyberem	32	C3	Prestbury	45	C3	Radstone	49	B1
Pontybodkin	66	A3	Presteigne	11	B4	Radway	48	B2
Pontyclun	22	A4	Prestleigh	11	B4	Radwell	51	A1
Pontycymer	33	B1	Preston	113	C1	Radwinter	51	D1
Pontypool	33	E2	Preston	5	F3	Radyr	22	B4
Pontypridd	33	C1	Preston	113	B3	Rafford	131	A2
Pontywaun	33	D1	Preston	87	B2	Ragdale	59	B4
Pool	85	A3	Preston	35	B2	Raglan	34	A2
Pool of Muckhart	116	E1	Preston	38	B4	Ragnall	81	A1
Pool Street	52	A1	Preston	30	B2	Rainford	76	B3
Poole	6	B4	Preston	83	C1	Rainham	27	F4
Poolewe	133	D2	Preston	107	E2	Rainow	78	B1
Pooley Bridge	95	B2	Preston	59	D2	Rainton	90	E1
Poolfold	67	B3	Preston	9	D4	Rainworth	69	B3
Poolhill	34	D4	Preston	52	C2	Raisthorpe	86	D4
Popham	25	C1	Preston	25	A3	Rait	117	B3
Porchfield	6	F4	Preston Bissett	37	A4	Raithby	82	A2
Porkellis	1	D3	Preston Brockhurst	55	D4	Raithby	71	C4
Port Appin	119	C1	Preston Brook	76	B1	Rake	15	A3
Port Askaig	108	C2	Preston Candover	25	C1	Rame	1	D3
Port Bannatyne	109	B2	Preston Capes	49	B2	Rame	3	B1
Port Carlisle	100	A1	Preston Gubbals	55	D4	Rampisham	11	A1
Port Charlotte	108	A1	Preston on Stour	48	A2	Rampside	88	D1
Port Ellen	103	A4	Preston on Wye	45	D1	Rampton	51	C3
Port Erin	137	B1	Preston Patrick	89	D1	Rampton	81	A1
Port Glasgow	109	E3	Preston upon the Weald Moors	56	A4	Ramsbottom	77	B4
Port Henderson	128	F4	Preston Wynne	46	A2	Ramsbury	24	D3
Port Isaac	2	D3	Preston-under-Scar	90	C3	Ramsdean	14	B3
Port Logan	93	B3	Prestonpans	112	C3	Ramsdell	25	C2
Port of Menteith	116	B1	Prestwich	78	A3	Ramsden	38	B3
Port Quin	2	D3	Prestwick	104	D2	Ramsden Bellhouse	40	C1
Port Ramsay	119	C1	Prickwillow	61	B1	Ramsey	60	C1
Port Soderick	137	C1	Priddy	23	A1	Ramsey	42	B4
Port St Mary	137	B1	Priest Hutton	89	B1	Ramsey	137	D3
Port Talbot	32	E1	Priestweston	55	B2	Ramsey Heights	60	C1
Port Wemyss	108	A1	Primrosehill	113	C1	Ramsey Island	42	B2
Port William	93	D3	Princes Risborough	37	B2	Ramsey Mereside	60	C1
Portachoillan	108	F1	Princethorpe	49	A4	Ramsey St Mary's	60	C1
Portavadie	109	A2	Princetown	3	C3	Ramsgate	30	C3
Portbury	23	A4	Priors Hardwick	49	A2	Ramsgill	90	C1
Portchester	14	A1	Priors Marston	49	A3	Ramshope	107	A1
Portencalzie	98	A2	Priston	23	B2	Ramshorn	68	A2
Portesham	5	E4	Privett	14	B3	Ramsnest Common	15	A3
Portfield Gate	31	C3	Prospect	94	D3	Ranby	82	A1
Portgate	3	A4	Prospidnick	1	C3	Ranby	80	D1
Portgordon	131	D3	Prudhoe	23	B3	Rand	81	D1
Porth	33	C1	Publow	23	B2	Randwick	35	A2
Porth Navas	1	D3	Puckeridge	39	B4	Rangemore	58	A4
Porthallow	1	D2	Pucklechurch	23	C4	Rangeworthy	23	B4
Porthallow	2	F1	Puddington	75	D1	Rankinston	104	E1
Porthcawl	21	D4	Puddington	9	B2	Rann	84	A1
Porthcothan	2	C4	Pudsey	85	A2	Rannoch Station	120	A2
Porthcurno	1	A3	Pulborough	16	A3	Ranskill	80	D2
Porthgain	31	B4	Pulford	66	B3	Ranton	56	C4
Porthgwarra	1	A3	Pulham	11	C2	Ranworth	63	B4
Porthkerry	22	A3	Pulham Market	62	C1	Rapps	10	B2
Porthleven	1	C3	Pulham St Mary	62	C1	Rashwood	47	B4
Porthmadog	64	E2	Pulloxhill	50	C1	Raskelf	91	A1
Porthoustock	1	E2	Pumsaint	44	C1	Ratby	59	A3
Porthpean	2	D1	Puncheston	31	D4	Ratcliffe Culey	58	B2
						Ratcliffe on Soar	69	A1
						Ratcliffe on the Wreake	59	B4
						Rathen	132	D3

Rathmell	84	A4
Ratho	112	A2
Rathven	131	D3
Ratley	48	B2
Ratling	30	B2
Ratlinghope	55	C2
Rattery	3	D2
Rattlesden	52	C3
Rattray	121	C1
Raunds	50	C4
Raven Meols	75	D3
Ravenfield	80	A2
Ravenglass	88	B3
Raveningham	63	B2
Ravenscar	92	B4
Ravenscliffe	67	B3
Ravensden	50	C2
Ravenshead	69	B3
Ravensthorpe	49	C4
Ravenstone	50	A2
Ravenstone	58	C3
Ravenstonedale	89	D4
Ravensworth	90	C4
Rawcliffe	86	B1
Rawling Street	29	B2
Rawmarsh	80	A3
Rawreth	41	A1
Rawridge	10	A1
Rawtenstall	84	B1
Raydon	52	D1
Rayleigh	41	A1
Rayne	40	C4
Reach	51	D3
Read	84	A2
Reading	26	A3
Reagill	95	C1
Rearsby	59	B3
Reay	136	B4
Reculver	30	A3
Red Ball	9	D2
Red Hill	47	C2
Red Lodge	52	A4
Red Roses	32	A3
Red Wharf Bay	74	C1
Redberth	31	E2
Redbourn	38	B3
Redbourne	81	C3
Redbrook	66	C2
Redbrook Street	20	A4
Redcar	97	B2
Redditch	47	B3
Rede	52	B2
Redenhall	63	A1
Redesmouth	101	A3
Redford	122	A1
Redford	15	B3
Redgrave	52	D4
Redhill	39	A4
Redhill	23	A2
Redhill	27	D1
Redisham	63	B1
Redlingfield	53	A4
Redlingfield Green	53	A4
Redlynch	11	C4
Redlynch	12	C3
Redmarley	46	C3
Redmarshall	96	D1
Redmile	70	B1
Redmire	90	C3
Rednal	66	B1
Redruth	1	D4
Redwick	23	A4
Redwick	22	D4
Redworth	96	C2
Reed	51	B1
Reedham	63	B2
Reedness	86	C1
Reepham	81	C1
Reepham	62	B4
Reeth	90	B4
Reigate	27	D1
Reighton	92	C1
Reiss	136	E3
Relubbus	1	B3
Remenham	26	B3
Rempstone	59	A4
Rendcomb	35	B2
Rendham	53	B3
Renfrew	110	A2
Renhold	50	D2
Renishaw	80	A1
Rennington	107	E2
Renton	109	E3
Renwick	95	C3
Repps	63	B4
Repton	68	C1
Rescassa	1	F4
Reskadinnick	1	C4
Resolven	33	A2
Reston	113	D2
Retford	80	C1
Rettendon	40	C1
Revesby	71	B4
Rew Street	6	F4
Rewe	9	C1
Reymerston	62	B3
Reynoldston	32	C1
Rhandirmwyn	44	D1
Rhayader	44	E3
Rhes-y-cae	65	E4
Rhewl	65	D3
Rhewl	65	E2
Rhiconich	135	B3
Rhigos	33	B2
Rhiwlas	64	E4
Rhoden Green	28	B1
Rhodiad-y-brenin	31	B4
Rhoose	22	A3
Rhos	43	E1
Rhos	32	E2
Rhos-on-Sea	74	F1
Rhos-y-gwaliau	65	C1
Rhosbeirio	74	B2
Rhoscolyn	74	A1
Rhoscrowther	31	C2
Rhosesmor	65	E4
Rhosgoch	45	B2
Rhoshill	43	C1
Rhoshirwaun	64	B1
Rhoslefain	54	A3
Rhosllanerchrugog	66	A2
Rhosmeirch	74	C1
Rhosneigr	74	B1
Rhostryfan	64	D3
Rhosybol	74	C2
Rhosymedre	66	A2
Rhu	109	D4
Rhuallt	75	B1
Rhuddlan	75	B1
Rhyd	64	E2
Rhyd-uchaf	65	C2
Rhyd-y pennau	54	A1
Rhyd-y-clafdy	64	C1
Rhyd-y-foel	75	A1
Rhydargaeau	32	C4
Rhydcymerau	44	B1
Rhydlewis	43	E2
Rhydowen	44	A2
Rhydyfro	32	E2
Rhyl	75	B1
Rhymney	33	C2
Rhynd	117	B3
Rhynie	126	E4
Ribbesford	46	C4
Ribchester	83	D2
Riby	81	D4
Riccall	86	B2
Riccarton	100	C4
Richards Castle	46	A4
Richmond	90	D4
Rickham	7	A4
Rickinghall	52	D4
Rickling	40	A4
Rickling Green	40	A4
Rickmansworth	38	A1
Riddlecombe	8	E2
Ridge	39	A2
Ridge	12	A4
Ridge Lane	58	B2
Ridgehill	23	A2
Ridgeway	80	A1
Ridgewell	52	A1
Ridgmont	50	C1
Riding Mill	101	B1
Ridlington	73	B1
Ridlington	59	C2
Ridsdale	101	A3
Rievaulx	91	B2
Rigg	100	A1
Rigsby	82	C1
Riley Green	83	D1
Rilla Mill	2	F3
Rillington	92	A1
Rimington	84	A3
Rimpton	11	B3
Rimswell	87	C1
Rinaston	31	D4
Rindleford	56	B2
Ringford	99	A1
Ringland	62	C3
Ringmer	18	A2
Ringmore	7	B4
Ringmore	4	B3
Ringsfield	63	B1
Ringshall	38	A3
Ringshall	52	D2
Ringshall Stocks	52	D2
Ringstead	50	C4
Ringstead	72	A2
Ringwood	12	B1
Ringwould	30	C1
Ripe	18	A2
Ripley	69	A3
Ripley	12	C1
Ripley	85	B4
Ripley	27	B2
Riplington	14	B3
Ripon	90	E1
Rippingale	71	A1
Ripple	47	A1
Ripponden	84	C1
Risbury	46	A2
Risby	52	B3
Risca	33	E1
Rise	87	B3
Risegate	71	B1
Riseley	50	C3
Riseley	26	A2
Rishangles	53	A4
Rishton	84	A2
Rishworth	78	B4
Risley	77	A2
Risley	69	A1
Risplith	90	D1
River	15	B3
Rivington	77	A4
Road Weedon	49	C3
Roade	50	A2
Roadmeetings	111	A1
Roadwater	9	D4
Roberton	106	B1
Roberton	105	C3
Robertsbridge	19	A3
Roberttown	85	A1
Robeston Wathen	31	E3
Robin Hood's Bay	92	A4
Roborough	8	E2
Rocester	68	A2
Roch	31	C3
Rochdale	78	A4
Roche	2	D1
Rochester	101	A4
Rochester	28	B3
Rochford	41	A1
Rochford	46	B4
Rock	2	C3
Rock	107	E2
Rock	46	C4
Rockbeare	4	C4
Rockbourne	12	B3
Rockcliffe	100	B1
Rockcliffe	94	B4
Rockfield	34	B3
Rockford	21	C1
Rockhampton	34	C1
Rockhill	45	C4
Rockland St Mary	63	A3
Rockland St Peter	62	A2
Rockley	80	C1
Rockley	24	C3
Rockwell End	37	B1
Rodbourne	24	B4
Rodden	5	E4
Rode	23	C2
Rode Heath	67	A3
Roden	55	D4
Rodhuish	9	D4
Rodington	56	A4
Rodley	34	D3
Rodmarton	35	B1
Rodmell	17	B1
Rodmersham	29	B2
Rodney Stoke	23	A1
Rodsley	68	B2
Roecliffe	90	E1
Rogate	15	A3
Rogerstone	33	E1
Rogiet	34	A1
Roke	37	A1
Rollesby	63	B4
Rolleston	59	B2
Rolleston	68	B1
Rolston	87	C3
Rolvenden Layne	19	B4
Romaldkirk	96	A2
Romanno Bridge	105	E4
Romansleigh	9	A3
Romford	12	B2
Romford	40	A1
Romiley	78	B2
Romsey	13	A3
Romsley	56	B1
Romsley	57	A1
Rookhope	96	A3
Rookley	7	A4
Rooks Bridge	22	D1
Rooks Nest	9	D4
Rookwith	90	D2
Roos	87	C2
Roothams Green	50	D3
Ropley	14	B4
Ropley Dean	14	B4
Ropsley	70	D1
Rora	132	E2
Rorrington	55	B2
Rose	2	B1
Rose Green	52	C1
Rose Green	52	C1
Rosebush	31	D4
Rosedale Abbey	91	C3
Rosehall	134	A2
Rosehearty	132	D3
Rosemarket	31	C2
Rosemarkie	130	C3
Rosemary Lane	10	A2
Rosenannon	2	C2
Rosewell	112	B2
Rosgill	95	B1
Rosley	94	F3
Roslin	112	B2
Rosliston	58	A4
Rosneath	109	D3
Ross	93	F3
Rossett	66	B3
Rossington	80	C3
Ross-on-Wye	34	C4
Rostherne	77	B1
Rosthwaite	94	F1
Roston	68	A2
Rosyth	111	C3
Rothbury	101	C4
Rotherby	59	B4
Rotherfield	18	B3
Rotherfield Peppard	26	A4
Rotherham	80	A2
Rothersthorpe	49	C3
Rotherwick	26	A2
Rothes	131	C2
Rothesay	109	C2
Rothiemay	131	E2
Rothienorman	132	B1
Rothley	59	A3
Rothwell	81	D3
Rothwell	59	C1
Rothwell	85	B1
Rottingdean	17	B1
Rottington	94	C1
Roucan	99	D2
Rougham	61	D4
Roughton	71	B4
Roughton	73	A1
Roughton	56	B2
Roundbush Green	40	B3
Roundway	24	B2
Rous Lench	47	B2
Rousdon	5	B4
Rousham	36	C4
Routh	87	B3
Row	2	E3
Row	89	A3
Row Green	40	C3
Rowanburn	100	B2
Rowarth	78	B2
Rowberrow	22	D2
Rowde	24	B2
Rowen	65	A4
Rowfoot	100	D1
Rowington	48	A4
Rowland	79	A1
Rowley	96	B4
Rowley	87	A2
Rowlstone	34	A4
Rowney Green	47	C4
Rownhams	13	A2
Rowrah	94	D1
Rowsham	37	B3
Rowsley	68	B4
Rowston	71	A3
Rowton	66	B4
Rowton	56	A4
Roxburgh	107	A3
Roxby	81	B4
Roxton	50	D2
Roxwell	40	B2
Roydon	39	B2
Roydon	61	C4
Roydon	62	B1
Roydon Hamlet	39	B2
Royston	79	B4
Royston	51	B1
Royton	78	A4
Rozel	137	B4
Ruabon	66	A2
Ruaig	118	B1
Ruan Lanihorne	1	E4
Ruan Major	1	D2
Ruan Minor	1	D2
Ruardean	34	C3
Ruardean Hill	34	C3
Ruardean Woodside	34	C3
Ruckhall	46	A1
Ruckinge	20	B4
Ruckley	55	D2
Rudby	91	A4
Rudchester	101	C1
Ruddington	69	B1
Rudgeway	23	B4
Rudgwick	16	B4
Rudley Green	41	A2
Rudloe	24	A3
Rudry	22	B4
Rudston	92	C1
Rudyard	67	C3
Rufford	76	A4
Rufforth	86	A3
Rugby	49	B4
Rugeley	57	B4
Rumbling Bridge	117	A1
Rumburgh	63	A1
Rumford	111	B3
Runcorn	76	B1
Runcton	15	B1
Runcton Holme	61	B3
Runfold	27	A1
Runhall	62	B3
Runham	63	B3
Runnington	10	A3
Runswick	97	D1
Runwell	40	C1
Rushall	46	B1
Rushall	62	C1
Rushall	24	C2
Rushbrooke	52	C3
Rushbury	55	D2
Rushden	39	A4
Rushden	50	B3
Rushford	62	A1
Rushlake Green	18	B3
Rushmere	63	C1
Rushmoor	15	B4
Rushock	45	C3
Rushock	47	A4
Rushton	66	D4
Rushton	59	C1
Rushwick	47	A2
Rushyford	96	D2
Ruskington	71	A3
Rusland	88	D3
Rusper	17	A4
Ruspidge	34	C3
Russ Hill	17	A4
Russell's Water	37	A1
Rustington	16	A1
Ruston	92	A2
Ruston Parva	87	A4
Ruswarp	92	A4
Rutherford	106	D3
Rutherglen	110	B2
Ruthernbridge	2	D2
Ruthin	65	E3
Ruthven	131	E2
Ruthven	121	D1
Ruthvoes	2	C2
Ruthwell	99	D1
Ruyton-XI-Towns	55	C4
Ryal	101	B2
Ryall	10	C1
Ryarsh	28	B2
Rydal	89	A4
Ryde	7	A4
Rye	20	A3
Rye Street	46	C1
Ryhall	60	A3
Ryhill	79	B4
Ryland	81	C1
Ryme Intrinseca	11	B2
Ryther	86	A2
Ryton	56	B2
Ryton	101	C1
Ryton-on-Dunsmore	48	B4
Sabden	84	A2
Sacombe	39	B3
Sacriston	96	C4
Sadberge	96	D1
Saddell	103	E3
Saddington	59	B2
Saddle Bow	61	B4
Saddlescombe	17	A2
Saffron Walden	51	C1
Sageston	31	D2
Saham Hills	62	A3
Saham Toney	62	A2
Saighton	66	B4
St Abbs	113	D2
St Agnes	2	A1
St Albans	38	B2
St Allen	2	B1
St Andrew	137	B4
St Andrews	117	E2
St Andrew's Major	22	B3
St Ann's Chapel	7	A4
St Anthony	1	D3
St Arvans	34	B1
St Asaph	75	B1
St Athan	22	A3
St Aubin	137	A3
St Austell	2	D1
St Bees	94	C1
St Boswells	106	D3
St Brelade	137	A3
St Brelade's Bay	137	A3
St Breock	2	D2
St Breward	2	E3
St Briavels	34	B2
St Bride's Major	21	E3
St Brides super-Ely	22	A4
St Brides Wentlooge	22	C4
St Buryan	1	A3
St Catherines	115	C2
St Chloe	35	A2
St Clears	32	A3
St Cleer	2	F2
St Clement	1	E4
St Clement	137	B3
St Clether	2	F4
St Columb Major	2	C2
St Combs	132	E3
St Cross South Elmham	63	A1
St Cyrus	122	C2
St David's	116	E3
St David's	31	B4
St Day	1	D4
St Decumans	22	A1
St Dennis	2	C1
St Dogmaels	43	C2
St Dominick	3	A2
St Donats	21	E3
St Endellion	2	D3
St Enoder	2	C1
St Erme	2	B1
St Erney	3	A1
St Erth	1	B3
St Erth Praze	1	C3
St Ervan	2	C2
St Ewe	1	F4
St Fagans	22	B4
St Fergus	132	E2
St Fillans	116	C3
St Florence	31	E2
St Gennys	8	A1
St George	75	A1
St Georges	22	D2
St Giles in the Wood	8	D3
St Giles-on-the-Heath	3	A4
St Harmon	44	E4
St Helen Auckland	96	C2
St Helena	62	C4
St Helens	7	B4
St Helens	76	B3
St Helier	137	B3
St Hilary	1	B3
St Hilary	22	A3
St Ippollitts	38	B4
St Ishmael's	31	B2
St Ive	3	A2
St Ives	51	B4
St Ives	1	B4
St John	3	A1
St John	137	B4
St John's	137	B2
St John's Chapel	8	D4
St John's Fen End	61	A3
St John's Town of Dalry	98	F3
St Jude's	137	C3
St Just	1	A3
St Just-in-Roseland	1	E3
St Keverne	1	D2
St Kew Highway	2	D3
St Keyne	2	F2
St Lawrence	41	B2
St Lawrence	7	A3
St Lawrence	137	B3
St Leonards	37	C2
St Leonards	12	B1
St Lythans	22	A3
St Mabyn	2	D3
St Margaret's at Cliffe	30	C1
St Margarets	45	D1
St Margarets	39	B3
St Marks	137	B1
St Martin	2	F1
St Martin	137	B4
St Martin	137	B3
St Martins	66	A1
St Mary	137	A3
St Mary Bourne	25	B1
St Mary Church	21	E3
St Mary in the Marsh	20	B3
St Mary's Bay	20	B3
St Mary's Hoo	29	A4
St Maughans Green	34	B3
St Mawes	1	E3
St Mawgan	2	C2
St Mellion	3	A2
St Merryn	2	C3
St Mewan	2	D1
St Michael Caerhays	1	F4
St Michael Church	10	B4
St Michael Penkevil	1	E4
St Michael South Elmham	63	A1
St Michael's on Wyre	83	B2
St Minver	2	D3
St Monans	117	E1
St Neot	2	E2
St Neots	50	D3
St Nicholas	43	A1
St Nicholas	22	A3
St Nicholas at Wade	30	B3
St Olaves	63	B2
St Osyth	42	B3
St Ouen	137	A3
St Owens Cross	34	B4
St Paul's Walden	38	B4
St Peter	137	A3
St Peter Port	137	B4
St Peter's	137	B4
St Sampson	137	B4
St Saviour	137	B4
St Saviour	137	B3
St Stephen	2	C1
St Stephen's Coombe	2	C1
St Teath	2	D3
St Tudy	2	D3
St Twynnells	31	C1
St Veep	2	E1
St Vigeans	122	B1
St Wenn	2	D2
St Weonards	34	B4
Saintbury	47	C1
Salcombe	7	A4
Salcott	41	B3
Sale	77	B2
Sale Green	47	B3
Saleby	82	C1
Salehurst	19	A3
Salem	54	B1
Salem	64	E3
Salen	118	F1
Salford	50	B1
Salford	78	A3
Salford	36	B4
Salford Priors	47	C2
Salfords	27	D1
Salhouse	63	A4
Saline	111	C4
Salisbury	12	B4
Salkeld Dykes	95	B3
Salle	62	B4
Salmonby	82	B1
Salperton	35	C3
Salsburgh	111	A2
Salt	67	C1
Saltash	3	B1
Saltburn	130	C4
Saltburn-by-the-Sea	97	C1
Saltby	70	B1
Saltcoats	104	C4
Salterforth	84	B3
Salterton	12	B4
Saltfleet	82	C2
Saltfleetby All Saints	82	C2
Saltfleetby St Clement	82	C2
Saltfleetby St Peter	82	C2
Saltford	23	B3
Salthouse	72	D2
Saltmarshe	86	C1
Salton	91	C2
Saltrens	8	D3
Salwarpe	47	A3
Salwayash	10	C1
Sambourne	47	C3
Sambrook	56	B4
Samlesbury	83	D2
Sampford Arundel	9	D3
Sampford Brett	9	D4
Sampford Courtenay	8	E1
Sampford Moor	9	D2
Sampford Peverell	9	D2
Sampford Spiney	3	B3
Samuelston	113	A2
Sanaigmore	108	A2
Sandbach	67	A4
Sancreed	1	A3
Sand Hills	85	B2
Sand Hole	86	C2
Sand Hutton	86	B4
Sandal Magna	79	B4
Sandend	131	E3
Sandford	95	D1
Sandford	12	C1
Sandford	22	D2
Sandford Orcas	11	B3
Sandford St Martin	36	C4
Sandhaven	132	D3
Sandhead	93	B4
Sandhoe	101	B1
Sandhurst	26	B2
Sandhurst	35	A4
Sandhurst	19	B3
Sandhutton	90	E2
Sandilands	82	C1
Sandleigh	36	C2
Sandon	40	C2
Sandon	51	B1
Sandon	67	C1
Sandon Bank	67	C1
Sandown	7	A4
Sandplace	2	F1
Sandridge	38	B3
Sandringham	72	A1
Sandsend	97	E1
Sandtoft	81	A4
Sandway	29	B1
Sandwith	94	C1
Sandy	50	D2
Sandy Lane	24	B3
Sandwich	30	B2
Sandygate	137	C3
Sandyhills	94	C4
Sanquhar	105	B1
Santon Bridge	88	B4
Santon Downham	61	D1
Sapcote	58	C2
Sapey Common	46	C3
Sapiston	52	C4
Sapperton	35	B2
Sapperton	70	D1
Saracen's Head	71	C1
Sarn	64	B1
Sarn	54	D2
Sarn	55	A1
Sarnau	43	E2
Sarnau	55	B4
Sarnesfield	45	D2
Saron	32	D3
Sarratt	38	A2
Sarre	30	B3
Sarsden	36	B4
Satley	96	B3
Satterleigh	9	A3
Satterthwaite	88	D3
Sauchen	127	B3
Saul	34	D2
Saundby	81	A2
Saundersfoot	31	E2
Saunderton	37	B2
Sausthorpe	71	C4
Sawbridge	49	B3
Sawbridgeworth	40	A3
Sawdon	92	A2
Sawley	84	A3
Sawley	90	D1
Sawston	51	C2
Sawtry	60	B1
Saxby	59	C4
Saxby	81	C2
Saxby All Saints	81	C4
Saxelbye	59	B4
Saxham Street	52	D3
Saxilby	81	B1
Saxlingham	72	D2
Saxlingham Green	63	A2
Saxlingham Thorpe	62	C2
Saxmundham	53	C3
Saxon Street	52	A3
Saxondale	70	A2
Saxtead	53	B3
Saxtead Green	53	B3
Saxthorpe	72	D1
Saxton	85	C2
Sayers Common	17	A3
Scackleton	91	C1
Scaftworth	80	C2
Scagglethorpe	91	D1
Scalasaig	108	C4
Scalby	86	C1
Scalby	92	B3
Scaldwell	50	A4
Scaleby	100	B1
Scalebyhill	100	B1
Scales	94	F2
Scales	88	D1
Scalford	59	C4
Scaling	97	D1
Scamblesby	82	A1
Scampston	92	A1
Scampton	81	B1
Scapegoat Hill	78	C4
Scarborough	92	B3
Scarcewater	2	C1
Scarcliffe	69	A4
Scarcroft Hill	85	B2
Scargill	90	C4
Scarinish	118	B1
Scarisbrick	76	A4
Scarning	62	A3
Scarrington	70	A2
Scawby	81	C3
Scawton	91	B2
Scayne's Hill	17	B3
Scethrog	33	C4
Scholes	79	B3
Scholes	79	A4
Scissett	79	A4
Scleddau	43	A1
Scofton	80	C1
Scole	53	A4
Sconser	123	D4
Scopwick	70	D3
Scorborough	87	A3
Scorrier	1	D4
Scorton	83	C3
Scorton	90	D4
Scotby	95	A4
Scotch Corner	90	D4
Scothern	81	C1
Scotlandwell	117	B1
Scotter	81	B3
Scotterthorpe	81	B3
Scotton	81	B3
Scotton	90	D3
Scotton	85	B4
Scoulton	62	A2
Scourie	135	A2
Scrabster	136	C4
Scraesburgh	106	D2
Scrane End	71	C2
Scraptoft	59	B3
Scratby	63	C4
Scrayingham	86	B4

Scredington	71	A2
Scremerston	113	E1
Screveton	70	A2
Scriven	85	B4
Scrooby	80	C2
Scropton	68	B1
Scruton	90	E3
Sculthorpe	72	C1
Scunthorpe	81	B4
Sea Palling	73	C1
Seaborough	10	C1
Seaford	18	A1
Seagrave	59	A4
Seaham	97	A4
Seahouses	107	E3
Seal	28	A2
Seale	27	A1
Seamer	91	A4
Seamer	92	B2
Seamill	104	C4
Searby	81	C3
Seascale	88	B4
Seathwaite	88	C3
Seatoller	94	F1
Seaton	2	F1
Seaton	94	D2
Seaton	5	B4
Seaton	87	B3
Seaton	102	B2
Seaton	59	D2
Seaton Delaval	102	B2
Seaton Ross	86	C2
Seatown	5	C4
Seave Green	91	B4
Seaview	7	B4
Seaville	94	E4
Seavington St Mary	10	C2
Sebergham	95	A3
Seckington	58	A3
Sedbergh	89	C3
Sedbusk	90	A3
Sedgeberrow	47	B1
Sedgebrook	70	C2
Sedgefield	96	D2
Sedgeford	72	A1
Sedgehill	11	D3
Sedgwick	89	B2
Sedrup	37	B3
Seend Cleeve	24	B2
Seer Green	37	C1
Seething	63	A2
Sefton	76	A3
Seighford	56	C4
Seion	64	E4
Seisdon	56	C2
Selattyn	66	A1
Selborne	15	A4
Selby	86	A2
Selham	15	B3
Selkirk	106	C3
Sellack	34	B4
Sellindge	20	B4
Selling	29	C2
Sells Green	24	B2
Selmeston	18	A2
Selsey	7	D4
Selside	89	D1
Selston	69	A3
Selworthy	21	E1
Semer	52	C2
Semington	24	A2
Semley	11	D3
Send	27	B2
Senghenydd	33	C1
Sennen	1	A2
Sennen Cove	1	A3
Sennybridge	33	B4
Sessay	91	A1
Setchey	61	B3
Settle	84	B4
Settrington	91	D1
Seven Sisters	33	A2
Seven Wells	47	C1
Sevenhampton	35	B3
Sevenhampton	36	A1
Sevenoaks	27	F2
Sevenoaks Weald	27	F1
Severn Beach	23	A4
Severn Stoke	47	A1
Sewards End	51	D1
Sewell	38	A4
Sewerby	92	D1
Seworgan	1	D3
Sewstern	59	D4
Shabbington	37	A2
Shackerstone	58	B3
Shackleford	27	A1
Shadforth	96	D3
Shadingfield	63	B1
Shadoxhurst	20	A4
Shadwell	62	A1
Shaftenhoe End	51	B1
Shafton	80	A4
Shaftesbury	11	D3
Shalbourne	25	A2
Shalden	26	A1
Shalford	40	C4
Shalford	27	B1
Shalford Green	40	C4
Shalstone	49	C1
Shamley Green	27	B1
Shandon	109	D4
Shangton	59	B2
Shanklin	7	A3
Shap	95	B1
Shapwick	12	A1
Shapwick	10	C4
Shardlow	69	A1
Shareshill	57	A3
Sharlston	85	C1
Sharnbrook	50	C3
Sharnford	58	C2
Sharow	90	E1
Sharpenhoe	38	A4
Sharperton	107	C1
Sharpness	34	C2
Sharrington	72	D1
Shatterford	56	B1
Shaugh Prior	3	B2
Shavington	67	A3
Shaw	78	B4
Shaw	24	A3
Shaw Mills	85	A4
Shawbury	55	D4
Shawell	59	A1
Shawhead	99	B2
Shearsby	59	B1
Shearston	10	B4
Shebbear	8	D2
Shebdon	56	B4
Sheen	68	A4
Sheepscombe	35	A2
Sheepstor	3	C2
Sheepwash	8	D1
Sheepy Magna	58	B2
Sheering	40	A3
Sheerness	29	B3
Sheet	15	A3
Sheffield	79	B2
Shefford	50	D1
Sheinton	56	A3
Shelderton	45	D4
Sheldon	68	B4
Sheldon	10	A2
Sheldwich	29	C2
Shelfanger	62	B1
Shelford	70	A2
Shelley	52	D1
Shelley	79	A4
Shellingford	36	B1
Shellow Bowells	40	B2
Shelsley Beauchamp	46	C3
Shelsley Walsh	46	C3
Shelton	50	C4
Shelton	62	C1
Shelton	70	B2
Shelve	55	B2
Shelwick	46	A1
Shenington	48	B1
Shenley	38	B2
Shenley Brook End	50	A1
Shenley Church End	50	A1
Shenmore	45	D1
Shenstone	57	B3
Shenstone	47	A4
Shenton	58	B2
Shepherdswell	30	B1
Shepley	79	A4
Shepreth	51	B2
Shepshed	58	C4
Shepton Mallet	23	B1
Shepton Montague	11	B4
Sheraton	97	A3
Sherborne	36	A3
Sherborne	23	B2
Sherborne St John	26	A2
Sherbourne	48	A3
Sherborne	11	B2
Sherburn	96	D3
Sherburn	92	A2
Sherburn in Elmet	85	C2
Shere	27	B1
Shereford	72	B1
Sherfield English	13	A3
Sherford	7	B4
Sherford	6	A4
Sheriff Hutton	91	C1
Sheriffhales	56	B3
Sheringham	73	A2
Sherington	50	B2
Shernborne	72	A1
Sherrington	12	A4
Sherston	24	A4
Shevington	76	B4
Sheviock	3	A1
Shibden Head	84	D1
Shidlaw	107	A4
Shiel Bridge	124	A3
Shieldaig	128	F2
Shieldhill	111	B3
Shifnal	56	B3
Shilbottle	107	E1
Shildon	96	C2
Shillingford	9	C3
Shillingford Abbot	4	B4
Shillingford St George	4	B4
Shillingstone	11	D2
Shillington	50	D1
Shilton	36	A2
Shilton	58	C1
Shimpling	62	C1
Shimpling	52	B2
Shimpling Street	52	B2
Shincliffe	96	D3
Shiney Row	96	D4
Shipbourne	28	A1
Shipdham	62	A3
Shipham	22	D2
Shiplake	26	B4
Shipley	84	D2
Shipley	16	B3
Shippon	36	C1
Shipston on Stour	48	A1
Shipton	35	B3
Shipton	86	A4
Shipton	55	D2
Shipton Bellinger	24	D1
Shipton Gorge	5	D4
Shipton Green	15	A1
Shipton Moyne	35	A1
Shipton-on-Cherwell	36	C3
Shipton-under-Wychwood	36	B3
Shiptonthorpe	86	D3
Shirburn	37	A1
Shirdley Hill	76	A4
Shirebrook	69	B4
Shirenewton	34	B1
Shireoaks	80	B1
Shirland	69	A3
Shirley	68	B2
Shirrell Heath	14	A2
Shirwell	8	E4
Shiskine	103	F3
Shobdon	45	D3
Shoby	59	B4
Shocklach	66	B3
Shop	8	B2
Shop	2	C3
Shop Street	53	A4
Shoreditch	10	B3
Shoreham-by-Sea	17	A1
Shorley	14	A3
Shorne	28	B3
Shortgate	18	A2
Shortlanesend	1	E4
Shortstown	50	C2
Shorwell	6	F3
Shoscombe	23	C2
Shotesham	63	A2
Shotley	53	A1
Shotley Bridge	96	B4
Shotley Gate	53	B1
Shotley Street	53	A1
Shottenden	29	C2
Shotteswell	49	A2
Shottisham	53	B1
Shottle	68	C3
Shottlegate	68	C2
Shotts	111	A1
Shotwick	66	A4
Shouldham	61	C3
Shouldham Thorpe	61	C3
Shoulton	47	A3
Shrawardine	55	C4
Shrawley	46	C3
Shrewley	48	A3
Shrewsbury	55	D3
Shrewton	24	C1
Shrivenham	36	A1
Shropham	62	A2
Shucknall	46	B1
Shudy Camps	51	D1
Shurdington	35	A3
Shurlock Row	26	B3
Shurton	22	B1
Shustoke	58	A1
Shut Heath	56	C4
Shute	10	B1
Shutford	48	B1
Shuthonger	47	A1
Shutlanger	49	C2
Shuttington	58	A3
Shuttlewood	80	A1
Shuttleworth	77	B4
Sibbertoft	59	B1
Sibdon Carwood	55	C1
Sibford Ferris	48	B1
Sibford Gower	48	B1
Sible Hedingham	52	B1
Sibley's Green	40	B4
Sibsey	71	C3
Sibson	60	B2
Sibson	58	B2
Sibthorpe	70	B2
Sicklesmere	52	B3
Sicklinghall	85	B3
Sidbury	5	A4
Sidbury	56	A1
Sidcot	22	D2
Siddington	67	B4
Siddington	35	B2
Sidestrand	73	B2
Sidmouth	5	A4
Sigglesthorne	87	B3
Sigingstone	21	E3
Silchester	26	A2
Sileby	59	A4
Silecroft	88	C2
Silfield	62	B2
Silk Willoughby	70	D2
Silkstone	79	B3
Silkstone Common	79	B3
Silloth	94	D4
Silpho	92	B3
Silsoe	50	D1
Silton	11	C3
Silver End	41	A3
Silverburn	112	A1
Silverdale	89	A1
Silverstone	49	C1
Silverton	9	C1
Silvington	46	B4
Simonburn	101	A2
Simons Burrow	10	A2
Simonsbath	9	B4
Simonstone	84	A2
Simpson	50	B1
Sinclair's Hill	113	D1
Sinclairston	104	E2
Sinderby	90	E2
Sinderland Green	77	B2
Sindlesham	26	B3
Singleton	83	B2
Singleton	15	B2
Sinnington	91	D2
Sinton	47	A3
Sissinghurst	19	B4
Siston	23	B3
Sithney	1	C3
Sittingbourne	29	B2
Six Ashes	56	B1
Six Mile Bottom	51	D3
Sixhills	81	D2
Sixpenny Handley	12	A2
Skares	104	E2
Skateraw	127	C1
Skeeby	90	D4
Skeffington	59	C2
Skeffling	87	D1
Skegby	70	B4
Skegness	71	E4
Skelbrooke	80	B4
Skeldyke	71	C1
Skellingthorpe	70	C4
Skellow	80	B4
Skelmanthorpe	79	A4
Skelmersdale	76	A3
Skelmorlie	109	C2
Skelton	95	A3
Skelton	86	C1
Skelton	97	C1
Skelton	90	E1
Skelton	86	A4
Skelwith Bridge	88	D4
Skendleby	71	D4
Skenfrith	34	A3
Skerne	87	A4
Skerray	135	F4
Skewsby	91	C1
Skidby	87	A2
Skilgate	9	C3
Skillington	59	D4
Skinburness	94	E4
Skinflats	111	B3
Skipness	109	A1
Skipsea	87	B4
Skipton	84	C3
Skipton-on-Swale	90	E2
Skipwith	86	B2
Skirlaugh	87	B2
Skirling	105	D4
Skirmett	37	B1
Skirpenbeck	86	C4
Skirwith	95	C2
Skye Green	41	A4
Slack	84	C1
Slad	35	A2
Slade	9	B3
Slade Hooton	80	B2
Slaggyford	95	C4
Slaidburn	84	A3
Slaithwaite	78	C4
Slaley	101	B1
Slamannan	111	A3
Slapton	37	C3
Slapton	7	B4
Slapton	49	C2
Slaugham	17	A3
Slaughterford	24	A3
Slawston	59	C2
Sleaford	15	A4
Sleaford	70	D2
Sleagill	95	C1
Sleapford	56	A4
Sledmere	92	A1
Sleightholme	90	B4
Sleights	92	A4
Sligachan	123	C4
Slimbridge	34	D2
Slindon	67	B1
Slindon	15	B2
Slinfold	16	B4
Slingsby	91	C1
Slip End	38	A3
Slip End	51	A1
Slipton	50	B4
Slitting Mill	57	A4
Sloncombe	3	D4
Sloothby	71	D4
Slough	27	B4
Slough Green	10	B3
Slyne	89	B1
Smailholm	106	D3
Small Dole	17	A2
Small Hythe	20	A4
Smallburgh	63	A4
Smalley	69	A2
Smallfield	27	E1
Smallridge	10	B1
Smallworth	62	B1
Smannell	25	A1
Smarden	29	A1
Smarden Bell	29	A1
Smart's Hill	27	F1
Smeatharpe	10	A2
Smeeth	20	B4
Smeeton Westerby	59	B2
Smestow	56	C2
Smisby	58	B4
Smith's Green	52	A1
Smithfield	100	B1
Smithstown	128	F4
Smithton	130	C1
Snailbeach	55	C2
Snailwell	51	D3
Snainton	92	A2
Snaith	86	B1
Snape	90	D2
Snape	53	C3
Snape Street	53	C3
Snarestone	58	B3
Snarford	81	C1
Snargate	20	A3
Snave	20	B4
Sneaton	92	A4
Snelland	81	C1
Snelston	68	A2
Snetterton	62	A1
Snettisham	72	A1
Snig's End	34	D4
Snitter	107	C1
Snitterby	81	C2
Snitterfield	48	A3
Snitton	46	A4
Snodland	28	B2
Snow End	39	B4
Snowshill	47	C1
Soake	14	B2
Soberton	14	A2
Soberton Heath	14	A2
Sockburn	90	E4
Soham	51	D4
Soldridge	14	B4
Sole Street	28	A3
Sole Street	29	C1
Solihull	48	A4
Sollers Dilwyn	45	D2
Sollers Hope	34	C4
Solva	31	B4
Somerby	59	C3
Somerby	81	C3
Somercotes	69	A3
Somerford Keynes	35	B1
Somerleyton	63	C2
Somersal Herbert	68	A1
Somersby	82	B1
Somersham	51	B4
Somersham	52	D2
Somerton	36	C4
Somerton	11	A3
Sompting	16	B1
Sonning	26	B3
Sonning Common	26	A4
Sopworth	24	A4
Sorbie	93	E4
Sorn	104	F3
Sosgill	94	D2
Sotby	82	A1
Sots Hole	71	A4
Sotterly	63	B1
Soughton	66	A4
Soulby	95	D1
Souldern	36	D4
Souldrop	50	C3
Sourton	3	B4
Soutergate	88	C2
South Acre	61	D3
South Alkham	30	B1
South Anston	80	B1
South Baddesley	13	A1
South Barrow	11	B3
South Benfleet	28	B4
South Brent	3	D1
South Brewham	11	C4
South Broomhill	102	A4
South Burlingham	63	B3
South Carlton	81	B1
South Cave	86	D2
South Cerney	35	C1
South Charlton	107	E2
South Cheriton	11	B3
South Cliffe	86	D2
South Cockerington	82	B2
South Cornelly	21	D4
South Cove	63	C1
South Creake	72	B1
South Croxton	59	B3
South Dalton	86	D3
South Duffield	86	B2
South Elkington	82	A2
South Elmsall	80	A4
South Fambridge	41	A1
South Fawley	25	B4
South Ferriby	87	A1
South Gorley	12	C2
South Green	29	A2
South Green	62	B3
South Hanningfield	40	C1
South Hayling	14	B1
South Heath	37	C2
South Hetton	96	D3
South Hiendley	80	A4
South Hill	3	A3
South Hinksey	36	D2
South Holmwood	27	C1
South Huish	7	A4
South Hykeham	70	C4
South Kelsey	81	C3
South Killingholme	81	D4
South Kilvington	91	A2
South Kilworth	59	A1
South Kirkby	80	A4
South Kyme	71	A3
South Lawn	36	B3
South Leigh	36	C2
South Leverton	81	A1
South Lopham	62	B1
South Luffenham	59	D2
South Marston	36	A1
South Milford	85	C2
South Milton	7	A4
South Mimms	39	A2
South Molton	9	A3
South Moreton	36	D1
South Mundham	15	B1
South Newbald	86	D2
South Newton	12	B4
South Normanton	69	A3
South Ockendon	28	A4
South Ormsby	82	B1
South Owersby	81	C2
South Perrott	11	A2
South Petherton	10	C2
South Petherwin	3	A3
South Pickenham	61	D3
South Pool	7	B4
South Poorton	11	A1
South Queensferry	112	A3
South Radworthy	9	A4
South Rauceby	70	D2
South Raynham	61	D4
South Runcton	61	B3
South Scarle	70	B4
South Shields	102	B1
South Stainley	85	B4
South Stoke	23	C2
South Stoke	16	A2
South Street	17	B3
South Street	29	C2
South Tawton	3	C4
South Thoresby	82	B1
South Tidworth	24	D1
South Weald	40	B1
South Willingham	81	D1
South Wingate	97	A3
South Wingfield	68	C3
South Witham	59	D4
South Woodham Ferrers	41	A1
South Wraxall	24	A3
South Zeal	3	C4
Southam	35	B4
Southam	49	A3
Southampton	13	B2
Southborough	28	A1
Southbourne	15	A1
Southburgh	62	A3
Southburn	87	A4
Southcott	8	B1
Southcott	8	E1
Southcott	3	D3
Southease	17	B1
Southend	103	D1
Southend-on-Sea	29	A4
Southerndown	21	D3
Southerness	94	C4
Southerton	4	C4
Southery	61	B2
Southfleet	28	A3
Southgate	32	D1
Southill	50	D1
Southleigh	5	A4
Southminster	41	B2
Southmoor	36	C1
Southoe	50	D3
Southorpe	60	A3
Southowram	84	D1
Southport	75	D4
Southrepps	73	B1
Southrey	71	A4
Southrop	36	A2
Southrope	26	A1
Southsea	14	B1
Southside	96	B2
Southwaite	95	A3
Southwater	16	B3
Southwell	70	A3
Southwick	14	B2
Southwick	60	A2
Southwick	24	A2
Southwold	53	D4
Sowerby	91	A2
Sowood	84	D1
Sowton	3	B2
Soyland Town	84	C1
Spain's End	52	A1
Spalding	60	C4
Spaldington	86	C2
Spaldwick	50	D4
Spalford	70	B4
Spanby	71	A2
Sparham	62	B4
Spark Bridge	88	D2
Sparkford	11	B3
Sparkwell	3	C1
Sparrowpit	78	C1
Sparsholt	36	B1
Spaunton	91	C3
Spaxton	10	A4
Spean Bridge	119	F4
Speen	37	B2
Speeton	92	C1
Speldhurst	28	A1
Spen Green	67	B3
Spennithorne	90	C3
Spennymoor	96	C2
Spetisbury	11	D1
Spexhall	63	B1
Spey Bay	131	D3
Spinkhill	80	A1
Spinningdale	134	C1
Spital Hill	80	B2
Spittal	136	D3
Spittal	31	D4
Spittal of Glenshee	121	B3
Spittalfield	117	A4
Spixworth	63	A4
Splatt	8	E1
Splayne's Green	18	A3
Spofforth	85	B3
Spooner Row	62	B2
Sporle	61	D3
Spott	113	B3
Spratton	49	C4
Spreakley	26	B1
Spreyton	9	A1
Spriddlestone	3	B1
Spridlington	81	C2
Springfield	100	A1
Springfield	117	C2
Springholm	99	B2
Springthorpe	81	B2
Springwell	102	B1
Sproatley	87	B2
Sproston Green	67	A4
Sprotbrough	80	B3
Sproughton	52	D1
Sprouston	107	A3
Sproxton	59	D4
Sproxton	91	B2
Spurstow	66	C3
Spyway	5	D4
Stableford	56	B2
Stacey Bank	79	B2
Stackhouse	90	A1
Stackpole	31	D1
Staddiscombe	3	B1
Stadhampton	36	D1
Staffield	95	B3
Staffin	128	C3
Staffin	3	I11
Stafford	56	C4
Stagsden	50	C2
Stainburn	94	D2
Stainburn	85	A3
Stainby	59	D4
Staincross	79	B4
Staindrop	96	B1
Stainforth	90	A1
Stainforth	80	C4
Staining	83	A2
Stainland	84	D1
Staines	27	B3
Stainsacre	92	A4
Stainton	95	B2
Stainton	89	B2
Stainton	96	B1
Stainton	80	B2
Stainton by Langworth	81	C1
Stainton le Vale	81	D2
Stainton with Adgarley	88	D1
Staintondale	92	B3
Stair	104	E2
Stair Haven	93	C4
Staithes	97	D1
Stalbridge	11	C2
Stalbridge Weston	11	C2
Stalham	63	B4
Stalisfield Green	29	B2
Stallen	11	B2
Stallingborough	81	D4
Stalmine	83	B3
Stalybridge	78	B3
Stambourne	52	A1
Stambourne Green	52	A1
Stamford	107	E2
Stamford	60	A3
Stamford Bridge	66	C4
Stamford Bridge	86	B4
Stamfordham	101	C2
Stanbridge	37	C4
Stanbury	84	C2
Standburn	111	B3
Standeford	56	C3
Standen	19	B4
Standerwick	24	A1
Standford	15	A4
Standingstone	94	D2
Standish	76	B4
Standon	13	B3
Standon	39	B4
Standon	67	B1
Stane	111	A1
Stanfield	62	A4
Stanford	50	D1
Stanford	20	C4
Stanford Bishop	46	B2
Stanford Bridge	46	C3
Stanford Dingley	25	C3
Stanford le Hope	28	B4
Stanford on Avon	49	B4
Stanford on Soar	59	A4
Stanfree	80	A1
Stanghow	97	C1
Stanhoe	72	B1
Stanhope	96	A3
Stanion	59	D1
Stanley	69	A2
Stanley	96	C4
Stanley	117	A4
Stanley	67	C3
Stanley Crook	96	C3
Stanley Pontlarge	35	B4
Stanmer	17	B2
Stannersburn	100	E3
Stannington	102	A2
Stannington	79	B2
Stannington Station	102	A3
Stansbatch	45	C3
Stansfield	52	B2
Stanstead	52	B2
Stanstead Abbots	39	B3
Stansted	28	A2
Stansted Mountfitchet	40	A4
Stanton	47	C1
Stanton	101	C3
Stanton	68	A2
Stanton	52	C4
Stanton by Bridge	68	C1
Stanton by Dale	69	A2
Stanton Drew	23	B2
Stanton Fitzwarren	36	A1
Stanton Harcourt	36	C2
Stanton in Peak	68	B4
Stanton Lacy	46	A4
Stanton Lees	68	B4
Stanton Long	55	D1
Stanton St John	36	D2
Stanton St Quintin	24	A4
Stanton Street	52	C3
Stanton under Bardon	58	C3
Stanton upon Hine Heath	55	D4
Stanton Wick	23	B2
Stanway	41	B4
Stanway	35	C4
Stanwick	50	C4
Stape	91	D3
Stapeley	66	D3
Staple	30	B2
Staple	22	A1
Staple Cross	9	D3

Staple Fitzpaine	10	B3
Staplefield	17	A3
Stapleford	39	A3
Stapleford	59	C4
Stapleford	70	C3
Stapleford	69	A1
Stapleford	12	B4
Stapleford Abbotts	40	A1
Staplehay	10	A3
Staplehurst	29	A1
Staplestreet	29	C2
Stapleton	45	C3
Stapleton	58	C2
Stapleton	96	C1
Stapleton	55	D3
Stapleton	10	C3
Stapley	10	A2
Staploe	50	D3
Staplow	46	B1
Star	117	C1
Star	43	D1
Starbotton	90	B1
Starcross	4	B3
Stareton	48	B4
Starlings Green	40	A4
Starston	62	C1
Startforth	96	B1
Startley	24	B4
Statenborough	30	B2
Stathe	10	C3
Stathern	70	B1
Staughton Green	50	D3
Staughton Highway	50	D3
Staunton	34	B3
Staunton	34	D4
Staunton on Arrow	45	D3
Staunton on Wye	45	D1
Staveley	89	A2
Staveley	89	B3
Staveley	80	A1
Staveley	85	B4
Staverton	35	A4
Staverton	49	B3
Staverton	24	A2
Stawell	10	C4
Stawley	9	D3
Staxigoe	136	F3
Staxton	92	B2
Staynall	83	B3
Stean	90	C1
Steane	49	B1
Stearsby	91	B1
Steart	22	C1
Stebbing	40	C4
Stebbing Green	40	C4
Stedham	15	B3
Steel	101	B1
Steen's Bridge	46	A3
Steep	15	A3
Steep Lane	84	C1
Steeple	6	A3
Steeple	41	B2
Steeple Ashton	24	A2
Steeple Aston	36	C4
Steeple Bumpstead	52	A1
Steeple Claydon	37	A4
Steeple Gidding	60	B1
Steeple Langford	12	A4
Steeple Morden	51	A1
Stelling Minnis	30	A1
Stembridge	10	C3
Stenalees	2	D1
Stenhousemuir	111	A3
Stenton	113	B3
Stepaside	31	E2
Steppingley	50	C1
Sternfield	53	C3
Stert	24	B2
Stetchworth	51	D3
Stevenage	39	A4
Stevenston	104	C4
Steventon	25	C1
Steventon	36	C1
Steventon End	51	D1
Stevington	50	C2
Stewartby	50	C1
Stewarton	104	D4
Stewkley	37	C4
Stewley	10	B3
Steyning	16	B2
Steynton	31	C2
Stibb	8	B2
Stibb Cross	8	D2
Stibb Green	24	D2
Stichill	107	A4
Sticker	2	D1
Stickford	71	C3
Sticklepath	3	C4
Stickling Green	40	A4
Stickney	71	C3
Stiffkey	72	C2
Stillingfleet	86	A2
Stillington	96	D2
Stillington	91	B1
Stilton	60	B1
Stinchcombe	34	D1
Stinsford	5	F4
Stiperstones	55	C2
Stirling	111	A4
Stisted	41	A4
Stithians	1	D3
Stixwould	71	A4
Stoak	76	A1
Stobo	105	E4
Stoborough	6	A4
Stobswood	102	A4
Stock	40	C2
Stock	22	D2
Stock Green	47	B3
Stock Wood	47	B3
Stockbridge	13	A4
Stockcross	25	B3
Stockerston	59	C2
Stocking	34	C4
Stocking Pelham	40	A4
Stockland Bristol	22	C1
Stockleigh Pomeroy	9	B1
Stockley	24	B3
Stockport	78	A2
Stocklinch	10	C2
Stocksbridge	79	A3
Stocksfield	101	C1
Stockton	46	A3
Stockton	56	B4
Stockton	56	B2
Stockton	49	A3
Stockton-on-Tees	97	A1
Stockton on Teme	46	C3
Stockton on the Forest	86	B4
Stockwood	11	B2
Stodmarsh	30	A2
Stody	72	D1
Stoford	11	A2
Stogumber	9	D4
Stogursey	22	B1
Stoke	8	B3
Stoke	25	B1
Stoke	14	B1
Stoke	29	A3
Stoke Abbott	10	C1
Stoke Albany	59	C1
Stoke Ash	52	D4
Stoke Bardolph	70	A2
Stoke Bliss	46	B3
Stoke Bruerne	50	A2
Stoke by Clare	52	A1
Stoke Canon	9	C1
Stoke Charity	13	B4
Stoke Climsland	3	A3
Stoke Cross	46	B2
Stoke Doyle	60	A1
Stoke Dry	59	D2
Stoke Ferry	61	C2
Stoke Fleming	7	B4
Stoke Gabriel	4	A1
Stoke Golding	58	C2
Stoke Goldington	50	A2
Stoke Hammond	37	C4
Stoke Holy Cross	62	C2
Stoke Lacy	46	B2
Stoke Lyne	36	D4
Stoke Mandeville	37	B2
Stoke-on-Trent	67	B2
Stoke Orchard	35	A4
Stoke Poges	27	B4
Stoke Prior	46	A2
Stoke Prior	47	B3
Stoke Rivers	8	E4
Stoke Rochford	70	C1
Stoke Row	26	A4
Stoke St Michael	23	B1
Stoke St Milborough	55	D1
Stoke sub Hamdon	11	A2
Stoke Talmage	37	A2
Stoke Trister	11	C3
Stoke upon Tern	66	D1
Stoke Wake	11	C1
Stoke-by-Nayland	52	C1
Stokeford	6	A4
Stokeham	81	A1
Stokeinteignhead	4	B2
Stokenchurch	37	B1
Stokenham	7	B4
Stokesby	63	B3
Stokesley	91	B4
Stolford	9	D4
Stolford	22	B1
Ston Easton	23	B2
Stondon Massey	40	B2
Stone	37	B3
Stone	34	C1
Stone	20	A3
Stone	80	B2
Stone	47	A4
Stone	67	B1
Stone Allerton	22	D1
Stone Street	28	A2
Stone Street	63	B1
Stonebridge	22	D2
Stonebridge	58	A1
Stonebroom	69	A3
Stonecrouch	19	A4
Stonegate	19	A3
Stonegrave	91	C2
Stonehall	47	A2
Stonehaven	122	D4
Stonehouse	66	C4
Stonehouse	34	D2
Stonehouse	105	A4
Stoneleigh	48	B4
Stones Green	42	B4
Stonesby	59	C4
Stonesfield	36	C3
Stoney Middleton	79	A1
Stoney Stanton	58	C2
Stoney Stoke	11	C4
Stoney Stratton	11	B4
Stoney Stretton	55	C3
Stoneyburn	111	B2
Stoneykirk	93	B4
Stoneywood	127	C3
Stonham Aspal	53	A3
Stonor	37	A1
Stonton Wyville	59	C2
Stony Houghton	69	A4
Stoodleigh	9	A4
Stoodleigh	9	C3
Stopham	16	A3
Stormy Corner	76	B4
Storrington	16	B2
Storwood	86	B3
Stotfold	51	A1
Stottesdon	56	A1
Stoughton	59	B2
Stoughton	15	A2
Stoulton	47	A2
Stourbridge	56	C1
Stour Provost	11	C3
Stour Row	11	D3
Stourport-on-Severn	47	A4
Stourton	56	C1
Stourton	48	B1
Stourton	11	C4
Stourton Caundle	11	C2
Stow	106	B4
Stow	81	B1
Stow Bardolph	61	B3
Stow Bedon	62	A2
Stow cum Quy	51	C3
Stow Longa	50	D4
Stow Maries	41	A2
Stow-on-the-Wold	36	A4
Stowbridge	61	B3
Stowe	45	C4
Stowe by Chartley	67	C1
Stowell	11	B3
Stowford	8	D1
Stowford	21	B1
Stowford	3	B4
Stowlangtoft	52	C3
Stowmarket	52	D3
Stowting	30	A1
Stowting Common	30	A1
Stowupland	52	D3
Strachan	127	A1
Strachur	115	C1
Stradbroke	53	A4
Stradsett	61	C3
Stragglethorpe	70	C3
Straiton	104	D1
Straloch	121	B2
Stramshall	68	A1
Strang	137	C2
Strangford	34	B4
Stranraer	98	A1
Stratfield Saye	26	A2
Stratfield Turgis	26	A2
Stratford St Mary	52	D1
Stratford-upon-Avon	48	A2
Strath	128	F4
Strathblane	110	B3
Strathcanaird	133	D2
Strathdon	126	D3
Strathaven	105	A4
Strathkinness	117	D2
Strathmiglo	117	B2
Strathpeffer	130	A3
Strathtay	121	A2
Strathwhillan	104	A3
Strathy	136	A4
Strathyre	116	B2
Stratton	8	B1
Stratton	5	E4
Stratton	35	B2
Stratton Audley	36	D4
Stratton St Michael	62	C2
Stratton Strawless	62	C4
Stratton-on-the-Fosse	23	B1
Stream	9	D4
Streat	17	B2
Streatley	38	A4
Streatley	25	C4
Street	11	A4
Street Ashton	58	C1
Street Dinas	66	A2
Street End	15	B1
Street Gate	102	A1
Street on the Fosse	11	B4
Streethay	57	B3
Streetlam	90	E3
Streetly End	51	D2
Strelley	69	B2
Strensall	86	B4
Strete	7	B4
Stretford	77	B2
Strethall	51	C1
Stretham	51	C4
Stretton	77	A1
Stretton	69	A4
Stretton	59	D4
Stretton	56	C3
Stretton	68	B1
Stretton on Fosse	48	A1
Stretton under Fosse	58	C1
Stretton Westwood	56	A2
Stretton-on-Dunsmore	49	A4
Strichen	132	D2
Stringston	22	B1
Strixton	50	B3
Stroat	34	B1
Stromeferry	129	A1
Stronachlachar	115	E2
Strone	109	C3
Stronmilchan	115	C3
Strontian	119	B2
Stroud	35	A2
Stroud	14	B3
Stroud Green	34	D2
Stroxton	70	C1
Struan	128	B1
Struan	120	E3
Strumpshaw	63	A3
Struy	129	E1
Stuartfield	132	D2
Stubbington	14	A1
Stubbins	77	B4
Stubton	70	C2
Studham	38	A3
Studholme	94	F4
Studland	6	B3
Studley	47	C3
Studley	24	B3
Studley Royal	90	E1
Stuntney	51	D4
Sturmer	52	A1
Sturminster Common	11	C2
Sturminster Marshall	12	A1
Sturminster Newton	11	C2
Sturry	30	A2
Sturton	81	C3
Sturton by Stow	81	B1
Sturton le Steeple	81	A2
Stuston	53	A4
Stutton	85	C2
Stutton	53	A1
Styal	78	A1
Styrrup	80	B2
Suckley	46	C2
Sudborough	60	A1
Sudbourne	53	C2
Sudbury	52	B1
Sudbrook	70	D2
Sudbrook	34	B1
Sudbrooke	81	C1
Sudbury	68	B1
Suddington	47	A3
Suffield	92	B3
Suffield	73	A1
Sugnall	67	A1
Sugwas Pool	45	D1
Sulby	137	C3
Sulgrave	49	B1
Sulhamstead	26	A3
Summerbridge	85	A4
Summercourt	2	C1
Summerfield	72	A2
Summerhouse	96	C1
Summerseat	77	B4
Sunbury	27	C3
Sunderland	94	E3
Sunderland	83	B4
Sunderland	102	C1
Sundridge	27	F2
Sunningwell	36	C2
Sunniside	96	B3
Surfleet	71	B1
Surlingham	63	A3
Sustead	73	A1
Susworth	81	A3
Sutcombe	8	C2
Sutcombemill	8	C2
Sutterby	82	B1
Sutterton	71	B1
Sutton	51	A2
Sutton	60	B2
Sutton	51	C4
Sutton	7	A4
Sutton	27	D2
Sutton	30	B1
Sutton	85	C1
Sutton	63	B4
Sutton	80	C2
Sutton	70	B1
Sutton	56	B1
Sutton	56	B4
Sutton	53	B2
Sutton	16	A2
Sutton at Hone	28	A3
Sutton Bassett	59	C1
Sutton Bonington	59	A4
Sutton Bridge	61	A4
Sutton Cheney	58	C2
Sutton Coldfield	57	B2
Sutton Courtenay	36	D1
Sutton Grange	90	E1
Sutton Green	27	B2
Sutton Howgrave	90	E2
Sutton Maddock	56	B2
Sutton Mallet	10	C4
Sutton Mandeville	12	A3
Sutton Montis	11	B3
Sutton on Sea	82	C1
Sutton on the Hill	68	B1
Sutton on Trent	70	B4
Sutton Scotney	13	B4
Sutton St Edmund	60	D3
Sutton St James	60	D4
Sutton St Nicholas	46	A2
Sutton upon Derwent	86	B3
Sutton Valence	29	A1
Sutton Veny	24	A1
Sutton Waldron	11	D2
Sutton Weaver	76	B1
Sutton Wick	36	C1
Sutton Wick	23	A2
Sutton-in-Craven	84	C3
Sutton-on-the-Forest	91	B1
Sutton-under-Brailes	48	B1
Sutton-under-Whitestonecliffe	91	A2
Swadlincote	58	B4
Swaffham	61	D3
Swaffham Bulbeck	51	D3
Swaffham Prior	51	D3
Swafield	73	B1
Swainby	91	A4
Swainsthorpe	62	C2
Swainswick	23	C3
Swalcliffe	48	B1
Swallow	81	D3
Swallowcliffe	12	A3
Swallowfield	26	A3
Swan Green	77	B1
Swanage	6	B3
Swanbourne	37	B4
Swanland	87	A1
Swanley	27	F3
Swanmore	14	A2
Swannington	58	C4
Swannington	62	C4
Swansea	32	E1
Swanton Abbot	63	A4
Swanton Morley	62	B4
Swanton Novers	72	D1
Swanwick	69	A3
Swarby	70	D2
Swardeston	62	C2
Swarkestone	68	C1
Swarland	102	A4
Swarraton	14	A4
Swarthmoor	88	D2
Swaton	71	A1
Swavesey	51	B4
Swayfield	60	A4
Sweetham	9	B1
Sweethaws	18	A3
Sweets	8	A1
Sweetshouse	2	E2
Swefling	53	B3
Swepstone	58	B3
Swerford	36	B4
Swettenham	67	A4
Swiftsden	19	A3
Swilland	53	A2
Swillington	85	B2
Swimbridge	8	E4
Swinbrook	36	B3
Swincliffe	85	A4
Swinderby	70	C4
Swindon	56	C1
Swindon	24	C4
Swine	87	B2
Swinefleet	86	C1
Swineshead	50	C3
Swineshead	71	B2
Swinford	49	B4
Swingfield Minnis	30	A1
Swingfield Street	30	A1
Swingleton Green	52	C2
Swinhoe	107	E3
Swinithwaite	90	B3
Swinside	94	F1
Swinstead	60	A4
Swinton	107	B4
Swinton	77	B3
Swinton	90	D2
Swinton	80	A3
Swithland	59	A3
Swynnerton	67	B1
Swyre	5	D4
Sychtyn	54	D3
Syde	35	B3
Sydenham	37	A2
Sydenham Damerel	3	A3
Syderstone	72	B1
Sydling St Nicholas	11	B1
Syerston	70	B2
Sykehouse	80	C4
Symington	104	D3
Symington	105	C3
Syreford	35	B3
Syresham	49	C1
Syston	59	B3
Syston	70	C2
Sywell	50	A3
Tackley	36	C3
Tacolneston	62	C2
Tadcaster	85	C3
Taddington	68	A4
Taddington	35	C4
Tadlow	51	A2
Tadmarton	49	A1
Tain	134	D1
Taff's Well	22	B4
Taibach	33	A1
Takeley	40	B3
Takeley Street	40	B3
Tal-y-Bont	65	A4
Tal-y-bont	54	A4
Tal-y-coed	34	A3
Tal-y-garn	22	A4
Talaton	9	D1
Talbenny	31	B3
Talerddig	54	D2
Talgarreg	43	E2
Talgarth	45	B1
Taliesin	54	B2
Talkin	100	C1
Talladale	129	A4
Tallarn Green	66	B2
Tallentire	94	D3
Talley	32	D4
Tallington	60	B3
Talmine	135	E4
Talog	32	B4
Talsarn	44	B2
Talsarnau	64	E1
Talskiddy	2	C2
Talwrn	74	C1
Talybont	54	A1
Talybont-on-Usk	33	C4
Talysarn	64	D3
Tamworth	58	A3
Tan Office Green	52	B3
Tan-y-groes	43	D2
Tanfield	96	C4
Tanfield Lea	96	C4
Tangley	25	A1
Tankersley	79	B3
Tannadice	122	A2
Tannington	53	B3
Tannochside	110	C2
Tansley	68	C3
Tansor	60	A1
Tantobie	96	C4
Tanton	91	B4
Tanworth in Arden	47	C4
Taplow	27	A4
Tarbert	108	E1
Tarbet	115	E1
Tarbet	123	F1
Tarbert	109	A2
Tarbolton	104	E3
Tardebigge	47	B4
Tarfside	122	A4
Tarland	126	E2
Tarleton	83	B1
Tarlton	35	B2
Tarnock	22	D2
Tarporley	66	C4
Tarr	9	B4
Tarr	9	D4
Tarrant Crawford	11	D1
Tarrant Gunville	11	D2
Tarrant Hinton	12	A2
Tarrant Keyneston	12	A1
Tarrant Launceston	12	A2
Tarrant Monkton	12	A2
Tarrant Rawston	12	A2
Tarrant Rushton	12	A1
Tarrington	46	B1
Tarskavaig	123	D2
Tarves	127	C4
Tarvin	66	C4
Tasburgh	62	C2
Tatenhill	58	A4
Tathwell	82	B1
Tatsfield	27	E2
Tattenhall	66	C3
Tatterford	72	B1
Tattersett	72	B1
Tattershall	71	B3
Tattershall Thorpe	71	B3
Tattingstone	53	A1
Taunton	10	A3
Taverham	62	C3
Tavernspite	31	E3
Tavistock	3	B3
Taw green	9	A1
Tawstock	8	E4
Taxal	78	B1
Tayinloan	103	D4
Taynton	34	D4
Taynton	36	A3
Taynuilt	115	B4
Tayport	117	D3
Tayvallich	108	F4
Tealby	81	D2
Teangue	123	E2
Tebay	89	C4
Tebworth	38	A4
Tedburn St Mary	4	A4
Teddington	35	B4
Tedstone Delamere	46	B3
Tedstone Wafer	46	B3
Teeton	49	C4
Teffont Evias	12	A4
Teffont Magna	12	A4
Tegryn	32	A4
Teigh	59	D4
Teignmouth	4	B3
Telford	56	B3
Tellisford	23	C2
Templand	99	D3
Temple	2	E3
Temple	112	B1
Temple Bar	44	A2
Temple Cloud	23	B2
Temple Grafton	47	C2
Temple Guiting	35	C4
Temple Hirst	86	A1
Temple Normanton	69	A4
Temple Sowerby	95	C2
Templecombe	11	C3
Templeton	9	B2
Templeton	31	E3
Tempsford	50	D2
Ten Mile Bank	61	B2
Tenby	31	E2
Tendring	42	B4
Terling	40	C3
Ternhill	66	D1
Terrington	91	C1
Terrington St Clement	61	B4
Teston	28	B2
Tetbury	35	A1
Tetchill	66	B1
Tetcott	8	C1
Tetford	82	B1
Tetney	82	B3
Tetsworth	37	A2
Teversal	69	A4
Teversham	51	C3
Teviothead	106	B1
Tewin	39	A3
Tewkesbury	35	A4
Thakeham	16	B2
Thame	37	A2
Thankerton	105	C4
Tharston	62	C2
Thatcham	25	C3
Thaxted	40	B4
The Braes	128	D1
The Bungalow	137	C2
The City	37	B1
The Den	109	E1
The Forstal	29	B1
The Forstal	20	B4
The Green	88	C2
The Green	40	C3
The Hill	88	C2
The Holt	26	B4
The Lee	37	C2
The Lhen	137	C4
The Mythe	47	A1
The Strand	24	A2
Theakston	90	E2
Thealby	81	B4
Theale	26	A3
Theale	22	D1
Thearne	87	A2
Theberton	53	C3
Theddingworth	59	B1
Theddlethorpe All Saints	82	C2
Theddlethorpe St Helen	82	C2
Thelnetham	52	D4
Thelveton	62	C1
Themelthorpe	62	B4
Therfield	51	B1
Thetford	61	D1
Theydon Bois	40	A2
Thickwood	24	A3
Thimbleby	71	B4
Thimbleby	91	A3
Thirkleby	91	A2
Thirlby	91	A2
Thirlspot	94	F1
Thirn	90	D2
Thirsk	91	A2
Thistleton	83	B2
Thistleton	59	D4
Thistley Green	52	A4
Thixendale	86	C4
Thockrington	101	B2
Tholomas Drove	60	D3
Tholthorpe	91	A1
Thomastown	131	E1
Thompson	62	A2
Thong	28	B3
Thoralby	90	B2
Thoresway	81	D3
Thorganby	82	A3
Thorganby	86	B2
Thorgill	91	C3
Thorington	53	C4
Thorington Street	52	D1
Thorlby	84	C3
Thorley	40	A3
Thorley Street	6	E4
Thormanby	91	A1
Thorn's Flush	16	A4
Thornage	72	D1
Thornborough	37	B4
Thornborough	90	E2
Thornbury	8	C2
Thornbury	34	C1
Thornbury	46	B3
Thornby	49	C4
Thorncliff	67	C3
Thorncombe	10	C1
Thorndon	53	A4
Thorndon Cross	3	B4
Thorne	80	C4
Thorne St Margaret	9	D3
Thorner	85	B2
Thornes	57	B3
Thorney	60	C3
Thorney	81	B1
Thorney	10	C3
Thornfalcon	10	B3
Thornford	11	B2
Thorngrafton	100	E1
Thorngumbald	87	C1
Thornham	72	A2
Thornham Magna	52	D4
Thornham Parva	52	D4
Thornhaugh	60	A2
Thornhill	99	B4
Thornhill	116	C1
Thornhill	85	A1
Thornholme	87	B4
Thornicombe	11	D1
Thornington	107	B3
Thornley	96	B3
Thornley	96	D3
Thorns	52	A2
Thornsett	78	B2
Thornthwaite	94	E2
Thornthwaite	85	A4
Thornton	121	E1
Thornton	50	A1
Thornton	86	C3
Thornton	117	C1
Thornton	83	A3
Thornton	58	C3
Thornton	71	B4
Thornton	97	A1
Thornton	107	C4
Thornton	84	D2
Thornton Curtis	81	D4
Thornton Dale	91	D2
Thornton Hough	75	D1
Thornton in Lonsdale	89	C1
Thornton le Moor	81	C3
Thornton Rust	90	B3
Thornton Steward	90	D2
Thornton Watlass	90	D2
Thornton-in-Craven	84	B3
Thornton-le-Beans	91	A3
Thornton-le-Clay	91	C1
Thornton-le-Moor	91	A3
Thornton-le-Moors	76	A1
Thornton-le-Street	91	A2
Thorntonhall	110	B1
Thornythwaite	95	A2
Thoroton	70	B2
Thorp Arch	85	C3
Thorpe	68	A3
Thorpe	87	A3
Thorpe	84	C4
Thorpe	70	B3
Thorpe Abbotts	62	C1
Thorpe Arnold	59	C4
Thorpe Audlin	80	A4
Thorpe Bassett	92	A1
Thorpe by Water	59	D2
Thorpe Constantine	58	A3
Thorpe End	63	A3
Thorpe Green	42	B4
Thorpe Green	52	C2

lx

DISTANCES CHART

1 MILE = 1.6 KILOMETRES

	London	Aberdeen	Aberystwyth	Ayr	Berwick-upon-Tweed	Birmingham	Blackpool	Bournemouth	Braemar	Brighton	Bristol	Cambridge	Cardiff	Carlisle	Doncaster	Dover	Dundee	Edinburgh	Exeter	Fishguard	Fort William	Glasgow	Gloucester	Great Yarmouth	Harwich	Holyhead	Inverness	John o'Groats	Kingston upon Hull	Kyle of Lochalsh	Land's End	Leeds	Leicester	Lincoln	Liverpool	Manchester	Newcastle upon Tyne	Norwich	Nottingham	Oban	Oxford	Plymouth	Portsmouth	Sheffield	Shrewsbury	Southampton	Stranraer	Swansea	York
London		517	211	394	352	117	234	107	482	52	122	54	157	301	171	71	448	390	181	260	510	397	109	128	76	269	550	663	184	586	297	189	97	131	202	185	286	114	122	499	57	218	70	159	160	77	402	194	207
Aberdeen	517		445	183	182	420	308	564	59	573	493	471	505	221	344	588	67	125	569	504	149	145	468	517	535	439	105	232	364	189	692	327	414	383	341	340	235	496	393	178	483	615	560	360	399	547	228	507	319
Aberystwyth	211	445		317	311	114	153	207	405	253	125	214	105	224	176	292	376	320	201	56	430	320	102	294	281	111	486	601	223	499	313	169	153	199	104	129	257	276	164	412	154	237	222	159	77	201	325	73	195
Ayr	394	183	317		134	289	180	436	143	446	370	357	382	93	235	478	117	73	446	373	133	33	330	402	425	305	199	328	251	212	570	212	299	274	213	212	149	382	274	94	353	492	430	245	269	417	51	379	214
Berwick-upon-Tweed	352	182	311	134		274	181	412	148	409	362	306	368	87	184	424	113	57	428	371	190	101	318	345	372	311	215	342	185	263	552	156	252	224	219	196	64	328	221	180	324	474	401	190	265	388	170	383	148
Birmingham	117	420	114	289	274		123	147	385	163	81	100	103	196	94	194	349	292	157	170	392	292	56	180	167	148	458	574	134	471	281	113	39	90	93	80	207	166	50	384	64	203	141	76	45	128	297	119	130
Blackpool	234	308	153	180	181	123		270	281	286	204	208	209	87	94	312	239	183	282	209	296	183	174	252	275	141	348	478	127	372	405	72	140	128	49	48	129	232	111	285	187	328	264	86	98	251	188	216	96
Bournemouth	107	564	207	436	412	147	270		524	92	82	154	117	343	235	174	495	439	82	222	539	439	96	240	187	288	597	724	264	618	205	255	158	209	234	227	347	214	183	530	90	128	52	216	185	31	444	167	269
Braemar	482	59	405	143	148	385	281	524		534	477	438	483	196	310	553	52	91	550	493	125	110	443	477	504	426	75	202	187	288	507	318	318	201	457	353	141	465	587	320	371	532	194	505	285				
Brighton	52	573	253	446	409	163	286	92	534		147	116	182	370	236	82	517	456	184	291	575	468	159	180	338	334	617	741	245	651	308	200	266	197	272	257	352	175	193	565	108	224	226	41	475	222	275		
Bristol	122	493	125	370	362	81	204	82	477	147		169	45	277	175	202	430	373	76	154	486	373	35	275	217	206	539	668	233	552	200	194	120	183	161	161	299	252	145	465	74	122	97	161	103	76	378	85	222
Cambridge	54	471	214	357	306	100	208	154	438	116	169		190	264	116	125	406	345	249	270	479	372	123	82	67	270	505	630	139	555	374	145	68	85	194	165	241	62	83	468	83	293	144	120	159	148	379	227	165
Cardiff	157	505	105	382	368	103	209	117	483	182	45	190		289	209	238	441	385	121	112	485	385	56	284	246	216	549	680	244	564	245	232	154	208	165	183	325	262	172	477	108	167	142	194	111	121	390	41	244
Carlisle	301	221	224	93	87	196	87	343	196	370	277	264	289		142	389	152	96	353	297	206	96	247	320	336	231	262	391	158	275	477	119	206	191	120	119	57	289	194	188	260	399	348	152	176	324	101	309	121
Doncaster	171	344	176	235	184	94	94	235	310	236	175	116	209	142		242	275	219	251	247	357	249	150	167	194	181	383	507	47	432	374	29	74	39	86	61	114	147	43	346	145	297	234	18	109	209	257	232	34
Dover	71	588	292	478	424	194	312	174	553	82	202	125	238	389	242		523	462	248	331	596	488	191	185	125	360	622	747	256	671	381	260	185	202	299	276	358	174	205	585	141	300	130	245	251	143	496	274	282
Dundee	448	67	376	117	113	349	239	495	52	517	430	406	441	152	275	523		56	518	460	187	83	410	484	469	394	132	259	295	186	642	258	349	314	286	285	166	422	328	117	433	552	514	291	300	500	167	473	250
Edinburgh	390	125	320	73	57	292	183	439	91	456	373	345	385	96	219	462	56		450	399	144	44	349	386	413	333	158	285	234	216	574	202	295	258	216	215	110	366	262	123	372	496	453	235	274	438	124	412	194
Exeter	181	569	201	446	428	157	282	82	550	184	76	249	121	353	251	248	518	450		230	560	449	111	335	279	282	618	744	309	628	123	270	196	247	237	236	364	308	221	549	156	46	135	237	179	105	454	161	287
Fishguard	260	504	56	373	371	170	209	222	493	291	154	270	112	297	247	331	460	399	230		486	376	153	366	337	167	542	671	280	567	353	237	209	272	160	197	329	343	220	481	205	264	251	215	145	233	392	67	261
Fort William	510	149	430	133	190	392	296	539	125	575	486	479	485	206	357	596	127	144	560	486		101	454	527	543	438	66	195	369	79	686	329	422	399	329	329	253	504	401	49	472	595	555	348	382	541	195	496	330
Glasgow	397	145	320	33	101	292	183	439	110	468	373	372	385	96	224	488	83	44	449	376	101		346	419	432	330	166	295	254	179	573	215	314	291	216	215	148	385	293	92	356	495	448	248	272	433	84	409	217
Gloucester	109	468	102	330	318	56	174	99	443	159	35	123	56	247	150	191	410	349	111	153	454	346		225	196	191	504	628	198	528	235	174	85	159	140	126	266	204	110	441	52	157	119	126	77	105	343	89	189
Great Yarmouth	128	517	294	402	345	180	252	240	477	180	275	82	284	320	167	185	484	386	335	366	527	419	225		82	334	553	677	169	602	446	196	140	128	240	212	281	20	153	515	200	365	221	166	225	220	426	329	201
Harwich	76	535	281	425	372	167	275	187	504	128	217	67	246	336	194	125	469	413	279	543	432	196	82	82		349	569	693	196	611	390	223	147	155	265	228	308	73	150	524	145	309	166	187	240	164	435	267	228
Holyhead	269	439	111	305	311	148	141	288	426	334	206	270	216	231	181	360	394	333	282	167	438	349	174	216	102		124	272	311	185	427	238	328	311	168	113	293	338	184	204									
Inverness	550	105	486	199	215	458	348	597	75	617	539	505	549	262	383	622	132	158	618	542	66	166	504	553	569	474		129	394	84	741	360	461	427	382	373	268	613	393	438	598	262	572	352					
John o'Groats	663	232	601	328	342	574	478	724	202	741	668	630	680	391	507	747	259	285	744	671	195	295	628	677	693	603	129		518	189	868	487	588	554	511	500	395	654	557	244	656	790	737	520	567	723	379	696	479
Kingston upon Hull	184	364	223	251	185	134	127	264	327	245	233	139	244	158	47	256	295	234	309	280	369	254	198	169	196	231	394	518		445	421	55	102	44	130	95	132	149	90	346	192	355	264	16	192	159	256	259	37
Kyle of Lochalsh	586	189	499	212	263	471	372	618	159	651	552	555	564	275	432	671	186	216	628	567	79	179	528	602	611	514	84	189	445		763	394	500	476	407	406	318	582	479	126	550	674	633	427	451	616	263	594	407
Land's End	297	692	313	570	552	281	405	205	665	308	200	374	245	477	374	381	642	574	123	353	686	573	235	446	390	405	741	868	421	763		405	320	371	361	361	498	421	345	665	274	89	259	361	303	228	585	285	411
Leeds	189	327	169	212	156	113	72	255	293	260	194	145	232	119	29	260	258	202	270	237	329	215	174	196	223	176	360	487	55	394	405		95	68	75	40	92	176	70	307	168	316	257	33	109	232	220	248	24
Leicester	97	414	153	299	252	39	140	158	389	166	120	68	154	206	74	185	349	295	196	209	422	314	85	140	147	190	461	588	102	500	320	95		51	130	92	187	119	25	419	73	242	162	62	84	137	330	177	108
Lincoln	131	383	199	274	224	90	128	209	357	197	183	85	208	191	39	202	314	258	247	272	399	291	159	128	155	216	427	554	44	476	371	68	51		129	84	159	105	35	387	137	293	201	46	133	204	298	233	75
Liverpool	202	341	104	213	219	93	49	234	318	272	161	194	165	120	86	299	286	216	237	160	329	216	140	240	265	102	382	511	130	407	361	75	130	129		35	168	220	98	308	172	283	254	72	58	239	221	195	99
Manchester	185	340	129	212	196	80	48	227	318	257	161	165	183	119	61	276	285	215	236	197	329	215	126	212	228	124	373	500	95	406	361	40	92	84	35		132	185	73	307	144	283	236	38	69	221	220	187	64
Newcastle upon Tyne	286	235	257	149	64	207	129	347	201	352	299	241	325	57	114	358	166	110	364	329	253	148	266	281	308	272	268	395	132	318	498	92	187	159	168	132		264	157	233	260	410	337	125	201	324	158	347	84
Norwich	114	496	276	382	328	166	232	214	457	175	252	62	262	289	147	174	422	366	308	343	504	385	204	20	73	311	529	654	149	582	421	176	119	105	220	185	264		130	492	145	343	207	146	205	206	403	301	181
Nottingham	122	393	164	274	221	50	111	183	353	193	145	83	172	194	43	205	328	262	221	220	401	293	110	153	150	185	430	557	90	479	345	70	25	35	98	73	157	130		390	109	267	191	37	93	176	290	192	77
Oban	499	178	412	94	180	384	285	530	141	565	465	460	477	188	346	585	117	123	549	481	49	92	441	515	524	427	117	244	346	128	665	307	419	387	308	307	233	492	390		462	587	545	339	364	530	148	506	309
Oxford	57	483	154	353	324	64	187	90	465	108	74	83	108	260	145	141	433	372	156	205	472	356	52	200	145	238	532	656	192	550	274	168	73	137	172	144	260	145	109	462		199	77	135	106	64	379	141	181
Plymouth	218	615	237	492	474	203	328	128	587	224	122	293	167	399	297	300	552	496	46	264	595	495	157	365	309	328	664	790	355	674	89	316	242	293	283	283	410	343	267	587	199		176	283	225	151	500	206	333
Portsmouth	70	560	222	430	401	141	264	48	597	144	97	144	142	348	234	130	514	453	135	251	555	448	119	221	166	311	613	737	269	633	259	257	162	201	254	236	337	207	191	545	77	176		230	207	21	461	182	278
Sheffield	159	360	159	245	190	76	86	216	320	226	161	120	194	176	18	245	291	235	237	215	348	248	126	166	187	168	393	520	65	427	361	33	62	46	72	38	125	146	37	339	135	283	230		82	199	263	217	52
Shrewsbury	160	399	77	269	265	45	98	185	371	226	103	159	111	176	109	251	330	274	179	145	382	272	77	225	240	113	438	567	169	451	303	109	84	133	58	69	201	205	93	364	106	225	207	82		185	277	118	133
Southampton	77	547	201	417	388	128	251	31	532	61	76	148	121	324	209	143	500	438	105	233	541	433	105	220	164	293	598	723	256	618	228	232	177	204	239	221	324	206	176	530	64	151	21	199	185		445	161	258
Stranraer	402	228	325	51	170	297	188	444	194	475	378	379	390	101	257	496	167	124	454	392	195	84	343	426	435	338	262	379	259	263	585	220	330	298	221	220	158	403	290	148	379	500	461	263	277	445		417	222
Swansea	194	507	73	379	383	119	216	167	505	222	85	227	41	309	232	274	473	412	161	67	496	409	89	329	267	184	572	696	264	594	285	248	177	233	195	187	347	301	192	506	141	206	182	217	118	161	417		272
York	207	319	195	214	148	130	96	269	285	275	222	165	244	121	34	282	250	194	287	261	330	217	189	201	228	204	352	479	37	407	411	24	108	75	99	64	84	181	77	309	181	333	278	52	133	258	222	272	